PHYSICS
A PRACTICAL APPROACH

SECOND EDITION

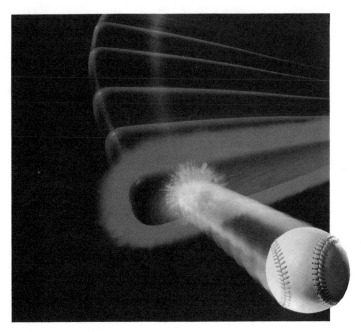

There is a great deal of practical physics information in the cover photograph. By using a strobe light that flashed on at regular intervals, a camera was able to capture the motion of a bat striking a baseball. An artist then enhanced the photograph by adding colour and placing a border around the image.

Much of what you will learn in this text may be summarized by studying this photograph. Knowing the time between flashes of the strobe could help reveal the speed of the bat. The bat applies a force to the ball, and in doing so gives some of its energy to the ball. Some of the energy goes to the ball's motion, and a small amount goes to sound and thermal energy. As you study physics, you will see many examples of measurement, motion, forces, and various types of energy.

You may wish to select a photograph, poster, or picture from a magazine that appeals to you. Write down how you think measurement, motion, forces, and energy might be connected to the image you have selected. When you have completed this course, read your ideas again and compare them to what you now know about physics and the way it is part of your everyday life.

PHYSICS
A PRACTICAL APPROACH

SECOND EDITION

Alan J. Hirsch

WILEY

John Wiley & Sons

Toronto   New York   Chichester   Brisbane   Singapore

Canadian Cataloguing in Publication Data

Hirsch, Alan J.
  Physics: a practical approach

2nd ed.
For use in secondary schools.
ISBN 0-471-79524-0

1. Physics. I. Title.

QC21.2.H57 1990   530   C90-093426-3

Cover Design: Jack Steiner
Typesetting: Compeer Typographic Services Limited
Photo Research: Elaine Freedman/Will Woods
Acquisitions Editor: Wilson Durward

Printed and bound in Canada by T.H. Best
10 9 8 7 6 5 4 3 2 1

Acknowledgements

I would like to thank the staff of John Wiley & Sons Canada Limited for their help during the development of both editions of *Physics: A Practical Approach*. Particular appreciation goes to Wilson Durward for his early support and initiative, and to Lee Makos, Oliver Salzmann, and Jeffrey Aberle for their ongoing editorial assistance and help in obtaining photographs and reviews. Special thanks are extended to Roy Bowland for his contribution in the preparation of the unit openers. Most of all, I must thank Ann Downar for her encouragement and guidance on this edition.

The reviewers of the first edition of *Physics: A Practical Approach* provided valuable criticism throughout that book's development, for which they must be acknowledged. So must those who reviewed and gave advice on this, the second edition:

Doug Bannister, Meadowvale Secondary School
Paul Crysler, Chairman of Science, Upper Canada College
Jim Dawson, Coordinator of Pure and Applied Science, Windsor Board of Education
Carole Escobar, Bellport Senior High School, Brookhaven, NY
Kevin Oikawa, Brampton Centennial Secondary School
Walt Sigmund, Head of Physics, Bathurst Heights Secondary School
Numerous teachers who have offered suggestions throughout the past ten years

I am especially indebted to my wife, Judy, for her assistance, understanding, and support as the project developed.

Finally, I want to thank the hundreds of students I have had the privilege of teaching in the past years. They provided the inspiration and rewards that have made the writing of this book a pleasure.

Alan J. Hirsch

Preface

The second edition of *Physics: A Practical Approach* has incorporated features of the first edition that were well received by students and teachers alike. Some have been modified, and new material has been added. The main features of the second edition are:

- Twenty-seven chapters grouped into nine units of study in the areas of: measurement; motion; properties of solids; fluids; heat; sound; electrical energy; light and colour; and nuclear energy.
- *Unit Openers* which emphasize careers that apply principles of physics, drawing students' attention to practical applications of the concepts involved and making them aware of career possibilities in the field of science and technology.
- *Chapter Openers* that stimulate interest with photographs and examples from common experience, as well as providing a set of "main ideas."
- Practical, "hands-on" *Activities* (inserted at appropriate intervals), which range from those with detailed instructions to those that require creativity.

- *Safety Precautions* clearly indicated where appropriate.
- Fundamental principles of physics, developed in a concise and logical fashion using many practical examples to maintain student motivation.
- *Did You Know?* features, which apply physics to personal life experience.
- A carefully controlled reading level.
- Numerous applications and practical examples.
- Many illustrations.
- Numerous clearly outlined *Sample Problems*.
- *Practice Questions* at the end of each reading section.
- A list of *Words to Know* in every chapter to help check vocabulary.
- A list of *Chapter Objectives* and a comprehensive set of *Review Questions* at the end of each chapter.
- Answers to selected questions.
- Extra information in the appendixes.
- A comprehensive index.

General Safety Rules

Your school laboratory need not be dangerous. Understanding how to use materials and equipment and following proper procedures will help you maintain an accident-free environment.

Care has been taken to ensure a safe environment for all activities in this textbook. Take special note of the CAUTION symbol (ⓘ) associated with certain activities. This alerts you to the fact that you will be working with potentially dangerous equipment, or materials that require special care.

Follow the guidelines and general safety rules listed below. Your teacher will give you specific information on additional safety procedures recommended in your province and on routines that apply to your school. You will also be informed about the location and proper use of all safety equipment.

1. Read through each activity before you begin.
2. Clear the laboratory bench of all materials except those you are using in the activity.
3. Learn the location and use of the safety equipment available to you, such as safety goggles, protective aprons, fire extinguishers, fire blankets, eyewash fountains, and showers. Find the location of the nearest fire alarm.
4. Do not begin an activity until you are instructed to do so.
5. Do not taste any material unless you are asked to do so by your teacher.
6. If you are instructed to smell a chemical in the laboratory, hold the container with the chemical in one hand and gently wave the air above the container towards your nostrils. Only this technique should be used to smell chemicals. Never sniff a chemical by placing it close to your nose.
7. Use flames only when instructed to do so. Read the special Bunsen burner safety rules that follow.
8. When heating materials, wear safety goggles. Make sure the test tubes you use are Pyrex and are clean and not cracked. Always keep the open end of the test tube pointed away from other people and yourself. Move the test tube through the flame so heat is distributed evenly.
9. Handle hot objects carefully. If you suffer a burn, immediately inform your teacher.
10. If any part of your body comes in contact with a harmful chemical, inform your teacher. Wash the area immediately and thoroughly with water. If your eyes are affected, do not touch them, but wash them immediately and continuously for at least 10 minutes.
11. Never pour harmful substances into the sink. Dispose of them as instructed by your teacher.
12. Clean all apparatus before putting it away.
13. Always unplug electric cords by pulling on the plug, not the cord.
14. Watch for sharp or jagged edges on all apparatus. Do not use broken or cracked glassware. Place broken glass only in specially marked containers.
15. Report to your teacher all accidents (no matter how minor), broken equipment, damaged or defective facilities, and suspicious looking substances.

BUNSEN BURNER SAFETY RULES

If a Bunsen burner is used in your science classroom, make sure you follow the procedures listed below. (Note: hot plates should be used in preference to Bunsen burners whenever possible.)

1. Do not wear scarves or ties, long necklaces, or earphones suspended around your neck. Tie back loose hair, and roll back and secure loose sleeves before you light a Bunsen burner.
2. Obtain instructions from your teacher on the proper method of lighting and using a Bunsen burner.
3. Never heat a flammable material (for example, alcohol) over a Bunsen burner.
4. Be sure there are no flammable materials nearby before you light a Bunsen burner.
5. Never leave a lighted Bunsen burner unattended.
6. Always turn off the gas at the valve, not at the base of the Bunsen burner.

WHAT TO DO IF A FIRE OCCURS

Your teacher will review procedures for fires. Always follow those instructions.

1. Shut off all gas supplies at the desk valves.
2. Notify your teacher immediately. Since every second is vital, move quickly to provide help in an emergency.
3. Here are some other recommendations for action.
    (a) If clothing is on fire, roll on the floor to smother the flames. Use a fire blanket to smother the flames if a fellow student's clothing has caught fire.
    (b) A small fire can be smothered by using sand or a small container such as an inverted large beaker or can.
    (c) Make sure you know how to operate the fire extinguishers in order to assist your teacher.
    (d) If the fire is not quickly and easily put out, leave the building in a calm manner.

CONTENTS

Unit 3   Rigid Bodies, Stability, and Elasticity   88

UNIT 4 Fluids ... 136

UNIT 5 Heat ... 164

UNIT 6 Waves, Sound, and Music208

UNIT 7 Electricity and Electromagnetism260

UNIT 8 Light and Colour   344

Appendixes

Measurement

You have been relying on measurements all your life. We all need measurements with clear meanings — 5.0 kg, 80 W, $4.00 — in our daily activities. Accurate measurements are also necessary in such areas as office procedures, factories, warehousing, various types of sales jobs, international trade, medicine, and other scientific technologies. This unit is about measurements with clear meanings.

The information in this unit will be useful to you as you consider your future career possibilities. Knowledge of mass, area, volume, and linear measurement will be essential if you are considering a career in construction, cooking, photography, music, sales, fashion design, tool-and-die making, drafting, or sports and the industries built around it. Careers in the space industry as well as other technological jobs also rely on a solid knowledge of measurement.

Here are two examples of careers related to the use of measurement:

- Rapid technological changes in recent years have caused a revolution in methods used in business and industry. More of the product is expected to be produced in a shorter period of time. Even in a computer-orientated environment, however, the need for measurements with clearly defined meanings remains the same. For example, because of the development of ceramic tooling and electrical discharge machinery, a tool-and-die maker now

designs and builds tools, dies, and moulds that could never before be imagined. Yet despite new developments, the basic knowledge of measurement is still essential to the tool-and-die maker.

- The fashion industry's final products are garments and accessories that will properly fit people of various sizes. This demands a clear understanding of measurement, patterns, body shapes, and dimensions. As well, the knowledge of particular characteristics — elasticity, density, and durability — of fabrics, thread, and other fashion materials is extremely important.

Knowing the information in this unit will be especially useful if you plan a career in any of the areas already mentioned, as well as the following: transportation, auto mechanics, surveying, clock and watch manufacturing or maintenance, lab technology, fishing, farming, industrial manufacturing, or astronomy. Choose any career possibility mentioned and find out more about it. You might interview someone already on that career path. If it still appeals to you, contact your local community college, university, guidance office, or counselling centre for more information on training for the career of your choice.

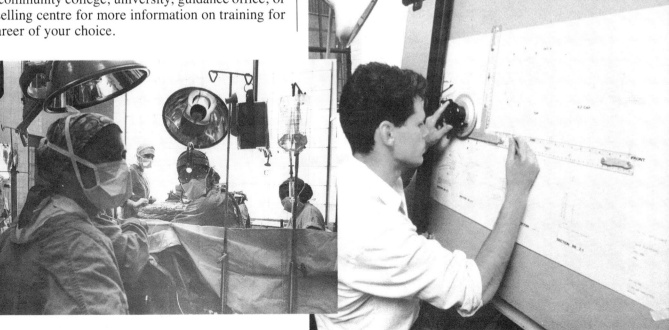

Measurement of Time

The structure in the photograph is called Stonehenge. It is a collection of large standing stones built thousands of years ago in western England. Stonehenge may have been just a meeting place for an ancient religion. Or it may have been much more. Evidence shows it could be one of the biggest clocks ever built! Some of the stones are lined up so that events occurring in the sky every year could be predicted and observed. These events signalled the changing seasons.

If Stonehenge had been used to indicate the changing seasons, it was doing what all timepieces do: measuring a repeated event. In this chapter you will learn about some events that take a long time to repeat, and others that take a very short time. Most of what you learn will be found through experimentation.

Main Ideas

- Time is measured by keeping track of events that repeat regularly.
- To be useful for measuring time, the repeated events must be standardized.
- The period and frequency of a repeated event can be measured.
- All measurements have some error.

1.1 Measuring Time Without Clocks

The measurement of time is so common we tend to forget how important it is. Many people's salaries are based on time measurements of hours, days, or weeks. Long-distance telephone charges are based on time measurements of minutes as well as the time period of the day. A person who wants a soft-boiled egg learns from experience how many minutes and seconds the egg must remain in the boiling water. Some racing events, such as ski and swim races, are timed to the closest fraction of a second.

But the measurement of exact times has not always been so important. About 500 years ago, there were no watches or clocks, so people did not have an exact measure of time. Perhaps they measured time by daylight. Of course, they did not have to worry about long-distance telephone charges because there were no telephones. But we can assume that people then liked to eat well-prepared food, so how did they measure the time needed to cook a perfect soft-boiled egg? One way may have been by counting pulse beats. Other ways may have involved something being pulled downward by the force of gravity, such as sand or salt falling through a narrow opening, or water dripping out of a hole in a container (Figure 1-1).

In the activity that follows you will measure the time of certain events using both your pulse and a water clock. The activity will introduce you to the experimental side of physics. You will get practice in co-ordinating events with other students, making careful observations, recording data, and interpreting observations.

Figure 1-1 Two possible ways of measuring time

(a) The sand or salt takes about the same time to fall through the hole each time the container is turned over.

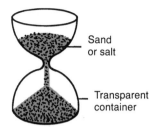

Sand or salt

Transparent container

(b) A transparent dripping water device could be marked off to indicate certain events.

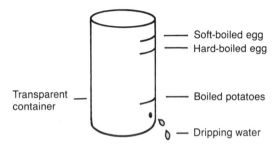

Transparent container

Soft-boiled egg
Hard-boiled egg

Boiled potatoes

Dripping water

Activity 1A   Using Primitive Timing Devices

PROBLEM ■ What difficulties occur when measuring time with pulse beats and a water clock?

APPARATUS ■ large beaker; pop can with a very small hole near the bottom; several small, equal-size containers for catching water (e.g., small beakers or plastic film containers); catch basin or sink; water; other apparatus related to the event to be timed

PROCEDURE ■

1. Choose an event to be timed by all students in the class. It must be an event that can be repeated at least three times. (The "event" may be a timed alarm, a portion of a song played on a cassette recorder or portable synthesizer, or a ball rolling down a ramp and then along the floor for a set distance, etc.)

2. Practise counting your own pulse beat found on your wrist (Figure 1-2).

3. Start the event and measure the time using your pulse beat for the entire event. Record your measurement.

 CAUTION Do not try the next step if you have heart or breathing problems. Discuss with your teacher.

4. Briefly perform an appropriate exercise (e.g., running on the spot or doing sit-ups). Then repeat #3.

5. Set up the water clock so you can catch water from the can in small containers while keeping the water in the can at about the same level. See Figure 1-3. Be sure that any water that spills goes into a catch basin or sink. Notice that it is possible to require only two small containers if you empty one out each time it is filled and keep track of the number emptied.

6. Start the event and measure the time for the event in the number of containers collected. Fractions are allowed (e.g., $13\frac{1}{2}$ containers). If the measurement is uncertain, try it again.

ANALYSIS ■

1. Make a list of the first pulse measurements of the event found by all students.

2. Make a list of the second pulse measurements (after exercise) found by all students.

3. Make a list of the water clock times of the groups in the class.

4. Would the water clock used in this activity be more or less accurate if it were not kept filled up? How would you prove your answer?

5. Is the pulse a good way of measuring time? Why or why not?

6. Is a water clock a good device for measuring time? Why or why not?

7. Describe any difficulties students had in measuring time with pulse beats or the water clock.

Figure 1-2 Measuring your pulse beat

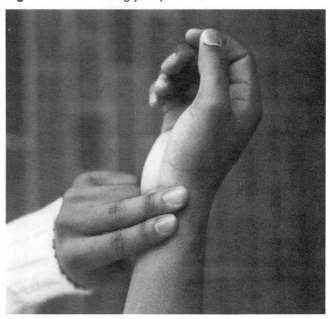

Figure 1-3 A water clock

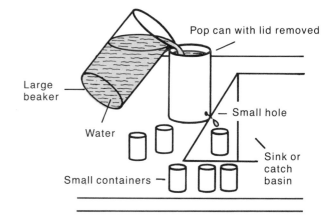

APPLICATIONS ■

1. How reliable would your pulse be to measure the time to cook a soft-boiled egg? Explain your answer.

2. If a recipe to cook a certain food called for a time of 500 heart beats, would everybody using the recipe get the same results? Explain your answer.

1.2 Developments in Time Measurement

Thousands of years ago people did not have clocks or calendars, so they needed other ways of determining when to plant crops or hunt for fish, birds, and other animals. People learned how to use *repeated* natural events to measure time. For example, a day was determined by observing the apparent motion of the sun in the sky. A month was determined by observing the moon. This was possible because every certain number of days the phases of the moon are repeated, from full moon to half moon to new moon, and back eventually to full moon (Figure 1-4).

Figure 1-4 The phases of the moon are repeated once every 29 or 30 risings of the sun.

(a) Motion of the moon around the earth, showing the sun's rays and four phases

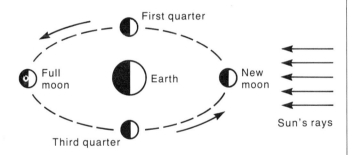

(b) View of the moon as seen from the earth

New moon	First quarter	Full moon	Third quarter	New moon

The seasons were determined by observing repeated positions of the sun. For example, the sun is lowest in the sky in winter and highest in the sky in summer. Between winter and summer, rivers could flood and birds and other animals could be seen migrating to cooler regions. (In many areas we still use the arrival of the first robin as a sure sign of spring.)

Other methods of measuring time were used, including various types of water clocks and sundials, and perhaps an arrangement of stones like that shown on the first page of this chapter. Almost all of the methods had one feature in common: they measured time by using *repeated* events. About 500 years ago, advances were made in various fields of science. People began to need more reliable methods of measuring time, especially short intervals of time. Eventually, the time for the earth to rotate once on its axis (one day) was split into 24 equal intervals called hours. Each hour was split into 60 equal intervals called minutes, and each minute was split into 60 equal intervals called seconds. This meant that one second was 1/86 400 of the time it takes the earth to rotate once on its axis.

We now use the second (symbol, s) as the standard measurement of time. A **standard measurement** is a measurement that has the same value everywhere. Other standard measurements are described in Chapters 2 and 3.

In our everyday lives, seconds are probably the smallest time intervals we need. But some events require much smaller time intervals. For example, some Olympic sports records are recorded to the closest millisecond (1/1000 s). Even shorter time intervals are needed for computers, or events observed in scientific experiments. Thus, time intervals of one microsecond (1/1000 000 s) or one nanosecond (1/1000 000 000 s) are used nowadays.

Notice in the above paragraph that the prefixes milli, micro, and nano are used. There are several other prefixes used in the metric system. The meanings and symbols of all the prefixes are summarized in Appendix A at the back of the book. Notice also in Appendix A that time is a fundamental quantity having the second as its base unit.

With our ability to measure smaller and smaller times, the definition of a second has become more exact. Currently, one second is defined as the time for 9 192 631 770 vibrations of a certain colour of light emitted by atoms of cesium. This quantity is believed to remain constant, so it is an appropriate standard. Notice that this definition involves another example of a repeated event (the vibration of an atom).

Period and frequency

Every event having a cycle that is repeated regularly has a period and a frequency. The **period**, symbol T, is the amount of time required for one complete cycle. If the time for several cycles is known, the period can be found using this equation:

$$T = \frac{\text{total time}}{\text{number of cycles}}$$

The unit of period is the second per cycle, or simply the second.

The **frequency**, symbol f, is the number of cycles that occur in a specific amount of time. One way to calculate the frequency of a repeated event is to use this equation:

$$f = \frac{\text{number of cycles}}{\text{total time}}$$

Frequency is measured in cycles per second, or hertz (Hz). This unit is named after a German physicist, Heinrich Hertz (1857–1894).

Sample Problem 1

The time for a ball to bounce 20 times is found to be 8.3 s. Determine the (a) period and (b) frequency of the bouncing.

Solution

(a) $T = \dfrac{\text{total time}}{\text{number of cycles}}$

$= \dfrac{8.3\,\text{s}}{20\,\text{cycles}}$

$= 0.415$ s or 0.42 s (rounded)

Thus, the period is 0.42 s.

(b) $f = \dfrac{\text{number of cycles}}{\text{total time}}$

$= \dfrac{20\,\text{cycles}}{8.3\,\text{s}}$

$= 2.4$ Hz (rounded)

Thus, the frequency is 2.4 Hz.

The answers to the sample problem have been rounded to two significant digits. No measurements are perfect; they all have some error. So, the answers to calculations using measurements should be rounded. In this text, we will tend to round answers to two or three significant digits. Information about significant digits and rules for rounding numbers are found in Appendixes C and D at the back of the book.

Since period is measured in seconds per cycle and frequency is measured in cycles per second, they are reciprocals of each other.

$$f = \frac{1}{T} \quad \text{and} \quad T = \frac{1}{f}$$

Thus, if either the period or frequency is given, the other can be found.

Sample Problem 2

Find the period of a bird's wings vibrating at 4.5 Hz.

Solution $T = \dfrac{1}{f} = \dfrac{1}{4.5\,\text{Hz}} = 0.22$ s (rounded)

Sample Problem 3

Find the frequency of a squirrel's paw scratching the ground with a period of 0.28 s.

Solution $f = \dfrac{1}{T} = \dfrac{1}{0.28\,\text{s}} = 3.6$ Hz (rounded)

PRACTICE

1. What problems occur when trying to use objects in the sky to measure time?
2. Could a human pulse, or a water clock (both used in Activity 1A), be used to measure longer times, such as a year? Explain your answer.
3. Could a human pulse, or a water clock, be used to measure short times, such as the time for a pen to fall from the table to the floor? Explain your answer.
4. In an AC electric circuit, the electrons vibrate 330 times in 5.5 s. Determine the (a) period and (b) frequency of this repeated event.
5. Calculate the period of vibration if the frequency is:
   (a) 4.0 Hz   (b) 0.020 Hz   (c) 0.13 Hz
6. Find the frequency of an object that vibrates with a period of:
   (a) 5.0 s   (b) 0.025 s   (c) 1.7 s

1.3   The Scientific Method

The scientific method is a process that people use for solving problems, often without thinking much about it. It is not necessarily the same process for everybody. Thus, it is hard to define. However, we can list the main steps involved in the process. Using the scientific method, a problem solver would:

1. State the problem to be solved.
2. Make a hypothesis, which is a scientific attempt to answer the problem, based on experience and research of related facts.
3. Perform a controlled experiment to test the hypothesis.
4. Analyse the experiment.
5. Offer predictions or applications for related situations.

Various forms of this method have helped in the development of science. The method can also be used to solve problems we may face daily, such as "Why does the light not come on when I turn on the switch?" or "What is causing this cactus plant to appear to be dying?"

Controlled experimentation

An important step in the scientific method is to perform a *controlled experiment*. To learn the meaning of the word "controlled", consider the problem you will be asked to solve in the next activity. It involves a pendulum.

A **pendulum** is a mass (on the end of a string or other support) that swings back and forth with a regular period and frequency. A playground swing is an example of a pendulum. To study the motion of a pendulum, some definitions must be introduced. One **cycle** of a pendulum is a complete vibration of the mass, from one side to the other *and back again*. The **rest position** is the location of the mass when the swinging is stopped. The **amplitude** of vibration is the maximum distance, to one side, that the mass moves from the rest position. The **length** of the pendulum is the distance from the support position to the *middle* of the mass. These definitions are illustrated in Figure 1-5 (overleaf).

Figure 1-5 Definitions associated with a pendulum

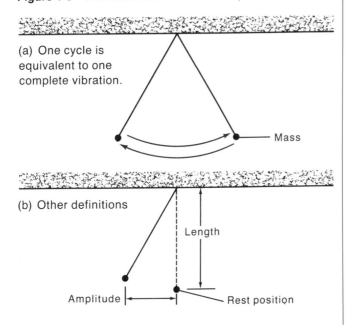

(a) One cycle is equivalent to one complete vibration.

Mass

(b) Other definitions

Length

Amplitude

Rest position

How does the frequency of a pendulum depend on the amplitude of vibration, the size of the mass, and the length of the pendulum? This one problem has three parts to it. Each part must be solved separately in order to grasp the significance of any numbers measured. Thus, to find how the frequency of a pendulum depends on the amplitude, the mass and length must remain constant as you try different amplitudes. You should be able to decide what must be kept constant in order to find how the frequency depends on the size of the mass or the length of the pendulum.

An investigation in which only one variable is changed at a time while keeping all the other variables constant is called a **controlled experiment**. You will perform this type of investigation in the following activity.

Activity 1B The Pendulum

PROBLEM ■ What happens to the frequency of a pendulum when you change the pendulum's amplitude, mass, and length, one at a time?

APPARATUS ■ support stand; clamp; string; stopwatch; split rubber stopper; metre stick; metal masses (200 g, 100 g, and 50 g); graph paper

Note: When measuring, try to reduce errors as much as possible. Appendix C describes the types of errors to watch for.

PROCEDURE ■

1. Set up a table of data based on Table 1-1.

Table 1-1 Observations for Activity 1B

Length (cm)	Mass (g)	Amplitude (cm)	Time for 20 cycles (s)	Frequency (Hz)

SAMPLE

2. Obtain a string about 110 cm long and attach a 200 g mass to one end of it. Place the other end of the string into the split rubber stopper (Figure 1-6). Adjust the pendulum length to 100 cm, and clamp the rubber stopper firmly. Remember that the length is measured to the middle of the mass.
3. Set the pendulum swinging with an amplitude of 10 cm, and measure the time for 20 complete cycles. Repeat once or twice more for accuracy. Enter the data in your table.
4. Repeat #3 with amplitudes of 20 cm and 30 cm to determine how frequency depends on amplitude. (If a computer program is available to check your results, use it before you proceed.)
5. Determine how the frequency depends on the mass. Do this in a controlled way, using masses of 200 g, 100 g, and 50 g. Again, remember to measure the length to the *middle* of each mass used.
6. Determine how the frequency depends on the length of the pendulum. Do this in a controlled way using lengths of 100 cm, 80 cm, 60 cm, 40 cm, and 20 cm. Enter the data in your table.

Figure 1-6 Setting up the pendulum

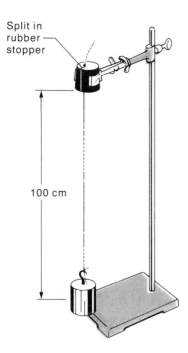

Split in rubber stopper

100 cm

ANALYSIS ■

1. On a single piece of graph paper, and using a different type (or colour) of line for each part of the activity, plot a graph of all the data. The graph should have frequency along the vertical axis. (If you don't know why, see Appendix E.) Place the following variables along the horizontal axis:
   (a) amplitude (when the length and mass are constant)
   (b) mass (when the amplitude and length are constant)
   (c) length (when the amplitude and mass are constant)
2. Which variables, if any, had little or no effect on the frequency of the pendulum?
3. Which variable, if any, had the greatest effect on the frequency of the pendulum?
4. What happens to the frequency of a pendulum when you change the pendulum's amplitude, mass, and length, one at a time?

APPLICATION ■ A pendulum clock is running slower than normal. What should be done to increase its frequency?

1.4 Measuring Short Time Intervals

The observation that a pendulum swings with a regular frequency and period of vibration (Activity 1B) can be applied to the measurement of time intervals. In fact, the first accurate clocks were made with pendulums having a constant period of vibration. However, a swinging pendulum is not helpful when trying to measure short time intervals. For example, a person concerned with highway safety may need to measure the time it takes a driver to apply the brakes after seeing an emergency. This is the **human reaction time**, the time between seeing an event and reacting to it.

A simple stopwatch would be useless to measure reaction time because reaction time is needed to operate the stopwatch. A more appropriate device for measuring short time intervals is called a *recording timer*. This timer has a mechanism that produces dots with a regular period and frequency. These dots are recorded on a paper strip pulled through the timer. To determine the time of an event, count the spaces *between* the dots, *not* the dots themselves. In one type of recording timer, shown in Figure 1-7 (overleaf), a metal arm vibrates at a constant frequency. The next activity introduces you to the use of a recording timer to measure short time intervals, and shows you how to use the timer to measure your own reaction time.

Activity 1C The Recording Timer and Reaction Time

PROBLEM ■
(a) What are the period and frequency of the dots produced by a recording timer?
(b) What is your reaction time?

APPARATUS ■ recording timer and related apparatus; three paper strips with lengths about 30 cm, 50 cm, and 70 cm; stopwatch; metal mass (e.g., 100 g); masking tape

Figure 1-7 One type of recording timer: A needle on the arm strikes carbon paper and records dots on a paper strip pulled through the timer.

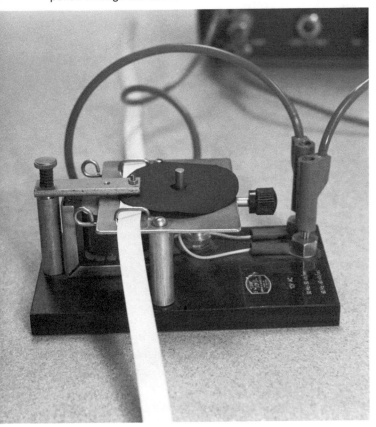

 CAUTION Some timers are spark timers, and could give you an electric shock. Make sure you understand how to use your timer.

PROCEDURE ■

1. Use the shortest paper strip to determine if the timer is working properly. If it isn't, inform your teacher.
2. Position the longest paper strip in the recording timer. Turn on the timer and use the stopwatch to determine how long it takes to pull the tape through at a fairly slow speed. Count the number of spaces between the dots, then calculate the frequency of the timer (f = number of cycles/time). Before going on to the next step, check with your teacher or a computer to discover if your result is acceptable.

3. Use masking tape to attach the metal mass to one end of the 50 cm strip. Place a mark on the tape about 5 cm from the mass. Have one person in your group hold the timer so the mass can fall vertically through it. Have another person hold the top of the tape, as shown in Figure 1-8. Position your hand so your thumb and index finger line up with the mark on the tape without touching the tape. As you watch the strip, have the person holding it drop it without warning. Grasp the tape as soon as possible, and mark where you caught it.
4. Repeat #3 for other students who want to find their reaction time.

Figure 1-8 Measuring reaction time

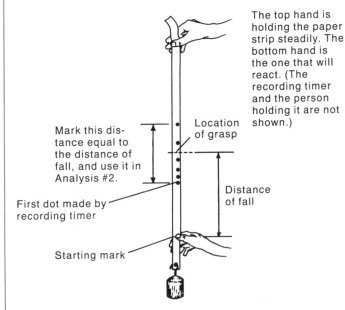

The top hand is holding the paper strip steadily. The bottom hand is the one that will react. (The recording timer and the person holding it are not shown.)

Location of grasp

Mark this distance equal to the distance of fall, and use it in Analysis #2.

First dot made by recording timer

Distance of fall

Starting mark

ANALYSIS ■

1. Use the measured frequency of the timer to determine the time between dots produced by the timer. In other words, calculate the period of the timer.

2. Measure the distance from the starting mark to where you caught the strip. Mark off the same distance from the starting point of the dots made by the timer. Count the spaces produced in that distance (Figure 1-8). Use the number of spaces and the period of the timer to calculate your reaction time. (Repeat this for everyone whose reaction time was measured.)

APPLICATION ■ Some people claim that it is impossible to grab a paper currency bill (such as a five-dollar bill) if it is dropped lengthwise without warning through the gap between a person's thumb and finger. (The bottom of the bill should start off at the same level as the thumb and finger.) Based on the reactions observed in this activity, do you agree with this claim?

Words to Know

standard measurement	rest position of a pendulum
period	amplitude of vibration
frequency	length of a pendulum
scientific method	controlled experiment
pendulum	human reaction time
cycle of a pendulum	recording timer

(You should also be aware of the terminology in Appendixes A to E.)

Chapter Objectives

Having completed this chapter, you should now be able to:

1. Describe ways in which time may have been measured before clocks were invented.

2. Recognize the disadvantages of measuring time using a pulse, dripping water, or other similar methods.

3. State examples of repeated events that have been used to measure time.

4. Describe why the second is a standard measurement.

5. Define period and frequency and state their units.

6. Calculate period or frequency using their defining equations (period = time/number of cycles; frequency = number of cycles/time).

7. Given one of period or frequency, calculate the other $\left(f = \frac{1}{T} \text{ and } T = \frac{1}{f}\right)$.

8. Arrange in order a given set of steps of the scientific method.

9. Define the amplitude of vibration and the length of a pendulum.

10. Carry out a controlled experiment involving at least three variables.

11. State what affects the frequency and period of a pendulum.

12. Set up and use a recording timer.

13. Describe how to find a person's reaction time experimentally.

Chapter Review

1. List three examples of measuring time using repeated events that are not standard. (1.1, Act. 1A)

2. (a) Give one example of a standard measurement. (b) Why is it called standard? (1.2)

3. During hibernation, a black bear's heart beats only about eight times each minute. Determine the (a) period and (b) frequency of the heartbeat in the proper units (seconds and hertz). (1.2)

4. A butterfly beats its wings at a frequency of 9.0 Hz. What is the period of vibration of the wings? (1.2)

5. The horned sungem is an African bird with the fastest wing-beat of any bird. If the period of vibration of the wings is 0.011 s, what is the frequency? (1.2)

6. List these steps of problem solving in a logical order:
   - analyse the experiment.
   - research to help make a hypothesis
   - perform a controlled experiment (1.3)

7. Research and report on the development of science before the scientific method evolved. In particular, find out about the ancient Greek philosophers and science during the so-called Middle Ages.

8. What happens to the period of vibration of a pendulum when you increase the
   (a) amplitude?   (b) mass?   (c) length?

9. The diagram shows the motion of a paper strip pulled through a recording timer. What is the time interval from the start to the finish of the motion if the frequency of the timer is:
   (a) 10 Hz?   (b) 60 Hz?   (Act. 1C)

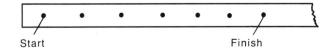

Start   Finish

10. For each problem listed below, state at least three factors you would vary to perform a controlled experiment.
    (a) What factors affect the rate of growth of a bean plant?
    (b) What factors affect the rate at which water evaporates from a container?
    (c) What factors affect the rate at which milk becomes sour?

11. Make a list of competitive sports that you think measure events to the closest hundredth of a second. Research to determine how accurate and complete your list is. (One resource is the *Guinness Book of World Records*.)

12. Describe why time measurement is important to each of the following people: an air traffic controller; a photographer; a chef; an Olympic swimmer; a musician.

CHAPTER 2

Measurement of Distances

Road signs, like the one shown here in rural Ireland, often indicate the direction to a destination. But they also indicate a quantity we are all concerned with: distance. Distances are often called by other names, such as length, width, height, depth, thickness, and diameter. Distance is important to vacation travellers, long-haul truckers, building and road construction crews, fabric manufacturers, airline pilots, sailors, surveyors, astronomers, and a host of other people. In this chapter, you will learn how distance can be measured both directly and indirectly. You will measure small distances, such as the thickness of your hair. And you will get practice in "thinking metric."

Main Ideas

- Triangulation is a method of measuring distances that cannot be measured directly.
- The metre is the base unit of distance in the metric system.
- The metric system has distinct advantages over other systems of measurement, especially once it becomes familiar.
- Instruments with double scales are used to provide measurements of high precision.

2.1 Measuring Distances Indirectly

Imagine a climbing team has reached the top of a mountain and is now descending by a different path. On a glacier, the team members suddenly come to a huge gap in the ice, several metres across and hundreds of metres deep. To cross the gap they hope to use their sturdy ladder, which can be extended to 4.0 m. But will the ladder reach all the way across? Before leaning the ladder across the gap, they could estimate the distance across the gap using *indirect measurement*. Various methods of indirect measurement are possible; the one discussed here is called triangulation.

Triangulation is the method of measuring distances indirectly by drawing a scale diagram of a triangle. The triangle has one side of known length, called the **baseline**, and two measured angles adjacent to the baseline. Figure 2-1 illustrates that the angles adjacent to the baseline must be measured to a common point.

Figure 2-1   In the method of triangulation, the baseline and two angles measured to a common point must be known.

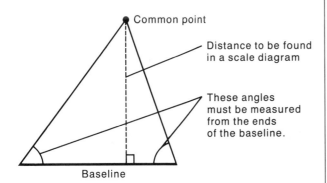

Sample Problem 1

The mountain-climbing team described above measures a baseline of 4.0 m. (They use their ladder to measure this distance.) Then they choose a common point on the opposite side of the gap in the ice, and measure the angles from each end of the baseline to the common point. The angles are found to be 58° and 66° respectively. How wide is the gap?

Solution   A diagram is drawn to scale, as shown. (The scale chosen is 1.0 cm = 1.0 m. It produces a small diagram. When more space is available, draw a larger diagram to obtain better accuracy.) The baseline is AB and the common point is C.

Figure 2-2   Scale diagram

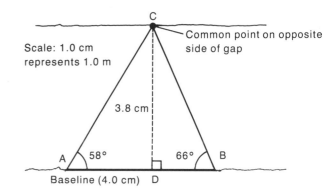

The shortest distance across the gap is CD, which is drawn perpendicular to AB from point C. It is 3.8 cm in the diagram, or 3.8 m in the actual situation. Thus, the ladder is just long enough to bridge the gap.

The method of triangulation can be used to determine very large distances, such as the distance from the sun to a distant planet (as in Review #4). It can also be used to measure vertical distances, such as the height of a tree (as in Activity 2B).

Activity 2A Using Triangulation to Measure a Horizontal Distance

PROBLEM ■ What are the main steps to follow in measuring a horizontal distance indirectly using triangulation?

APPARATUS ■ small protractor and metric ruler for drawing a scale diagram; large protractor (or piece of cardboard to make one)

Note: The instructions for this activity require that the distance be in units related to the human body, such as paces or hand spans. If distances measured in metric units are preferred, a metre stick must be used to measure the baseline.

CAUTION Take care that you do not injure yourself, or anyone else, as you move around, or as you use the metre stick.

PROCEDURE ■

1. Choose at least one unknown distance to find indirectly. An outdoor example is the distance from the school to a distant pole. An indoor example is the distance from your desk to a light switch.
2. If only a small protractor is available, use it to make a larger one on cardboard (Figure 2-3). A large protractor provides a greater chance of good results.

Figure 2-3 Making a large protractor

Use the small protractor to draw lines on the cardboard. Then label the angles appropriately.

Cardboard

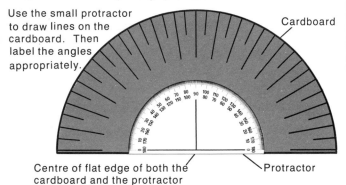

Centre of flat edge of both the cardboard and the protractor

Protractor

3. Mark off and measure an appropriate baseline (Figure 2-4) using only yourself as the measuring device. For example, if the baseline is large, use natural paces or lengths of your shoe. If the distance is small, use hand spans. For best results, use as large a baseline as possible.

Figure 2-4 Choosing a baseline and measuring the angles from it

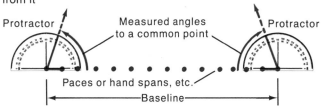

Protractor

Measured angles to a common point

Protractor

Paces or hand spans, etc.

Baseline

4. Measure the angle from each end of the baseline to a common point, as shown in Figure 2-4. Be sure the protractor is placed exactly along the baseline. Record these angles.
5. Repeat the steps to find another unknown distance.

ANALYSIS ■

1. Using an appropriate scale, draw a large scale diagram to determine each unknown distance. (Use sample problem 1 as a reference.)
2. Compare your results with the results of anyone else who measured the same distance.
3. List the main steps you followed to measure a horizontal distance indirectly using triangulation.

APPLICATION ■ A surveyor (Figure 2-5) measures off a baseline of 130 m along the shore of a river. She then uses a transit (a type of telescope) to measure the angle from each end of the baseline to a rock on the opposite shore. The two angles found are 71° and 52°. Draw a scale diagram to determine the width of the river.

Figure 2-5 A surveyor can measure angles with a transit.

Activity 2B Using Triangulation to Measure a Vertical Height

PROBLEM ■ How can triangulation be used to determine the height of a tall tree?

PROCEDURE ■ Design your own technique to determine the height of a tall tree (or building) indirectly.

CAUTION Have your design checked by your teacher before you begin your procedure. There may be harmful aspects.

Write a report of your activity, including procedure, calculations, and analysis. Figure 2-6 illustrates clues about one way to solve the problem.

Figure 2-6 Some clues that may help in finding the height of a tree

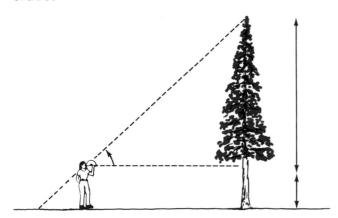

2.2 Standardized Distances

Distance measurements in paces or hand spans (Activity 2A) are examples of measurements that are not standard. Two people with paces of a different size may find the same distance to be 25 paces and 30 paces. Centuries ago, units of distance measurement included the pace and hand span, as well as the digit, hand, yard, foot, fathom, cubit, and so on. Some of these units are illustrated in Figure 2-7. Often these were defined according to the measurements of a nation's leader. Of course, this practice did not provide standard units of measurement.

Figure 2-7 Units of the past that related to the human body

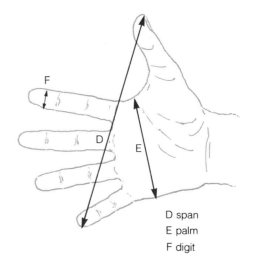

D span
E palm
F digit

The British or Imperial system of measurement has standard units of distance. Some examples are the inch, foot, yard, and mile. However, this system is awkward for conversion purposes because it is not based on the number 10. For instance, there are 12 inches per foot, 3 feet per yard, 1760 yards per mile, and 5280 feet per mile. Another problem with this system is that some units are not standardized the same everywhere. For instance, a Canadian gallon is larger than an American gallon. Thus, the Imperial system is obsolete for science, and almost obsolete for world trade.

The metric system is an easier system of measurement to use. As you know, it is based on multiples of 10. It does not vary from one place to another. In other words, all the distance units, and other units, are standardized. And it is used throughout most countries in the world. Internationally, the metric system is called the *Système International d'Unités*, or simply the SI. (The metric system is summarized in Appendix A.)

Converting metric distances

In the metric system, the base unit of distance is the metre (m). However, you will often use other standard units, such as the millimetre (mm), centimetre (cm), and kilometre (km). It is useful, and sometimes necessary, to be able to convert measurements from one of these units to another. Before seeing how to perform such conversions in the next three examples, look at Appendix A to refresh your memory about the meaning of prefixes such as milli, centi, and kilo.

Sample Problem 2

Convert 7.6 km to metres.

Solution $1\,km = 1000\,m$

$$7.6\,km = 7.6\,km \times \frac{1000\,m}{1\,km}$$

$$= 7600\,m$$

Sample Problem 3

Convert 2.45 m to centimetres.

Solution $1\,m = 100\,cm$

$$2.45\,m = 2.45\,m \times \frac{100\,cm}{1\,m}$$

$$= 245\,cm$$

Sample Problem 4

Convert 485 mm to metres.

Solution $1\,m = 1000\,mm$ or $1\,mm = 0.001\,m$

$$485\,mm = 485\,mm \times \frac{0.001\,m}{1\,mm}$$

$$= 0.485\,m$$

Estimating distances using body measurements

The switch from the British system of measurement to the metric system in North American schools seems to be almost complete. However, outside the schools, the switch is proceeding rather slowly, and many people still think in terms of feet, inches, and so on. One way of improving your chances of "thinking metric" is to know the approximate metric sizes of your own pace, arm span, hand span, and perhaps a few other measurements. These sizes can then be used to estimate distances.

Sample Problem 5

A man wants to buy some wire fencing to keep a young puppy safe in the yard. An advertisement indicates that the fencing comes in lengths of 5 m, 10 m, 15 m, etc. The man does not have a metric measuring device, but he knows his shoe length is 28 cm. He steps off the distance where the fencing is needed, and finds it to be about 50 shoe lengths. What length of fencing should he buy?

Solution   The estimated distance is

$$28\,\frac{cm}{pace} \times 50\,paces = 1400\,cm \;\; or \;\; 14\,m$$

Thus, he should buy a 15 m length of fencing. Notice that the "pace" units divide out, leaving centimetres only.

The next activity will give you practice in estimating distances using the metric system.

Activity 2C Estimating Distances Using Metric Units

PROBLEM ■ How well can you estimate distances?

APPARATUS ■ metre stick(s)

PROCEDURE ■

1. Determine the measurements listed below as accurately as possible in the metric units indicated in brackets. Try to prevent the error caused by parallax by looking straight at the metre stick, not at an angle to it. (Parallax and other types of errors are described in Appendix C.)
   (a) your hand span (in centimetres and millimetres)
   (b) your height with shoes (in centimetres and metres)
   (c) your arm span (in centimetres and metres)
   (d) the sole of your shoe (in centimetres and decimetres)
   (e) the length of your natural pace (in centimetres and metres)
2. Set up a table based on Table 2-1.
3. Choose several distances, some short, some medium, and some long. (Some examples are the length of a desk and the length of the classroom.) Name these distances in the first column of your data table. Then complete the table using these steps:
   (a) Just by looking, estimate each distance in the most convenient metric unit.
   (b) Measure each distance in an appropriate body unit, such as your hand span, arm span, pace, etc.
   (c) Use the results in (b) combined with the results in #1 to calculate each distance in a metric unit. Show your calculations, and round each value to 2 or 3 significant digits. One example is shown in Table 2-1. (Rules for rounding numbers to the correct number of significant digits are found in Appendix D.)
4. To determine how accurate your final results are, measure each distance with a metre stick and compare your calculated distances with these measured values.
5. If you performed Activity 2A, use the data from this activity to calculate the distance found then.
6. Which body measurements are most useful to memorize?
7. Describe how you could improve your ability to estimate distances.

APPLICATION ■ Two joggers always jog along the same path around a park. They use the technique applied in this activity to estimate the length of the path. The jogger with an estimated pace of 130 cm counts 1420 steps. The jogger with an estimated pace of 110 cm counts 1710 steps.
(a) Determine the two estimated lengths in metres.
(b) Explain reasons why the two estimates are not identical.

Table 2-1 Data for Activity 2C

Description of distance	Estimated distance (in a metric unit)	Measured distance (in a body unit)	Calculated distance (in a metric unit)
Length of desk	60 cm	3 hand spans	3 spans × 22 cm/span = 66 cm

2.3 Precision Measurements

Suppose three people are using measuring devices to find the width of a wooden board used to make a picture frame. The first person is a child who is learning how to use a children's metric ruler. The second is a worker in a picture-framing store using an ordinary metric ruler. You are the third person, with a part-time job responsible for the manufacture of the wood to an exact specification. You would use a device with a special scale that would let you to be more exact than the child or the picture framer. The three measuring devices are shown in Figure 2-8.

Figure 2-8 Three different measurements of the same object

(a) With a children's ruler, the width measured is $4\frac{1}{2}$ cm.

(b) With an ordinary metric ruler, the width is 4.4 cm.

(c) With a more exact instrument, the width is 4.42 cm.

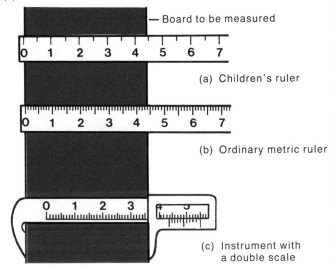

— Board to be measured

(a) Children's ruler

(b) Ordinary metric ruler

(c) Instrument with a double scale

Figure 2-8 illustrates that how precise a measurement is depends on the precision of the instrument used. **Precision** is an indication of the smallest division of a measurement or an instrument. Let us compare the precision of the three examples in Figure 2-8.

- The smallest division of the children's ruler is $\frac{1}{2}$ centimetre or 0.5 cm; this ruler has low precision.

- The smallest division on the ordinary ruler is $\frac{1}{10}$ cm or 0.1 cm; this ruler has medium precision.

- The smallest division on the ruler with the double scale is $\frac{1}{100}$ cm or 0.01 cm; this device has high precision.

Although the precision of a measurement depends a lot on the scale on the measuring device, it also depends on the person using the device. For example, an experienced person using the ordinary ruler or the double-scale device could obtain one more digit in each measurement than an inexperienced person could. The important thing here is that the double scale provides a precise measurement.

To learn how to read the double scale, consider Figure 2-9(a). The top scale is an ordinary metric scale with centimetres and millimetres. We will call this scale the *main scale*. The bottom scale is called a *vernier scale* (after its inventor, Pierre Vernier, a French mathematician who lived from 1580 to 1637). Notice that 10 divisions on the vernier scale correspond to 9 divisions on the main scale. In Figure 2-9(b), we take a reading by finding the approximate distance (in this case, between 4.4 and 4.5 cm), then by searching for the mark on the vernier scale that lines up best with a mark on the main scale. In this case, it lines up with the second mark, or 2. Thus, the reading is 4.42 cm.

Figure 2-9 The vernier scale

(a) In one example of a vernier scale, 10 divisions on the vernier scale correspond to 9 divisions (9 mm) on the main scale.

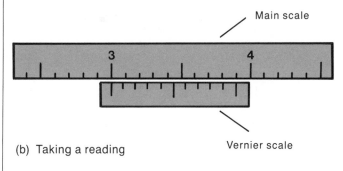

Main scale

Vernier scale

(b) Taking a reading

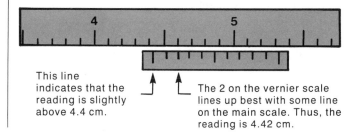

This line indicates that the reading is slightly above 4.4 cm.

The 2 on the vernier scale lines up best with some line on the main scale. Thus, the reading is 4.42 cm.

A double scale can be placed on various types of instruments. One common instrument is the *vernier calliper*, shown in Figure 2-10(a). (Calliper may also be spelled caliper.) It is used to measure the outside diameter of a cylinder or the inside diameter of a hollow cylinder. Another instrument with a double scale is the *micrometer calliper*, shown in Figure 2-10(b). The one shown has a scale with 50 divisions wrapped around a barrel. Two rotations of the barrel correspond to a gap of 1 mm, or 0.1 cm. Thus, the smallest division on this micrometer is $\frac{1}{100}$ mm, or 0.001 cm. This is a very high-precision instrument.

Figure 2-10 Two instruments that use a double scale

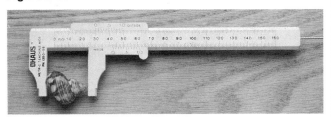

(a) A vernier calliper

(b) A micrometer calliper

When using high-precision instruments, such as the vernier calliper or micrometer calliper, it is necessary to check the zero setting before taking a reading. If, for example, the instrument is supposed to read 0.000 cm but instead reads 0.002 cm, the error must be taken into consideration with each reading. (Recall from Appendix C that this type of error is called a systematic error. Eliminating systematic error increases the accuracy of a measurement. In other words, it gives a reading closer to the true value. Notice that accuracy is different from precision.)

Activity 2D Measuring Distances with Precision Instruments

PROBLEM ■ When, and how, are high-precision measuring instruments used?

APPARATUS ■ vernier calliper; micrometer calliper; small glass beaker; various other objects

PROCEDURE ■
1. Familiarize yourself with the scales of the high-precision instruments you will use. (The double scales on some instruments are different from the ones shown in Figures 2-9 and 2-10.) Especially learn how to adjust the micrometer using the small safety knob on the end of the large cylinder.
2. Set each instrument to the zero setting, and discover if it reads zero. If it does not, learn how to add or subtract the systematic error for each measured value.
3. Measure several distances using either the vernier calliper or the micrometer calliper, or both. Record all your measurements. Some suggested distances are:

- outside diameter of a beaker
- inside diameter of a beaker
- inside depth of a beaker
- thickness of a piece of paper
- thickness of a hair
- diameter of a metal wire, such as an earring clasp or electrical wire
- thickness of a metal or plastic ruler
- diameter of a marble or metal ball
- other distances you can think of

4. If time permits, devise a way to measure the thickness of the wall of the glass beaker using both instruments.

ANALYSIS ■
1. For which measurements was the vernier calliper more useful than the micrometer calliper?
2. For which measurements was the micrometer calliper more useful than the vernier calliper?
3. Do the two instruments provide the same amount of precision? Explain.
4. When used to find the thickness of the curved glass of a beaker, which instrument provides the more accurate measurement? Why?

APPLICATION ■ A dial balance uses a double scale. If this type of balance is available for inspection, describe the scale on it.

Words to Know

triangulation   vernier scale
baseline   vernier calliper
precision   micrometer calliper

(Refer also to the terminology in Appendixes A to D.)

Chapter Objectives

Having completed this chapter, you should now be able to:

1. Draw a scale diagram using metric units.
2. Use the method of triangulation to determine an unknown distance indirectly.
3. Know the base unit of distance in the metric system.
4. Perform basic conversions of distances in millimetres, centimetres, metres, and kilometres.
5. Use your body measurements to determine estimates of unknown distances.
6. Define precision, and recognize how it differs from accuracy. (Accuracy is described in Appendix C.)
7. Use instruments with double scales to measure distances to a high degree of precision.

Chapter Review

1. A scale diagram is drawn with the scale
   1.0 cm = 20 m.
   (a) How long would a baseline be drawn for a distance of 150 m?
   (b) An unknown distance measured in the diagram is 12 cm long. What is this distance in real life?   (2.1, Act. 2A)
2. A hiker uses triangulation to determine the approximate distance across a canyon. The baseline parallel to one side of the canyon is 120 paces long. The angles from the ends of the baseline to a common point on the far side of the canyon are 65° and 75°.
   (a) Use a scale diagram to determine the width of the canyon in paces.
   (b) If the hiker's average pace is 80 cm, how wide is the canyon in metres?   (2.1, Act. 2A)
3. A student is standing 13 m from a school wall, and measures an angle of 38° between a horizontal line and the top of the wall. If the person's eyes are 1.5 m above the ground, how high is the top of the wall above the ground? (Use a scale diagram to solve this problem.)   (2.1, Act. 2B)

4. An astronomer uses the diameter of the earth's orbit around the sun as a baseline to estimate the radius of Saturn's orbit around the sun. (Saturn is the sixth planet from the sun.) As illustrated in the diagram, the diameter of the earth's orbit is 3.0×10^8 km, and the angles to Saturn (taken six months apart) are both 84°. Use a scale diagram to determine the distance from Saturn to the sun. (When astronomers use triangulation to measure such large distances, they take into consideration the motion of the distant object.)   (2.1)

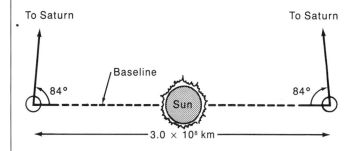

5. Convert these measurements:
   (a) 420 mm = ? cm = ? m
   (b) 33.8 cm = ? m = ? mm
   (c) 400 km = ? m
   (d) 0.019 km = ? m = ? cm
   (e) 150 m = ? km   (2.2)
6. The smallest division on ruler A is 2 mm, and the smallest division on ruler B is 1 mm. Which ruler provides the greater precision? Explain.   (2.3)
7. List these measurements in order of highest to lowest precision: 12 m; 12.22 m; 12.2 m   (2.3)
8. The main scale of the vernier calliper shown in the diagram has small divisions of 1 mm. What is the reading of the calliper?   (2.3)

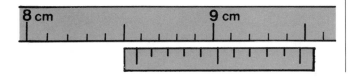

9. Explain how a micrometer calliper, which has high precision, could give a reading of low accuracy. (Hint: Consider systematic error, which is described in Appendix C.)
10. List careers or jobs that would involve distance measurements that are:
    (a) larger than about 1000 m
    (b) between about 1 m and 1000 m
    (c) between about 1 mm and 1 m
    (d) less than about 1 mm
11. Use a reference book to research the development of the metric system, starting in the late 1700s. Write a report on the development.

CHAPTER 3

Measurement of Derived Quantities

Oil, whether in the crude or refined form, is transported and stored in large tanks. The people who manufacture and use tanks for oil and other liquids must know the capacity (or volume) of the tanks. Volume is just one example of a quantity that is derived from other quantities.

A glance at the summary of the metric system in Appendix A reveals that there are seven fundamental quantities of measurement. You have studied two of these, time and distance, in the previous two chapters, and you will see a third one, mass, in this chapter. The seven fundamental quantities are used to derive (or make up) numerous other quantities. In this chapter, you will study three derived quantities: area, volume, and density. Other derived quantities will be presented later in the text.

Main Ideas

- Area, volume, and density are examples of derived quantities.
- The area of regular surfaces can be found using equations.
- The volume of regular solids can be found using equations, and the volume of irregular solids can be found using the displacement of water.
- Density is a property of matter derived from mass and distance.

3.1 Surface Area

Interior decorators, fashion designers, tailors, farmers, construction workers, and many other people use area calculations to determine required quantities of materials, and the costs of those materials. **Area** is the calculation of the number of square units of the surface of an object. Area is derived from length. Length is a one-dimensional quantity having units such as the metre (m). Area is a two-dimensional quantity having units such as the metre squared (m²).

An application of surface area is the measurement of land area. In the metric system, the unit commonly used for land area is the hectare (ha). It is equivalent to the area of a square that is one hectometre (1.0 hm or 100 m) on each side. To imagine the size of a hectare, remember that a high-school football field is 100 m long. A field that is as long as a football field and equally wide has a surface area of 1.0 ha (Figure 3-1).

Figure 3-1   A surface area of one hectare (1.0 ha)

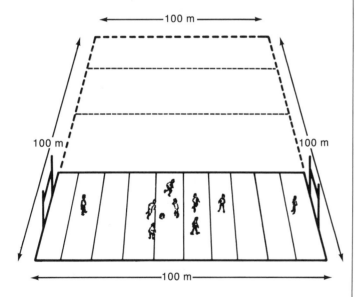

The equation used to calculate the surface area of an object depends on the shape of the object. We will consider only the rectangle and circle here.

For a rectangle,   area = length × width   or

$$A = lw$$

For a circle,   area = π (radius)² or

$$A = \pi r^2$$

If the diameter of a circle is given, divide by 2 to find the radius before using the equation for the area of a circle.

Sample Problem 1

A rug must cover a floor that is 3.8 m long and 2.6 m wide. The unit cost of the rug chosen is $40/m².
(a) Calculate the surface area of the required rug.
(b) Determine the total cost of the rug.

Solution
(a) $A = lw$
$ = (3.8 \text{ m})(2.6 \text{ m})$
$ = 9.88 \text{ m}^2$
When rounded to two significant digits, the answer is 9.9 m².
(b) Total cost = (unit cost)(area)
$$= \frac{(\$40)}{\text{m}^2}(9.9 \text{ m}^2)$$
$$= \$396$$
Thus, the total cost is about $400.

(Rules for rounding numbers to the correct number of significant digits are found in Appendix D.)

PRACTICE

1. Calculate the surface area of each rectangular shape in the most appropriate units:
   (a) material for a curtain measures 1.9 m by 3.6 m
   (b) the light-gathering panel of a solar calculator measures 16 mm by 54 mm
   (c) a potato field measures 100 m by 100 m (This is equivalent to 1.0 ha.)
2. A public playground is 300 m long and 200 m wide. Determine the surface area in:
   (a) square metres
   (b) hectares   (Hint: See #1(c) above.)
3. Calculate the surface area of each circular shape.
   (a) A round cookie cutter has a radius of 4.4 cm.
   (b) The distance from the hole to the edge of a circular green on a golf course is 15 m.
   (c) A camera lens is adjusted so its diameter is 31 mm.
4. A window pane that measures 1.2 m by 2.5 m must be replaced at a unit cost of $12/m².
   (a) Determine the surface area of the window pane.
   (b) Calculate the cost of the new pane.
5. A building contractor requires bundles of material to insulate an attic that is 12.4 m long and 8.5 m wide. Each bundle covers 10 m². Determine the:
   (a) surface area of the attic
   (b) number of bundles the contractor needs
6. Estimate the surface area of a five-dollar bill in a convenient unit. Then check your estimate by measuring the dimensions of the bill and calculating its area.
7. (a) Use metric graph paper (or a similar grid marked off in square centimetres) to determine the approximate surface area of your flattened hand with the fingers and thumb close together.
   (b) Use the area found in (a) to estimate the amount of material you would need to make your own pair of ski mitts.

3.2   Volume

Consumers are often required to pay for products by their volume. These products include toothpaste, milk, gasoline, propane, and large loads of gravel or concrete. **Volume** is the total space occupied by a substance or an object. It is derived from length, by extending length to three dimensions (length, width, and depth). For solid objects, volume is usually measured in cubic units, such as the metre cubed (m^3). For liquids and gases, volume can also be expressed in cubic units, but more commonly they are stated in capacity units, such as litres (L) and millilitres (mL). To convert from cubic units to capacity units and vice versa, the following facts are useful:

$$1.0\,cm^3 = 1.0\,mL$$
$$1.0\,dm^3 = 1.0\,L$$
$$1.0\,m^3 = 1000\,L$$

Volume of a regular solid object
A regular solid object has the shape of a box. Its volume is the product of its length and width and depth. Thus,

$$V = lwd$$

Sample Problem 2

The box of a truck is 6.1 m long, 2.8 m wide, and 2.2 m high.
(a) What is the volume of the box in metres cubed?
(b) What is the capacity of the box in litres?

Solution
(a) $V = lwd$
   $= (6.1\ m)(2.8\ m)(2.2\ m)$
   $= 37.576\ m^3$
   This answer should be rounded to two significant digits, so the volume is 38 m³.
(b) Since 1.0 m³ is equivalent to 1000 L, the capacity of the box is about 38 000 L.

Volume of a sphere

The volume of a sphere can be found using the equation

$$V = \frac{4}{3}\pi r^3 \quad \text{where } r \text{ is the radius of the sphere}$$

As with a circle, the radius is half of the diameter.

Volume of a liquid

The volume of a liquid can be measured using a graduated cylinder. When liquid is placed in a glass graduated cylinder, a curved shape, called a **meniscus**, may be formed. Readings are most accurate if taken from the bottom of the meniscus, assuming the curve is lower in the middle, as shown in Figure 3-2.

Figure 3-2 The volume of a liquid

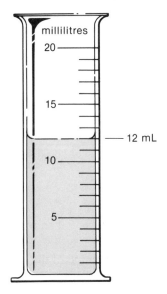

Volume of a small, irregular, solid object

If the volume of a solid irregular object, such as a small stone, is required, a technique called the **displacement of water** can be used. For example, assume a graduated cylinder contains 20 mL of water. A stone is lowered into the water, and the water rises to the 23 mL level. The volume of the stone is 3 mL, which is 3 cm³.

Volume of a large, irregular, solid object

The volume of a large irregular object can be found by the displacement of water using an overflow can. Refer to Figure 3-3. The can should be filled with water, and the excess water allowed to drip out of the spout. The object, when lowered gently into the water, will force some water out of the can's spout. The water is then caught and measured in a graduated cylinder.

Figure 3.3 Measuring volume by the displacement of water

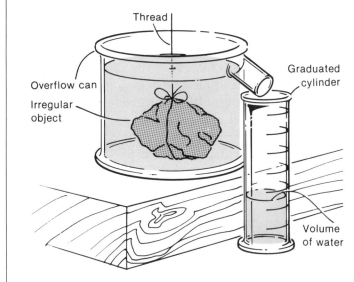

Activity 3A Measuring and Estimating Volume

PROBLEM ■ What is the most appropriate method to measure the volume of:
(a) a regular solid?
(b) a uniform sphere?
(c) a small irregular object?
(d) a large irregular object?
(e) lung capacity?

APPARATUS ■ metric ruler; vernier calliper; graduated cylinder; overflow can; rubber tubing; large container with a narrow opening (e.g., a plastic or metal container used for distilled water); various objects whose volumes are to be measured (e.g., regular solid blocks, marble, irregular solid objects)

PROCEDURE ■
1. Measure the dimensions of a regular solid and calculate its volume in an appropriate unit. Remember to round your answer.
2. Measure the diameter of a sphere using the vernier calliper and calculate the sphere's volume in an appropriate unit.
3. Use the displacement of water in a graduated cylinder to measure the volume of selected small, irregular objects.
4. Estimate the volume of a large rubber stopper or similar object. Use the displacement of water in an overflow can to measure the volume of the stopper.
5. Estimate the volumes of some mystery objects or containers set up by your teacher.

CAUTION Anyone with respiratory problems should consult the teacher before trying Procedure #6.

6. Estimate to the closest half-litre the volume of air you can exhale from your lungs. Check your estimate by blowing into an inverted water-filled container that is submerged in water (Figure 3-4). Place your hand tightly over the mouth of the container. Invert the container in the air and measure the volume of water required to refill it.

ANALYSIS ■
1. In your opinion, which provides a more accurate determination of volume, displacement of water or calculations with measured lengths? Explain your answer.
2. Describe how you could improve your ability to estimate volume.

APPLICATIONS ■
1. An upright freezer has inside dimensions of 1.8 m by 0.80 m by 0.90 m.
   (a) What is the inside volume of the freezer?
   (b) How many litres of ice cream can the freezer hold?
2. The diameter of a spherical storage tank at an oil refinery is 10 m.
   (a) Determine the volume that the tank can hold in metres cubed.
   (b) Convert your answer to litres.
   (c) Convert your answer to megalitres.

Figure 3-4 Estimating lung capacity

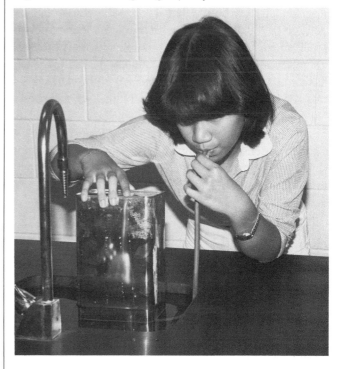

3.3 Density

From your past experience, you should have a general idea about the meaning of density. You know that cork floats on water, but iron sinks in water. This indicates that cork has a lower density than water, and iron has a higher density. Density is derived from two quantities, mass and volume, so before we define density, let us review the meaning of mass.

Mass is a measure of the quantity of matter contained in an object. It is a fundamental measurement, just as time and distance are. The SI base unit of mass is the kilogram (kg). Other metric units of mass are the milligram (mg), gram (g), and metric tonne (t).

The kilogram is the only base unit with a prefix. The gram proved to be too small for practical purposes. The one-kilogram standard is a block of iridium alloy kept in France. Copies of the standard kilogram are kept in major centres around the world.

We can now define **density**: it is the mass per unit volume of a substance. The expression ''per unit volume'' means that we must compare the masses of equal volumes of substances. For example, 1.0 m³ of brass has a mass of about 8500 kg, and 1.0 m³ of water has a mass of 1000 kg. So for the same volume (1.0 m³), brass has 8.5 times as much mass as water. Thus, the density of brass is 8.5 times greater than the density of water.

Since density is defined as the quantity of matter (mass) per unit volume, the equation for density is written in terms of mass and volume. The equation is:

$$D = \frac{m}{V}$$

Sample Problem 3

A 2.5 m³ sample of ore has a mass of 10 000 kg. Calculate the density of the ore.

$$
\begin{aligned}
Solution \quad D &= \frac{m}{V} \\
&= \frac{10\ 000\ \text{kg}}{2.5\ \text{m}^3} \\
&= 4000\ \frac{\text{kg}}{\text{m}^3}
\end{aligned}
$$

Sample Problem 4

Assume that 2.0 L of gasoline has a mass of 1400 g. Calculate the density of the gasoline.

$$
\begin{aligned}
Solution \quad D &= \frac{m}{V} \\
&= \frac{1400\ \text{g}}{2.0\ \text{L}} \\
&= 700\ \frac{\text{g}}{\text{L}}\ \text{(grams per litre)}
\end{aligned}
$$

The preferred unit for density in the SI is kilograms per metre cubed (kg/m³). In sample problem 4, the density of 700 g/L can be expressed as 700 kg/m³ because

$$\frac{1.0\ \text{g}}{1.0\ \text{L}} = \frac{1000\ \text{g}}{1000\ \text{L}} = \frac{1.0\ \text{kg}}{1.0\ \text{m}^3}$$

In other words, 1000 g = 1.0 kg and
1000 L = 1.0 m³.
Thus, density expressed in grams per litre is equivalent to density expressed in kilograms per metre cubed.

DID YOU KNOW?

People who work with minerals and jewels use density to determine the purity of a sample. For example, there is a big difference between the density of gold and the density of lead coated with gold.

Density is a characteristic property of matter. This means that any sample of a pure substance has the same density. It does not matter how large or small the sample is, where the sample is taken from, or where in the world the density is measured. It also means that the density of a sample of some unknown pure substance can be used to identify the substance. For example, if an investigation conducted to determine the density of an unknown metal finds the density to be 2700 kg/m³, then the unknown substance is aluminum. The densities of several common substances are listed in Table 3-1.

Table 3-1   Densities of Some Common Substances

Substance	State	Density (kg/m³)
Hydrogen	Gas (0°C)	0.089
Helium	Gas (0°C)	0.178
Air	Gas (0°C)	1.29
Cork	Solid	240
Ethyl alcohol	Liquid	790
Ice	Solid (0°C)	920
Water	Liquid (4°C)	1000
Salt water	Liquid (0°C)	1030 (varies)
Glycerin	Liquid	1260
Aluminum	Solid	2700
Iron	Solid	7860
Brass	Solid	8500
Copper	Solid	8950
Mercury	Liquid	13 600
Gold	Solid	19 300

Note: Values listed are at 20°C unless otherwise stated.

PRACTICE

8. A 0.20 m³ sample of a substance has a mass of 540 kg.
   (a) Determine the density of the substance.
   (b) Use Table 3-1 to identify the substance.
9. A 1.5 L sample of liquid has a mass of 2100 g.
   (a) Calculate the density of the liquid in grams per litre.
   (b) Convert your answer in (a) to the preferred metric unit of density.
10. A mining engineer has a mineral sample that looks like pure gold. The sample is found to have a mass of 400 kg and a volume of 0.025 m³. Determine the density of the sample, and use it to decide if the sample is pure gold. (Reference: Table 3-1)
11. Rearrange the equation $D = \frac{m}{V}$ to determine an equation for:
    (a) m by itself   (b) V by itself
12. Determine the unknown quantity in each case:
    (a) $D = 4200$ kg/m³; $V = 0.20$ m³;
       $m = ?$ kg
    (b) $D = 640$ g/L; $m = 3520$ g; $V = ?$ L

Activity **3B**   **Density**

PROBLEM ■
(a) How can graphing be used to determine the density of a liquid?
(b) How can the density of various solid objects be found?

APPARATUS ■

For Problem (a): triple-beam balance; 100 mL graduated cylinder; liquid whose density will be measured
For Problem (b): You will make up this list after you read the procedural instructions.

Note: Part of this activity involves plotting a graph of measured data and finding the slope of the line on the graph. If your graphing skills need updating, refer to Appendix E at the back of the book.

CAUTION   *Take care when choosing a liquid — some may be hazardous. Consult your teacher.*

PROCEDURE ■
1. Design and perform an investigation to find the mass in grams of these volumes of the same liquid: 0.0 mL, 20 mL, 40 mL, 60 mL, 80 mL, and 100 mL. Plot the data on a graph with mass on the vertical axis. (Do you know why mass should be on the vertical axis?) Draw the line of best fit, and find the slope of the line. This slope represents the density of the liquid in grams per millilitre. Convert your answer to grams per litre.
2. Design and perform an investigation to measure the density of various solid objects. Try to choose interesting objects. Write a report of this investigation, including the apparatus, the procedure, and analysis.

Words to Know

area	displacement of water
volume	mass
meniscus	density

Chapter Objectives

Having completed this chapter, you should now be able to:

1. Recognize the difference between fundamental and derived quantities, and give examples of each.
2. State and use the metric units of area, volume, mass, and density.
3. Describe how to find the area, volume, and density of a variety of objects experimentally.
4. Identify a substance by determining its density and referring to a table of densities.
5. Apply the equation for density $\left(D = \dfrac{m}{V}\right)$ to find any one of the three variables, given the other two.

Chapter Review

1. The following are symbols of some of the units seen in this chapter: m, m², m³, mL, L, g, kg, g/L, kg/m³
   (a) Which of these units belong to fundamental quantities?
   (b) Which units are capacity units?
   (c) Which unit is the preferred metric unit of density?
   (d) Which are units of derived quantities?

2. A rectangular plot of land with dimensions 200 m by 450 m is for sale.
   (a) Determine the area of the plot in square metres.
   (b) What is the area in hectares?
   (c) At a cost of $2000/ha, what is the asking price of the land?   (3.1)

3. A drill bit has a diameter of 1.8 cm. Determine the cross-sectional area of the hole made by this bit.   (3.1)

4. A 2500 kg sample of a liquid has a volume of 2.5 m³.
   (a) Calculate the density of the liquid.
   (b) Identify the liquid.   (3.3)

5. A block of metal is 50 cm long, 20 cm wide, and 15 cm deep. It has a mass of 127.5 kg.
   (a) Write the dimensions of the block in metres.
   (b) Calculate the volume of the block in metres cubed.
   (c) Determine the density of the block.
   (d) What is the identity of the metal? (Reference: Table 3-1)   (3.2, 3.3)

6. A 660 g rock is lowered into an overflow can filled with water. The volume of water it displaces is 120 mL.
   (a) What is the volume of the rock in cubic centimetres?
   (b) Calculate the density of the rock in grams per cubic centimetre.   (3.2, 3.3)

7. A student performed an experiment to find the density of glycerin (a liquid). The measurements are shown below. Use them to calculate the density of glycerin in grams per litre.

   mass of graduated cylinder 12.4 g
   volume of glycerin added 82 mL
   mass of cylinder and glycerin 117.4 g (3.3)

8. A chunk of cork has a volume of 0.15 m³. What is the mass of the block? (See Table 3-1.) (3.3)

9. One winter it was estimated that one million kilograms of ice had formed on a small lake. What is the volume of this amount of ice, to 2 significant digits? (Reference: Table 3-1) (3.3)

10. Estimate the total mass of water found in an Olympic-size swimming pool. Show all your calculations.

11. State which of the derived quantities (area, volume, and density) each of the following people would be concerned with, and state why.
    (a) a real estate agent
    (b) an architect
    (c) a grain farmer
    (d) a dairy farmer
    (e) a pharmacist
    (f) an engineer at a gold mine
    (g) a chemist at an oil refinery

Motion and Mechanical Energy

You are very familiar with the motion of objects, and possibly even with the forces that affect those movements. Laws that describe motion enable us to predict a fly's movement, the path of a satellite around a planet, or the safest design for a new automobile. In this unit you will study more about the laws that describe motion.

Energy allows us to do work. Earlier peoples consumed energy stored in food that enabled them to work with their bodies. As civilization progressed more forms of energy were found. Today energy is used to heat homes in winter, cool homes in summer, manufacture necessities and luxuries, cook food, transport people and goods—the list is endless. Energy exists in many forms; in this unit you will investigate two: kinetic energy, which is the energy of motion, and gravitational potential energy, which is the energy an object possesses because of its position.

Together, kinetic energy and gravitational potential energy are called mechanical energy.

Information about motion and mechanical energy gathered in this unit will be useful to you as you consider future careers in the automotive, aviation, or construction industries. Knowledge of motion and mechanical energy is also useful in such fields as space technology, machine design, medical technology, urban design, sports, and energy conservation.

- People who design, plan, and build roads and bridges need to be keenly aware of motion and mechanical energy. Knowledge of how best to use reinforced concrete and steel, of highway technology, plane surveying, and computer-aided construction practices is now basic for careers in this area.

Knowing the information in this unit will be especially useful if you plan a career in any of the areas already mentioned, as well as the following: environmental technology, traffic control and safety, trucking and/or shipping, or energy resources. You can get more information about any career possibility mentioned by interviewing someone already on that career path, and by contacting your local community college, university, guidance office, or counselling centre.

CHAPTER 4

Uniform Motion

When traffic becomes heavy on the city expressway shown in the photograph, the vehicles in one lane tend to travel at approximately the same speed. Although motion at a constant speed in one direction is not very common, it is the easiest type of motion to study. The main portion of this chapter is devoted to an examination of motion at a constant speed. Experimenting and graphing will help you analyse such motion.

Main Ideas

- The speed of an object moving with uniform motion can be calculated using the distance travelled and the time taken.
- On a distance-time graph, uniform motion is represented by a straight line.
- The slope of the line on a distance-time graph indicates the speed of the moving object.
- A recording timer or similar device can be used to determine time in activities involving motion.

4.1 Non-Uniform and Uniform Motion

Motion is very common in our universe. Our solar system moves through space. The earth moves around the sun. People, animals, the air, and many other things move on the earth's surface. Tiny particles, many of which are too small to see, are also in motion.

Motion may be classified as either non-uniform or uniform. **Non-uniform motion** is movement involving change in speed, or direction, or both. Your motion to get from home to school is non-uniform: you speed up, slow down, stop, move up or down stairs, and so on. Another example of non-uniform motion is shown in Figure 4-1.

Figure 4-1 A car travelling at a constant speed around a corner is experiencing non-uniform motion. In this case, the direction of the car's motion is changing.

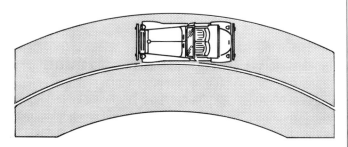

Uniform motion is movement in a straight line at a constant speed. If you were jogging along a straight path with a constant speed of 3 m/s, your motion would be uniform.

Sample Problem 1

Decide whether each motion listed below is uniform or non-uniform.
(a) A steel ball is dropped from your raised hand to the floor.
(b) A car is travelling north at a constant speed of 80 km/h for two hours.
(c) A jogger is running around a circular track at a constant speed.

Solution
(a) non-uniform motion (The speed of the ball increases as it falls.)
(b) uniform motion
(c) non-uniform motion (The jogger's direction is constantly changing.)

PRACTICE

1. Describe each motion below as either uniform or non-uniform. If you think it is non-uniform, explain why.
   (a) A car is travelling a steady 60 km/h due west.
   (b) A leaf flutters toward the ground.
   (c) A rocket is launched from the earth toward the moon.
   (d) A motorcycle rider applies the brakes in order to come to a stop.
   (e) A ball on the end of a rope is whirled around a person's head at a constant speed of 8.0 m/s.

4.2 Speed

In order to analyse motion, we must be able to measure speed. **Speed** is the total *distance travelled* divided by the *time*. Writing this in equation form:

$$\text{speed} = \frac{\text{distance travelled}}{\text{time}} \quad \text{or}$$

$$v = \frac{d}{t}$$

Since the base unit of distance is the metre and the base unit of time is the second, the metric unit of speed is metres per second (m/s). Speed may also be expressed in other units, such as centimetres per second and kilometres per hour. (Most texts use the symbol v for speed from the word velocity, which is speed with a direction.)

Sample Problem 2

Calculate the speed of a runner who takes 500 s to run 2000 m.

Solution $\quad v = \dfrac{d}{t}$

$$= \frac{2000\,\text{m}}{500\,\text{s}}$$

$$= 4.0 \text{ m/s}$$

PRACTICE

2. Calculate the speed if:
   (a) $d = 8.0$ m and $t = 4.0$ s
   (b) $d = 25$ m and $t = 0.5$ s
   (c) $d = 6.2$ m and $t = 0.1$ s
3. In 3.0 s sound travels 1000 m in air. What is the speed of sound in air?

4. In the human body blood travels in the largest blood vessel, the aorta, faster than in any other blood vessel. Calculate the blood's speed (in centimetres per second) in the aorta if the blood takes 0.2 s to travel 6.0 cm.
5. Rewrite the equation $v = \dfrac{d}{t}$ to express:
   (a) d by itself
   (b) t by itself
6. Calculate the unknown quantities:
   (a) $v = 14.5$ m/s; $t = 12$ s; $d = ?$ m
   (b) $v = 16$ m/s; $d = 256$ m; $t = ?$ s
7. How far would a cyclist travel in 120 s at a constant speed of 12 m/s?
8. At a speed of 950 km/h, how many kilometres would an airplane travel in 12 h?
9. Assume the distance around the earth at the equator is 40 000 km (4.0×10^4 km). Calculate how many hours it would take a supersonic jet to travel once around the world at a speed of 1600 km/h.

4.3 Graphing Uniform Motion

In experiments involving motion, the variables usually measured are distance and time. The third variable, speed, is often found by calculation rather than direct measurement.

In uniform motion, the speed is constant, so the distance moved is the same in equal time intervals. For instance, assume that an object moves exactly 3.0 m every second. Then its speed is steady at 3.0 m/s and we can make a table of ordered pairs of its motion:

time (s)	0	1	2	3	4
distance (m)	0	3	6	9	12

Figure 4-2 shows a graph of this motion. Notice that for uniform motion a graph of distance against time yields a straight line.

Figure 4-2 A distance-time graph of uniform motion

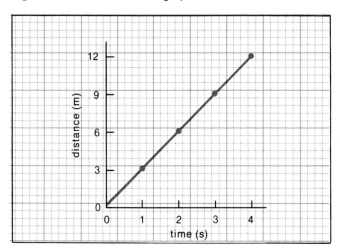

PRACTICE

10. On one distance-time graph, draw the line for each set of ordered pairs listed below. Remember to label each axis of the graph.

(a) time (s)   0   10   20   30

     distance (m) 0   2   4   6

(b) time (s)   0   10   20   30

     distance (m) 0   5   10   15

(c) time (s)   0   5   10   15

     distance (m) 0   5   10   15

11. Which lines on the distance-time graph shown represent uniform motion? How can you tell?

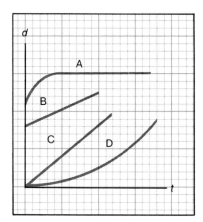

4.4   Measuring Time

Time is an important quantity in the study of motion. (Remember that speed = distance/time.) You will be required to measure time in various activities involving motion. A simple *stopwatch* gives acceptable values of time intervals, but if accurate results are required, a better method must be used.

Most physics laboratories have instruments that measure time very accurately for demonstration purposes. A *digital timer* is an electronic device that measures time intervals to a fraction of a second. An *electronic stroboscope* has a light that flashes on and off at time intervals controlled by adjusting a dial. A stroboscope is used to light up a moving object in a dark room as a camera records the object's motion on film. The motion can be analysed knowing the time between flashes of the strobe. A *computer* with the appropriate software measures time intervals to the nearest millisecond (ms).

Devices that produce dots at regular periods of time provide another way to measure time intervals. One such device is the *recording timer*, described in Section 1.4 and shown in Figure 1-7. (A recording timer may also be called a spark timer.) A paper strip is pulled through the timer and dots are made on the strip. The recorded dots give an exact picture of the motion. The faster the motion, the greater is the space between the dots.

Figure 4-3 Measuring time using a recording timer: Notice that it takes seven dots, including the starting one, to obtain six spaces.

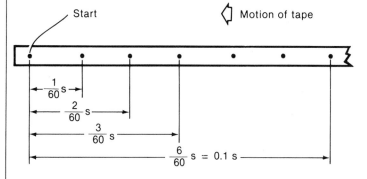

Most recording timers make 60 dots each second. We say they have a frequency of 60 Hz or 60 vibrations/s. (Hz is the symbol for hertz.) Figure 4-3 illustrates why an interval of six spaces on a recording tape represents a time of 0.1 s.

Sample Problem 3

A student pulls a tape through a 60 Hz recording timer and obtains the tape shown. Plot a graph of distance (from the starting position) against time.

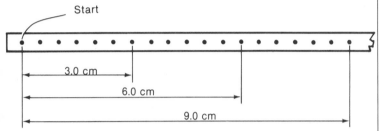

Solution   The ordered pairs are:

time (s)	0	0.1	0.2	0.3
distance (cm)	0	3.0	6.0	9.0

The required graph is shown below. The line is straight, which means that the tape was pulled at a constant speed.

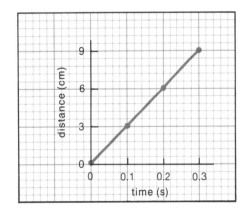

Motion can also be studied on an air table with one or two pucks that move with little or no friction. In one type of air table, a spark timer produces dots on paper at intervals of 100 ms, 50 ms, or as low as 10 ms. The analysis of the motion recorded on the paper is similar to that for the recording timer, although it may take a different number of spaces to produce 0.1 s.

PRACTICE

12. The motion of a tape pulled through a 60 Hz recording timer is shown in the diagram below. Use the results to plot a graph of distance (from the starting position) against time.

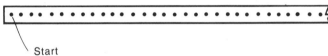

13. (a) How can you judge from the dots produced by a recording timer whether or not the motion was uniform?
    (b) How can you judge from a distance-time graph whether or not the motion was uniform?

Activity 4A   Graphing Motion

PROBLEM ■   How does a graph of attempted uniform motion reveal how constant the speed was?

APPARATUS ■   recording timer and related apparatus; battery-operated toy vehicle; masking tape; metre stick; graph paper

Note: The procedure for this activity suggests only one of many possible ways of producing motion that can be timed. The analysis applies to any choice of procedure.

PROCEDURE ■

1. Check whether the recording timer is working properly by pulling a short strip of paper through it. If the timer is skipping, double-dotting, or making unclear dots, inform your teacher.
2. Obtain a paper strip about 80 to 100 cm long, and attach it to the battery-powered vehicle. With the timer off, arrange the strip so the timer can record the motion of the vehicle, as shown in Figure 4-4.

Figure 4-4 Using a recording timer to determine the motion of a toy vehicle

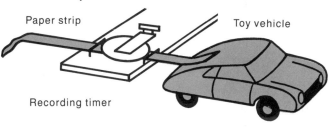

Paper strip
Toy vehicle
Recording timer

3. Turn on the timer, start the vehicle moving, and obtain a record of the motion on the strip of paper.
4. On the tape, find the first distinct dot and label it A. From A count six spaces to B. Measure AB, which is the distance travelled in the first time interval.
5. From point B count another six spaces to point C. Measure AC to find the total distance travelled to the end of the second interval. See Figure 4-5.

Figure 4-5 Motion during the first two intervals of time

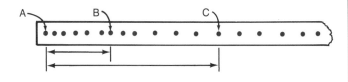

A   B   C

6. Repeat this procedure for a maximum of 10 intervals, always measuring the distance from point A.

ANALYSIS ■

1. Set up a table of data indicating the *time* elapsed and the total *distance* from the starting position.
2. Plot a distance-time graph of the motion. (If your graphing skills need reviewing, see Appendix E near the back of the book.)
3. According to the graph, was the speed constant at the beginning of the motion? How can you tell?
4. Did the speed become constant or nearly so later in the motion? How can you tell from the graph?

APPLICATION ■ Sketch a distance-time graph of a battery-powered toy moving first with a constant speed, then experiencing a change of speed as the battery becomes weak and finally "dies."

4.5 Slopes of Lines on Distance-Time Graphs

If a graph of distance against time is drawn for uniform motion at various speeds, a set of straight lines at different slopes will result. In order to calculate the value of the slope of a straight line on a graph, we use the equation:

$$\mathbf{slope} = \frac{\mathbf{rise}}{\mathbf{run}} \quad \text{or}$$

$$m = \frac{\triangle y}{\triangle x}$$

In this equation, m is the slope of the line, $\triangle y$ is the change in the value of the y variable, and $\triangle x$ is the change in the value of the x variable. ($\triangle$ is the letter *delta* from the Greek alphabet.)

On a distance-time graph, distance is the y variable and time is the x variable, so the equation for slope is

$$m = \frac{\triangle d}{\triangle t}$$

Units of measurement must be included when calculating the slope of a line on a graph. This is shown in the example that follows.

Sample Problem 4

Calculate the slope of the line on the distance-time graph shown.

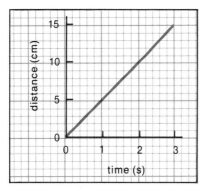

Figure 4-6 The motion from 0 s to 2 s is faster than from 2 s to 5 s.

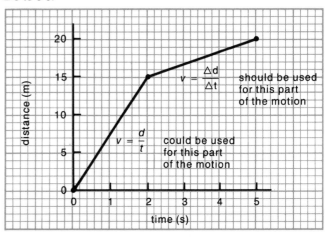

$$Solution \quad m = \frac{\Delta d}{\Delta t}$$

$$= \frac{15\,cm}{3.0\,s}$$

$$= 5.0 \text{ cm/s}$$

The answer to sample problem 4 has units of centimetres per second, which represent speed. Thus, we can conclude that *the slope of a line on a distance-time graph indicates speed*.

In Section 4.2 the equation for speed was $v = \frac{d}{t}$, whereas here the equation for speed is $v = \frac{\Delta d}{\Delta t}$. The first equation applies when considering a single motion only. The second equation can be used with a single motion. But it is more general, because it can also be used when more than one motion at a constant speed is involved. An example of two motions represented on the same distance-time graph is shown in Figure 4-6.

PRACTICE

14. Calculate the slope of each line on the distance-time graphs shown:

(a)

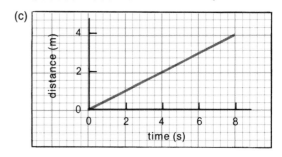

(b)

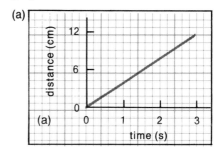

(c)

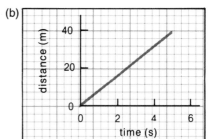

4.6 Graphs of Speed Against Time for Uniform Motion

Speed can be found by calculating the slope of the line on a distance-time graph. Since the slope of a straight line is constant, this means that the speed is constant. This fact can be used to plot a speed-time graph of the motion. For example, if the slope of a line on a distance-time graph is 5.0 m/s, then the line on the corresponding speed-time graph is horizontal (constant) at a value of 5.0 m/s.

DID YOU KNOW?

If you are in a car travelling at 60 km/h and another car is travelling toward you at 80 km/h, it *seems* as if the approaching car is travelling at 140 km/h. The speed of one car relative to the other is 140 km/h.

Sample Problem 5

Given the distance-time graph shown, determine the speed of the motion and plot the corresponding speed-time graph.

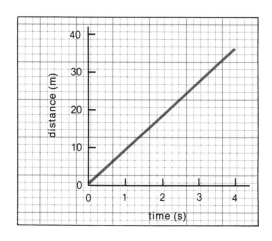

Solution
$$\text{speed} = \text{slope}$$
$$= \frac{\Delta d}{\Delta t}$$
$$= \frac{36 \text{ m}}{4.0 \text{ s}}$$
$$= 9.0 \text{ m/s}$$

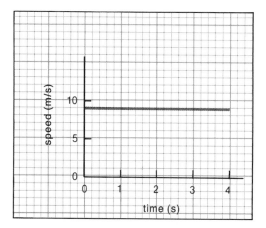

The line on the speed-time graph in sample problem 5 ends at the same time as the line on the distance-time graph. This is because we do not have data after that time.

PRACTICE

15. Plot a speed-time graph that corresponds to each distance-time graph in Practice # 14, at the end of the previous section.

Activity 4B Uniform Motion at Varying Speeds

PROBLEM ■ What is revealed by plotting distance-time and speed-time graphs of uniform motion at varying speeds?

APPARATUS ■ Read the procedure, then indicate what apparatus you will be using.

PROCEDURE ■
1. Use a technique approved by your teacher to obtain observations of motion at three distinct constant speeds — slow, medium, and fast. (It is important to try to obtain *constant speeds*. Thus, if you use a recording timer, you may have to omit several dots at the beginning of the motion where the speed is not constant.)
2. Record all the data in a table indicating the distance from the start of the uniform motion, and the time.

ANALYSIS ■
1. On one distance-time graph plot lines representing all three motions. Remember to label each axis as well as each line. (If the points plotted do not lie on a straight line, draw the line of best fit so that the slope can be found.)
2. Calculate and compare the slopes of the three lines.
3. On one speed-time graph, plot the speeds of the three motions. Be sure each line ends at the appropriate time. Explain how this graph relates to the activity.

4. What is revealed by plotting distance-time and speed-time graphs of uniform motion at varying speeds?

APPLICATION ■ The graph shown reveals four different motions that you might observe while standing outdoors. State which line best matches each of these motions:

(a) a cyclist rides by you at top speed
(b) a jogger runs past you
(c) some geese are flying overhead
(d) a single-engine aircraft is flying overhead

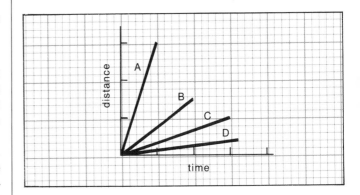

Words to Know

non-uniform motion
uniform motion

speed
slope of a line
(on a distance-time graph)

Chapter Objectives

Having completed this chapter, you should now be able to:
1. Define uniform motion and non-uniform motion.
2. Apply the equation for speed in terms of distance and time $\left(v = \dfrac{d}{t}\right)$.

3. Draw line graphs of distance against time, given a table of distance-time data.
4. Measure time accurately in activities.
5. Examine lines on a distance-time graph to determine whether the motion plotted is uniform and whether one motion is faster than another.
6. Calculate the slope of a straight line on a graph, using the equation for slope $\left(m = \dfrac{\Delta y}{\Delta x}\right)$.
7. Know that the slope of a line on a distance-time graph represents speed.
8. Plot a speed-time graph, given a distance-time graph.

Chapter Review

1. Define and give an example of uniform motion. (4.1)
2. Define and give an example of non-uniform motion. (4.1)
3. What speed is needed by a bionic track star in order to run 100 m in 8.0 s? (4.2)
4. Light travels from the sun to the earth, a distance of 1.5×10^{11} m, in only 500 s. Calculate the speed of light. (4.2)
5. The highest average lap speed on a closed circuit in motorcycling is about 72 m/s (or 258 km/h). If a cyclist takes 56 s to complete one lap of the circular track, what is the distance around the track? (4.2)
6. The record lap speed for car racing is about 112 m/s (or 402 km/h). The record was set on a track 12.5 km in circumference. How long did the driver take to complete one lap? (4.2)
7. The motion of a tape pulled through a 60 Hz recording timer is shown in the diagram below.

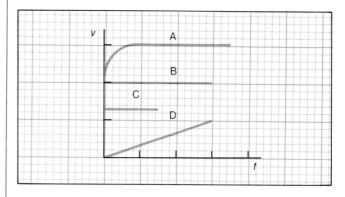

Start

   (a) What is the time interval between the beginning of the tape and the end?
   (b) Is the motion uniform? Explain your answer. (4.4)
8. What does the slope of a line on a distance-time graph represent? (4.5)

9. Find the slope of each line on the distance-time graph shown. Then draw the corresponding speed-time graph for the motions. (4.5, 4.6)

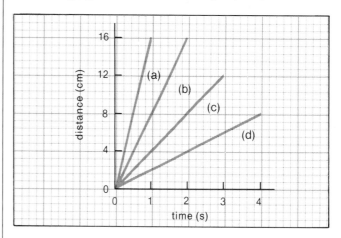

10. Which lines on the speed-time graph shown represent uniform motion? Explain your answer. (4.6)

11. (a) Estimate your average walking speed in metres per second.
    (b) Estimate the total distance from the Pacific Coast to the Atlantic Coast of mainland Canada. Express your answer in both kilometres and metres.
    (c) Use your answers in (a) and (b) to calculate approximately how long you would take to walk across Canada. Express your answer in seconds, and in hours.

CHAPTER 5

Uniformly Accelerated Motion

accelerated motion (slowing down) as well as positive accelerated motion (speeding up). There are many applications (both useful and unwanted) in our daily lives.

Main Ideas

- Accelerated motion can be positive or negative.
- Acceleration can be found using an equation involving change of speed and the time for that change.
- Acceleration can also be found from a speed-time graph.
- Graphing can be used to analyse accelerated motion.
- The acceleration of objects near the surface of the earth is commonly called the acceleration due to gravity.

Vehicles tend to come to a stop much more quickly than they can speed up. This is especially true if one vehicle crashes into a wall or another vehicle. A test vehicle with a dummy, like the one shown in the photograph, is used to discover the effects of crashes on the human body. Knowing this information helps engineers design safer vehicles. In this chapter, you will study negative

5.1 Comparing Uniform Motion and Uniformly Accelerated Motion

In Chapter 4 you studied uniform motion in which an object travels at a steady speed in a straight line. Figure 5-1 reminds you that a line on a speed-time graph of uniform motion is horizontal.

time (s)	0	1	2	3	4
speed (m/s)	15	15	15	15	15

Most moving objects do not display uniform motion. Any change in an object's speed or direction means that its motion is not uniform. This non-uniform motion is called **accelerated motion**. An example of accelerated motion is a car ride at rush hour in a city when the car has to speed up, slow down, and turn corners.

One type of accelerated motion is called **uniformly accelerated motion**. This is motion of an object that travels in a straight line and has its speed changing steadily with time. Figure 5-2 gives an example of uniformly accelerated motion for an object that starts from rest and increases its speed by 5.0 m/s every second.

time (s)	0	1	2	3	4
speed (m/s)	0	5	10	15	20

Uniformly accelerated motion also occurs when an object, travelling in a straight line, is slowing down steadily. In this case, the object is actually undergoing *decelerated motion*, or is said to have **negative accelerated motion**. Refer to Figure 5-3, which gives an example of uniformly negative accelerated motion in which a moving object slows down steadily from 20 m/s to 0.0 m/s in 4.0 s.

time (s)	0	1	2	3	4
speed (m/s)	20	15	10	5	0

Figure 5-1 Uniform motion

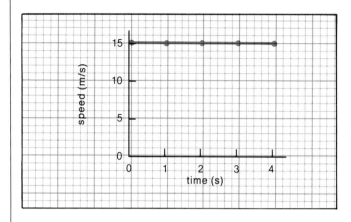

Figure 5-2 Uniformly accelerated motion

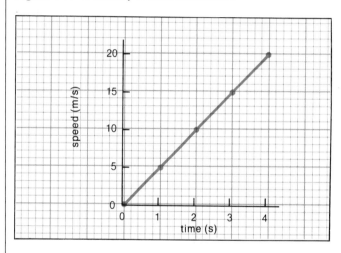

Figure 5-3 Uniformly negative accelerated motion

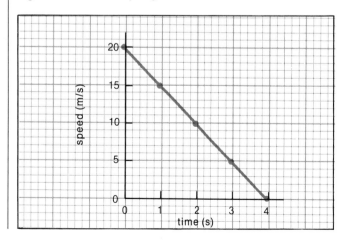

If an object is changing its speed in an unsteady fashion, its accelerated motion is non-uniform. Such motion is difficult to analyse, but an example is given in Figure 5-4 for comparison purposes.

time (s)	0	1	2	3	4
speed (m/s)	0	10	16	19	20

Figure 5-4 Non-uniformly accelerated motion

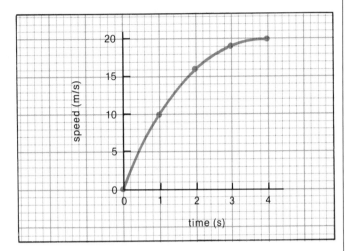

PRACTICE

1. The table shows five different sets of speeds at times of 0, 1, 2, and 3 s. Which sets represent uniformly positive or negative accelerated motion?

time(s)	0	1	2	3
(a) speed (m/s)	0	10	20	30
(b) speed (m/s)	0	5	10	10
(c) speed (m/s)	5	5	5	5
(d) speed (m/s)	15	16	17	18
(e) speed (m/s)	15	10	5	0

2. Choose which speed-time graphs represent uniformly positive or negative accelerated motion.

(a)

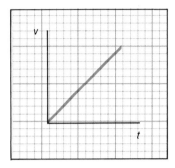

(b)

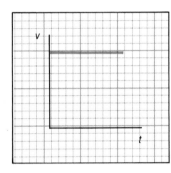

(c)

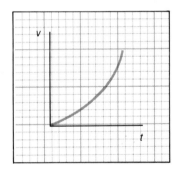

(d)

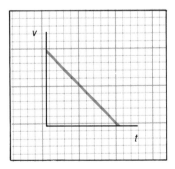

5.2 Calculating Acceleration

For motion in a straight line, **acceleration** is defined as the rate of change of speed. In order to calculate an object's acceleration, we must know its *change of speed* and the *time during which that change occurred*. In equation form:

$$\textbf{acceleration} = \frac{\textbf{change of speed}}{\textbf{time}} \quad \text{or}$$

$$a = \frac{\Delta v}{\Delta t}$$

The units of acceleration must be units of speed divided by units of time. In the SI, speed is measured in metres per second, so acceleration is stated in metres per second $\div$ seconds, or (m/s)/s. SI units will be necessary in Chapters 6 and 7, but for now it is acceptable to use centimetres per second per second, (cm/s)/s, and kilometres per hour per second, (km/h)/s.

Sample Problem 1

A motorbike, starting from rest, reaches a speed of 20 m/s in 8.0 s. Find the bike's acceleration.

Solution $a = \dfrac{\Delta v}{\Delta t}$

$\qquad = \dfrac{20\,\text{m/s}}{8.0\,\text{s}}$

$\qquad = 2.5\,\dfrac{(\text{m/s})}{\text{s}} \quad \text{or} \quad 2.5\,(\text{m/s})/\text{s}$

In sample problem 1, the acceleration of 2.5 (m/s)/s means that the speed of the motorbike increases 2.5 m/s every second. Thus, the bike's speed is 2.5 m/s after 1.0 s, 5.0 m/s after 2.0 s, and so on.

Sample Problem 2

An airline flight is behind schedule so the pilot increases the air speed from 135 m/s to 165 m/s in 60 s. What is the aircraft's acceleration?

Solution $a = \dfrac{\Delta v}{\Delta t}$

$\qquad = \dfrac{30\,\text{m/s}}{60\,\text{s}}$

$\qquad = 0.5\,\dfrac{(\text{m/s})}{\text{s}} \quad \text{or} \quad 0.5\,(\text{m/s})/\text{s}$

If an object is slowing down, its acceleration is negative, as shown in the next example.

Sample Problem 3

A cyclist, travelling at a speed of 12 m/s, brakes smoothly and stops in 4.0 s. What is the cyclist's acceleration?

Solution The change in speed (Δv) is negative because the speed decreases from 12 m/s to 0.0 m/s. Thus,

$a = \dfrac{\Delta v}{\Delta t}$

$\qquad = \dfrac{-12\,\text{m/s}}{4.0\,\text{s}}$

$\qquad = -3.0\,\dfrac{(\text{m/s})}{\text{s}} \quad \text{or} \quad -3.0\,(\text{m/s})/\text{s}$

PRACTICE

3. Calculate the acceleration if:
   (a) Δv = 72 m/s and Δt = 6.0 s
   (b) Δv = 8.4 m/s and Δt = 0.5 s
   (c) Δv = -35 m/s and Δt = 7.0 s
4. The world record for motorcycle acceleration occurred when a cycle took only 6.0 s to go from rest to 78 m/s (281 km/h). Calculate the record acceleration.
5. A car, travelling at 60 km/h, increases its speed to 100 km/h in 10 s. What is its acceleration?
6. Calculate the acceleration needed by a train, travelling at 12 m/s, to stop in 120 s.
7. Rewrite the equation $a = \dfrac{\Delta v}{\Delta t}$ to express:
   (a) Δv by itself
   (b) Δt by itself
8. Calculate the unknown quantities:
   (a) a = 4.2 (m/s)/s; Δt = 15 s; Δv = ? m/s
   (b) a = 2.1 (m/s)/s; Δv = 42 m/s; Δt = ? s
9. In the second stage of a rocket launch the rocket's speed increased from 1000 m/s to 10 000 m/s with an average acceleration of 30 (m/s)/s. How long did the acceleration last?
10. A truck driver, travelling at 90 km/h, applies the brakes to prevent hitting a stalled car. In order to prevent a collision, the truck would have to be stopped in 20 s. At an acceleration of -4.0 (km/h)/s, will a collision occur?
11. Assume that when a ball is thrown upwards it accelerates at a rate of -10 (m/s)/s. With what speed must a ball leave a thrower's hand in order to climb for 2.0 s before stopping?

5.3 Using Speed-Time Graphs to Find Acceleration

In Chapter 4 you learned that the slope of a line on a distance-time graph indicates the speed. Let us now use the equation $m = \dfrac{\Delta y}{\Delta x}$ to see what the slope of a line on a speed-time graph gives.

Consider the graph in Figure 5-5. The slope of the line is

$$
\begin{aligned}
m &= \frac{\Delta y}{\Delta x} \\
&= \frac{\Delta v}{\Delta t} \\
&= \frac{30\,\text{m/s}}{10\,\text{s}} \\
&= 3.0\,\frac{\text{m/s}}{\text{s}} \quad \text{or} \quad 3.0\,\text{(m/s)/s}
\end{aligned}
$$

Figure 5-5   Speed-time graph

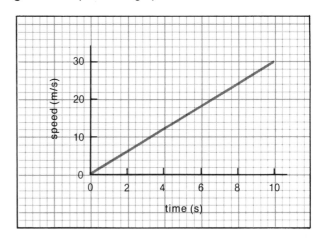

The units for this slope represent acceleration. Thus, we can conclude that *the slope of a line on a speed-time graph equals the acceleration.* In equation form:

acceleration = slope on a *v-t* graph   or
$$
a = \frac{\Delta v}{\Delta t}
$$

Sample Problem 4

Find the acceleration of the motion shown in the graph.

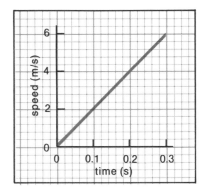

Solution $a = \dfrac{\Delta v}{\Delta t}$

$\qquad = \dfrac{6\,\text{m/s}}{0.3\,\text{s}}$

$\qquad = 20\dfrac{(\text{m/s})}{\text{s}} \quad \text{or} \quad 20\,(\text{m/s})/\text{s}$

PRACTICE

12. For the motions shown in the following graph, which line represents the greatest acceleration? Explain why.

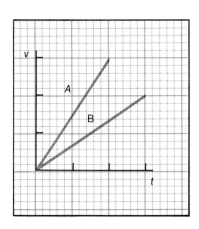

13. Calculate the acceleration for the motion in each of the three following graphs.

(a)

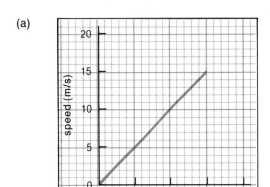

(b)

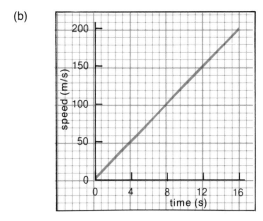

(c)

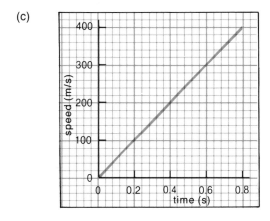

5.4 Investigating Acceleration in the Laboratory

Assume you are asked to calculate the acceleration of a car as it goes from 0.0 km/h to 100 km/h. The car has a speedometer that can be read directly, so the only instrument you need is a watch. The average acceleration can be calculated knowing the time it takes to reach 100 km/h. For instance, if the time taken is 10 s, the average acceleration is

$$a = \frac{\Delta v}{\Delta t} = \frac{100 \text{ km/h}}{10 \text{ s}}$$
$$= 10 \frac{(\text{km/h})}{\text{s}} \quad \text{or} \quad 10 \text{ (km/h)/s}$$

In a science laboratory, however, an acceleration experiment is not so simple. Objects that move (e.g., a cart, ball, or metal mass) do not have speedometers, so the speed cannot be observed directly.

This problem can be solved by measuring distance travelled and time, rather than change of speed and time. Then a distance-time graph of the motion can be plotted and a procedure followed to calculate the average acceleration.

An example of how to calculate acceleration from a distance-time graph is described below. The calculations are based on the assumption that the accelerated motion is uniform, which is the only type we will study. Similar calculations will be done in the next two activities.

To begin, consider Figure 5-6, which shows a typical distance-time graph of uniformly accelerated motion for a skier starting from rest and accelerating downhill. Notice that the line is curved, not straight as for uniform motion. This is because the skier travelled 1.0 m in the first 1.0 s, 3.0 m in the next 1.0 s, 5.0 m in the next 1.0 s, and 7.0 m in the last 1.0 s.

Figure 5-6   Distance-time graph of uniformly accelerated motion

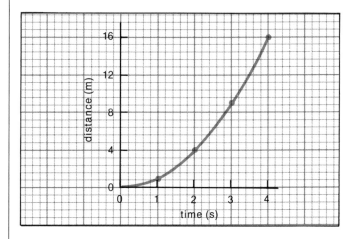

Because the line is curved, we cannot find its slope easily, the way we did for uniform motion in Chapter 4. In fact, the slope keeps changing. Thus, we will find the slope of the curved line at one instant. The instant we will choose is 2.0 s, at "half-time" in the motion.

To find the slope of the curved line at the "half-time", we draw a straight line from the final point to the origin of the graph. Refer to Figure 5-7(a). Then we find the slope of that straight line, which has the same slope as the curved line at 2.0 s. Now we know the "half-time" speed.

Next we plot a speed-time graph of the motion, using the fact that at "half-time" (2.0 s) the skier's speed is 4.0 m/s. In order to complete the graph, as shown in Figure 5-7(b), we assume that the acceleration is constant so we extend the straight line to 4.0 s.

Finally, we calculate the slope of the line on the speed-time graph. This tells us that the average acceleration is 2.0 (m/s)/s, which is constant. The resulting acceleration-time graph is shown in Figure 5-7(c).

Figure 5-7 Graphing uniformly accelerated motion

(a)

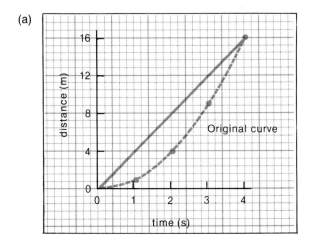

Original curve

(b)

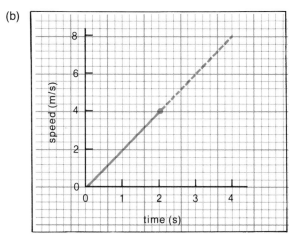

(c)

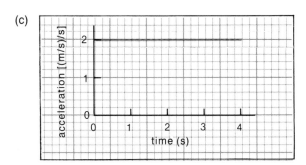

PRACTICE

14. In the tables below are three sets of distance-time data for uniformly accelerated motion. In each case:
    (a) plot a distance-time graph
    (b) find the "half-time" speed of each motion
    (c) plot a speed-time graph
    (d) plot an acceleration-time graph

(i)	time (s)	0	2	4	6	8
	distance (m)	0	8	32	72	128

(ii)	time (s)	0	1	2	3	4
	distance (m)	0	5	20	45	80

(iii)	time (s)	0	0.1	0.2	0.3	0.4
	distance (m)	0	1	4	9	16

Activity 5A   Measuring Acceleration

PROBLEM ■ How accurately can acceleration be found using the graphing technique?

APPARATUS ■ recording timer and related apparatus; cart with low-friction wheels; masking tape; stiff board 2.5 m long; metre stick; graph paper

Note: As with the motion activities in Chapter 4, only one of several possible procedures is described (overleaf). The analysis applies to other procedures besides this one.

PROCEDURE ■

1. Check the recording timer to be sure it is working properly.
2. Elevate one end of the board so it has a slope of 1/10, i.e., if the board is 2.5 m long elevate one end 0.25 m or 25 cm. Be sure the board is not sagging in the middle.
3. Use masking tape to attach a 2.0 m long paper strip to the cart. Feed the strip through the timer as shown in Figure 5-8, with the cart close to the timer. Have someone ready to catch the cart at the bottom of the ramp.
4. Hold the cart still, turn on the timer, then release the cart.

Figure 5-8   Set-up for Activity 5A

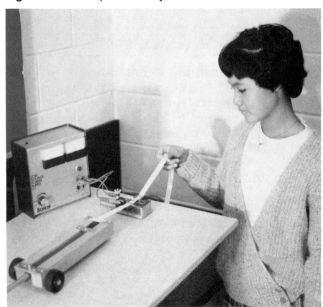

5. Choose as a starting position the first distinct point, A. Count 6 spaces to the next position, B, and measure AB. See Figure 5-9.

Figure 5-9   Measuring the distance from the starting position

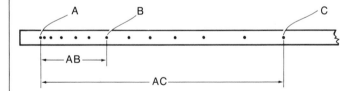

6. From B count another 6 spaces to C and measure AC, again shown in Figure 5-9. Continue this procedure for as many sets of 6 spaces as possible, always measuring the distance from the starting position, A. Tabulate the data:

time (s)	0	0.1	0.2	. . .
distance (cm)	0			

ANALYSIS ■

1. Plot the data on a distance-time graph. Determine from the smoothness of the line joining the ordered pairs whether or not the accelerated motion was uniform.
2. From the distance-time graph find the "half-time" speed of the motion. Use that speed to plot a speed-time graph. Remember to extend the line on this graph to the full time of the motion.
3. From the speed-time graph calculate the acceleration and plot an acceleration-time graph.
4. Use as a reference a computer program (or your teacher) to determine an acceptable value of acceleration for your set-up. Compare your answer with the acceptable one.
5. List any possible sources of error in this activity.
6. How accurately can acceleration be found using the graphing technique?

5.5 Acceleration Near the Surface of the Earth

If two solid metal objects of different mass (e.g., 50 g and 100 g) are dropped from the same height above the floor, they should land at the same time. This means that the acceleration of falling objects near the surface of the earth does not depend on mass.

The acceleration of falling objects does depend, however, on air resistance. To observe this, drop a piece of loose-leaf paper and a rubber stopper from the same height. Then repeat the drop, this time with the paper crumpled into a ball. Crumpling the paper eliminates much of the air resistance on the paper.

It was Galileo Galilei, an Italian scientist (1564-1642) who first proved that, if we do not consider air resistance, the acceleration of falling objects is constant. He proved this by measuring the acceleration of steel balls rolling down a ramp. He found that, for a constant slope of the ramp, the acceleration was constant, no matter what the mass of the ball. The reason he could not measure vertical acceleration was that he had no way of measuring short periods of time accurately. You might appreciate the difficulty of measuring time when you perform the next activity.

The acceleration of objects falling freely near the surface of the earth is 9.8 (m/s)/s. This value does not apply to objects influenced by air resistance. It is an average value that changes slightly, depending on factors to be discussed in Chapter 6. It is an acceleration caused by the force of gravity.

The quantity of 9.8 (m/s)/s is so common that from now on we will give it the symbol g, the **acceleration due to gravity**. (Do not confuse this g with the g used as a symbol for gram.)

PRACTICE

15. A steel ball falls freely from rest for 3.0 s at an acceleration of 9.8 (m/s)/s. Calculate the speed of the ball after:
    (a) 1.0 s   (b) 2.0 s   (c) 3.0 s

Activity 5B   The Acceleration Due to Gravity

PROBLEM ■   How does the experimental acceleration due to gravity found in the classroom compare to 9.8 (m/s)/s?

APPARATUS ■   If you choose the recording timer for this activity, you will need a 200 g metal mass, masking tape, a support stand and clamp, a metre stick, and something for the mass to land on. (See Figure 5-10.) If you choose a different device for performing the activity, list the apparatus you intend to use.

Figure 5-10   Using a recording timer to determine an approximate value of the acceleration due to gravity

PROCEDURE ■   Design and perform an activity to determine the acceleration of a mass falling with as little friction as possible. Write a report, including procedure, observations, and analysis. Use the analysis questions in Activity 5A as a reference.

 CAUTION   Have your design checked by your teacher before you begin your procedure. There may be harmful aspects.

5.6 Applications of Uniformly Accelerated Motion

Galileo Galilei began the mathematical analysis of accelerated motion, and the topic has been studied by physicists ever since. However, only during the twentieth century has it become a topic that relates closely to our everyday lives.

The study of accelerated motion is important in the field of transportation. Humans undergo such motion in automobiles, airplanes, rockets, and other vehicles. The positive acceleration in cars and airplanes is small, but in a rocket or military aircraft it can be great enough to cause damage to the human body.

In 1941, a Canadian pilot and inventor named W.R. Franks designed an ''anti-gravity'' suit to prevent pilot blackouts in military planes undergoing high-speed turns and dives. Blackouts occur when blood drains from the head and goes to the lower part of the body. To prevent this, Franks designed a suit with water encased in the inner lining to prevent the blood vessels from expanding outwards (Figure 5-11).

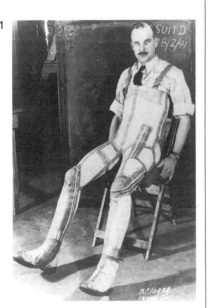

Figure 5-11 This 1941 photograph shows W.R. Franks in the ''anti-gravity'' suit he designed.

Modern experiments have shown that the maximum acceleration a human can withstand is 30 *g* [294 (m/s)/s]. Astronauts experience up to 10 *g* [98 (m/s)/s] when a rocket is launched. At that acceleration, if the astronauts were standing, they would faint due to loss of blood to the head. To prevent this problem, the astronauts must be lying down during blast-off (Figure 5-12).

Figure 5-12 Two astronauts participate in a launch simulation exercise as a backup crew member assists.

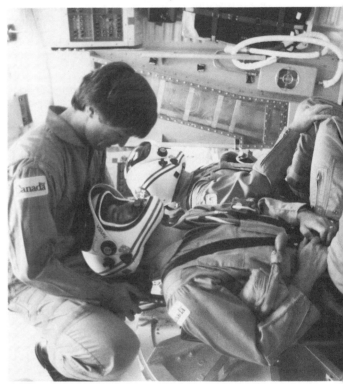

In our day-to-day lives we are more concerned with the negative accelerated motion in cars and other vehicles than with the positive accelerated motion in rockets. Studies are continually being made to determine the effect on the human body when a car has a collision or must stop quickly. Seat belts, headrests, and air bags help prevent many injuries caused by a large negative acceleration. The photograph at the beginning of the chapter shows a dummy hitting an air bag during a test crash.

Another application is the study of the effect of acceleration rates on gasoline consumption of cars. It is logical that a driver with a "heavy foot" wastes valuable resources by accelerating at excessive rates. Some cars are now equipped with a light that indicates when the acceleration is greater than a certain energy-saving value.

In the exciting sport of sky diving, the diver jumps from an airplane and accelerates toward the ground, experiencing "free fall." See Figure 5.13. The parachute is not opened until the diver is at a predetermined distance from the ground. During free fall, the diver's speed will increase to a maximum amount called **terminal speed**. Air resistance prevents a higher speed. At terminal speed the acceleration becomes zero; in other words, the speed remains constant. For humans, terminal speed in air is about 53 m/s or 190 km/h.

One other application is the acceleration due to gravity on heavenly bodies other than the earth. If an astronaut standing on the moon dropped a ball, it would accelerate at about one sixth of that on the earth, or about 1.6 (m/s)/s. Table 5-1 lists the acceleration caused by gravity on the nine planets in our solar system.

Table 5-1

Planet	Acceleration Due to Gravity [(m/s)/s]
Mercury	3.8
Venus	8.9
Earth	9.8
Mars	3.7
Jupiter	25.8
Saturn	11.1
Uranus	10.5
Neptune	13.8
Pluto*	uncertain

*Until 1999 Neptune will be the farthest planet from the sun. After that date, Pluto will again be farthest, so it is placed last in this table.

Figure 5-13   This sky diver experiences "free fall" immediately upon leaving the aircraft.

PRACTICE

16. How do you think the terminal speed of a stone and a mouse compare to that of a human?
17. Sketch a speed-time graph for a sky diver who accelerates, then reaches terminal speed, then opens the parachute.

5.7   Review of Motion

Two types of motion, uniform motion and uniformly accelerated motion, have been studied in Chapters 4 and 5. Both types deal with motion in a straight line. Uniform motion is motion at a constant speed. Uniformly accelerated motion is motion with a steady change in speed. Refer to Figures 5-14 and 5-15 (overleaf).

The acceleration due to gravity near the surface of the earth is 9.8 (m/s)/s, assuming air resistance is not considered.

Figure 5-14   Summary of uniform motion

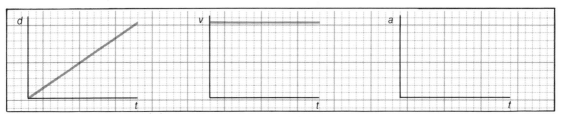

The $d - t$ graph is a straight line.
The slope of the line $\left(m = \dfrac{\Delta d}{\Delta t}\right)$
gives the speed.

The $v - t$ graph is horizontal because the speed is constant.

There is no acceleration.

Figure 5-15   Summary of uniformly accelerated motion

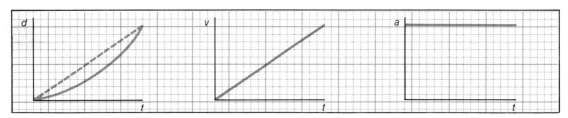

The $d - t$ graph is curved.
The slope of the line $\left(m = \dfrac{\Delta d}{\Delta t}\right)$
gives the speed at "half-time".

The $v - t$ graph is a straight line whose slope $\left(m = \dfrac{\Delta v}{\Delta t}\right)$
gives the acceleration.

The acceleration graph is horizontal because the acceleration is constant.

Words to Know

accelerated motion
uniformly accelerated
   motion
negative accelerated motion
positive accelerated motion

acceleration
"half-time" speed
acceleration due to gravity
terminal speed

Chapter Objectives

Having completed this chapter, you should now be able to:
1. Define uniform accelerated motion that is either positive or negative.
2. Calculate the acceleration of an object, given its change in speed and the time during which that change occurred $\left(a = \dfrac{\Delta v}{\Delta t}\right)$.

3. State the SI unit of acceleration and recognize other metric units of acceleration.
4. Determine the slope of a straight line on a speed-time graph and use it to plot an acceleration-time graph.
5. Given a distance-time graph of uniform accelerated motion, be able to plot a speed-time graph and calculate the acceleration.
6. Determine experimentally the acceleration of an object that, starting from rest, accelerates down a sloping ramp.
7. State the average acceleration due to gravity at the surface of the earth.
8. Determine experimentally the acceleration due to gravity.
9. State applications of accelerated motion.

Chapter Review

1. What is uniformly accelerated motion? (5.1)
2. Sketch a speed-time graph that represents:
   (a) uniformly accelerated motion that is positive
   (b) uniformly accelerated motion that is negative
   (5.1)
3. In drag racing a car accelerates from rest and must reach a maximum speed in about 400 m. Calculate the world-record accelerations of the cars in each situation described below:
   (a) A piston-engine car reached 112 m/s (403 km/h) in 5.6 s.
   (b) A rocket-powered car reached 170 m/s (608 km/h) in 4.6 s. (5.2)
4. Give reasons we should or should not waste gasoline on sports activities such as the races described in #3.
5. Find the acceleration of a truck that increases its speed from 22 m/s to 28 m/s in 30 s. (5.2)
6. What acceleration is needed by a car, travelling at 100 km/h, to come to a stop in 5.0 s? (5.2)
7. Determine the change of speed of a bullet that accelerates at 400 (m/s)/s for 0.1 s. (5.2)
8. At an acceleration of 6 (m/s)/s, how long would it take a car to change its speed from rest to 21 m/s? (5.2)
9. What does the slope of a line on a speed-time graph indicate? (5.3)
10. Calculate the acceleration for each line on the speed-time graph shown. (5.3)

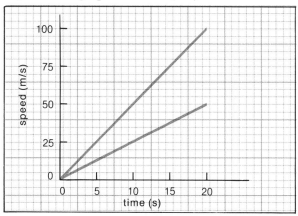

11. The table shows the results of an activity involving uniformly accelerated motion.

time (s)	0	2	4	6	8
distance (m)	0	16	64	144	256

   (a) Plot the results on a *d-t* graph. Is the curve smooth?
   (b) Calculate the "half-time" speed of the motion.
   (c) Draw a *v-t* graph of the motion.
   (d) Calculate the acceleration. (5.4)

12. A 60 Hz recording timer is used in an activity to measure the acceleration of a cart travelling down a ramp. Use the results, shown in the table, to calculate the acceleration. (5.4, Act. 5A)

time (s)	0	0.1	0.2	0.3	0.4
distance (cm)	0	0.8	3.2	7.2	12.8

13. What is the average value of the acceleration due to gravity at the surface of the earth? (5.5)
14. Calculate the acceleration experienced by the driver of a rocket-powered dragger rated at 3.5 *g*. (5.5)
15. Describe an experiment that could be set up to show that, in the absence of air resistance, a feather and a steel ball fall at the same rate under the influence of gravity. (5.5)
16. The maximum acceleration a human can survive is 294 (m/s)/s. In a head-on collision with a solid wall, a car stops in about 0.05 s. Determine whether or not a person, wearing a safety belt, can possibly survive such a collision in a car travelling at:
   (a) 28 m/s (This is about 100 km/h.)
   (b) 14 m/s (5.2, 5.6)
17. The acceleration due to gravity on a planet increases as the mass of the planet increases. Which planet listed in Table 5-1 has the greatest mass? (5.6)

18. A stroboscope with a period of flashes of 0.05 s is used to observe a falling ball. The ball appears at the locations shown in the diagram. Determine the distance-time data needed to plot a graph of the motion. Use the analysis steps found in Activities 5A and 5B to determine if the ball was undergoing free fall.

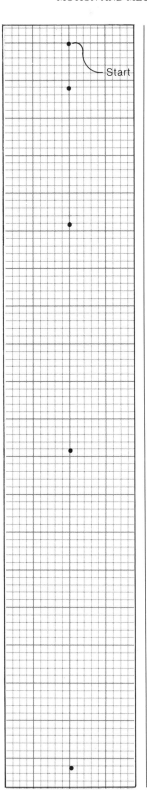

Force and Newton's Laws of Motion

to overcome the downward force of the earth's gravity. In this chapter you will study various forces, such as gravity, friction, and the force that causes the launching of a rocket. Many of the examples and applications of forces relate to your everyday experiences.

Main Ideas

- Forces cause accelerated motion.
- The force of gravity pulls us toward the earth.
- Friction is a force that acts against the motion of an object.

The launching of a space shuttle, such as the one shown here, requires a large upward force. This force is needed

6.1 Forces

A **force** is a push or a pull. Forces act on everything from the smallest particles imaginable to the largest objects in the universe. The main types of force in nature, with an example of each, are listed below. These forces can act when the objects are not in direct contact.

- *Gravitational forces* keep the earth revolving around the sun.
- *Nuclear forces* act between tiny particles that make up the centres of atoms.
- *Magnetic forces* arrange patterns of information in computers.
- *Electric forces* help objects maintain their shape.

Electric forces are important in causing other forces called *mechanical forces*. These forces can act when objects or particles are in direct contact with each other. Here are some familiar examples of mechanical forces:

- *Frictional forces* help keep a car on the road.
- *Tension forces* act within the strap of a purse.
- *Compression forces* act on vertical beams that support a building.
- *Shear forces* can cause a bone struck from the side to break.

Some of these forces will be studied more in this chapter; others will be presented later in the book.

PRACTICE

1. State the type or types of force related to each example given below.
   (a) prevents air particles from escaping from the earth
   (b) occurs in the bones of your legs when you are standing
   (c) causes "static cling"
   (d) allows the use of a compass to find direction
   (e) occurs when you tear a piece of paper

6.2 Measuring Force

The title of this chapter refers to one of the greatest scientists in history, Sir Isaac Newton (Figure 6-1). Newton was born the same year Galileo Galilei died. Many of Newton's ideas resulted from Galileo's discoveries. Since Newton developed important ideas about force, it is fitting that the unit of force is called the **newton** (symbol N).

Figure 6-1 Sir Isaac Newton (1642-1727)

The newton is an SI unit, so it is necessary to measure distance in metres, mass in kilograms, and time in seconds.

If you have not had experience measuring force in newtons, you should arrange to do so now. One way to do this is to hang a 100 g mass on the end of a force scale available in the laboratory. The force needed to hold up the mass is about 1.0 N. You could also try pulling on the force scale (Figure 6-2). Each force scale has a spring that extends when a pulling force is applied. The spring is attached to a needle that indicates the force.

Figure 6-2 Force measured in newtons using a spring scale

PRACTICE

2. What force would be required to hold up a mass of:
   (a) 200 g?
   (b) 400 g?
   (c) 1000 g?

6.3 Balanced and Unbalanced Forces

To study the effects of forces acting on objects, we must distinguish between forces that are balanced and forces that are unbalanced. Imagine that you are holding a book as shown in Figure 6-3. Two forces affect it. One is the force of gravity, which acts to pull the book downward. The other is the force exerted by your hand holding up the book. Those forces are equal and act in opposite directions. When such forces act on a single object, they are called **balanced forces**.

Figure 6-3 An example of balanced forces

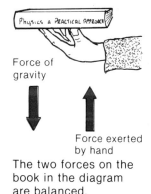

Force of gravity

Force exerted by hand

The two forces on the book in the diagram are balanced.

Now consider forces that are not balanced. Imagine that the hand holding the book in Figure 6-3 is suddenly removed. The only force acting on the book now is the downward pull of gravity. This force will cause the book to accelerate downward. In this case, the force of gravity is an example of an **unbalanced force**, one that is greater in one direction than any other.

PRACTICE

3. A brick is at rest on a table. Draw a diagram showing the forces acting on the brick.
4. Name the type of force that causes accelerated motion.

6.4   Newton's First Law of Motion

An object is either at rest or in motion. One that is at rest requires an unbalanced force to get it to move. One that is in motion requires an unbalanced force to get it to stop. In both cases, the object tends to resist change. For instance, a train is hard to get moving, and once it is in motion, it is hard to stop.

These facts are summarized by Newton's **first law of motion**. It states that:

An object maintains its state of rest or uniform motion unless it is acted upon by an unbalanced force.

First, think about objects that are at rest. They will remain at rest unless an unbalanced force acts on them. Here are examples of this:

- It is hard to push a stalled truck to the side of the road.
- Some "magicians" can jerk a smooth tablecloth from beneath a table setting of glasses and silverware.
- A passenger standing on a bus or subway train tends to fall backward as the vehicle accelerates forward from rest.

Now consider an object in uniform motion. It will continue in a straight line at a constant speed unless an unbalanced force acts on it. A toboggan in uniform motion is subject to balanced forces, as shown in Figure 6-4. The downward force of gravity is balanced by the upward force of the snow on the toboggan. The backward force of friction is balanced by the forward force produced by the tension in the rope. As long as the forces remain balanced, the toboggan does not accelerate.

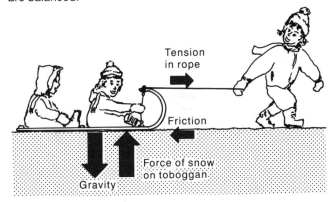

Figure 6-4   Forces acting on an object in uniform motion are balanced.

Here are examples of objects in motion tending to remain in motion:

- A spacecraft travelling toward Mars does not need its engine on most of the time. Outer space is basically a vacuum, so there is no moving friction on the craft. The craft tends to maintain a constant speed in a straight line (uniform motion).
- A speeding car approaching a curve on an icy highway has the tendency to continue in a straight line, thus failing to follow the curve. That is why care must be taken when driving on slippery roads.
- People in cars and other vehicles have the tendency to maintain uniform motion. This can be dangerous for them if the vehicle comes to a sudden stop, and the passengers keep on going. The danger can be greatly reduced by the proper wearing of safety belts.

PRACTICE

5. Explain why astronauts are placed horizontally in the space capsule during blast-off from the launching pad.
6. Some thrill rides at exhibitions or fairs create sensations that may be explained using Newton's first law of motion. Describe two such rides.
7. Draw a diagram showing the forces acting on each object described below. Then state whether the forces on the object are balanced.
   (a) A box of groceries is being pushed with a force of 25 N forward across the floor. The floor is exerting a frictional resistance of 25 N backwards. Gravity is pulling down on the box with a force of 75 N, and the floor is pushing up with a force of 75 N.
   (b) A cross-country skier is skiing on level ground. The downward force of gravity is 600 N, and the upward force of the trail on the skier is 600 N. The forward force is 5 N and the backward force of friction is 12 N.

Activity 6A Force, Mass, and Acceleration

PROBLEM ■ How does the acceleration of an object depend on:
(a) the unbalanced force applied to the object?
(b) the mass of the object?

APPARATUS ■ cart of known mass; two 1.0 kg masses; spring scale (to 10 N); piece of string; some means of determining acceleration (optional)

Note: This activity can be done qualitatively, without measuring actual accelerations. Or, it can be done quantitatively by determining the acceleration in each case.

PROCEDURE ■ Design and perform a procedure to determine answers to Problems (a) and (b). Clues for setting up the apparatus to make qualitative observations are shown in Figure 6-5. If quantitative observations are to be made, more apparatus will be required.

CAUTION *Have your design checked by your teacher before you begin your procedure. There may be harmful aspects.*

Figure 6-5 Set-up for Activity 6A

(a) Increasing the force applied to a constant mass: Use three different forces, e.g., 1.0 N, 2.0 N, 3.0 N.

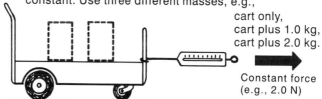

(b) Increasing the mass while keeping the applied force constant: Use three different masses, e.g.,
cart only,
cart plus 1.0 kg,
cart plus 2.0 kg.

Constant force
(e.g., 2.0 N)

ANALYSIS ■ Analyse the observations made in your investigation. Your analysis depends on whether the activity was done qualitatively or quantitatively, but focus on the following.
1. For an object of constant mass, what happens to the acceleration as the unbalanced force increases?
2. For an object with a constant force applied to it, what happens to the acceleration as the mass increases?

6.5 Newton's Second Law of Motion

Newton's first law deals with situations in which the forces on an object are balanced. No acceleration occurs. His second law deals with situations in which the forces on an object are unbalanced (greater in one direction than any other). The object accelerates in the direction of the unbalanced force.

Newton's **second law of motion** states that:

The acceleration of an object increases as the unbalanced force increases, and it decreases as the mass increases.

This statement agrees with what you observed in the previous activity. It can be summarized in the form of an equation.

$$\text{acceleration} = \frac{\text{unbalanced force}}{\text{mass}} \quad \text{or}$$

$$a = \frac{F}{m}$$

This equation is often written in the rearranged form

$$\textbf{unbalanced force} = \textbf{mass} \times \textbf{acceleration} \quad \text{or}$$

$$F = ma$$

In these equations, the units used must be from the SI. Force must be measured in newtons, mass in kilograms, and acceleration in metres per second per second.

The equation $F = ma$ can be used to define the newton in terms of metres, kilograms, and seconds.

$$F = ma$$

$$N = (\text{kg})\frac{\text{m/s}}{\text{s}}$$

Thus, **one newton** is the force required to give a 1.0 kg object an acceleration of 1.0 (m/s)/s.

Sample Problem 1

Calculate the acceleration of a 5.0 kg cart being pushed by a 40 N unbalanced force.

Solution $a = \dfrac{F}{m}$

$$= \frac{40\,\text{N}}{5.0\,\text{kg}} \qquad \frac{\cancel{\text{kg}}\left(\frac{\text{m}}{\text{s}}\right)}{\cancel{\text{kg}}}\frac{}{\text{s}}$$

$$= 80\,\frac{\text{m/s}}{\text{s}}$$

Sample Problem 2

Calculate the unbalanced force required to give a 1500 kg car an acceleration of 2.0 (m/s)/s.

Solution $F = ma$

$$= 1500\,\text{kg} \times 2.0\,\frac{\text{m/s}}{\text{s}}$$

$$= 3000\,\text{N}$$

PRACTICE

8. Compare the direction of the acceleration of an object with the direction of the unbalanced force causing that acceleration.
9. Calculate the acceleration in each situation.
    (a) A cyclist exerts an unbalanced force of 15 N to a total mass (cyclist + bicycle) of 60 kg.
    (b) A bowler exerts an unbalanced force of 17.5 N on a 7.0 kg bowling ball.
    (c) An unbalanced force of 8.0 N is applied to a 0.1 kg model rocket.
10. Find the unbalanced force if:
    (a) A cannon gives a 5.0 kg shell an acceleration of 5000 (m/s)/s before it leaves the muzzle.
    (b) A 0.05 kg arrow is given an acceleration of 2500 (m/s)/s.
    (c) A 500-passenger Boeing 747 jet (with a mass of 1.64×10^5 kg) undergoes an acceleration of 1.0 (m/s)/s.

11. Rearrange the equation $F = ma$ to express m by itself.
12. In parts of outer space where the gravitational force is practically zero, mass cannot be measured using a balance. However, it can be measured by experiment using Newton's second law of motion. Calculate the mass of an object in such an experiment if an unbalanced force of 8.0 N gives a measured acceleration of 5.0 (m/s)/s.

6.6 The Force of Gravity

We can apply Newton's second law of motion, in the form $a = \dfrac{F}{m}$, to calculate the acceleration due to gravity at the surface of the earth. For example, if a 1.0 kg object is held up by a force scale, the scale reads 9.8 N. This means that the force of gravity pulling down on a 1.0 kg object is 9.8 N. If this object is allowed to fall freely, it will accelerate at a value

$$a = \frac{F}{m}$$
$$= \frac{9.8\,\text{N}}{1.0\,\text{kg}}$$
$$= 9.8\,\frac{\text{m/s}}{\text{s}}$$

This value is, of course, the acceleration due to gravity (g) discussed in Section 5.5.

Now we can use the value $g = 9.8$ (m/s)/s to calculate the force required to hold up an object, even though the object is not accelerating. The equation we use is:

$$\mathbf{F} = \mathbf{mg} \quad \text{where} \quad \mathbf{g} = \mathbf{9.8\ (m/s)/s}$$

The F in this equation may be called the force required to hold up an object, the force of gravity acting on an object, or the force required to lift an object without acceleration.

Sample Problem 3

What is the force of gravity acting on a 0.5 kg book?

Solution $\quad F = mg$
$$= 0.5\,\text{kg} \times 9.8\,\frac{\text{m/s}}{\text{s}}$$
$$= 4.9\,\text{N}$$

Some textbooks refer to the force of gravity as "weight". What is important to remember is that mass is measured in kilograms and the force of gravity, or weight, is measured in newtons.

From the equation $F = mg$, it is evident that the force of gravity on a known mass changes if g changes. Although the average value of g on earth is 9.8 (m/s)/s, that value may change slightly, depending on location. In general, the *farther you are from the centre of the earth, the less the value of g*. Thus g would be less at the top of a mountain than at the bottom of a valley. Also, g at the equator is somewhat less than at the North or South Pole because the earth is slightly flattened at the poles. Table 6-1 lists the values of g at various locations on the earth. From that list it is apparent that the force of gravity changes with location.

Table 6-1 Acceleration Due to Gravity at Various Locations on Earth

Location	Latitude	Altitude (m)	g [(m/s)/s]
Equator	0°	0	9.781
North Pole	90°	0	9.832
Toronto	44°	162	9.805
Brussels	51°	102	9.811
Denver	40°	1638	9.796

If you were to travel to the moon, you would find that the force of gravity there is only 1/6 of that on the earth. That is why the acceleration caused by gravity on the moon is only 1.6 (m/s)/s. Accelerations caused by the force of gravity on different planets were shown in Table 5-1, Section 5.6.

Sample Problem 4

Calculate the force of gravity on a fully outfitted astronaut (mass 110 kg)
(a) on the earth
(b) on the moon

Solution
(a) $F = mg$

$$= 110 \text{ kg} \times 9.8 \frac{\text{m/s}}{\text{s}}$$

$$= 1078 \text{ N} \quad \text{or} \quad \text{about } 1100 \text{ N}$$

(b) $F = ma$

$$= 110 \text{ kg} \times 1.6 \frac{\text{m/s}}{\text{s}}$$

$$= 176 \text{ N} \quad \text{or} \quad \text{about } 180 \text{ N}$$

Notice, of course, that the mass does not change when the astronaut is on the moon.

In Section 6.1 it was mentioned that the force of gravity keeps the earth revolving around the sun. Gravity also keeps our moon revolving around the earth. Not only does the earth exert a force on the moon, but the moon also exerts a force on the earth. That force is evident in the creation of ocean tides on the earth.

PRACTICE

13. Calculate the force of gravity acting on:
    (a) a 300 kg piano   (b) yourself
14. (a) Determine the force of gravity pulling down on a 15 kg curling stone (on the earth).
    (b) What force would you have to exert to lift the curling stone in (a) off the ice (without any acceleration)?
15. The 1968 Summer Olympics were held in Mexico City, which has an elevation of 2200 m above sea level and a latitude of about 20°. Several jumping records were broken at those Olympics. Explain what conditions helped contribute to this.
16. Calculate the force of gravity on a 10 kg object on the surface of
    (a) Venus
    (b) Jupiter (Refer to Table 5-1, Section 5.6.)

17. Some science-fiction movies and television programs show people walking around spacecraft the way we walk around a room. How scientifically accurate is this representation?

6.7   Newton's Third Law of Motion

Newton's first law of motion is descriptive and his second law mathematical. In both cases we consider the forces acting on only one object. When a force is applied to one object, however, it must be applied by a second object. This brings us to the third law, which considers forces acting as pairs on two objects.

Newton's **third law of motion**, often called the action-reaction law, states that:

For every action force on an object there is an equal reaction force in the opposite direction on a second object.

To understand the third law, imagine a high jumper pushing off the ground with one foot, as illustrated in Figure 6-6. The foot (or running shoe) exerts a downward force on the ground. This is called the **action force**. The ground exerts an upward force on the foot. This is called the **reaction force**. The action and reaction forces are equal in size, but opposite in direction, and act on different objects.

Figure 6-6   An example of an action-reaction pair of forces

Action force   Reaction force
(foot on ground)   (ground on foot)

As you read the examples of the third law that follow, remember there are always two objects to consider. One object exerts the *action force*, and the other exerts the *reaction force*. In certain cases, one of the "objects" may be a gas, such as air.

- In swimming the *action force* is exerted by the hands moving backward against the water. The water exerts a *reaction force* forward against the hands, pushing the body forward.
- The propeller blades on a helicopter are designed to force air in one direction as the propeller spins rapidly. Thus, the *action force* is exerted downward by the blades against the air. The *reaction force* is exerted by the air upward against the blades, sending the helicopter in a direction opposite to the motion of air.
- A jet engine on an aircraft allows air to enter a large opening at the front of the engine. The engine heats the air and expels it rapidly out the rear. The *action force* is exerted by the engine backward on the expelled air. The *reaction force* is exerted by the expelled air forward on the engine, forcing the engine, and thus the entire airplane, in the opposite direction.
- A squid is a marine animal with a body size ranging from about 3 cm to 6 m. The squid propels itself by taking in water and expelling it in sudden spurts. The *action force* is applied by the discharged water backward on the surrounding water. The *reaction force* of the sea water forward against the discharged water sends the squid in the opposite direction.

PRACTICE

18. Explain each event described in terms of Newton's third law of motion. In each case draw a diagram illustrating the situation and label the action and reaction forces.
    (a) When a toy balloon is blown up and released, it flies violently around the room.
    (b) A paddle is used to propel a canoe.
    (c) A person with ordinary shoes is able to walk on a sidewalk.
    (d) A space shuttle, like the one shown in the photograph at the start of the chapter, is launched.

6.8 The Force of Friction

Friction has been mentioned previously in this chapter, but it has not been described in detail.

Friction is a force that resists motion. It occurs at the surfaces of two objects in contact. No one would put on a pair of ice skates to try to glide along a concrete sidewalk! It is the friction between the sidewalk and the blades that would prevent any skating.

One type of friction, called **static friction**, is the force that prevents a motionless object from starting to move. (Static means at rest.) Assume, for example, that the maximum force of static friction between an exercise mat and a gymnasium floor is 100 N. In order to get the mat to start sliding across the floor, a force of at least 100 N would have to be exerted on it. See Figure 6-7.

Figure 6-7 Static friction must be overcome before an object begins moving.

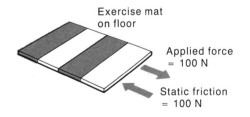

Exercise mat on floor

Applied force = 100 N

Static friction = 100 N

Sometimes static friction is helpful, and sometimes it is not. A carpenter wearing boots can stand safely on a sloping roof with the help of the friction between the boots and the roof. However, a person trying to move a heavy filing cabinet across a room does not appreciate static friction.

Once the force applied to an object overcomes static friction, the object begins moving. Then **kinetic friction** replaces static friction. (Kinetic stems from the Greek word *kinema*, which means motion.) Kinetic friction is the force that acts against an object's motion in a direction opposite to the direction of motion.

Different types of kinetic friction have different names, depending on the situation. *Sliding* friction would affect a toboggan, *rolling* friction would affect a clothes washer, and *air resistance* would affect a sky diver.

PRACTICE

19. State one example of each of the following types of friction. (Choose examples different from those given in this section.)
    (a) static friction that is useful
    (b) static friction that is unwanted
    (c) sliding friction
    (d) rolling friction
    (e) air resistance

Activity 6B   Factors that Affect Sliding Friction

PROBLEM ■   What factors affect the amount of sliding friction between two rigid surfaces?

APPARATUS ■   friction block; masses to be used as loads; force scale; various types of rigid surfaces on which the block can move

PROCEDURE ■   Design and carry out an investigation to find answers to the problem. The following questions provide clues to some of the factors to consider.

1. Is maximum static friction the same size as kinetic friction? (To measure kinetic friction, be sure to keep the object moving at a constant speed.)
2. Does the total mass of the object (including the load) affect the kinetic friction?
3. Do the types of materials in contact affect the kinetic friction?
4. Does the area of contact between the objects affect the kinetic friction?

 CAUTION   Have your design checked by your teacher, before you begin your procedure. There may be harmful aspects.

Write a report of your activity, including your analysis. Add some applications related to your experiences, such as friction during skiing, skating, or playing basketball.

6.9   Friction and Technology

More than 4500 years ago the Egyptians built enormous pyramids using huge stone blocks that were difficult to move by sliding. To move the blocks they placed logs underneath them and pushed. By doing this, they were taking advantage of the fact that rolling friction is much less than sliding friction.

Modern technology uses the same principles as the Egyptians, though in a more sophisticated way. We try to reduce unwanted friction for many reasons. For instance, all machines have moving parts that rub together during operation causing friction. We know that friction can wear out the machines, reduce efficiency, and cause unwanted heat. (If you rub your hands hard together you can feel the heat produced by friction.) Excess friction in machines can be overcome by making smooth surfaces, lubricating with grease or oil, and using bearings.

Bearings function on the principle of the rolling logs used by the Egyptians to move stones. A **bearing** is a device containing many rollers or balls that reduce friction while supporting a load. Bearings change sliding friction into rolling friction, reducing friction by up to 100 times. Figure 6-8 illustrates the application of bearings to the wheel-and-axle assembly of a common device.

Figure 6-8 Ball bearings reduce friction in the wheel of a skate board.

To compare the friction between various types of materials, a number called the **coefficient of friction** can be measured. This number is the friction force divided by the force between the surfaces in contact. Thus,

$$\textbf{coefficient of friction} \ = \ \frac{\textbf{friction force}}{\textbf{force between surfaces}}$$

The force between the surfaces is perpendicular to the friction force, so we call it a *normal force*, or simply the *normal*. Using *f* for friction, *N* for normal, and the Greek letter μ for coefficient, we can write the above equation using symbols.

$$\mu \ = \ \frac{\textbf{friction}}{\textbf{normal}} \ \text{or}$$

$$\mu \ = \ \frac{f}{N}$$

Since both *f* and *N* are measured in newtons, the units cancel out. Thus, the coefficient of friction has no units.

For objects on horizontal surfaces, the normal is easy to find. It is equal in size to the force of gravity on the object. This situation is shown in Figure 6-9.

Figure 6-9 Forces acting on an object moving on a horizontal surface

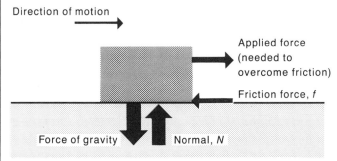

Although friction is often unwanted, it can also be useful. Consider the technology involved in designing roads, bridges, and automobile tires. Without friction, driving on highways would not only be dangerous, it would be impossible. Friction between tires and roads aids all types of accelerated motion—speeding up, slowing down, and changing direction. Engineers consider friction when they design treads for tires and surfaces of roads and bridges.

Sample Problem 5

A wooden box is dragged along a flat stone patio at a constant speed. The force of gravity on the box is 800 N and the horizontal force required to pull the box is 320 N. Find the coefficient of sliding friction between the wood and the stone.

Solution

$$\mu = \frac{f}{N} = \frac{320\,N}{800\,N} = 0.4$$

The coefficients of friction between several pairs of materials are listed in Table 6-2. (The coefficient of friction between rigid materials does not depend on the surface area in contact. However, if one or both of the materials is flexible or elastic, the coefficient does depend somewhat on the surface area.)

Table 6-2 Approximate Coefficients of Sliding Friction

Materials in Contact	Coefficient
Rubber on dry asphalt	0.70
Stone on stone or brick	0.65
Leather on metal	0.55
Wood on wood (dry)	0.35
Rubber on wet asphalt	0.30
Well-oiled metal on metal	0.05
Cartilage on bone	0.015
Rubber on ice	0.010

Notice that friction between wet asphalt and rubber is much less than between dry asphalt and rubber. Notice also that friction between ice and rubber hardly exists. All drivers of vehicles should be aware of the consequences of the reduction of helpful friction. One way of increasing friction in hazardous conditions is shown in Figure 6-10.

An easy way of measuring the approximate coefficient of sliding friction is found in the next activity.

Figure 6-10 It is dangerous to drive on steep mountain roads covered with snow or ice in the winter. The danger can be reduced by putting chains on tires.

DID YOU KNOW?

The coefficient of friction at the joints in a healthy human body are extremely small. Modern technology has difficulty in making joints having such low coefficients, for artificial limbs.

PRACTICE

20. Explain why it is necessary to streamline modern aircraft and rockets.
21. Some students in a certain physics class refused to believe that friction helps us walk. In an effort to show that friction is needed, one student threw some hard plastic beads onto the floor and asked the others to walk out of the room as fast as possible. What point would be proved by such a demonstration? (Do not include safety concerns in your answer.)
22. Sliding friction occurs in gasoline engines as the pistons move back and forth in the cylinders. What two methods would help reduce that sliding friction?

23. Explain why friction between your hand and a doorknob helps you open the door.

24. Give an explanation involving friction for a sign that reads "Reduce speed on wet highway"

25. Determine the coefficient of sliding friction in each case. Assume the object is moving at a constant speed.

    (a) The force between a sleigh and the snow is 500 N and the force needed to pull the sleigh is 30 N.

    (b) The force between a car and the road is 12 000 N and the force of friction as the car skids to a stop is 3600 N.

26. Rearrange the equation $\mu = \frac{f}{N}$ to express f by itself.

27. A leather suitcase slides along a metal ramp. Determine the force of friction if the force between the surfaces is 200 N. (See Table 6-2.)

Figure 6-11 Measuring the coefficient of sliding friction

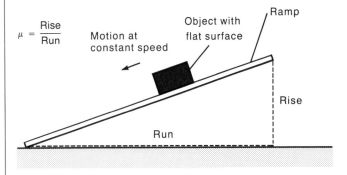

$$\mu = \frac{Rise}{Run}$$

Motion at constant speed

Object with flat surface

Ramp

Rise

Run

DID YOU KNOW?

You can use the tan function on your calculator to find the slope of the line. Measure the angle the ramp makes with the horizontal, then find the tan of that angle.

Activity 6C   The Coefficient of Sliding Friction

PROBLEM ■   How can a ramp be used to determine the coefficient of sliding friction?

APPARATUS ■   wooden board at least 1.2 m in length; metre stick; objects that can slide along the board (e.g., wooden block, steel block, plastic block, book, leather shoe, athletic shoe, etc.)

PROCEDURE ■

1. Place the first object to be tested near the top of the wooden ramp, as shown in Figure 6-11. Gradually raise the end of the ramp with the object until the object begins to slide down the ramp. Find the position of the ramp that allows the object to move down it at a constant speed. Try this several times until you are sure of the best position. Then use the metre stick to measure the slope of the ramp $\left(\text{slope} = \frac{\Delta y}{\Delta x}\right)$. This value is the coefficient of sliding friction. Record your data and calculations.

2. Repeat #1 for various objects.

3. Predict whether increasing the mass of the object will have any effect on the coefficient of friction. Then experiment to determine if your prediction was correct.

ANALYSIS ■

1. Which material had the greatest friction with wood? the least?

2. How did the coefficients you found in this activity compare with the coefficients listed in Table 6-2?

3. How can a ramp be used to determine the coefficient of sliding friction?

APPLICATION ■   Why are leather-soled shoes not recommended for use on gymnasium floors?

Words to Know

force	third law of motion
newton	action force
balanced force	reaction force
unbalanced force	static friction
first law of motion	kinetic friction
second law of motion	bearing
force of gravity	coefficient of friction
(or weight)	normal force (or normal)

Chapter Objectives

Having completed this chapter, you should now be able to:

1. Define force and state the SI unit used to measure it.
2. State the difference between balanced and unbalanced forces.
3. Draw diagrams showing the forces acting on objects.
4. State Newton's first law of motion and describe examples to illustrate it.
5. Write and apply Newton's second law of motion in equation form $\left(a = \dfrac{F}{m} \text{ and } F = ma \right)$.
6. Calculate the force of gravity on an object of known mass.
7. State how the force of gravity on an object varies with location.
8. State Newton's third law of motion and describe examples to illustrate it.
9. Define friction and describe factors that affect it.
10. Compare static friction with kinetic friction.
11. State examples of both unwanted and useful friction.
12. Describe means of reducing unwanted friction.
13. Define and calculate the coefficient of friction $\left(\mu = \dfrac{f}{N} \right)$.
14. Determine the coefficient of sliding friction experimentally.

Chapter Review

1. Define force. (6.1)
2. State the SI unit used to measure force. (6.2)
3. A parachutist is falling at a constant speed straight toward the ground. Draw a diagram showing the forces acting on the parachute. Are those forces balanced? (6.3)
4. State what happens (if anything) to an object that is:
   (a) at rest and has balanced forces acting on it
   (b) in motion and has balanced forces acting on it
   (c) at rest and has an unbalanced force applied to it   (6.3, 6.4)
5. Explain why it is wise to wear a safety belt when riding in a car. (6.4)
6. An unbalanced force of 5.0 N is applied to a toy electric train. The mass of the train is 2.5 kg. Calculate the acceleration of the train. (6.5)
7. What unbalanced force is needed to give a 120 kg boat an acceleration of 2.5 (m/s)/s? (6.5)
8. An unbalanced force of 29.4 N causes a certain object to accelerate at 9.8 (m/s)/s. Calculate the mass of the object. (6.5)
9. Calculate the force of gravity pulling down on a 60 kg person. [Use $g = 9.8$ (m/s)/s.] (6.6)

10. Describe how the force of gravity on an object depends on location. (6.6)
11. A jet aircraft is travelling at a constant speed, at a constant altitude, and in a constant direction. Draw a diagram showing the forces acting on the aircraft. Label everything you can about the forces. (6.7)
12. A rocket in outer space, where there is no air, can change its direction by firing a small engine on the side of the rocket. Explain how this is possible. (6.7)
13. Imagine you are stranded in the middle of a *frictionless* pond of ice the size of a football field. You have in your hand a basketful of hockey pucks, which you don't mind losing. Describe how you would get to one side of the pond. (Try to use all three of Newton's laws of motion to explain your answer.)
14. In general, which is greater in size, static friction or kinetic friction? (6.3, Act. 6B)
15. List factors that affect the force of friction. (Act. 6B)
16. A meteor or "shooting star" is a chunk of rocky material from outer space that burns and gives off light as it enters the earth's atmosphere. What is the likely cause of the burning? (6.9)
17. A surface that appears smooth to the human eye may appear irregular under the magnification of a microscope. For example, the surface of a "smooth" block of wood may look like this:

Use a diagram to explain why friction occurs between such a surface and another surface that is even smoother. (6.8, 6.9)

18. A 15 kg wooden table requires a horizontal force of 50 N to push it across a floor at a constant speed.
    (a) What is the normal force acting on the table?
    (b) Determine the coefficient of sliding friction between the table and the floor.
    (c) According to Table 6-2, what material is the floor likely made of? (6.9)
19. A 500 N girl is roller skating when she trips and slides across the floor. The coefficient of sliding friction between the girl and the floor is 0.12. What is the force of friction on the girl? (6.9)
20. A demolition worker places a ramp from a window on the second floor of an old building to a trolley bin below, as shown in Figure 6-12. The chunks of material slide down the ramp at constant speed. Use the information in the diagram to determine the coefficient of sliding friction between the material and the ramp. (Act. 6C)

Figure 6-12   Scale 1.0 cm = 1.0 m

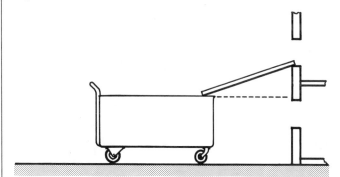

CHAPTER 7

Mechanical Energy and Power

As the amount of energy consumed in the world increases, we are finding new ways of obtaining energy from nature. One example is the energy from tides. The photograph shows Canada's first tidal generating station, located in Nova Scotia's Bay of Fundy area. As it moves through the station, the water gives some of its energy to generators that produce electricity. In this chapter you will see why moving objects have energy, and how energy can do work for us. You will also learn how power relates to energy and work.

Main Ideas

- The scientific meanings of work, energy, and power are somewhat different from the everyday meanings.
- Two types of mechanical energy are gravitational potential energy and kinetic energy.
- Energy is not created or destroyed; it simply changes form.
- Power is related to both energy and time.

7.1   The Importance of Energy

Energy is important both in physics and in our everyday lives. Earlier peoples consumed only the energy stored in the food they ate. That energy helped them perform work with their hands. As civilization progressed, more energy was used. The greater the progress, the greater was the consumption of energy.

Nowadays the nations in the world with the most advanced technology consume the most energy. That energy is used to heat homes in winter, cool homes in summer, manufacture necessities and luxuries, cook food, transport people and goods — the list is endless. People living in our society should learn about the advantages and disadvantages of consuming energy for such purposes.

Energy exists in many forms. That is why we will not try to give a simple definition of it. Table 7-1 gives a list of forms of energy.

Table 7-1   Forms of Energy

Form of energy	Comment
Radiant	Examples include visible light and X rays
Thermal	Results from the motion of particles
Electrical	Results from the forces of repulsion and attraction of charged particles
Nuclear	Stored in the central parts of atoms
Sound	Allows us to hear vibrations
Chemical potential	Stored in materials such as fuel and food
Gravitational potential	Energy of position
Kinetic	Energy of motion
Elastic potential	Stored in stretched or compressed objects

The forms of energy listed in Table 7-1 can change from one to another. For example, in a microwave oven, electrical energy is transformed into radiant energy (the microwaves). This energy is then transformed into thermal energy in the food being cooked. Figure 7-1 shows another example of an energy transformation. More examples are discussed in various parts of this textbook.

In this chapter the forms of energy studied are gravitational potential energy and kinetic energy, which together are called *mechanical energy*.

Figure 7-1   Radiant energy from the sun is transformed into the thermal energy of air particles in the production of wind. The wind can drive windmills like the one shown, which is used to pump water in a game park in Africa.

PRACTICE

1. Name at least one form of energy associated with each object in italics:
   (a) A *bonfire* roasts a marshmallow.
   (b) A *baseball* smashes a window.
   (c) A *solar collector* heats water for a swimming pool.
   (d) The *siren* of an ambulance warns of an emergency.
   (e) A watch's *spring* is fully wound.
   (f) Ocean *water* is used to produce electrical energy in a tidal generating station.

7.2 Using Force to Transfer Energy

Consider a situation in which some groceries must be lifted from the floor to a higher level. An example of this is shown in Figure 7-2. In order to lift the groceries up, a force must be exerted over a certain distance. When a force is exerted to move an object some distance, energy is transferred to the object.

Figure 7-2 Energy was transferred to box #72 to lift it from the floor to the rollers.

When energy is transferred to an object, we say that **work** has been done on the object. The amount of work done depends on the force exerted and the distance moved, as shown in the relation:

work = force × distance or

$$E = Fd$$

The symbol E is used to remind you that work done on an object is a measure of the energy transferred to that object.

Since force is measured in newtons and distance in metres, work is measured in newton metres, N·m. The newton metre is called a joule, J, in honour of James Joule, an English physicist (1818-1889) who studied heat and electrical energy.

The equation $E = Fd$ applies when the force and distance moved are in the same direction. This is true whether the force pushes an object horizontally, lifts it vertically, or anything in between.

When calculating the work done in lifting an object vertically, you may have to find the force needed to lift the object. If the object's mass is known, use the equation $F = mg$ to find the force. (Refer to Section 6.6.)

Sample Problem 1

The mass of the box #72 with groceries in Figure 7-2 is 20 kg, and the vertical distance it is raised is 1.0 m. Calculate the:
(a) force required to lift the box
(b) work done on the box in raising it to the rollers

Solution
(a) $F = mg$
$\quad = 20 \text{ kg} \times 9.8 \text{ (m/s)/s}$
$\quad = 196 \text{ N} \quad \text{or} \quad 2.0 \times 10^2 \text{ N}$
(b) $E = Fd$
$\quad = 196 \text{ N} \times 1.0 \text{ m}$
$\quad = 196 \text{ J} \quad \text{or} \quad 2.0 \times 10^2 \text{ J}$

Sample Problem 2

A 200 N force, parallel to the ramp, is needed to push a loaded wheelbarrow up the ramp. If the ramp is 6.0 m long, calculate the work done on the wheelbarrow.

Solution $E = Fd$
$\quad = 200 \text{ N} \times 6.0 \text{ m}$
$\quad = 1200 \text{ J}$

Sample Problem 3

A dog team is pulling a loaded sled across the snow with a total force of 150 N. The team and sled move with uniform motion on a level surface.
(a) What is the function of the 150 N force?
(b) Calculate the work done after the team and sled have travelled 1.0 km (1000 m).

Solution
(a) The force of 150 N is needed to overcome the sliding friction of the sled in the snow.
(b) $E = Fd$
$$= 150 \text{ N} \times 1000 \text{ m}$$
$$= 150\,000 \text{ J} \quad \text{or} \quad 1.5 \times 10^5 \text{ J}$$

In sample problem 3 the force exerted by the dogs balances the force of friction. This allows uniform motion. In such a situation the work that is done simply overcomes friction.

DID YOU KNOW?

*T*he calorie, symbol C, is a unit of food energy. It is equal to 4200 J or 4.2 kJ. Thus, a chocolate milk-shake rated at 250 C contains about one million joules or 1.0 MJ of chemical potential energy. It would take about a half-hour of swimming for an average person's body to consume this amount of energy.

PRACTICE

2. A boy pushes a box 5.0 m with a force of 25 N. How much work has he done on the box?
3. A girl pushes against a large maple tree with a force of 150 N. How much work has she done on the tree?
4. A 0.1 kg book is lifted vertically from the floor to a shelf 2.0 m above. Calculate the:
   (a) force needed to lift the book
   (b) work done on the book in lifting it to the shelf
5. Calculate the amount of work you would have to do in climbing 3.0 m vertically up a ladder.
6. A cyclist exerts an average force of 40 N in a uniform motion trip and covers a distance of 2.0 km (2000 m).
   (a) What is the function of the 40 N force?
   (b) How much work does the cyclist do?
7. Express joules in terms of metres, kilograms, and seconds. (Hint: Refer to the definition of a newton in Section 6.5.)
8. Rearrange the equation $E = Fd$ to express:
   (a) F by itself   (b) d by itself
9. Calculate the unknown quantities:
   (a) $E = 620$ J; $d = 31$ m; $F = ?$ N
   (b) $E = 40$ J; $F = 80$ N; $d = ?$ m

DID YOU KNOW?

*O*ne litre of gasoline contains about 34 million joules, or 34 MJ, of chemical potential energy.

7.3 Gravitational Potential Energy

Suppose that you must pound a peg part of the way into the ground using only a rock. You could lift the rock above the peg, as shown in Figure 7-3. At the raised position, the rock will have the potential to help you do some work on the peg. This potential is due to the fact that the force of gravity is pulling down on the rock.

Figure 7-3 Raising a rock gives it gravitational potential energy.

The type of energy possessed by an object because of its position is called **gravitational potential energy**, E_P. This potential energy can be used to do work on some object.

In order to lift the rock in Figure 7-3 a vertical height h, you would have to transfer energy ($E = Fh$) to it. That transferred energy, or work, equals the change in the rock's potential energy; that is $E_P = Fh$, where E_P is the potential energy of the object that is a vertical height h above some level. Since the force F is the force due to gravity, we can now write the common equation for potential energy.

$$E_P = (F)h \quad \text{and} \quad F = mg$$
$$\therefore \quad E_P = (mg)h, \quad \text{or:}$$
$$E_P = mgh \quad \text{where} \quad g = 9.8 \, (\text{m/s})/\text{s}$$

In the SI, energy is measured in joules, mass in kilograms, and vertical height (or distance) in metres.

When performing calculations of potential energy, be careful about your choice of *reference level*, the level to which an object may fall.

Sample Problem 4

The 20 kg box (#72) of groceries (Figure 7-2 and sample problem 1) is 0.5 m above the level of the loading platform outside the store. Calculate the potential energy of the box relative to that level.

Solution $E_P = mgh$
$= 20 \, \text{kg} \times 9.8 \, (\text{m/s})/\text{s} \times 0.5 \, \text{m}$
$= 98 \, \text{J}$

Sample problem 4 illustrates a useful application of potential energy. An object is lifted to a higher position, then gravity helps it accelerate down a slope. The object's speed helps it move a required distance. Ski lifts provide an example of this application. Another example is shown in Figure 7-4 in which a type of roller coaster is at a high position where its potential energy is greatest. Then gravity causes the coaster to accelerate downward. The rest is fun.

Figure 7-4 At the instant shown the cars in this thrill ride have a large amount of gravitational potential energy.

Sample Problem 5

Assume a loaded roller coaster has a mass, including passengers, of 5000 kg. From the loading platform it is raised vertically 12 m to its highest level. What is the potential energy of the coaster relative to the platform?

Solution $E_P = mgh$
$$= 5000 \text{ kg} \times 9.8 \text{ (m/s)/s} \times 12 \text{ m}$$
$$= 588\,000 \text{ J} \quad \text{or} \quad 5.9 \times 10^5 \text{ J}$$

Figure 7-5 shows another application of potential energy. A pile driver is about to be lifted by motor high above the pile. Then it will have the potential energy to do the work of driving the pile into the ground.

PRACTICE

10. A 0.5 kg book is resting on a desk that is 0.6 m high. Calculate the potential energy of the book relative to the:
    (a) desk
    (b) floor
11. Calculate the potential energy of a skier (total mass 70 kg, including equipment) at the top of a 100 m hill.
12. Rearrange the equation $E_P = mgh$ to express:
    (a) m by itself
    (b) h by itself
13. Calculate the unknown quantities:
    (a) $E_P = 19.6 \text{ J}$; $h = 4.0 \text{ m}$; $m = ? \text{ kg}$
    (b) $E_P = 29.4 \text{ J}$; $m = 2.0 \text{ kg}$; $h = ? \text{ m}$

Figure 7-5 An application of gravitational potential energy

7.4 Kinetic Energy

A bowling ball resting on the floor has no energy of motion. One that is rolling along a bowling alley has energy of motion. Energy due to the motion of an object is called **kinetic energy**, E_K. (Recall from Chapter 6 that "kinetic" relates to motion.)

Two factors determine the amount of kinetic energy possessed by a moving object. They are the mass and speed of the object. If either quantity increases, the kinetic energy increases. This is evident in the equation used to calculate kinetic energy:

$$E_K = \frac{mv^2}{2}$$

Again, the energy is measured in joules, mass in kilograms, and speed in metres per second.

Although the derivation of $E_K = \frac{mv^2}{2}$ is beyond the goals of this chapter, you should be aware that the equation stems from the fact that energy must be transferred to an object to increase its speed. For example, if 100 J of work is done on an object to increase its speed, its kinetic energy increases by 100 J. (The derivation of the equation is shown in Appendix F.)

Sample Problem 6

Find the kinetic energy of a 6.0 kg bowling ball rolling at 5.0 m/s.

Solution $E_K = \frac{mv^2}{2}$

$\quad\quad = \frac{(6.0\,\text{kg})(5.0\,\text{m/s})^2}{2}$

$\quad\quad = 3.0\,\text{kg} \times 25\,\text{m}^2/\text{s}^2$

$\quad\quad = 75\,\text{J}$

PRACTICE

14. Calculate the kinetic energy of each object:
    (a) A 4.0 kg shot leaves an athlete's hand during a shot-put event at a speed of 10 m/s.
    (b) A 2000 kg car is travelling at 20 m/s.
    (c) A 0.15 kg hockey puck has a speed of 40 m/s.

15. Rearrange the equation $E_K = \frac{mv^2}{2}$ to express:
    (a) m by itself
    (b) v by itself

16. Calculate the unknown quantities:
    (a) $E_K = 50\,\text{J}$; $v = 5.0\,\text{m/s}$; $m = ?\,\text{kg}$
    (b) $E_K = 25\,\text{J}$; $m = 2.0\,\text{kg}$; $v = ?\,\text{m/s}$

Activity 7A Comparing Work and Energy

PROBLEM ■ When work is transformed to gravitational potential energy and then to kinetic energy, does the total energy remain constant?

APPARATUS ■ cart; board (up to 2.5 m long); balance; force scale (to 10 N); metre stick; masking tape; recording timer and related apparatus (or an alternative way of measuring speed)

PROCEDURE ■
1. **Getting ready**
   (a) Check the force scale to see if it is properly adjusted to use at a slight angle to the horizontal. If it isn't, inform your teacher.
   (b) Elevate and support one end of the board so it makes an angle of about 20° to the horizontal, as shown in Figure 7-6(a). Be sure there is no sag in the middle of the board.
   (c) Use masking tape to mark off a position two cart lengths above the bottom end of the board (position A in the diagram).
   (d) Set up the recording timer (or other device used to determine speed). Check to be sure it is working properly.
   (e) Draw a diagram similar to Figure 7-6(b) on which you can record measurements and calculations.

Figure 7-6   Activity 7A

(a) The basic set-up: Position A is two cart lengths above the bottom of the board.

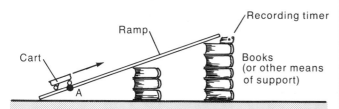

(b) Required distance measurements: Notice that E is half-way between C and A.

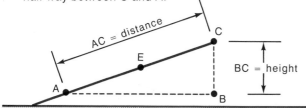

2. **Basic measurements**
   (a) Measure the mass of the cart in kilograms.
   (b) Measure the distance AC in metres. [See Figure 7-6(a).]
   (c) Measure the height BC in metres.
3. **Experimental measurements**
   (a) Measure the average force, F, in newtons required to pull the cart up the ramp from A to C at a constant speed. Repeat this procedure for accuracy.
   (b) Tape a paper strip to the cart and feed it into the recording timer. With the cart initially at rest at the top of the ramp, allow the cart to accelerate down the ramp while recording the motion. Catch the cart at the bottom of the ramp. Save the paper strip for analysis.

ANALYSIS ■
1. Calculate the work done in pulling the cart up the ramp ($W = Fd$, where d is the distance AC).
2. Calculate the gravitational potential energy of the cart above position A when it is at the top of the ramp ($E_P = mgh$, where h is the height BC).
3. Calculate the gravitational potential energy of the cart above position A when it has moved halfway down the ramp ($E_P = mgh$, where h is half of BC).
4. Determine the speed of the accelerating cart in metres per second at positions E and A. (These calculations require careful planning. Ask your teacher if you need help.)
5. Calculate the kinetic energy of the cart at positions C, E, and A $\left(E_K = \dfrac{mv^2}{2}\right)$.
6. Summarize your data in a chart based on the one shown here. The total energy is the sum of E_P and E_K at any position.

Position	E_P (J)	E_K (J)	Total Energy (J)
Top of ramp			
Middle of ramp			
Bottom of ramp			

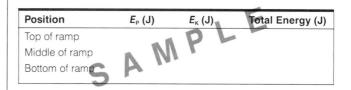

7. How does the work done in pulling the cart up the ramp compare to the gravitational potential energy at the top of the ramp?
8. Describe any possible sources of error in this activity.
9. Write a sentence about the total amount of energy in this activity.

APPLICATION ■   What is the advantage of pulling an object up a ramp rather than lifting it vertically to the same height? What is the disadvantage?

7.5 The Law of Conservation of Energy

The quantities of energy transferred (or work), potential energy, and kinetic energy are all measured in joules, and one can change to another. Scientists say that, when any such change occurs, energy is "conserved". In other words:

When energy changes from one form to another, no energy is lost.

This statement is called **the law of conservation of energy**. (This law applies to other forms of energy. It does not, however, apply to nuclear reactions. Such reactions obey the law of conservation of mass-energy, mentioned in Chapter 27.)

As an example of the law of conservation of energy, consider a situation in which a man has the job of breaking a large rock into smaller chunks. The rock is too heavy for him to lift. The man has no tools, only a ramp and some smaller nearby stones. He can use physics to solve his unusual problem.

Figure 7-7 illustrates a logical solution that uses the resources available. First the man builds a ramp with the smaller stones as a base. Then he does work on the rock, rolling it up the ramp, as shown in diagram (a). Assume the amount of work he does is 1000 J. At the top of the ramp, in diagram (b), the rock has 1000 J of potential energy relative to he rocky ground below. (Recall from the previous activity that the work done moving an object up a ramp equals the gravitational potential energy at the top of the ramp.)

In diagram (c), the potential energy changes to kinetic energy as the rock accelerates downward. Just before striking the ground the rock has maximum speed and 1000 J of kinetic energy.

Then, in diagram (d), the kinetic energy changes into other types of energy, and the rock shatters into smaller chunks. Again, the amount of energy equals 1000 J.

Figure 7-7 The law of conservation of energy

(a) $E = Fd$

(b) $E_p = mgh$

(c) $E_k = \dfrac{mv^2}{2}$

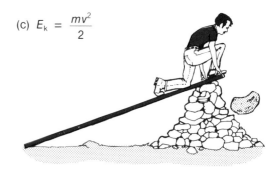

(d) The energy is conserved.

The law of conservation of energy can also be applied to several situations already mentioned in this chapter:

- sending groceries to a pick-up area (Figure 7-2)
- using a rock to pound a peg (Figure 7-3)
- operating a thrill ride (Figure 7-4)
- using a pile driver (Figure 7-5)

PRACTICE

17. An object, moving with a kinetic energy of 20 J, has 30 J of energy transferred to it.
    (a) What is the new kinetic energy?
    (b) What law is this based on?
18. Use the law of conservation of energy to describe the energy changes that occur in the operation of a pile driver, shown in Figure 7-5.
19. A ball is dropped vertically from a height of 1.5 m and bounces back to a height of 1.3 m. Does this violate the law of conservation of energy? Explain your answer.

7.6 Power

It takes approximately 2000 J of work for an average person to climb one flight of stairs. The amount of work remains the same whether the person climbs the stairs in 5 s or 30 s. If the work is the same but the time changes, something else must change. That something else is called power.

Power is the rate of doing work or transforming energy.

$$P = \frac{E}{t}$$

Since energy is measured in joules and time in seconds, power is measured in joules per second. This SI unit has the special name watt (W), in honour of James Watt, a Scottish physicist (1736-1819) who was the first to invent a practical steam engine. Watts and kilowatts are commonly used to indicate the power of electrical appliances.

Sample Problem 7

What is the power of a cyclist who transfers 20 000 J (2.0×10^4 J) of energy in 100 s?

Solution $P = \frac{E}{t}$

$$= \frac{20\,000\,J}{100\,s}$$

$$= 200\,W$$

Sample Problem 8

A 60 kg student takes 6.0 s to climb vertically up a 3.0 m ladder. Calculate the:

(a) potential energy of the student at the top of the ladder
(b) student's power for the climb

Solution
(a) $E_P = mgh$
$$= 60\,kg \times 9.8\,(m/s)/s \times 3.0\,m$$
$$= 1764\,J \quad or \quad 1.8 \times 10^3\,J$$

(b) $P = \frac{E}{t}$

$$= \frac{1764\,J}{6.0\,s}$$

$$= 294\,W \quad or \quad 3.0 \times 10^2\,W$$

PRACTICE

20. If 150 J of work are done in 30 s, what is the power?
21. An electric clock uses 150 J of electrical energy every 60 s. What is the clock's power rating?
22. A certain stereo uses 1.44×10^5 J of energy in 1 h (3600 s). Calculate its power rating.
23. Rearrange the equation $P = \frac{E}{t}$ to express:
    (a) E by itself (b) t by itself
24. Calculate the unknown quantities:
    (a) $P = 120\,W$; $t = 60\,s$; $E = ?\,J$
    (b) $P = 15\,W$; $E = 750\,J$; $t = ?\,s$
25. Express watts in terms of metres, kilograms, and seconds. (Hint: Refer to Practice #7 in this chapter.)

Activity 7B Student Power

PROBLEM ■ How powerful are you?

APPARATUS ■ stopwatch; metre stick; 4 or 5 hard-cover textbooks; bathroom scales (in kilograms or newtons); heavy object, such as a trunk, to be dragged or pushed

PROCEDURE ■

1. Measure the vertical height of a flight of stairs. (The greater the height, the better!) Determine the time it takes you to run up the stairs as quickly and safely as possible. (A running start is allowed.) Calculate your own power for the run.

 CAUTION Exercise common sense in this activity. Run up stairs only if you are wearing athletic shoes. Be careful not to trip. Also, be careful not to strain your arm muscles during any of the suggested activities. Anyone with heart or breathing problems should consult the teacher.

2. Obtain four or five textbooks and measure their total mass. Find the time it takes you to lift the books a known vertical distance for 25 repetitions. Calculate your own power for this activity.
3. Determine the horizontal force required to push or pull a heavy object across a floor. Find the time it takes you to move the object a known distance. Calculate your power for this activity.

ANALYSIS ■

1. Compare your power for each activity with the power of the other students in the class. From the comparison try to determine factors that affect "student power".
2. Name other activities that may be interesting in this type of experiment.

Words to Know

forms of energy
work
joule
gravitational potential
  energy

kinetic energy
law of conservation of
  energy
power
watt

Chapter Objectives

Having completed this chapter, you should now be able to:

1. Describe forms of energy, in particular the two forms of mechanical energy called gravitational potential energy and kinetic energy.
2. Calculate the work done on an object that moves a given distance under a known force ($E = Fd$).
3. Use the SI unit of energy.
4. Calculate the gravitational potential energy of an object given its mass and height above a reference level ($E_P = mgh$).
5. Describe applications of gravitational potential energy.
6. Calculate the kinetic energy of an object given its mass and speed $\left(E_K = \dfrac{mv^2}{2}\right)$.
7. State the law of conservation of energy and give examples that illustrate it.
8. Define power and use the SI unit to measure it.
9. Calculate the power of an object consuming energy for a given amount of time $\left(P = \dfrac{E}{t}\right)$.
10. Determine experimentally the power of a person participating in an activity.

DID YOU KNOW?

*T*he "horsepower" is a unit of power in the Imperial system of measurement. It is equal to about 750 W, which is the amount of power exerted by an average working horse for an extended period of time. You may want to compare your maximum power to one horsepower.

Chapter Review

1. What is the scientific term for:
   (a) energy of position?
   (b) energy of motion?   (7.1)
2. A black bear's greatest enemy is a grizzly bear. To escape a grizzly attack, a black bear does what its enemy cannot do — it climbs a tree. Calculate the work done by a 150 kg black bear in climbing 20 m up a tree.   (7.2)
3. A baseball is given 120 J of energy by a pitcher who exerts a force over a distance of 1.0 m. Calculate the force exerted.   (7.2)
4. A force of 200 N is required to keep a motorcycle moving with uniform motion. How far will 6.0×10^5 J of work take that motorcycle?   (7.2)
5. In April 1981, Arnold Boldt of Saskatchewan set a world high-jump record for disabled athletes in Rome, Italy, jumping to a height of 2.04 m. (At the age of three, Arnold had his right leg amputated above the knee after an accident.) Calculate Arnold's gravitational potential energy at the top of the record jump. (Assume that his mass at the time of the jump was 68 kg.)   (7.3)
6. An object of unknown mass, located 10 m above the ground, has a potential energy of 98 J relative to the ground. Calculate the object's mass.   (7.3)
7. How high above the floor must a 0.1 kg ball be lifted to give it a potential energy of 4.9 J relative to the floor?   (7.3)
8. Find the kinetic energy of a 2.0 kg ball that is travelling:
   (a) 2.0 m/s
   (b) 4.0 m/s
   (c) 6.0 m/s   (7.4)
9. A discus travelling at 20 m/s has 400 J of kinetic energy. Find the mass of the discus.   (7.4)
10. Calculate the speed of a 16 kg curling stone that has a kinetic energy of 72 J.   (7.4)

11. An interesting and practical feature of the Montreal subway system is that, in some cases, the level of the station is higher than the level of the adjoining tunnel, as illustrated in Figure 7-8. Explain the advantages of this design. (Take into consideration such concepts as force, acceleration, work, potential energy, and kinetic energy.)

Figure 7-8   The Montreal subway system

12. Calculate the power rating of a light bulb that uses 3600 J of energy each 60 s.   (7.6)
13. Some people perform difficult tasks to raise money for charity. For example, walking up the stairs in Toronto's CN Tower helps charity and personal fitness. If a 70 kg person climbs the vertical distance of 342 m 10 times in 4 h, calculate the:
    (a) work done each trip up the stairs
    (b) total work for the 10 trips
    (c) power   (7.2, 7.6)
14. How much energy is used by a 1200 W electric kettle during 5 min (300 s) of operation?   (7.6)
15. Find the time it takes a 60 W light bulb to consume the energy stored in 1.0 kg of coal (3.0×10^7 J).   (7.6)

Rigid Bodies, Stability, and Elasticity

Chewing food, walking, and using scissors and screwdrivers have been part of your daily life for years. Perhaps you have paddled a canoe, played on a seesaw with a small child, rowed a boat, or used a wrench to tighten or loosen a bolt. All these actions produce movement through some form of rotation of a rigid body around a pivot point. The turning effect that tends to cause rotation is called torque. Torque is important in understanding why some objects have stability, that is, are less likely to tip over than other objects.

Some solid bodies (such as a rubber ball) bend and give way when force is applied, and then return to their original shape. These objects are called elastic bodies. This unit examines rigid bodies, the stability of objects and how to achieve stability, the elasticity of solid bodies, and the design and construction of buildings, bridges, and other structures.

Information gained in this unit will be useful as you consider future careers in tool-and-die making, machine design or operation, construction, and mechanics. The natural resources industries such as mining, oil, and forestry (as well as the energy conservation industry

involving power systems and mechanics) all require thorough knowledge of rigid bodies, stability, and elasticity. This knowledge is required, too, if you are considering any of the fields of maintenance and repairs, sports, fashion design, theatre, and dance.

- The construction industry is one of Canada's largest employers. This industry offers a wide variety of jobs such as carpentry, plumbing, and tiling. A construction engineer technologist is highly trained in surveying, drafting, and construction methods. As well, the study of mechanics and mechanical installations is needed, as is the ability to use a well-equipped laboratory to test the composition and quality control of construction materials and components.

Knowing the information in this unit will be especially useful if you plan a career in any of the areas already mentioned, as well as the following: figure skating, acrobatics (including circus performance), toy design and manufacture, architecture, fabric manufacture, and boat building. For more information about any of the careers mentioned, you might talk to someone already on that career path. If it still appeals to you, contact your local community college, university, guidance office, or counselling centre.

CHAPTER 8

Rigid Bodies and Stability

How can an elephant balance on a ball? How can a swan rest peacefully while standing on one skinny leg? Or how does a ballerina stand motionless on the toes of one foot? The study of such examples of balance involves the concept of stability. Stability, in turn, is understood in terms of the concepts of torque and centre of mass. We begin this chapter with a study of torque, which will lead to an examination of many interesting applications of centre of mass, and stability.

Main Ideas

- Torque is a turning effect, often applied to a lever.
- The centre of mass of an object is the point about which all the torques are balanced.
- A body is stable only when its centre of mass lies above its support base.

8.1 Torque

Previously in this textbook we treated all objects as if they were a single concentrated mass. For example, if we calculated the kinetic energy of a swimmer, we needed to know the mass and speed of the swimmer. We did not need to know about the swimmer's arms, legs, bones, and so on. In this topic, however, we look at objects differently. Here we are concerned with forces that act on various parts of solid objects. The forces are not large enough to break the objects or even bend them noticeably. Solid objects that do not deform or break under applied forces are called **rigid bodies**. An example of a rigid body is a seesaw (Figure 8-1). When two people are on a seesaw they hope it won't bend or break.

Figure 8-1 A seesaw is a typical example of a rigid body.

DID YOU KNOW?

In pairs figure skating and ballet, one partner can help the other partner perform a spin by producing two torques. One torque is caused by pushing on one side, the other by pulling on the other side.

When a force or set of forces cause a rigid body to tend to rotate, we say a torque has been set up. A **torque** is a turning effect on a rigid body around a pivot support. Every time you apply a force to open or close a door, you are producing a torque on the door. With a door, the hinges act as the pivot support. You know from experience that a small force applied far from the hinges can produce the same torque as a large force applied closer to the hinges. Refer to Figure 8-2.

Figure 8-2 Producing torque on a door

A large force applied at a small distance from the pivot support (a) can cause the same torque as a small force applied at a large distance (b).

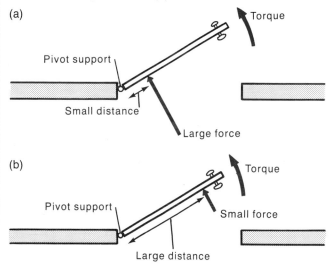

A good way to get a "feel" for torque is to try to push on a door at various distances from the hinges. You will notice the effect shown in Figure 8-2. But you will also discover one other fact. Our natural tendency is to apply the force at an angle of 90° to the door. We have learned from experience that this causes the largest turning effect on the door. If you try applying the same force at various angles to the same point on the door, you will see that the torque is reduced.

In this text we will consider only situations in which the applied force is perpendicular to the rigid body. See Figure 8-3.

Figure 8-3 The torque is biggest when the applied force is perpendicular to the rigid body.

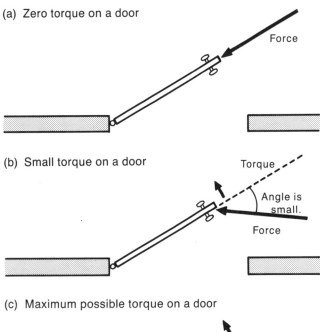

(a) Zero torque on a door

(b) Small torque on a door

(c) Maximum possible torque on a door

We can see from the example with the door that the amount of torque produced on a rigid body depends on two main factors. One factor is the force (F) applied to the rigid body. The other is the distance (d) between the pivot support and the applied force. Using the symbol T for torque, the following statements hold true:

T increases as F increases

T increases as d increases

Thus, **torque = force × distance**

or $T = Fd$ (with F perpendicular to the rigid body)

Using SI units, force is measured in newtons (N) and distance in metres (m), so torque is measured in newton metres (N·m). Do not confuse the equation for torque with the equation for work ($W = Fd$). The work equation applies when the force and the distance are *parallel* to each other. The torque equation applies when the force and the distance are *perpendicular* to each other. The units, too, are different. (Recall that work is measured in joules.)

Sample Problem 1

Determine the torque on the wrench shown in the diagram.

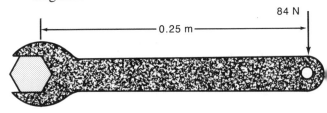

Solution $T = Fd$
$= 84 \text{ N} \times 0.25 \text{ m}$
$= 21 \text{ N·m}$

The concept of torque is applied in the construction and use of tools and machines, as well as other ways described later in this chapter.

PRACTICE

1. Describe the conditions under which a baseball bat would be considered:
   (a) an object of concentrated mass
   (b) a rigid body
2. A mechanic is able to apply a 500 N force at right angles to a wrench to loosen a nut. Calculate the torque if the distance from the nut to the applied force is:
   (a) 0.30 m   (b) 0.50 m
3. A door that swings inward or outward has hidden hinges and no handle. A person applies a force of 100 N at the hinges. What torque is produced on the door?
4. Rearrange the equation for torque to find an expression for:
   (a) the distance, d (b) the force, F
5. A cyclist is signalling with one hand and steering with the other hand to turn a corner. The cyclist applies a force of 4.5 N, which produces a torque of 0.99 N·m. What is the distance from the pivot support to the force applied by the cyclist?
6. A corral gate is partly open. A cow hits the gate with its head, at a distance of 3.6 m from the hinges. If the torque produced by the cow is 540 N·m, what force did the cow apply to the gate?

8.2   Levers

Anyone who tries to remove the lid of a paint can using his or her fingers soon discovers it is impossible. The task becomes much easier using a rigid device to pry the lid open. Figure 8-4 shows a screwdriver acting as a rigid body to remove a lid. Used this way, the screwdriver is called a lever. A **lever** is a rigid body that may rotate around a pivot support. With levers, the pivot support is called a **fulcrum**.

Figure 8-4   When a screwdriver is used to pry a lid open, it acts as a lever. A small effort force by the hand produces a large load force on the lid. The outer edge of the can is the fulcrum.

Specific terminology and symbols are used with levers. The **effort** or **effort force** (F_E) is the force in newtons applied to try to move an object. The **load** or **load force** (F_L) is the force required to move the object. The **effort arm** (d_E) is the distance from the fulcrum to the effort force. The **load arm** (d_L) is the distance from the fulcrum to the load force. These definitions are illustrated in Figure 8-5.

Figure 8-5   The four variables associated with the lever, illustrated for a first-class lever

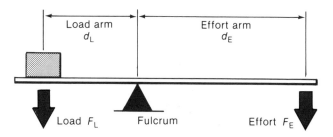

Classes of the lever

Levers are divided into three classes, depending on the positions of the load, effort, and fulcrum. The following are the definitions and examples of the three classes. Notice that for each class, one of the examples is found in the human body.

(1) A **first-class lever** has the fulcrum between the load and the effort.

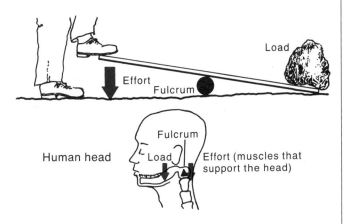

(2) A **second-class lever** has the load between the fulcrum and the effort.

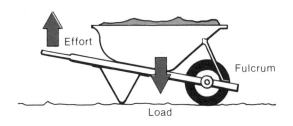

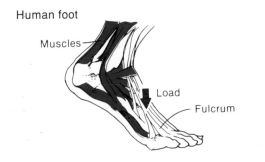

(3) A **third-class lever** has the effort exerted between the fulcrum and the load.

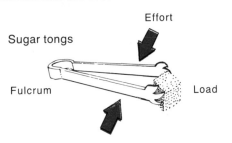

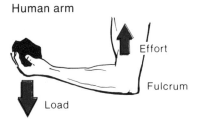

Torque and levers

In Section 8.1 you learned that the product of force and distance is the torque. There are two torques that can be calculated for a lever. One is the effort torque (T_E) and the other is the load torque (T_L). The equations to determine these torques are:

$$\textbf{effort torque} = \textbf{effort force} \times \textbf{effort arm} \text{ or}$$
$$T_E = F_E d_E$$

$$\textbf{load torque} = \textbf{load force} \times \textbf{load arm} \text{ or}$$
$$T_L = F_L d_L$$

Remember that torque is measured in newton metres (N·m) and in each case the force is perpendicular to the lever.

Sample Problem 2

A person is using a large plank as a first-class lever to move a rock. The effort force is 450 N and the distance from the fulcrum to the effort force is 2.2 m. What is the effort torque produced?

Solution $T_E = F_E d_E$
$$= 450 \text{ N} \times 2.2 \text{ m}$$
$$= 990 \text{ N} \cdot \text{m}$$

PRACTICE

7. State the class of lever illustrated by each device shown in Figure 8-6 and draw a diagram showing the fulcrum, load, and effort.

Figure 8-6 For Practice #7

(a) Nutcracker

(b) Paddling a canoe (Assume the fulcrum is at the top end of the paddle.)

(c) Human jaw

(d) Nailclipper

8. Determine the effort torque for each lever shown in Figure 8-7.

Figure 8-7 For Practice #8

(a)
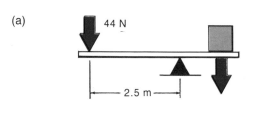

(b)
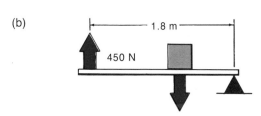

9. Determine the load torque for each lever shown in Figure 8-8.

Figure 8-8 For Practice #9

(a)
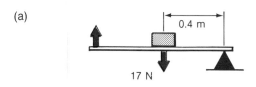

(b)
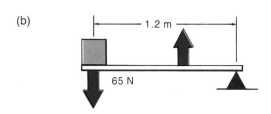

10. Estimate the maximum effort torque you could produce on a wheel nut using a tire wrench that is 50 cm long.

8.3   Static Balance of Rigid Bodies

The word *static* means *at rest*. A body that is in static balance is at rest in two ways. First, it is not moving in any direction. Second, and more important here, it is not rotating.

When a lever is in static balance, the size of the effort torque equals the size of the load torque.

This observation is called the **law of the lever**. It can be written in equation form, as follows:

effort torque = load torque

effort force × effort arm
= load force × load arm

$$F_E d_E = F_L d_L *$$

*Only the *sizes* of the quantities are considered in this equation. This eliminates the need to worry about positive and negative signs.

Any one of the four variables in the law of the lever equation can be found by rearranging the equation. For example, to find the effort force, F_E, the equation is:

$$F_E = \frac{F_L d_L}{d_E}$$

Sample Problem 3

A camper wants to mount a trailer on blocks for the winter. One corner of the trailer is lifted by placing a 3.0 m plank as shown in the diagram, and applying an effort force. Determine the size of the effort force required.

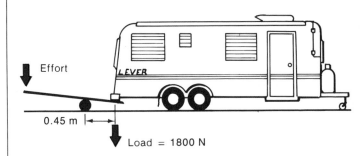

Solution
$$F_E = \frac{F_L d_L}{d_E}$$
$$= \frac{(1800\,\text{N})(0.45\,\text{m})}{1.8\,\text{m}}$$
$$= 450\,\text{N}$$

The law of the lever can be stated in more general terms for any rigid body. Rather than using the terms load and effort, the direction of rotation is considered. Also, the point about which the rotation can occur is no longer called a fulcrum. For now, we will call it the "balance point". Thus, *when any rigid body is in static balance, the clockwise torque is balanced by the counterclockwise torque.* Using convenient symbols, the general condition for static balance is:

$$T\,\circlearrowright = T\,\circlearrowleft$$

where $T\,\circlearrowright$ is the size of the clockwise torque on an object around the balance point, and $T\,\circlearrowleft$ is the size of the counterclockwise torque on the object. This is illustrated for a first-class lever in Figure 8-9.

This condition of static balance is applied in Activity 8A, where you will locate the balance point of a variety of objects.

Figure 8-9 When a lever is balanced, the size of the clockwise torque equals the size of the counterclockwise torque.

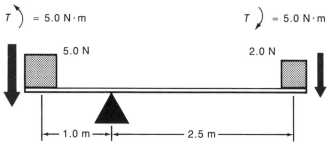

$T\,) = 5.0\ \text{N·m}$ $T\,) = 5.0\ \text{N·m}$

5.0 N   2.0 N

← 1.0 m →|← 2.5 m →

PRACTICE

11. Calculate the effort force for each situation shown in Figure 8-10.

Figure 8-10 For Practice #11

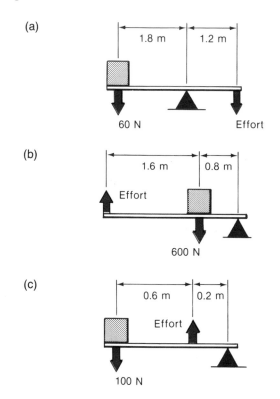

(a)

1.8 m   1.2 m

60 N   Effort

(b)

1.6 m   0.8 m

Effort

600 N

(c)

0.6 m   0.2 m

Effort

100 N

12. Rearrange the law of the lever equation to express:
    (a) d_E by itself   (b) F_L by itself   (c) d_L by itself

13. (a) Find d_E given $F_E = 10\ \text{N}$, $F_L = 50\ \text{N}$, and $d_L = 0.20\ \text{m}$.
    (b) Find F_L given $F_E = 60\ \text{N}$, $d_E = 3.5\ \text{m}$, and $d_L = 0.70\ \text{m}$.
    (c) Find d_L given $F_E = 30\ \text{N}$, $d_E = 2.0\ \text{m}$, and $F_L = 600\ \text{N}$.

14. A woman wants to raise one end of an upright piano so she can place coasters under the wheels. It takes 1600 N to raise one end of the piano, but she can apply only 400 N. She places a fulcrum 30 cm from the piano and uses a strong board as a first-class lever to raise the piano.
    (a) Draw a sketch of this situation showing the fulcrum, the lever, and the distances and forces involved.
    (b) What is the length of the effort arm required?
    (c) What is the total length of the board?

15. Each oar in a rowboat is held 40 cm from the oarlock (Figure 8-11). The oars exert a force on the water at an average distance of 1.4 m from the oarlock. If a rower can exert a force of 350 N with each arm, what is the *total* force exerted by the oars on the water?

Figure 8-11 For Practice #15

Oarlock

16. The effort force applied to the tweezers in Figure 8-12 is 12 N. If the force exerted on the load is 8.0 N, determine the:
    (a) distance from the fulcrum to the load
    (b) distance from the effort to the load

Figure 8-12 For Practice #16

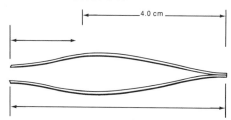

|← 4.0 cm →|

Activity 8A Finding the Balance Point

PROBLEM ■ How can the balance point of various rigid bodies be located?

APPARATUS ■

For Part A: metre stick; large rubber stopper; tape; various long thin objects (see Figure 8-13)

For Part B: various stiff cardboard shapes (see Figure 8-14); tape; pin or nail; plumb bob (mass on the end of a string or thread)

For Part C: large, rigid plank; two bathroom scales

PROCEDURE ■

Part A: The balance point of long rigid bodies

1. Locate the horizontal balance point of a metre stick in the following way. Place your two index fingers almost 1 m apart and rest the metre stick horizontally on them. *Slowly* slide your fingers toward each other until they meet. Try this a few times to be sure of the result. The point where your fingers meet is the balance point.

2. Tape a large rubber stopper on the top of one end of the metre stick and guess where the new balance point will be. Then experiment to find how good your guess was. Record your observations.

3. Predict and then find the location of the horizontal balance point of various other rigid objects that are long and thin. Some examples as shown in Figure 8-13.

Figure 8-13 Sliding fingers can be used to locate the horizontal balance point of long thin objects.

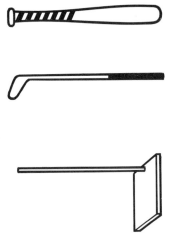

Part B: The balance point of irregular two-dimensional objects

1. Cut out various shapes of objects from stiff cardboard. Figure 8-14 shows examples of shapes you can use. Tape a piece of paper to the L-shaped object, as shown in diagram (c).

Figure 8-14 Examples of cardboard shapes

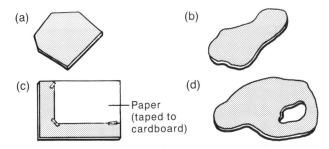

(a) (b)

(c) (d)

Paper (taped to cardboard)

2. Choose one cardboard body and with a pin poke a hole near the edge. Make the hole larger than the pin so when the body is held vertically it can rotate freely about the pin. Suspend a plumb bob from the pin, as shown in Figure 8-15(a), and carefully locate the plumb line made by the plumb bob. Draw the plumb line, and label it AB.

Figure 8-15 Using a plumb bob to locate the balance point and checking the result

(a) Finding the first plumb line

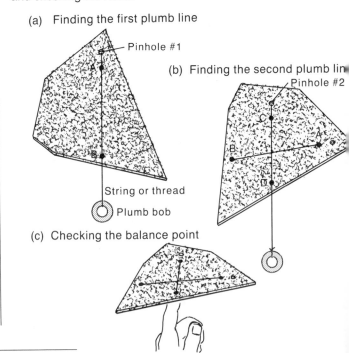

Pinhole #1

(b) Finding the second plumb line

Pinhole #2

String or thread

Plumb bob

(c) Checking the balance point

3. Poke another hole in the body and repeat #2, as shown in Figure 8-15(b). Label the new line CD. The point where line CD intersects with line AB is the balance point of the body.
4. Check the location of the balance point by using a third hole and perhaps a fourth one. Once you are certain of your results, try to balance the cardboard body horizontally on a finger, as shown in Figure 8-15(c).
5. Repeat #2 to #4 for the other cardboard bodies. What is unusual about the L-shaped body?

Part C: The horizontal balance point of a student
1. Place a bathroom scale under each end of a long, rigid plank of uniform construction. Check to be sure the scales read the same value. Mark the midpoint of the plank.

 CAUTION   Take care when moving the plank. Hold it firmly, with the leading edge down near the floor.

2. The student whose balance point is to be found should lie on the plank rigidly, with arms and legs extended. The student should move to a position such that the scales have the same reading (Figure 8-16). The horizontal balance point will be located along the midline of the plank.

Figure 8-16   Using bathroom scales to find the horizontal balance point of a student

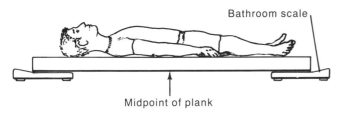

Midpoint of plank

3. If time permits, determine the effect on the balance point with the student's legs bent, or with other configurations.

ANALYSIS ■
1. Relate the concept of torque to the methods used to find the balance point of objects.
2. Can the balance point of a body be outside the body? State how you know.
3. Describe any possible sources of error in this activity.
4. How can the balance point of a rigid body be located? List the ways used to do this.

8.4   Centre of Mass

In Activity 8A you found the *horizontal* point about which the rigid bodies were balanced in one or two dimensions. If the balance point is found in all *three* dimensions, this point is called the centre of mass. As you have learned, the condition that determines the balance point is related to torques that are balanced. Thus, the **centre of mass** (c.m.) of a rigid body is the point about which all the torques are balanced. In other words, the clockwise torques balance the counterclockwise torques. Using symbols, $T \big\downarrow = T \big\uparrow$. This applies to all dimensions of the body. These concepts are illustrated for the centre of mass of a regular solid in Figure 8-17.

Figure 8-17   The centre of mass is the point about which all the torques are balanced. For a regular solid of uniform composition, the c.m. is at the exact centre.

Centre of mass

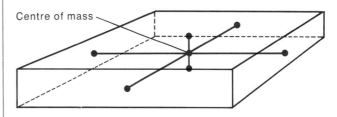

DID YOU KNOW?

The term centre of gravity is often used in place of centre of mass. The two points are located in the same position for objects considered in this textbook.

As shown in Figure 8-17, the c.m. of a regular solid of uniform composition is the exact centre of the object. The c.m. of other objects depends on the shape of the object as well as the distribution of mass. Figure 8-18 shows some examples of common objects. Other examples were found experimentally in Activity 8A (at least in one or two dimensions).

Figure 8-18 The c.m. of various objects

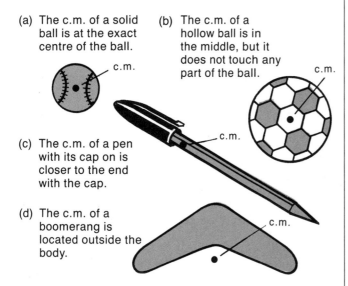

(a) The c.m. of a solid ball is at the exact centre of the ball.

(b) The c.m. of a hollow ball is in the middle, but it does not touch any part of the ball.

(c) The c.m. of a pen with its cap on is closer to the end with the cap.

(d) The c.m. of a boomerang is located outside the body.

The c.m. of a body suspended from a single point lies directly beneath the point of suspension. This observation is applied in the use of a plumb bob to locate the c.m. of a suspended body (Activity 8A, Figure 8-15). It is also applied in the construction of mobiles. Figure 8-19 shows how to build a mobile.

Figure 8-19 The c.m. of each part of a mobile lies directly beneath that part's point of suspension.

To build a mobile like the one shown, start from the bottom and work toward the top.

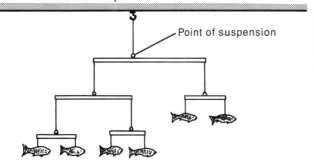

Point of suspension

PRACTICE

17. Are the c.m. and horizontal balance point of a metre stick exactly the same points? Explain your answer.
18. State the location of the c.m. of:
    (a) a golf ball
    (b) a doughnut (with a hole)
19. An open trailer in the shape of a box can be used to carry various loads. State the approximate vertical location of the c.m. of the trailer and its load when the trailer:
    (a) is filled with grain
    (b) is carrying a load of pigs
    (c) is carrying a load of standing horses
20. Describe how you would find the approximate c.m. of:
    (a) a golf club
    (b) a framed painting
    (c) a boomerang

Activity 8B   Centre of Mass and Stability

PROBLEM ■ How does the c.m. of an object relate to the object's stability?

APPARATUS ■ heavy object that can be lifted with one hand (e.g., a dumbbell); chair; various demonstrations and toys related to c.m.; brick (or similar metal or wooden block); ramp; various unbreakable objects whose stabilities are to be compared

 CAUTION Ensure that suspended objects are fastened securely. Also, if you have any physical difficulties in lifting objects or bending over, you should exercise care in choosing which procedure steps to follow. Discuss this with your teacher.

PROCEDURE AND ANALYSIS ■

1. For the parts of this step, refer to Figure 8-20, which shows two human feet (or rather shoes) and locations marked A to G. The region enclosed by the feet is shaded, and includes regions B, C, and D.

   (a) Stand upright with your arms at your side and your feet about 50 cm apart. Have your partner look at you from position F. Above what position (from A to G) does your c.m. lie?

   (b) With your feet still about 50 cm apart and your partner still watching from position F, slowly raise your *right* foot off the floor. Describe what happens to your c.m. Above what position (from A to G) does it appear to lie now?

   (c) Stand erect, this time with both feet together and a heavy object located near your right hand (at position E in the diagram). With your partner still at F, determine what happens to your body, especially your hips, as you raise the heavy object slightly. Where does your c.m. appear to lie now?

   (d) Stand upright with your two feet close together and your partner observing from one side, either A or E. Above what point does your c.m. appear to be? Now slowly bend forward, letting your arms fall toward the ground. Toward what direction does the top part of your body move? Toward what direction does the bottom part of your body (except your feet) move? Above what point is your c.m. now?

Figure 8-20 For Activity 8B, Procedure #1

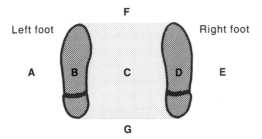

2. Try these.

   (a) Stand sideways against a wall with the side of one foot pressed against the wall. Slowly raise the other foot off the floor. What happens? Why?

   (b) Stand with your back to the wall and your heels pressed against the wall. Slowly bend over to try to touch your toes. What happens? Explain why.

   (c) Stand facing a wall with your toes pressed against the wall and your arms by your side. Try to rise up onto your tiptoes. What happens? Why?

   (d) With your back and heels to the wall, hold on to a chair, as shown in Figure 8-21. Now try to raise the chair slowly. Do girls tend to find this exercise easier or harder than boys? Why?

Figure 8-21 Lifting a chair from a bent position

3. Set up various kinds of apparatus that demonstrate the principle of c.m. These can range from toys to home-made demonstrations, some of which are shown in Figure 8-22. In each case, describe where the c.m. is located relative to the base over which it is balanced.

Figure 8-22 Examples of c.m. demonstrations

4. Choose a brick or solid block such that its length is greater than its width, and its width is greater than its depth. Try raising the c.m. of the object while keeping one of its edges touching the table. The way to do this is shown in Figure 8-23. In which of the three cases shown can the c.m. be raised the most? the least? Which situation is the most stable? the least stable?

Figure 8-23 Testing the stability of a brick or a block

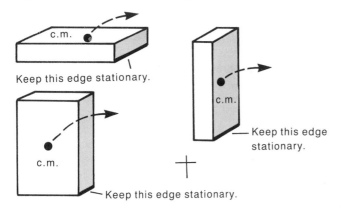

Keep this edge stationary.

c.m.

Keep this edge stationary.

Keep this edge stationary.

5. Discover what you can about how stability depends on the location of the c.m. of an object. To do this, you can place various unbreakable objects on a small board and slowly raise one end of the board until the object topples. Refer to Figure 8-24. Describe what you find out.

Figure 8-24 What shapes provide the greatest stability as the support base is raised?

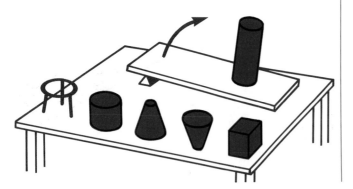

6. Summarize one important fact for each of the above five steps in this activity.

APPLICATIONS ■

1. The seats on a bus in which you are riding are full, so you are standing in the aisle facing the side windows of the bus. Are you more stable with your feet close together or spread apart? Why?
2. Design and build a toy that uses the principles of balance and c.m.

8.5 Stability

Imagine that the two vehicles shown in Figure 8-25 are travelling around a banked curve at the same speed. Which is more stable? In other words, which one is *less* likely to tip onto its side? Based on your intuition as well as what you discovered in Activity 8B, you know that the sports car has greater stability.

Figure 8-25 Which vehicle is more stable?

The sports car in Figure 8-25 has two features that help provide good stability. First, it has a low c.m. Secondly, it has a wide support base. **Objects with a low c.m. and wide support base tend to be stable.**

To maintain stability, the main condition is that **the c.m. must lie directly over the support base.** This is illustrated for an object on a horizontal support base in Figure 8-26.

Figure 8-26 The table is stable only as long as the c.m. lies above the support base.

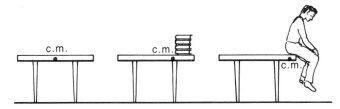

DID YOU KNOW?

The loon is a beautiful bird that is well adapted to water, where its feet help it dive and swim quickly. However, on land the loon is very awkward because its c.m. lies ahead of its feet, so it has to try to lean backward when it walks.

For an object on a slanted base, as the c.m. rises higher and higher the stability becomes lower. If the c.m. rises so high that it no longer lies above the support base, the object will fall over. This is illustrated in Figure 8-27 for a truck loaded in three different ways, going around a banked curve.

Figure 8-27 A low c.m. helps an object on a slanted base to maintain stability. The truck is unstable when its c.m. does not lie above the support base.

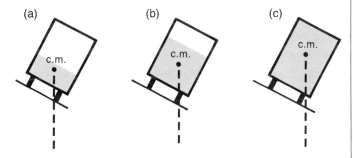

(a)   (b)   (c)

Stability is also important for ships, boats, and canoes. Various ways are used to provide stability in these vessels. Large ships are built with stabilizers which stretch into the water from the hull, increasing the support base of the ship. Some boats are built with a heavy keel to lower the c.m., thus providing greater stability. Canoeists know how important it is to maintain a low c.m. Standing in a canoe would be very foolish because it would cause the c.m. to be high, and the craft could easily turn over.

Some objects may appear to have a high c.m., but they are constructed and tested very carefully to ensure they are stable. For example, the double-decker buses used in England and some other countries are built to have a low c.m., even when filled with passengers on the upper level.

Stability and the human body

From a young age you learn to maintain stability as you move different parts of your body. When standing erect, your support base is the area enclosed by your two feet, and your c.m. lies above it. Now if you lean forward with the top part of your body, the bottom part of your body moves backward to keep the c.m. over the support base. Similarly, other movements require a repositioning of the c.m. These include rising up on your tiptoes, placing a load on your back, carrying a suitcase, and so on.

An application of stability of the human body occurs in tightrope walking. Acrobats who walk on tightropes carry a long pole that is heavy at both ends. The pole helps to lower the c.m. and thus provide greater stability.

Stability in other applications

The performing of various "tricks" and the design of some toys are based on the main condition of stability — the c.m. must lie above the support base. Examples of some toys and demonstrations that apply the principle of stability were shown in Figure 8-22.

Consider, also, the famous Leaning Tower of Pisa. This tower is located in Italy in a city where Galileo once lived. It leans slightly more each year, due to the sinking ground. The c.m. of the building is still above the support base, so the tower will remain stable for some time to come.

PRACTICE

21. What are the two features of a body that provide it with good stability?
22. State the condition for stability.
23. In Figure 8-28 the heavy dot in each diagram indicates the c.m. of the object. Determine which objects are stable and which are not.

Figure 8-28 For Practice #23

(a)

(b)

(c)

(d)

(e)

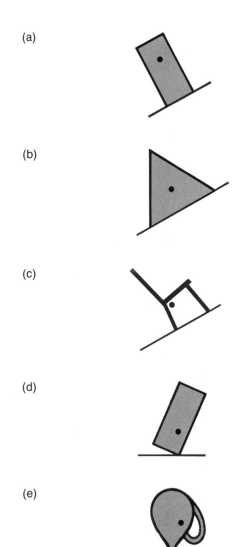

24. Describe how you could use your pen to illustrate:
    (a) a very stable body
    (b) a very unstable body
    (c) a body with medium stability
25. Rank the stability of the filing cabinets shown in Figure 8-29 from greatest to least. All the drawers are equally filled.

Figure 8-29 For Practice #25

(a)   (b)   (c)   (d)

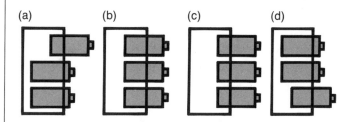

26. Describe which way you would shift your body, or part of it, to maintain stability in each case.
    (a) You use both hands to lift a heavy basket from a table top.
    (b) You lift a heavy suitcase with your left arm.
    (c) You are walking upstream in waist-deep water in a swift-flowing river.
    (d) You place a heavy backpack on your shoulders.
27. A tightrope walker has a choice of two long poles of equal mass. One pole is straight and the other is drooping down at the ends. Which pole would help the walker maintain stability better? Why?
28. Describe, from your own experiences, at least two situations that clearly illustrate the importance of centre of mass.

Words to Know

rigid body   effort arm
torque   classes of the lever
lever   law of the lever
fulcrum   centre of mass
load force   support base
effort force   stability
load arm

Chapter Objectives

Having completed this chapter, you should now be able to:

1. Define and give examples of a rigid body.
2. Define torque and recognize how to obtain a large torque.
3. Calculate the torque around a pivot support or fulcrum ($T = Fd$, where F and d are perpendicular to each other).
4. Use the SI unit of torque.
5. For a lever in any of the three classes, locate the fulcrum, load force, effort force, load arm, and effort arm.
6. State the law of the lever.
7. Apply the law of the lever to solve problems involving bodies in static equilibrium ($F_E d_E = F_L d_L$).
8. Describe three ways of finding the balance point (or centre of mass) of objects experimentally. (The three ways are for long rigid bodies, irregular two-dimensional objects, and human bodies.)
9. List two main features of objects with good stability.
10. State the main condition required for stability.
11. Describe applications of centre of mass and stability.

Chapter Review

1. What is the angle between a rigid body and the force applied to it that allows us to find torque using $T = Fd$?   (8.1)
2. Cars have smaller steering wheels than large buses and trucks. Explain why.   (8.1)
3. State an example in the human body of a:
   (a) third-class lever   (b) second-class lever   (8.2)
4. Calculate the effort torque on a wheelbarrow if a 300 N effort force is exerted 1.2 m from the fulcrum. (8.2)
5. What is the load torque on a 0.3 m arm holding a 20 N load?   (8.2)

6. State the law of the lever.   (8.3)
7. Use the data given below to determine if the lever is balanced.

   load force = 240 N   load distance = 3.5 m
   effort force = 180 N   effort distance = 4.5 m
   (8.3)

8. A 3.0 m first-class lever has a 600 N load located 0.5 m from the fulcrum.
   (a) Draw a diagram of the lever, showing the effort, load, and fulcrum.
   (b) Calculate the effort force needed to lift the load. (8.3)

9. A wheelbarrow has an 800 N load located 0.6 m from the fulcrum. If a girl needs to exert a 320 N effort to lift the handles of the wheelbarrow, what is the distance from her hands to the fulcrum? (8.3)

10. In a boy's arm, which acts like a third-class lever, the distance from the fulcrum to the muscle (the effort) is 4 cm (or 0.04 m) and the distance from the fulcrum to the hand (the load) is 30 cm (or 0.3 m). If the boy's muscle can exert an effort force of 1500 N, what load can the hand support? (8.3)

11. The distance between the effort and the fulcrum of a wheelbarrow is 1.5 m. An effort of 400 N can support a load of 1200 N.
    (a) What is the distance between the load and the fulcrum? (8.3)
    (b) What is the mass of the load? (Refer to Chapter 6.)

12. You are given a large, flat wooden block in the shape of a capital R.
    (a) Describe how you would find the c.m. of the block.
    (b) You are allowed to drill one hole in the block to hang it on a nail. Where would you drill the hole so the block would hang straight? (Act. 8A, 8.4)

13. Figure 8-30 shows the view from the back of a picture frame, with the c.m. labelled. Is the frame hanging motionless, or is the string slipping over the support nail? Explain. (Act. 8A, 8.4)

Figure 8-30 For Review #13

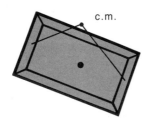
c.m.

14. A baton is made with one end heavier than the other. How would you find the c.m. of the baton? (Act. 8A, 8.3)

15. Why is it difficult to stand on stilts? (Act 8B, 8.5)

16. Why does a four-legged animal find it much easier to stand after birth than a two-legged one (like yourself)? (Act. 8B, 8.5)

17. A golfer is driving a cart up a steep hill (Figure 8-31) and begins to feel the front wheels lifting. Which way should she lean to gain greater stability? Why? (Act. 8B, 8.5)

Figure 8-31 For Review #17

18. Figure 8-32 shows three different ways of holding your arms and hands while doing sit-ups. Which way is the easiest? the hardest? Explain why. (8.2 to 8.5)

Figure 8-32 Doing sit-ups

(a)

(b)

(c)

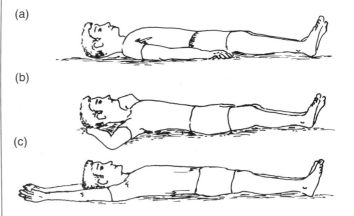

19. Why does a newly-purchased four-drawer filing cabinet have a warning that states "Caution: Fill bottom drawers first"? (Act. 8B, 8.5)

CHAPTER 9

Elasticity and Structural Design

The photographs show two modern ways of covering the large space of a stadium. The SkyDome in Toronto, Ontario, has a retractable roof that has a huge weight. What design features prevent the force of gravity from pulling the roof down when it is closed, or the force of the wind from damaging the roof when it is open? In Vancouver, British Columbia, B.C. Place has a permanent roof that is extremely light and is held up by air pressure. What design features provide this roof with both strength and beauty? What do these roofs have in common with the numerous smaller structures we see and use every day? Does nature have examples of structures that we can copy? By the end of this chapter you will know answers to these and many other questions. Many of the answers will come by performing activities.

Main Ideas

- Materials used for building structures must be able to withstand a stretching force, a compression force, and/or a sideways (shear) force.
- Various ways have been found to increase the strength of materials.
- Studying trusses, suspension bridges, and arches provides a basis for understanding numerous other structures.

9.1 Elastic Bodies

Pulling

In the previous chapter we examined rigid bodies. A body is rigid only if it does not deform or break under applied forces. But we know that objects can be deformed by being bent, dented, stretched, crunched, or twisted. They can also be broken. We begin this chapter by looking at objects that can return to their original shape after being deformed.

If you throw a tennis ball toward the floor, it will strike the floor and bounce back up. During the short time the ball is in contact with the floor, it experiences a force that deforms it. When this force is no longer there, the ball returns to its original shape, which you could observe by looking carefully at the ball.

The tennis ball is an example of an **elastic body**, which is a body that tends to return to its original shape after a deforming force is removed. Other examples of elastic bodies are rubber bands, commonly called elastics, and all balls used in sports.

When an elastic ball or other body strikes a surface, the time it is deformed is so short that we can't see the deformation. However, high-speed photography reveals the deformation. Figure 9-1 shows a tennis ball being struck by a racket. Both the ball and the strings of the racket are elastic. As the ball and strings are pressed together, they store energy in the form of *elastic potential energy*. Then this energy is changed to energy of motion of the ball, called *kinetic energy*. (Various forms of energy were described in Chapter 7.)

The tennis ball and the strings of the racket illustrate the two main ways that elastic bodies can be deformed. **Compression** is the pressing together of parts of a body. The ball is experiencing compression. **Tension** is the stretching of parts of a body. The strings of the racket are under tension. (Bodies can be deformed in other ways. But these other ways can be explained in terms of compression and tension, as you will see later in the chapter.) The diagrams in Figure 9-2 show what happens to the particles that make up a body during compression and tension.

Figure 9-1 A tennis ball and the strings of the racket are elastic bodies.

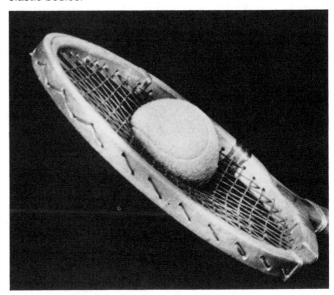

Figure 9-2 Illustrating compression and tension at the particle level

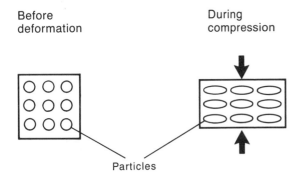

Before deformation

During compression

Particles

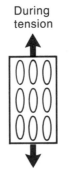

During tension

After deformation

The opposite of elastic is called inelastic. An **inelastic body** is one that remains deformed after the deforming force is removed. If you made a ball out of putty or pizza-crust dough and threw it to the floor, it would become deformed upon hitting the floor. And it would remain deformed.

Do you think steel is elastic or inelastic? A steel ball does not bounce well off an ordinary floor. However, a tennis ball does not bounce well off a soft pillow, yet we call the tennis ball elastic. To discover if steel is elastic, we could bounce a steel ball off a steel floor, or observe two steel balls as they collide. We would find that steel *is* elastic. That is one reason why it is an important material in building bridges and high-rise structures. It is also used in making springs that are under tension or compression. A tension spring starts off with its coils together, and it works by stretching. A Slinky toy is a tension spring. A compression spring has stiff coils that are apart. The springs in bicycle seats are compression springs. In the first activity in this chapter you will discover properties of elastic springs that are under tension.

PRACTICE

1. Describe a test you could perform to determine if each of the following objects is elastic:
   (a) a plastic billiard ball
   (b) an apple
   (c) a wooden metre stick
   (d) a tightly stretched guitar string
2. What is the difference between tension and compression?
3. State whether the springs used in each of the following objects is a compression spring or a tension spring.
   (a) a car suspension system when the car is stopped
   (b) a force scale
   (c) a bed mattress
   (d) a spring-loaded pen

Activity **9A**   Tension Springs

PROBLEM ■   What happens to an elastic tension spring when forces are applied to it?

APPARATUS ■   tension spring; support mechanism for spring; metre stick; various masses (your teacher will help you decide which masses are best with the spring you have chosen); graph paper

PROCEDURE ■

1. Design a chart to record data. On it use these headings: Suspended mass (kg), Applied force (N), Distance stretched (m)
2. Set up the apparatus as shown in Figure 9-3. Notice that the spring should be suspended, not clamped. Devise some means of fixing an indicator to record the position of the lowest point of the unloaded spring. You will be measuring the stretch from that fixed position.

Figure 9-3   Set-up for Activity 9A

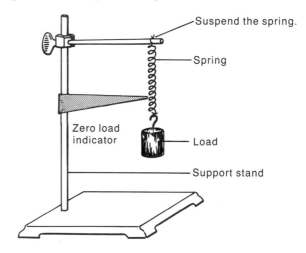

 CAUTION Toppling can occur as masses are hung onto the spring. Arrange the apparatus to avoid this problem. Also, do not overstretch the spring.

3. Add the first mass and measure the corresponding stretch that the spring undergoes. In your chart, record the mass in kilograms, the applied force in newtons caused by the mass ($F = mg$, where g is approximately 10 m/s²), and the stretch in metres.

4. Repeat #3 at least three more times using an increased mass each time. Record all the data.

5. Remove the masses. Does the lowest point of the spring return to its original position?

ANALYSIS ■

1. Plot a graph of the data by placing force along the vertical axis and stretch along the horizontal axis. Starting at the origin of the graph, draw the line of best fit through the points. (This graph is the reverse of the usual graph in which the dependent variable is placed along the vertical axis. The reason relates to Analysis #3 and 4.)

2. Does the graph indicate an exactly direct relationship between force and stretch? (Hint: How close were all the points on the graph to a straight line?)

3. Calculate the slope of the line of best fit on the graph. Be sure to include units in your calculations and answer.

4. The slope found in #3 has a special name, called the *spring constant*.
   (a) Compare the spring constant of your spring with the spring constant of the springs used by other groups.
   (b) Does a strong, stiff spring have a high spring constant or a low one? Explain your answer.

5. Is the spring you used an elastic body? Explain your answer.

6. List any possible sources of error in this activity.

7. Summarize what happens to an elastic tension spring when forces are applied to it.

APPLICATION ■ Describe how you would use a tension spring to make a device that measures:
(a) the weight of fish in newtons
(b) the mass of fish in kilograms

9.2 Hooke's Law

It is logical to suppose that if a 1 N force stretches a spring 1 cm, then a 2 N force will stretch it 2 cm, a 3 N force will stretch it 3 cm, and so on. This holds true for a tension spring that does not become overstretched. The discovery that a spring stretches equal amounts when equal forces are applied to it was made by a scientist named Robert Hooke (1635-1703). His discovery is now called **Hooke's law**. For a spring, Hooke's law states that **the change in length of a spring varies directly with the force applied to the spring**. This law applies to both tension springs, in which the force causes the length to increase, and compression springs, in which the force causes the length to decrease (Figure 9-4).

Figure 9-4 Hooke's law for tension and compression springs

(a) Tension spring

(b) Compression spring

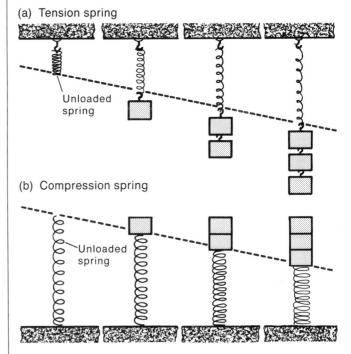

For a spring that obeys Hooke's law, a graph of the force applied to a spring against the change of length of the spring yields a straight line. Such a graph is usually plotted with the force along the vertical axis. The slope of the line is the ratio of the force to the change of length. Since the slope is constant, this ratio is constant and is called the spring constant. See Figure 9-5.

Figure 9-5 A typical graph of force against change of length for a spring that obeys Hooke's law

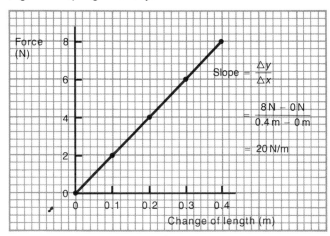

Thus, the **spring constant**, symbol k, is the ratio of the force applied to the change in length of the spring.

$$\text{spring constant} = \frac{\text{force applied to spring}}{\text{change in length of spring}} \quad \text{or}$$

$$k = \frac{F}{\Delta L}$$

This equation provides a way of stating Hooke's law as an equation. The spring constant is measured in newtons per metre (N/m), when force is measured in newtons and change in length in metres.

Sample Problem 1

A compression spring on a motorcycle suspension system is 38 cm long when no load is applied. When a load of 440 N compresses the spring, its length changes to 34 cm. What is the spring constant of the spring?

Solution The change in length of the spring is

$$\Delta L = 38\,\text{cm} - 34\,\text{cm}$$

$$= 4\,\text{cm}, \quad \text{or} \quad 0.04\,\text{m}$$

$$\text{Now } k = \frac{F}{\Delta L} = \frac{440\,\text{N}}{0.04\,\text{m}} = 11\,000\,\text{N/m}$$

Notice in the above sample problem that the spring constant is much higher than that of the spring you used in Activity 9A. You would expect this because the spring on a motorcycle must support not only the weight of the cycle but also the weight of the rider(s).

Hooke's law applies to a tension spring only if the spring is not overstretched. There are two main stages of overstretching. The **elastic limit** is the point of stretch after which the spring will not return to its original shape or length when the applied force is removed. A Slinky coil with parts of the coil that have been stretched to the elastic limit is shown in Figure 9-6.

Figure 9-6 The parts of this Slinky coil that have been stretched to the elastic limit will not return to their original shape.

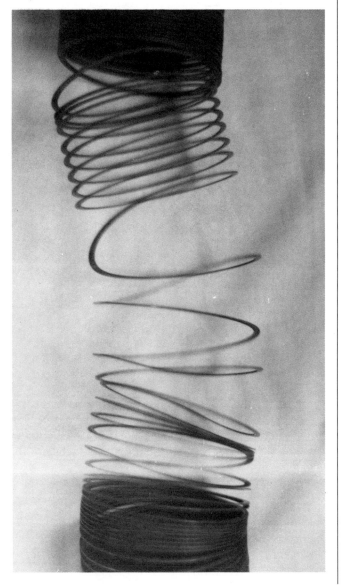

The **ultimate tensile strength** is the maximum force that the spring can withstand. After reaching this maximum, the spring weakens and soon breaks if the load is left on. In other words, the spring has reached its breaking point. The word tensile, in this case, refers to a tension force. It can also be used for compression forces when describing the ultimate tensile strength of objects undergoing compression. (You will learn more about tensile forces in Section 9.3.)

Notice that the ultimate tensile strength has been defined for a specific object, namely a spring. This definition is acceptable for the activities you will perform shortly. However, to compare the strengths of different materials we must know the ultimate tensile strength as well as the cross-sectional areas of the samples tested. The ultimate tensile strength *per unit area* is called the *ultimate tensile stress*. In other words, stress is a force divided by an area. Measuring stress is a useful way of comparing materials. After all, a thin spring will deform more than a thick spring of the same material when under the same applied force.

Most reference books list the ultimate tensile stress in newtons per square metre (N/m^2). The elastic limit can also be stated in the same units. In this book, we will use N/mm^2 rather than N/m^2 for comparing the strengths of materials. The elastic limit and ultimate tensile stress of some common materials are listed in Table 9-1.

To review, ultimate tensile strength is the force (in N) needed to break an object under tension or compression. Ultimate tensile stress is the force per unit area (in N/m^2 or N/mm^2, etc.) needed to break a sample of a material under tension or compression. It is used to compare materials.

Table 9-1 Approximate Elastic Limit and Ultimate Tensile Stress of Common Materials

Material	Elastic limit per unit area (N/mm²)	Ultimate tensile stress (N/mm²)
Aluminum	130	140
Brass	380	460
Copper	160	340
Iron	170	320
Steel, annealed	250	490
Steel, spring	410	690

PRACTICE

4. Three springs have a spring constant of 8000 N/m, 80 N/m, and 0.8 N/m. Which one would be used in:
   (a) a spring-loaded pen?
   (b) a car's suspension system?
   (c) a force scale used in a physics laboratory?
5. Determine the spring constant of the springs whose data are shown in the graph in Figure 9-7.

Figure 9-7 For Practice #5

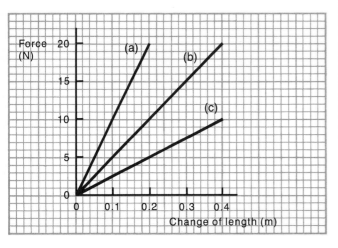

6. A tension spring is 12 cm long with no load. A fish that weighs 22 N is suspended from the spring. The spring stretches to a length of 17.5 cm.
   (a) What is the change in length of the spring in metres?
   (b) Determine the spring constant.
7. Rearrange the equation for Hooke's law to state:
   (a) F by itself
   (b) ΔL by itself
8. A compression spring in a type of bathroom scale has a spring constant of 25 000 N/m. A person steps on the scale and compresses it by 2.0 cm. What is the person's weight? (Recall that weight is the force of gravity, measured in newtons.)
9. A compression spring of spring constant 8000 N/m is used to make a child's jumping stick (a "Pogo" stick). By how much is the spring compressed when a 400 N (41 kg) child stands on it? Express your answer in metres and centimetres.

DID YOU KNOW?

You can make your own tension spring by wrapping a wire around a cylinder to make several equal-sized loops. To make a compression spring requires an extra step. A tension spring is stretched so there are spaces between the coils. Then the spring is heated to a high temperature and allowed to cool while the stretching force is still applied.

Activity 9B   Beyond the Elastic Limit

PROBLEM ■   How does graphing help to analyse the stretching and breaking of a thin rubber band?

PROCEDURE ■   This activity is similar to Activity 9A, so it is ideal for you to design yourself. You will need a small, thin rubber band and known masses that you can suspend from the band, one at a time. See Figure 9-8 for a clue about taking measurements of stretch. You should make observations before stretching begins. The band should be stretched until it breaks. Try to make observations that are both quantitative (numerical) and qualitative (descriptive).

CAUTION Because breakage is expected, it is very important to wear safety goggles. The rubber band should be small and thin. Also, the masses should fall onto something soft, such as a sponge.

Figure 9-8   Finding the amount of stretch of a rubber band

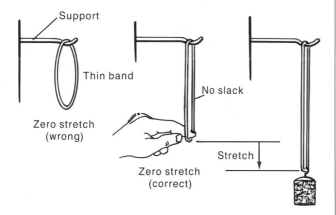

Write a report of your activity indicating the apparatus you used, the procedure you followed, and your answers to the following Analysis questions.

ANALYSIS ■
1. Plot a force-stretch graph of the data. For the first part of the graph, where the forces are small, draw a straight line of best fit. For the part of the graph where the points are in a curved path, draw a smooth curve.
2. Place the following labels where you think they should go on the graph:
   (a) elastic region (Hint: Remember the graph of a spring that obeys Hooke's law.)
   (b) elastic limit (This is where the line begins to curve.)
   (c) ultimate tensile strength (This was defined near the end of Section 9.2.)
3. From your graph, determine the spring constant of the rubber band in the elastic region.
4. By comparing your results with the results of other groups, discuss what factors affect the elastic limit of a rubber band.
5. List any possible sources of error in this activity.
6. What can be learned by plotting a force-stretch graph for a rubber band stretched beyond its elastic limit?
7. Does the elastic limit of an object depend on the cross-sectional area of the object? Explain your answer.

APPLICATION ■   Design and carry out an activity to determine the ultimate tensile strength of strands of various materials, such as dental floss, thread, and string.

Activity 9C   Failure Under Compression

PROBLEM ■
(a) How can materials be tested for strength under compression?
(b) How can the strength of materials under compression be increased?

APPARATUS ■   stick of fresh celery (one per group); knife; ruler; cutting board; metric bathroom scale (at least one per class); block of steel or wood; paper towelling; small elastic band; piece of string or thread 1.0 m long

PROCEDURE ■
1. From one stick of fresh celery, cut several pieces, each 2.0 cm long. Use a cutting board and avoid cutting on a slant.

> **CAUTION   Be careful when using a knife.**

2. Place paper towelling on the bathroom scale and stand a piece of celery on its cross-section on the towelling. Place the block on top of the celery. As you are observing the reading on the bathroom scale, slowly press straight down on the block (Figure 9-9). Determine the maximum compression force applied before the piece of celery undergoes failure (breaks). Call this force the *ultimate tensile strength* of the celery, and record it in newtons. (It is the control value for the rest of the activity.) Also, describe the broken piece of celery.

3. Determine the ultimate tensile strength of two pieces of celery placed side-by-side. Record your observations.

4. Repeat the test for the ultimate tensile strength of a piece of celery that has been reinforced by wrapping a rubber band three or four times around it. First try reinforcing the top part of the celery, then try reinforcing the bottom part of another piece. Record your observations.

5. Use exactly 1.0 m of string or thread to design the best reinforcement possible for a piece of celery. Test your design to determine the ultimate tensile strength when the reinforced celery undergoes failure. Describe the part of the celery that failed.

ANALYSIS ■
1. In one or two sentences, describe how to test a material for strength under compression.
2. What happens to the ability of a material to withstand compression when the total surface area increases? Which procedure steps proved this?
3. What effect does reinforcing have on the ultimate tensile strength of a material under compression?

APPLICATIONS ■
1. What do you think is meant by the term "reinforcing concrete with steel"?
2. Based on what you learned in this activity, what advice would you give to a person making a reinforced concrete floor for an apartment building?

Figure 9-9   Determining the ultimate tensile strength of a piece of celery under compression

9.3   Shear Forces

You have seen how materials act when forces are applied lengthwise, along the longitudinal axis of the material. A force in a material parallel to the longitudinal axis is called a *tensile force*. As you have learned, it can be tension, as in a rubber band or a tension spring; or it can be compression, as in the celery used in Activity 9C.

However, forces can also be applied from the side of a body, perpendicular to the longitudinal axis. A force set up in a material perpendicular to the longitudinal axis is called a **shear force**. If you break a toothpick, the break is usually caused by shear forces. See Figure 9-10.

Consider an obvious example of shear forces: the use of scissors, garden shears, pinking shears, metal cutting shears, etc. Shears are made of two blades with handles connected at a pivot point or fulcrum. When shears are used to cut a material, the two blades move in opposite directions, tearing the particles that make up the material. Both tension and compression occur, as illustrated in Figure 9-11.

If a force is applied from only one side of a body, shear forces within the body cause bending. The region of the bending depends on where the force is applied and where the body is supported. In any case, both tension and compression occur within the body. This is illustrated for two common examples of bending in Figure 9-12.

The diving board shown in Figure 9-12(b) is an example of a special category of structures. A structure that projects outward from a rigidly fastened end is called a **cantilever**. The limbs of trees and the wings of airplanes are cantilevers, as are the balconies of some apartment buildings. Does a wooden stick set up as a cantilever obey Hooke's law as forces are applied to the free end? This question will be explored in the next activity.

Figure 9-10   A force applied perpendicular to the longitudinal axis of a body causes shear forces within the body.

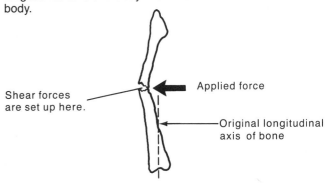

Figure 9-11   Using scissors or shears to cut paper
(a) The two blades move in opposite directions.

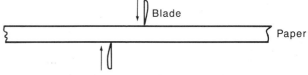

(b) Before cutting, the particles of paper do not experience compression or tension

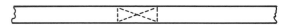

(c) During cutting, some of the particles get pulled apart (tension), and some get pushed together.

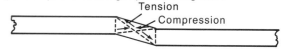

Figure 9-12   Planks used for simple bridges or diving boards are examples of bodies that experience shear forces.

(a) Simple bridge

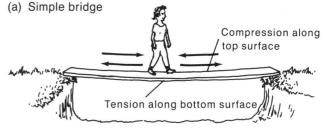

(b) Diving board

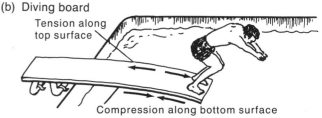

DID YOU KNOW?

Besides tensile and shear forces, there is a third category in which forces act in all directions to compress a body. This changes the volume of the body. People who build scuba-diving equipment, submarines, space craft, storage tanks for fluids, and numerous similar devices are concerned with these compression forces.

PRACTICE

10. Figure 9-13 shows a body in five different situations involving applied forces (the arrows). Choose the situation(s) in which the applied force causes:
    (a) only tension within the body
    (b) only compression within the body
    (c) shear forces within the body
    (d) cutting
    (e) tension along the top surface and compression along the bottom surface of the body
    (f) tension along the bottom surface and compression along the top surface of the body

Figure 9-13 For Practice #10

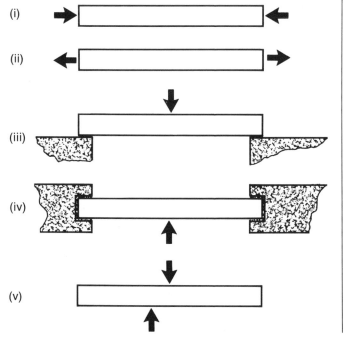

Activity 9D Bending a Wooden Stick

PROBLEM ■ How can graphing help to analyse the bending of a wooden stick under applied forces?

 CAUTION Do not add more masses than suggested by your teacher.

APPARATUS ■ wooden stick of uniform structure with a small hole at one end (e.g., a metre stick); metre stick (for measuring); clamp; two small wooden blocks; string or hook; various masses (depending on the strength of the stick being tested); graph paper

PROCEDURE ■

1. Design a chart to record data. In it use these headings: Mass added (kg), Applied force (N), Distance from floor (m), Distance bent (m)
2. Clamp the wooden stick to the lab bench using the two small wooden blocks as protection, as illustrated in Figure 9-14. Use a projection of about 75% of the length of the stick.

Figure 9-14 Set-up for Activity 9D

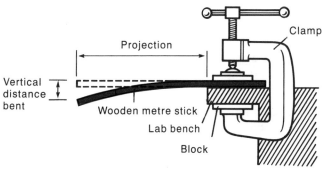

3. Measure the vertical distance from the floor to the free end of the stick as accurately as possible. Record this measurement in metres in your chart with "zero" mass added and "zero" applied force.

4. Choose an appropriate starting mass. (For example, if the stick can support 800 g, start with 200 g.) Support the mass from the free end of the stick using string or a hook. Measure the vertical distance from the floor to the free end of the stick. Subtract this measurement from the one found in #3 to determine the distance bent. Record your data.

5. Repeat #4 using other masses in equal steps (e.g., 400 g, 600 g, and 800 g). Record your measurements and calculations in your data chart. (Recall that force is found using $F = mg$, where g is approximately 10 (m/s)/s.)

6. Remove the masses. Determine if the free end of the stick returns to its original position.

ANALYSIS ■

1. Plot a graph of the data by placing the force applied along the vertical axis and the distance bent along the horizontal axis. Draw the line of best fit.

2. Compare this graph to the graph of force against stretch obtained for Hooke's law for a spring (Activity 9A and Section 9.2).

3. Calculate the slope of the line on the graph. Include proper units. (You can call this the ''spring constant'' for the wooden stick.)

4. During bending, which part of the stick experienced:
   (a) compression?
   (b) tension?
   (c) neither tension nor compression?

5. What can be learned about the bending of a wooden stick by drawing a graph?

6. Can a wooden stick be considered elastic? Explain your answer.

APPLICATION ■ Design and carry out a controlled experiment to determine the effect on the bending of a body when each of the following variables is changed, one at a time:
   (a) the thickness of the body
   (b) the width of the body
   (c) the length of the body

9.4 Building Strong Structures

Everything around you probably has been designed to serve a special function. Chairs, desks, window frames, sinks, clothing, and so on, all have design features that are different but are appropriate to their function. In this section we discuss four variables that affect the strength of structures:

(1) the type(s) of force the structure must withstand
(2) the size of the components of the structure
(3) ways of reinforcing the structure
(4) the shape and form of the structure

Forces on a structure

You have seen two important types of forces that a structure is built to withstand: tensile forces and shear forces. Tensile forces are *either* tension or compression, and shear forces are a combination of *both* tension and compression. The material chosen for a structure depends on whether a structure is under tension, compression, or shear. Installing a lamp provides an example of the different situations (Figure 9-15).

DID YOU KNOW?

Besides shear forces, there are also twisting or torsional forces that are a combination of tension and compression. Structures such as screwdrivers, garden hoses, and the centre posts of egg beaters must withstand torsional forces.

Based on your own experience and the concepts shown in Figure 9-15, two important conclusions can be made about materials under tension:

(1) To support a given load, materials under tension can be much lighter than materials under compression or shear.

(2) Materials under tension are flexible. (This may be an advantage or a disadvantage. In either case, it must be considered when designing structures.)

Figure 9-15 Installing a lamp using tension, compression, and shear

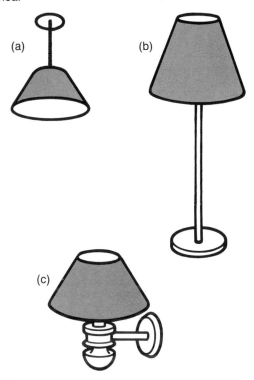

(a) A ceiling lamp is supported by a strong, thin, lightweight material under tension.
(b) A floor lamp is supported by a structure under compression.
(c) A wall lamp is supported by a structure under shear.

Another consideration related to the forces on a structure is whether the material is better used one way than another. Consider one of the oldest building materials in the world—stone blocks. These blocks can withstand a great amount of compression. That is why they have been used to build fences, castle walls, and much larger structures, such as the Egyptian pyramids, built approximately 4000 years ago. But if a stone block is used as a bridge, or a support across the top of columns or a doorway, it experiences shear forces. These forces are caused mainly by the block's own weight. The tension part of the shear forces causes the block to be weak. Thus, stone blocks used horizontally can span very short distances only. Refer to Figure 9-16.

Figure 9-16 Stone blocks are strong under compression but weak under shear.

(a) The Egyptian pyramids are made of stone blocks piled layer upon layer. The fact that these structures have survived more than 4000 years proves that stone is strong under compression.

(b) The doorway to this prehistoric hut is narrow. The stone across the top of the doorway is weak in shear, so it must remain narrow or it will break. This hut is found in Ireland.

Reinforcing

As described earlier, a stone block is weak under shear forces wherever tension exists. If the block is supported at its ends, the top surface of the block undergoes compression and the bottom surface undergoes tension. The same forces act in any structure built like a bridge. Concrete is a common building material that, like stone, is weak under shear (Figure 9-17).

Figure 9-17 A concrete slab that spans a space is weak under shear forces. Even its own weight can cause the slab to fail.

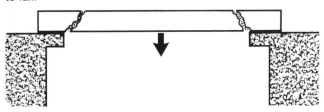

To strengthen materials, reinforcing can be used. For example, concrete can be reinforced by placing steel rods in a form where the wet concrete is to be poured. (Concrete is a mixture of sand, small stones, cement, and water.) As the mixture dries around the steel rods, it becomes much stronger than without the rods. Figure 9-18 shows various ways of placing the steel rods for maximum support with minimum mass.

Figure 9-18 Steel-reinforced concrete

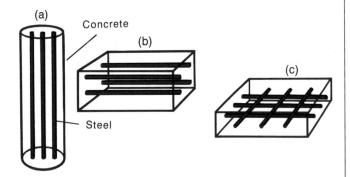

(a) A vertical column requires vertical reinforcing.
(b) A horizontal beam requires horizontal reinforcing.
(c) A horizontal slab requires reinforcing in two dimensions.

Another way of reinforcing is to exert a compression force on a material before the load is added. This process is called **prestressing a material**. (The prefix ''pre'' means before.) To prestress concrete, steel rods or cables are placed under tension as the concrete is poured over them. After the concrete has dried, the tension is removed. This puts the concrete under compression as the rods or cables try to come back to their original size. The concrete is now strong even when a load is added. (Remember, concrete is strong under compression but not under tension.) See Figure 9-19.

DID YOU KNOW?

Mortar is a building material that looks like concrete, but has a different composition and function. Mortar is a mixture of sand, cement, and water. It is used as a filler between bricks and cinder blocks to help distribute forces evenly. It is not meant to carry loads the way concrete does.

DID YOU KNOW?

Besides strengthening concrete by reinforcing or prestressing, a process called *poststressing* can be used. (The prefix ''post'' means after.) Steel rods or cables are in place as the concrete is poured. After the concrete has set, the steel can be tightened at the ends causing compression of the concrete. If more compression is needed after the load is applied, the steel can be tightened even more. This technique is used for large structures, such as concrete bridges.

Size of components

Can bigger support structures hold bigger loads? Not always. Certainly if you had to cross a stream on a wooden plank you would choose a thick, strong plank rather than a thin, flimsy one. But as the size of the support structure increases, so does its own weight. If it gets too big, it may barely support its own weight. Adding a load could cause structural failure.

Figure 9-19 Prestressing concrete with a steel rod

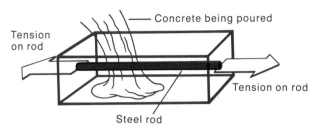

(a) A steel rod is placed under tension and the concrete is poured over it.

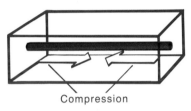

(b) After the concrete is dry, the tension on the steel rod is removed. This causes compression in the concrete.

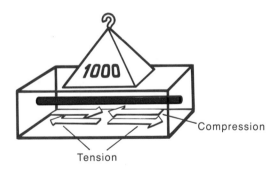

(c) The tension along the bottom surface caused by adding a load is balanced by the compression caused by the prestressing.

Shape and form

It is important to consider the *shape* of each component of a structure built to support a load. The shape chosen must provide strength without being too heavy. For instance, a steel beam may be used to support a house. Which of the possible shapes of such a beam shown in Figure 9-20 do you think would provide the greatest strength for its mass? You will discover more about this question in the next activity.

Figure 9-20 Possible shapes of a steel beam

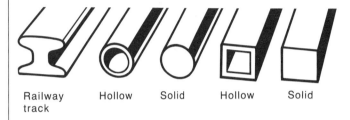

Railway track   Hollow   Solid   Hollow   Solid

Let us now consider the ways in which the components of a structure are put together. This is what we will call the *form* of the structure. Think of the many different forms of one of the most common support structures, the chair (Figure 9-21). Should the legs be vertical or slanted? Does a rectangular form work well, or are circular or triangular forms better? These questions, too, will be explored in the next activity.

Figure 9-21 Chairs have many different forms.

PRACTICE

11. A playground swing consists of two A-frame end supports, one horizontal cross-bar, two ropes, and one wooden seat. State which part or parts experience:
   (a) tension   (b) compression   (c) shear

12. What is the major advantage of using materials under tension rather than under compression or shear?

13. Is a wooden toothpick strong under:
   (a) tension?   (b) compression?   (c) shear?

14. What does the "pre" refer to in prestressing concrete?

15. Describe the difference between steel-reinforced concrete and prestressed concrete.

16. Use the chair or stool you are sitting on to explain the difference between shape and form.

Activity 9E   Beams and Trusses

PROBLEM ■

(a) How does the strength of a beam depend on its shape?

(b) What are ways of building strong trusses?

Note: A beam has one main component, whereas a truss has more than one component, usually many.

APPARATUS ■   6 identical pieces of stiff cardboard, such as Bristol board or cardboard, each with its length double its width (e.g., 24 cm by 12 cm); masking tape; two end supports; apparatus to test the applied force (a force scale or a set of masses); scissors; at least 11 equal-sized wooden sticks or cardboard strips with a small hole drilled near each end (e.g., popsicle sticks or coffee stir sticks); paper fasteners or toothpicks; string

PROCEDURE ■

Part A: Testing beams

1. Draw lines on five of the pieces of cardboard as illustrated in Figure 9-22. Fold each piece along the lines as shown, then tape each beam to hold it together. Notice that two rectangular beams are required.

Figure 9-22   Making five beams

(a) Flat beam: Fold the material accordion-style.

Draw these lines.

(b) Cylinder beam: Roll the material and tape it along the edges that join.

Tape

(c) Triangular beam: Fold the material and tape it along the edges that join.

Tape

(d) Rectangular beams (2 required): Fold the material and tape it along the edges that join.

Tape

2. Set up the flat beam as a bridge supported at the ends by two desks or stacks of books (Figure 9-23). The overlap at the ends should be the same (e.g., 3 cm). Attach the load-measuring device to the middle of the beam, and very carefully increase the load force. Measure and record the ultimate shear strength (i.e., the shear force that causes failure) of the bridge.

Figure 9-23   Setting up a beam bridge

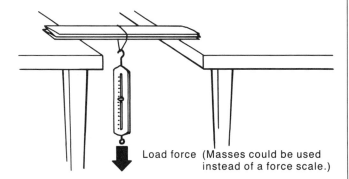

Load force (Masses could be used instead of a force scale.)

3. Repeat #2 for the cylinder beam, the triangular beam, and one rectangular beam.
4. Cut the sixth piece of cardboard to obtain four equal strips. Fold the strips, accordion-style, with each part of the fold being about 3 cm long. Place the folded strips inside the final rectangular beam, as shown in Figure 9-24. Determine the ultimate shear strength of this reinforced beam.

Figure 9-24   Reinforcing a beam

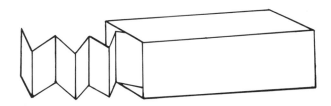

Part B: Testing trusses

Note: Do *not* test for failure in this part of the activity.

1. Use the equal-sized sticks to build a four-piece truss held together at the corners, as illustrated in Figure 9-25(a). With the truss upright, determine how sturdy it is. Record your observations.
2. Add a fifth component, as shown in Figure 9-25(b). The new structure is called a triangular truss.
   (a) Test the sturdiness of the truss, but don't break it.
   (b) What kinds of triangles are the ones in this truss?

Figure 9-25   Basic trusses

(a) Using four components

(b) Using five components

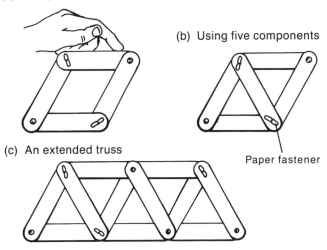

(c) An extended truss

Paper fastener

3. Make a larger truss using the triangular shape, as shown in Figure 9-25(c).
   (a) Does this truss feel sturdy when used as a bridge?
   (b) Is the truss sturdy when used as a cantilever?
4. Discover how to reduce the mass of a truss having many triangular components when it is suspended at the ends. Figure 9-26 shows how to begin to reduce the mass by replacing a stick with a string. This is based on the concept that a tension component (the string) is lighter than a compression component (the stick). Draw a diagram of your final truss bridge.

Figure 9-26   Reducing the mass of a suspended truss

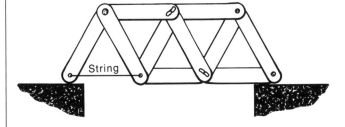

String

5. Turn over the truss bridge you made in #4. Describe what happens to its sturdiness.

6. Put the long truss back together and support it at one end only. (Recall that this is a cantilever.) Discover how to reduce the mass of the cantilever truss by replacing some sticks with pieces of string. Figure 9-27 shows you how to get started. Draw a diagram of your final cantilever truss.

Figure 9-27   Reducing the mass of a cantilever truss

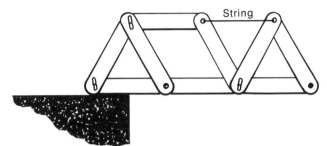

7. Does the shape of a beam affect its strength? Explain your answer.
8. What basic form provides a truss with strength?
9. How can a truss be reduced in mass while maintaining its strength?

APPLICATIONS ■

1. Why are metal support beams made in the shape of a capital L or capital I?
2. What is corrugated cardboard? Why is it strong?

9.5   Spanning a Space

Spanning a space means using a structure to reach from one place to another. The structure could be a beam to span a doorway or window opening, a bridge to span a river, or a roof to span a building. In this section we explore how such structures are built to span both large and small spaces.

Beams and trusses

The first beams used thousands of years ago were likely solid tree trunks and stone blocks. These had a limited size and strength. Today's beams are often made of metal shaped to provide strength without a large mass. Figure 9-28 shows examples of ancient and modern beams.

Figure 9-28   Beams of the past and present

(a) The horizontal beams of this 3000 year old Egyptian temple are made of stone blocks. They cannot span a large space, so the support columns must be close together.

(b) A bridge made of concrete beams

You have learned that a beam used as a bridge experiences compression along the top surface and tension along the bottom surface. In the middle is a neutral region where there is neither compression nor tension. Thus, a solid beam has a lot of mass in the middle that is not helping to provide strength. Much of this excess mass can be removed, leaving a different shape, such as the I beam. Figure 9-29 illustrates this principle as well as applications of it. (In Activity 9E you discovered other typical shapes that provide strength without being massive.)

Figure 9-29   The construction and use of the I beam

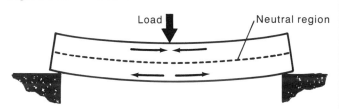

(a) A solid beam with a load experiences a neutral region between the compression and tension.

(b) An I beam has much of the mass removed from the middle.

(c) I beams are used in constructing buildings.

Now consider a U-shaped beam turned sideways, as shown in Figure 9-30(a). This beam would experience hardly any compression or tension along the middle. Thus, part of the middle can be removed to reduce the mass yet maintain the strength. We now have two L-shaped beams that can be joined by cross-pieces that form triangles. (Recall from Activity 9E that triangles provide great strength.) You will recognize the result as a typical truss, Figure 9-30(b).

Figure 9-30   Making a truss from a U beam

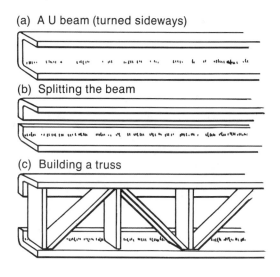

(a) A U beam (turned sideways)

(b) Splitting the beam

(c) Building a truss

DID YOU KNOW?

There are numerous ways of arranging the triangles of trusses. Most of them use a combination of compression and tension. However, the first truss you built in Activity 9E, using equilateral triangles, involves compression only. This type was invented in 1848, but has been used by nature for millions of years. The wing of a vulture has a bone called the metacarpal bone with a cross-section that looks like a truss having equilateral triangles.

Trusses can be constructed in many different ways to build numerous common structures. Trusses support chair lifts at ski resorts, huge electric power lines, roofs of houses and sports arenas, and oil-rig platforms. They are also used in cantilevers, such as cranes and cantilever bridges. Figure 9-31 shows examples of truss structures, including the longest cantilever bridge in the world, spanning the St. Lawrence River in Québec.

Figure 9-31   Structures that utilize trusses

Suspension bridges

One of the more beautiful structures used to span a space is a suspension bridge. It is made by suspending large cables from support towers, then suspending many vertical cables from the large cables to support the roadway. The towers are under compression, but the cables are under tension, so this type of bridge can span a very large space with less mass than other types of bridges. See Figure 9-32.

Figure 9-32   The Lion's Gate Bridge in Vancouver, BC, is a suspension bridge.

The use of suspension bridges is not new. For thousands of years people have known how to make rope from natural fibres. Ropes were used to make walking bridges across rivers and canyons. In some areas of the world this type of bridge can still be found.

Suspension bridges have one major disadvantage—they sway more easily in the wind than beam or cantilever bridges. A small amount of swaying is acceptable for cars and trucks, but not for trains. Few suspension bridges are built for rail traffic, but those that are must be constructed extremely well.

DID YOU KNOW?

One suspension bridge became famous when it swayed so much in the wind that it collapsed. You will learn about the collapse of the Tacoma Narrows Bridge in Chapter 14.

Arches

You have seen that a triangle is a strong and sturdy shape. Now if the top of the triangle becomes curved and the base of the triangle is removed, the new shape is an arch. The arch is a very stable and strong structure that transmits its load by compression forces to each side of its support base. Although the arch was known before the time of the Roman Empire, it was the Roman architects who were famous for constructing entrance ways, aqueducts, and other structures using arches. (Notice the word ''arch'' in architect.) See Figure 9-33.

DID YOU KNOW?

You might think that an arch made of bricks would collapse easily if one of the top bricks is knocked out. This is not the case. If one brick is removed, the other parts of the arch come together and form a new complete arch. To cause failure, the arch must be broken in two different places. Retreating armies sometimes used only one explosion to try to destroy an arched bridge, and met with a lack of success.

Figure 9-33 Arches

(a) This Roman aqueduct was built with arches.

(b) The arch is often used as a window frame or entrance way.

In order for an arch to be stable, the compression forces must fall within the support base. (This is similar to the concept of stability discussed in Chapter 8.) To be sure that this occurs, the lower part of a solid arch is usually thicker than the upper part (Figure 9-34).

Figure 9-34 Providing stability to an arch

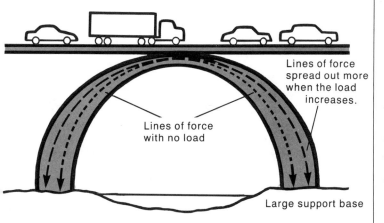

Lines of force spread out more when the load increases.

Lines of force with no load

Large support base

Domes

If several arches are joined together at the top, the resulting shape is a dome. Like the arch, the dome is strong and stable. The load is transmitted mainly by compression forces to the support base. Figure 9-35 shows some of the uses of domes. Examples of domes in modern structures will be described in the final section of this chapter.

Figure 9-35 Uses of domes

PRACTICE

17. What is the reason that a beam does not have to be built with a solid cross-section?
18. Why can truss bridges span longer spaces than beam bridges?
19. Why can suspension bridges span longer spaces than cantilever bridges?
20. (a) How are arches and domes similar?
    (b) How are they different?

Activity 9F   The Strongest Structure

PROBLEM ■   Who can build the strongest structure to span a space?

APPARATUS ■   These depend on the rules for the contest, as described next.

PROCEDURE ■

1. Decide on the rules for the contest. Questions to consider are:
   (a) Should the contest involve building a bridge, a cantilever projection, an arch, or a dome?
   (b) If the structure is to be a bridge, should it be a beam bridge, a basic truss bridge, a suspension bridge, an arch bridge, or a cantilever bridge?
   (c) Should compression components only be allowed, or both compression and tension?
   (d) What types and quantities of materials should be allowed? (For example, if the structure is a basic truss bridge, the rules could allow 40 stir sticks and 2.0 m of string, and either paper fasteners or white glue.)
   (e) How long should the span be?
   (f) Should the structure be designed with a road that has no spaces?
   (g) How should the contest be judged? (Be sure to consider how well the design applies the concepts presented in this chapter.)
   (h) When and where should the contest be held?
   (i) Are there any other questions that should be answered before the contest begins?

 CAUTION   Have your design checked by your teacher before you begin your procedure. There may be harmful aspects.

2. List the rules, then carry out the contest. Have fun, and good luck!.

ANALYSIS ■

1. Discuss the features of the structure that was strongest.
2. Describe what changes you would use to make your own structure stronger.

DID YOU KNOW?

An egg is shaped like two domes joined together. An egg shell is a very strong structure, especially when compressed from the ends. It provides protective shelter for the unborn chick while allowing air to pass into it.

9.6   Modern Structural Design

The number of modern structures we might discuss could easily fill a large book. In this section we will look at only a few examples of modern structures that apply the principles presented in this chapter. We will explore their composition and special design features.

Choice of materials

Some materials used today have been used for many centuries. Wood, stone, glass, mortar, clay, concrete, and some metals are examples. However, modern techniques have improved many of these materials. Safety glass used in automobiles is reinforced to prevent or reduce shattering. Concrete formed into thin panels for the fronts of buildings is reinforced with glass fibres.

DID YOU KNOW?

Like so many other products, clay bricks require heat to be manufactured. The process involves removing the air from crushed raw clay, shaping the clay into bricks, then heating them in a kiln. In modern manufacturing plants the process is controlled by computer.

DID YOU KNOW?

Curved wooden structures, such as some staircase railings, require heat to bend the wood. You can learn about the process by trying the following simple activity. Hold the middle of a popsicle stick under hot running water for several minutes. As the wood is being heated, gently bend the stick into a curved form. Place the stick between two rigid structures so the curved shape will be maintained until the wood is dry. Test the dried stick for strength.

Wood can make very strong panels by using reinforcing. For example, "waveboard" is a wavy reinforcing panel made by heating a mixture of wood and resin. When sandwiched between flat wooden panels, this provides a lightweight structure many times stronger than flat wood of equal mass (Figure 9-36).

Figure 9-36 Wood reinforced with waveboard

An old material that has found new uses in structures is air. The roof of the sports stadium in Vancouver, shown at the beginning of this chapter, uses compressed air. (You will learn more about this modern type of structure later in this section.)

Besides new ways of using old materials, many new materials have been developed recently. The petrochemical industry has provided us with plastics, polyesters, and other materials that have numerous uses. These materials made from chemicals can be flexible (for plastic bags, clothing, and so on), or they can be rigid (for sinks, bathtubs, safety helmets, surfboards, etc.). Despite their great versatility, however, these materials pose a serious problem for our society. They do not degrade back to their original form the way natural materials do, which means that they are difficult to dispose of.

Choosing the design to suit the use

The designer of a modern structure takes into consideration many factors, including the ones you have learned about in this chapter. For instance, the structure must be elastic, in other words, it must return to its original shape after being deformed. (It would not be good for a bridge or high-rise building to be permanently deformed by the wind, although it sometimes happens.) Also, the structure must be as light as possible while remaining strong. One way to achieve this is to use tension forces rather than compression forces wherever feasible.

Let us look more closely at high-rise buildings. The tallest ones are now over 100 storeys high. What features are used to build these huge structures? One feature is to have a low centre of mass. (Recall from Chapter 8 that a structure is stable if it has a low centre of mass and a large support base.) This is achieved partly by building a large foundation (Figure 9-37).

Another feature of high-rise buildings is that of using tension and trusses wherever possible. One way of doing this is shown in Figure 9-38. Truss members, using those wonderfully strong triangles, are connected under tension to the vertical support walls at the outsides of the building. These walls are under compression and rest on the foundation. Then several storeys are connected by tension to the truss members. This allows the building to be much lighter than it would be if the floors were piled up one on top of the other, under compression only.

Figure 9-37 A large foundation helps provide stability to a high-rise building.

Figure 9-38 One of many possible designs of a high-rise structure

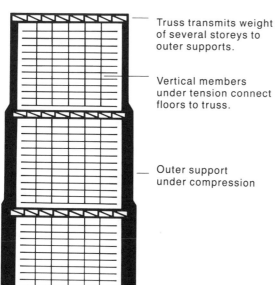

Truss transmits weight of several storeys to outer supports.

Vertical members under tension connect floors to truss.

Outer support under compression

Next, consider modern domes, which are much lighter and more versatile than the domes of the past. The "geodesic dome" is an interesting example. The original design of this structure was a sphere divided into many equilateral triangles. Refer to Figure 9-39. It was discovered that some of the cross-members of these triangles could be removed, leaving a lighter structure while maintaining good strength. The result is a sphere, or part of a sphere consisting of many hexagons (six-sided figures) and some pentagons (five-sided figures). Some of the uses of geodesic domes include enclosures for arenas and structures in the Arctic, and support structures for large radio telescopes.

Figure 9-39 The geodesic dome

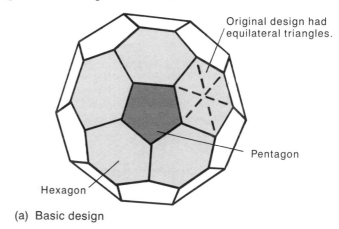

Original design had equilateral triangles.

Pentagon

Hexagon

(a) Basic design

(b) An example of a geodesic dome

Another modern type of dome is the air-filled dome, such as the one over the stadium at B.C. Place. Its basic design consists of two main membranes joined at their edges and supported there from below. When air is pumped into the space between the membranes, the membranes tend to bulge outward. To contain the membranes, cables are strung across them and are attached to the vertical supports. The entire roof is under tension, which allows strength along with a low weight. See Figure 9-40 as well as the photograph at the beginning of the chapter.

Figure 9-40   The basic design of an air-filled dome

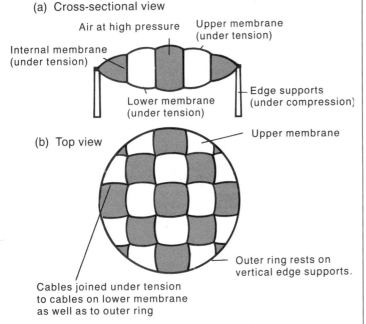

(a) Cross-sectional view

(b) Top view

Testing modern designs

Computers are used in the architectural design of modern structures in a process called computer-aided drafting, or CAD. With CAD, features can be checked and altered before a model of the structure or the structure itself are built. A typical hard-copy print-out of a CAD drawing is shown in Figure 9-41.

Figure 9-41   A small portion of an office building is shown in this architectural drawing produced by a computer-aided drafting system.

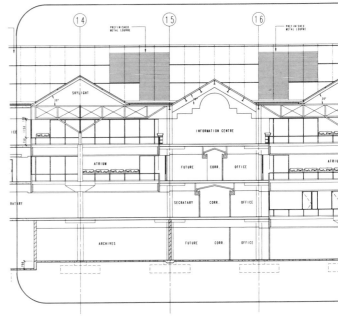

When a design is decided upon, a model is usually built and tested. The model can be tested for stability in a wind tunnel. It can be tested for regions of high stress by using modern methods such as ultrasound, X rays, and gamma rays. (More details about these methods are found in various chapters later in the text.) A plastic model can be tested by viewing it though two Polaroid sheets placed one on each side of the model. (These are the same types of sheets used to make Polaroid sunglasses.) The pattern seen indicates the regions of high and low stress.

DID YOU KNOW?

A soccer ball is a familiar geodesic sphere. If you count the figures on the surface of a soccer ball, you will discover there are 12 pentagons among all the hexagons. The interesting thing is that there are exactly 12 pentagons in any complete geodesic sphere, no matter how big or small it is, and no matter how many hexagons there are.

Designs of the future

As new uses for structures and materials are invented, new designs will be developed.

Are high-rise buildings going to keep getting taller? If they do, what design features will allow them to be stable? It is possible that buildings could be built much higher than they are today. One way to do this would be to build buildings within buildings. For example, if the structure shown in Figure 9-38 is supported by tall towers at the four corners instead of just the walls, the building could be built up to perhaps 200 storeys. Many questions about fire safety, earthquake hazards, sunlight interruption, and the effects on humans would have to be answered before such structures are built.

Travelling and living in outer space will provide more challenges to those who design structures. What will be the design features of orbiting space stations or colonies on the moon or Mars? These features will be extensions of what has been presented in this chapter. Materials will be strong and lightweight. The structures will contain many triangles and many components under tension. Air-filled spheres, with features similar to air-filled domes, may be common.

Smaller structures, too, will continue to be changed. The interesting thing is that no matter which structural design we come up with, chances are high that nature has been using that design for millions of years.

PRACTICE

21. Name structures that you have used that are made of plastic that are:
    (a) rigid and strong   (b) flexible and strong
22. Many fast-food restaurants serve food and beverages in structures made from chemicals. Discuss the advantages and disadvantages of this practice.
23. Look at the photograph of Toronto's SkyDome, the world's first stadium with a retractable roof, shown at the beginning of this chapter. What design features have been used in constructing the roof?
24. Use the information in this section to answer these questions.
    (a) What modern ways have been found to use glass, wood, and air as building materials?
    (b) What building materials are relatively new?
    (c) How is tension utilized in building high-rise structures?
    (d) What are the advantages of the designs of modern air-filled domes?

Words to Know

elastic body	shear force
inelastic body	cantilever
compression	reinforcing a material
tension	prestressing a material
Hooke's law	beam
spring constant	truss
elastic limit	suspension bridge
ultimate tensile strength	arch
tensile force	dome

Chapter Objectives

Having completed this chapter, you should now be able to:

1. Define and give an example of an elastic body.
2. Distinguish between compression and tension forces.
3. Use a graph to analyse how an elastic body stretches when a tension force is applied to it.
4. Calculate the slope of a straight line on a force-stretch graph, and state what that slope represents.
5. Apply Hooke's law for an elastic spring $\left(k = \dfrac{F}{\Delta L} \right)$ to determine the spring constant.
6. Define elastic limit and ultimate tensile strength, and recognize where to find them on a force-stretch graph.
7. Find the ultimate tensile strength of objects experimentally.
8. Recognize what is meant by ultimate tensile stress.
9. Recognize the difference between tensile and shear forces.
10. Show where shear forces in beams or cantilevers are in compression and where they are in tension.
11. Describe factors that affect the strength of a body.
12. Recognize the advantages of triangular shapes in trusses.
13. Build a truss structure using both compression and tension components.
14. Recognize the main properties of suspension bridges, arches, and domes.
15. Describe how basic principles of strength and design are applied to build structures.

Chapter Review

1. Under what conditions is a rubber band an elastic body? (9.1)
2. State whether the following parts of your body are built to withstand tension or compression:
   (a) your bones
   (b) your muscles
   (c) your tendons (which attach the muscles to the bones) (9.1)
3. Each line on the graph in Figure 9-42 represents a different spring.
   (a) Which spring is strongest?
   (b) Which spring has the lowest spring constant? (9.2)

Figure 9-42 For Review #3

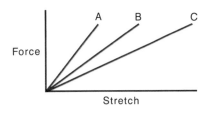

4. Describe how you would perform an experiment to see if Hooke's law applies to a compression spring. (9.2)
5. The free end of a diving board bends 6.0 cm when a 300 N child stands on it. It bends 12 cm when a 600 N teenager stands on it.
   (a) Does the diving board obey Hooke's law? Explain your answer.
   (b) Determine the "spring" constant of the diving board. (9.2)
6. The pilot's chair on a yacht has a compression spring with a spring constant of 7500 N/m. When seated, the pilot causes the spring's length to change by 8.0 cm. What is the pilot's weight in newtons? (9.2)
7. An air supply hose, attached to the ceiling of a repair garage, is coiled like a tension spring. The total weight it supports when hanging freely is 30 N. If it has a spring constant of 12 N/m, how far does it stretch when it is hanging freely? (9.2)
8. An experiment is performed by applying a force on one end of a tension spring. The force-stretch graph of the results is shown in Figure 9-43.

(a) Calculate the slope of the straight part of the line. Include proper units.

(b) What does this slope represent?

(c) What is the approximate elastic limit of the spring?

(d) What is the approximate ultimate tensile strength of the spring?   (9.2, Act. 9B)

Figure 9-43   For Review #8

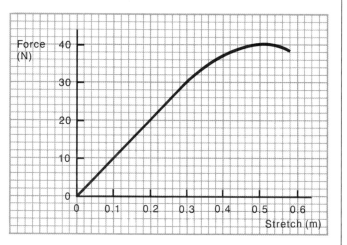

9. Are tension forces and tensile forces exactly the same? Explain your answer.   (9.1, 9.3)

10. (a) Name the type of structure that projects outward from a rigidly fastened end.

(b) Does this structure experience tensile or shear forces? Explain your answer.   (9.3)

11. The following statements are based on observations described in this chapter. Give one example of each observation.

(a) To reduce the mass of a load-bearing structure, tension components should be used as much as possible.

(b) A disadvantage of supporting a load under tension is that the load may swing in a wind.

(c) Stone is stronger under compression than under shear.

(d) Bigger support structures do not always support bigger loads.

(e) There are various ways of reinforcing materials.   (9.4)

12. Describe the features of the structure you would suggest for each function listed below:

(a) Cars and trucks must travel across a river that is about 1 km wide.

(b) Trains must travel across a canyon that is 400 m wide.

(c) An automobile expressway must pass over a railway track.

(d) A pedestrian cross-walk must span an expressway.

(e) A crane must lift shipping crates into and out of cargo ships.   (9.5)

13. Several examples were given in this chapter of materials that undergo changes when they are heated and then allowed to cool. Name at least two examples.

14. The first page of this chapter showed two stadiums, one with a heavy, retractable roof made with trusses, and the other with a permanent, air-filled roof. Assume you are given an unlimited amount of money to design and build a stadium having a roof that is *both* air-filled and has a retractable roof.

(a) Describe how you would go about designing the stadium.

(b) Describe the design features you would use.

15. Choose a research topic related to the concepts presented in this chapter. Find reference material on the topic, and prepare a report or presentation on the topic. The following are some possible titles of topics:

(a) non-destructive testing of materials

(b) destructive testing of materials

(c) metal fatigue

(d) arches, domes, and flying buttresses

(e) computer-aided drafting (CAD)

(f) designs of modern structures

(g) materials used for clothing

(h) materials used in the automobile industry

(i) structural design of aircraft

(j) careers involving the design and construction of structures

(k) tensegrity in space structures

Fluids

Air and water are called fluids because each flows and takes the shape of any container. Fluids at rest or in motion are vitally important to each of us every day. The study of fluids provides an understanding of the flow of rivers and blood, as well as the flight of animals and airplanes.

If you apply pressure to water, it reacts in a different way than if you were to apply the same pressure to a piece of steel. Every time you use a straw to drink liquid from a container, you have taken advantage of atmospheric or air pressure. As you suck the air from the straw, you reduce the pressure inside the straw. The air pressure on the surface of the liquid is greater than the pressure in the straw so it forces the liquid up the straw. This unit is about fluids and their characteristics, both at rest and in motion.

Information you gather in this unit will be useful as you consider future careers in medical technology, nursing, pharmacy, and sports. Knowledge of fluids will be equally useful should you consider weather forecasting, environmental science, fire fighting, or auto mechanics.

- More nurses are required every year for adequate care of our population. Knowledge of fluids is essential for the measurement of blood pressure, as well as the effects on the human body caused by chemicals or other required treatment. Constant advances in patient care, especially in nuclear medicine, laser

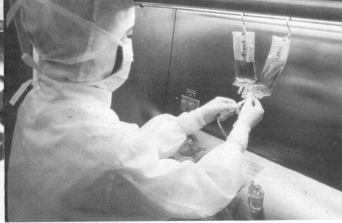

therapy, and ultrasound, require a knowledge of fluids. These advances also provide a broader range of areas in which a nurse may wish to specialize.

- In much the same way, and for many of the same reasons, employment opportunities for fitness instructors are quickly expanding beyond the field of sports and sports medicine. Because fitness instructors work with the human body, they must also have a basic understanding of fluids. As communities, businesses, and health-care centres shift their focus from curative to preventive health-care management, new job opportunities for fitness practitioners are constantly created.

Knowing the information in this unit will be especially useful if you plan a career in any of the areas already mentioned, as well as the following: dry cleaning, hygienics, deep-sea diving, hydraulic systems, pneumatic systems, vehicle design, navigation, aeronautics, or boat building. Choose any career possibility mentioned and find out more about it. You might interview someone already on that career path. If it still appeals to you, contact your local community college, university, guidance office, or counselling centre for more information on training for the career of your choice.

CHAPTER 10

Fluids at Rest

The shape of a boat is important in ensuring that it remains floating on top of the water. This is especially critical when considering a boat made of concrete, such as the one shown here moving along the Grand Canal in China. In this chapter, you will learn how dense materials, such as concrete or steel, can be made to float on water. You will also learn how concepts such as pressure and surface tension affect your daily lives.

Main Ideas

- Pressure involves both force and area.
- Atmospheric pressure and blood pressure are among fluid pressures measured with a variety of instruments.
- Buoyancy in fluids has many applications, including the use of ships and helium balloons.
- The surfaces of liquids display special properties.

10.1   General Properties of Fluids

A **fluid** is a substance that flows and takes the shape of its container. Both liquids and gases are fluids. Two common examples are water and air.

It is easy to observe that water has the properties of a fluid. Water flows readily when it is poured from one container into another, and it takes the shape of its container.

These properties are more difficult to observe for gases because gases are invisible. One way to show that air is a fluid is illustrated in Figure 10-1.

Figure 10-1   To show that air can flow and take the shape of its container, a flask filled with air is sealed and inverted under water. Then the seal is removed and the air flows into a different container, as shown.

Inverted container
initially filled with water

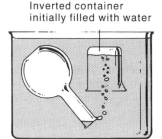

In some cases, it is difficult to decide if a substance is a fluid. For instance, butter at room temperature (20°C) is neither a rigid solid nor a readily flowing liquid. At a higher temperature, the butter melts and becomes a liquid. (The effect of heat on the states of matter will be discussed in the next unit.)

An important property of fluids (and solids as well) is density. *Density* is the mass per unit volume of a substance. It can be found using the equation $D = \frac{m}{V}$, where m is the mass of a sample of a substance and V is the volume of the sample. The SI unit of density is the kilogram per cubic metre (kg/m^3). However, the density of a fluid is sometimes expressed in grams per litre (g/L). For a more detailed discussion of density, refer to Section 3.3.

A useful property of liquids can be observed with two containers that are connected to each other and are open to the atmosphere. When one container is raised above the other, the liquid begins to flow toward the lower level until both levels are equal. Thus, *liquid in connected vessels open to the atmosphere reaches a common level*. Over 4500 years ago the Egyptians applied this principle to solve the problem of constructing level bases for their pyramids. First they marked off the outside dimensions of the pyramid, a size as large as 250 m on each side. They dug a set of trenches parallel to each other and deep enough to hold water, and then they dug another set of trenches at right angles to the first set. The ground likely resembled a huge checkerboard. Water was added to the trenches until they were nearly full. Because water is always level, it was used as a guide to make the ground level. Finally, the water was drained away, and construction of the pyramid could begin.

PRACTICE

1. Water (H_2O) can be found as ice, water, or steam. Which of these can be called a fluid?

10.2 Pressure

A person wearing skis or snowshoes stays on top of the snow, while a person of equal mass wearing boots sinks into the snow. The two people exert an equal force on the snow. However, the difference lies in the pressure each exerts on the snow. With skis or snowshoes, the force is spread out over a large surface area, so the pressure on any part of the snow is less.

Therefore, **pressure** is the force applied per unit area. In equation form,

$$p = \frac{F}{A}$$

In the SI, force is measured in newtons and area in metres squared. Thus, a force of 1.0 N applied over a surface area of 1.0 m² gives a pressure of:

$$p = \frac{F}{A}$$
$$= \frac{1.0\,\text{N}}{1.0\,\text{m}^2}$$
$$= 1.0\,\frac{\text{N}}{\text{m}^2}$$

The unit newtons per metre squared (N/m²) is called a **pascal**, symbol Pa. It is named after a French scientist, Blaise Pascal (1623-1662), who contributed greatly to our knowledge of fluids. (Pascal's law is discussed in Section 10.5.)

A pressure of 1.0 Pa is very small. It is approximately the pressure exerted by a single piece of newsprint resting flat on a table. Scientists prefer to use kilopascals (1.0 kPa = 1000 Pa). The pressure a chair exerts against your seat when you are sitting is approximately 3 or 4 kPa.

Sample Problem 1

A large wooden box has dimensions of 2.0 m × 3.0 m × 1.0 m high. The force of gravity pulling down on it is 1.2 × 10⁴ N (12 000 N). Calculate the pressure the box exerts on the floor when it is resting upright.

Solution First we must find the area of the box in contact with the floor.

$$A = lw$$
$$= 2.0\,\text{m} \times 3.0\,\text{m}$$
$$= 6.0\,\text{m}^2$$

Now $p = \dfrac{F}{A}$
$$= \frac{12\,000\,\text{N}}{6.0\,\text{m}^2}$$
$$= 2000\,\text{Pa} \quad \text{or} \quad 2.0\,\text{kPa}$$

Sample Problem 2

A circus elephant can easily balance on two of its feet. Calculate the pressure exerted by the elephant on a wooden floor when it is standing on two feet. Assume that the force of gravity pulling down on the elephant is 5 × 10⁴ N (50 000 N) and that the area of each foot is 0.01 m².

Solution The total area is
$$2 \times 0.01\,\text{m}^2 = 0.02\,\text{m}^2.$$

Then $p = \dfrac{F}{A}$
$$= \frac{50\,000\,\text{N}}{0.02\,\text{m}^2}$$
$$= 2\,500\,000\,\text{Pa}$$
$$= 2\,500\,\text{kPa (or } 2.5 \times 10^3\,\text{kPa)}$$

Another example can be used to show that pressure depends on area. Imagine if the sharp end of a nail were protruding out of a board that is lying on a floor. You would not want to stand on that nail in your bare feet because the pressure would be so great on such a small surface that the nail would easily pierce your skin. Now consider lying on a "bed" of nails, like the one shown in Figure 10-2. If the nails are spaced appropriately, the force will be spread out over the surface area of hundreds of nails, so that it is unlikely that any one nail would break through the skin.

Figure 10-2 The man sandwiched between two beds of nails is protecting his eyes as the concrete block is shattered.

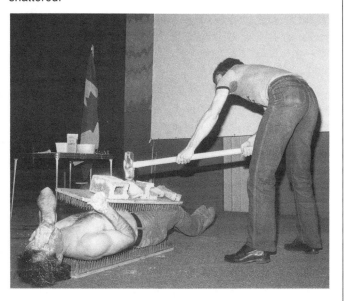

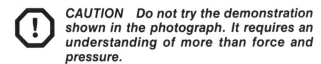

CAUTION   Do not try the demonstration shown in the photograph. It requires an understanding of more than force and pressure.

The examples in this section and the questions that follow do not relate directly to fluids. However, they provide a basis for understanding pressure in fluids, studied next.

PRACTICE

2. Try this. Place your left forearm flat on a desk or table. With the palm of your right hand, press down as hard as you can on your left forearm near your elbow. Now try to exert the same force downward using only the tip of the index finger of your right hand. Explain what you feel and why.

3. Explain each of the following statements, considering especially the difference between force and pressure.
   (a) An all-terrain vehicle has wide wheels.
   (b) If boxing gloves were allowed to be smaller, the sport of boxing would be more dangerous than it already is.
   (c) It is easier to break a walnut by hand using two walnuts pressed against each other than using a single walnut in the hand.

4. Calculate the pressure in each case:
   (a) $F = 20$ N, $A = 4.0$ m^2
   (b) $F = 400$ N, $A = 0.5$ m^2
   (c) $F = 600$ N, $A = 0.03$ m^2

5. Calculate the pressure applied by the toe of a ballet dancer's shoe when she balances, briefly, on that toe. Assume that the force of gravity on the dancer is 500 N and the surface area of her toe is only 2×10^{-4} m^2 (0.0002 m^2).

6. Compare your answer in #5 to the answer to sample problem 2 about the circus elephant.

7. Rewrite the equation $p = \dfrac{F}{A}$ to express:
   (a) F by itself   (b) A by itself

8. Calculate the unknown quantities:
   (a) $p = 2.5$ Pa, $A = 0.22$ m^2, $F = ?$ N
   (b) $p = 800$ Pa, $F = 640$ N, $A = ?$ m^2

9. Assume that the pressure in a bicycle tire is 400 kPa (or 400 000 Pa) higher than outside the tire, and that the pressure is spread over an area of 0.2 m^2. What total force acts on the tire?

10. Suppose that ground in a playground can withstand a pressure of 1.1×10^4 Pa (11 000 Pa), and you are asked to design a sandbox that could rest on the ground without sinking into it. The force of gravity on the sand and sandbox is 2.2×10^4 N (22 000 N). What should the surface area of the bottom of the box be? [Hint: Refer to #7(b).]

10.3 Atmospheric Pressure

One major reason our earth can support life as we know it is that it has an atmosphere. Our atmosphere (or air) is piled up layer upon layer, each layer pressing down on the one below. The result is a pressure that is called **atmospheric pressure**. It is greatest near the surface of the earth because it must support all the air above that level. The pressure becomes less at higher elevations.

Atmospheric pressure, like any other pressure, is measured in pascals or kilopascals. The standard atmospheric pressure, used by scientists for comparison purposes, is 101.3 kPa. This is the average atmospheric pressure at sea level, and is commonly called one atmosphere. Table 10-1 lists atmospheric pressures at elevations above sea level.

Table 10-1 Average Pressures at Various Elevations

Elevation (m)	Pressure (kPa)
0	101.3
1 500	85.0
3 000	70.0
5 500	50.0
9 000	30.0
12 500	20.0

Our ears are sensitive to changes in atmospheric pressure. No doubt you have experienced a "pop" in your ears when your elevation above ground level changed rapidly. This may happen when riding in an elevator in a tall building, in an airplane when it is taking off, or in a car on a mountain highway. The pop results when the pressure difference on either side of the eardrum is altered. Swallowing helps the pressure difference return to normal.

DID YOU KNOW?

At high altitudes, a lower atmospheric pressure also means a lack of oxygen. This can be dangerous for people who do not allow their bodies to adjust to the low oxygen supply before they exert themselves. For example, some mountain climbers have experienced altitude sickness or even brain damage due to lack of oxygen.

If atmospheric pressure conditions are known, forecasting the weather can be fairly accurate. If the pressure is constant, the weather will remain about as it is. Decreasing atmospheric pressure indicates stormier weather, while increasing pressure generally means fair weather.

Besides forecasting weather, there are other everyday uses of atmospheric pressure. Every time we use a straw to drink liquid from a container, we take advantage of atmospheric pressure. Sucking air out of the straw reduces the pressure inside the straw. The pressure on the surface of the liquid is greater than the pressure in the straw, and it forces the liquid up the straw. See Figure 10-3. A syringe, medicine dropper (eye dropper), and a vacuum cleaner work on the same principle as the straw. In the case of the vacuum cleaner, an electric motor drives a fan that pulls the air out of the hose. Then the atmosphere pushes the air up the hose, carrying dirt and dust with it.

Figure 10-3 The liquid rises in the straw when the atmospheric pressure on the liquid's surface is greater than in the straw.

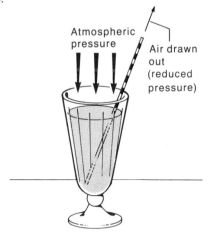

Atmospheric pressure

Air drawn out (reduced pressure)

DID YOU KNOW?

The drinking straw was patented in 1888. It is an example of an invention that some people might have thought too simple to bother obtaining a patent.

PRACTICE

11. Try this. Obtain a flask (with a capacity of at least 500 mL), a piece of paper (about 10 cm by 20 cm), and a match. Roll the paper loosely so it will fit into the mouth of the flask. Light one end of the paper with a match and insert the burning paper into the flask. Place the palm of your hand tightly onto the mouth of the flask and, after a few minutes, lift your hand gently. Describe and explain what happens.

 CAUTION *Make sure your hand does not come into contact with a flame.*

12. The elevator in Toronto's CN Tower takes only 60 s to rise to the main observation deck, 342 m above the ground. If a person's ears pop during the ride up the tower, would they pop inwards or outwards? Explain your reasoning.

13. Plot a graph of the data in Table 10-1. (Place atmospheric pressure along the vertical axis.) From the graph, determine the atmospheric pressure at 4000 m.

14. A certain weather report indicates that the atmospheric pressure has gone from 100.8 kPa to 100.1 kPa in 6 h. What prediction could be made about the weather?

15. Suppose that at sea level a student is able to suck water up a certain straw to a height of 100 cm. How would this value compare to the height if the same student tried the experiment with the same straw at the top of a high mountain? Explain your answer.

16. Research and report on how an ordinary flush toilet operates.

10.4 Instruments that Measure Pressure

The type of instrument that measures atmospheric pressure directly is called a **barometer**. The barometer was invented in Italy in 1640 by Evangelista Torricelli (1608-1647). Torricelli, whose teacher was Galileo Galilei, made the first barometer by filling a long glass tube with water so no air could get into the tube. The atmospheric pressure was great enough to hold about 10.3 m of water in the tube. A glass tube over 10 m long was impractical for a science laboratory, so Torricelli tried the same experiment using liquid mercury. He found that the tube needed to be only about 76 cm (0.76 m) long.

Torricelli's type of barometer, especially the kind using mercury, is still used today. However, it is not as convenient as the **aneroid barometer**. (The word aneroid means without liquid.) An aneroid barometer consists of an enclosed container having thin metal walls that are sensitive to pressure changes. A needle attached to the container indicates the pressure. (See Figure 10-4.) One use of an aneroid barometer is as an **altimeter**, a device that measures the altitude of an airplane above sea level.

Figure 10-4 The aneroid barometer

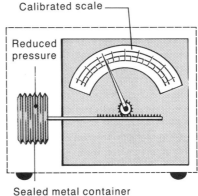

Calibrated scale

Reduced pressure

Sealed metal container with expandable sides

The type of instrument we will use to measure pressure other than atmospheric pressure is called a **manometer**. You will make a simple manometer when you perform Activity 10A. Such a manometer consists of two pieces of glass tubing (each about 30 cm long) connected by a rubber tube, as shown in Figure 10-5(a). Water is added to a depth of about 15 cm from the bottom of the instrument.

In Figure 10-6 air is being blown into one side of the manometer causing an increase in pressure there. This causes the water to fall in one side of the tube and rise in the other. The difference in pressure between one side of the manometer and the other can be calculated using the fact that:

> **For every centimetre difference between the water levels there is a pressure difference of 100 Pa or 0.1 kPa.** (Reference: Appendix F)

The statement also applies if air is removed from one side of the manometer.

Figure 10-5 A simple manometer

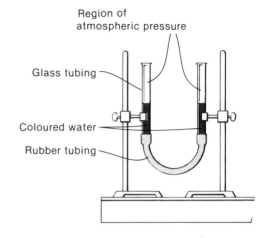

Figure 10-6 Using a manometer

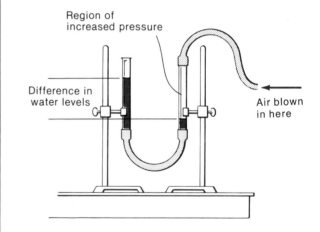

Sample Problem 3

A student blows into one side of a manometer. The distance between water levels is 12 cm. What is the difference in pressure between the levels?

Solution For every centimetre the difference in pressure is 0.1 kPa, so the answer is

$$12 \text{ cm} \times 0.1 \frac{\text{kPa}}{\text{cm}} = 1.2 \text{ kPa}$$

When an instrument is used to measure pressure other than atmospheric pressure, it is necessary to understand the difference between gauge pressure and absolute pressure. **Gauge pressure** is the reading obtained using some measuring device. For instance, you usually add air to a bicycle tire to a gauge pressure of about 400 kPa. But the **absolute pressure** inside the tire is greater than the gauge pressure because it must include the atmospheric pressure. In fact, the absolute pressure is the sum of the atmospheric and gauge pressures.

absolute pressure = atmospheric pressure + gauge pressure

In the example of the bicycle tire, the absolute pressure would be about 500 kPa (100 kPa + 400 kPa).

PRACTICE

17. The best suction pump in the world can pull water in an open tube no higher than about 10.3 m. Explain why.
18. A mountain climber takes a barometer reading and discovers an atmospheric pressure of 74 kPa. Later in the same day the climber reads the barometer at 83 kPa. Is the climber ascending or descending the mountain? How can you tell?
19. Calculate the difference in pressure between one side of a manometer and the other if the water levels differ by:
    (a) 10 cm
    (b) 18 cm
    (c) 34 cm
20. The gauge pressure in a tire is 203 kPa and the atmospheric pressure is 99.8 kPa. What is the absolute pressure in the tire?

Activity 10A   Pressure in Liquids

PROBLEM ■ How does the pressure beneath the surface of a liquid depend on the:
(a) direction?
(b) depth?
(c) size of the container holding the liquid?
(d) density of the liquid?

APPARATUS ■ fish tank; manometer; thistle tube with rubber diaphragm; glass cylinder (the same height as the fish tank); ruler; water; alcohol; glycerin (See Figure 10-7.)

Figure 10-7   For Activity 10A

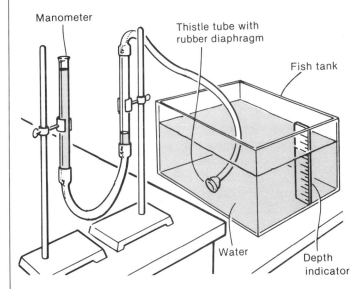

PROCEDURE ■
1. With the apparatus shown in Figure 10-7, hold the thistle tube so the diaphragm, facing sideways, is at a depth of 10 cm. Read the manometer and calculate the pressure. Now aim the diaphragm in other possible directions, including up and down. Be sure the depth remains constant. Record all manometer readings.
2. With the diaphragm on the thistle tube always facing downwards, determine how pressure changes with depth by finding the pressure at depths of 2 cm, 4 cm, . . . 20 cm or so.
3. Place water in the glass cylinder and measure the pressure at a depth of 10 cm. Compare this value to the one found at the same depth using the fish tank.

4. Replace the water in the cylinder with alcohol. Determine the pressure at the same depths used in #2.
5. Repeat #4 using glycerin.

ANALYSIS ■

1. Use the data from Procedure #2 to plot a graph of pressure (vertical axis) against the depth beneath the surface of the water.
2. To the graph for water, add a line for each of the other liquids used in this activity. (Use the data from Procedure #4 and #5.) Label the lines on the graph.
3. How do you think the density of a liquid affects the pressure beneath the liquid's surface? (Hint: Alcohol is less dense than water and glycerin is more dense.)
4. How do direction, depth, density, and size of container affect the pressure beneath the surface of that liquid?

APPLICATIONS ■

1. Assuming the pressure under water changes as you discovered in Procedure #2, determine the pressure at a depth of:
   (a) 100 cm
   (b) 170 cm (This could be enough pressure to damage the eardrums of a diver.)
2. A Bourbon gauge is a simple type of pressure gauge used by divers. Research to find out how a Bourbon gauge works, as well as its other uses.
3. A diver on SCUBA can remain underwater for extended periods of time. (SCUBA is short for "Self-Contained Underwater Breathing Apparatus.") Research and report on how it operates. (Aqualung is an alternate word to look up.)

10.5 Pascal's Law

An important property of liquid pressure was discovered by the French scientist, Blaise Pascal, mentioned in Section 10.2. His discovery, called **Pascal's law**, is based on the fact that liquids cannot be (easily) compressed. The law states that:

Pressure applied to an enclosed liquid is transmitted equally to every part of the liquid and to the walls of the container.

Pascal applied his law in the design of the hydraulic press. (The word hydraulic means operating by the force of a liquid.) Figure 10-8 illustrates how such a press works. A small downward force applied to the small movable cylinder can create a large upward force on the large movable cylinder. The way this relates to Pascal's law will become clear when you study sample problems 4 and 5.

Figure 10-8 The hydraulic press

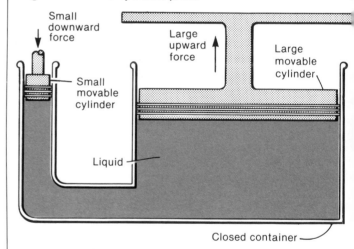

Sample Problem 4

Assume that for the hydraulic press in Figure 10-8 a force is applied to the small cylinder so that the pressure everywhere in the liquid is 2000 Pa. The surface area of the small cylinder is 0.1 m² and that of the large cylinder is 1.0 m². Calculate the force:
(a) applied on the small cylinder
(b) exerted by the liquid on the large cylinder

Solution If we take the equation $p = \dfrac{F}{A}$ and rearrange it to find F by itself, we get $F = pA$. According to Pascal's law the pressure (p) remains the same everywhere in the closed container, so we can find the required forces.

(a) $F = pA$
$= 2000 \text{ Pa} \times 0.1 \text{ m}^2$
$= 200 \text{ N}$
(b) $F = pA$
$= 2000 \text{ Pa} \times 1.0 \text{ m}^2$
$= 2000 \text{ N}$

Notice that if the area is 10 times as large, the force is also 10 times as large.

An important use of the hydraulic press is made in automobile service stations where force is applied to a small cylinder to hoist a large cylinder on which a car is perched.

Sample Problem 5

In an automobile service centre the hydraulic hoist can exert a maximum force on the small cylinder of 2000 N. If the surface area of the small cylinder is 0.1 m² and the surface area of the large cylinder is 2.0 m², then what is the maximum force that can be used to lift a car?

Solution The area is 20 times as large (2.0 m² ÷ 0.1 m²),
so the force is 20 times as large or
$20 \times 2000 \text{ N} = 40\ 000 \text{ N} (4.0 \times 10^4 \text{ N})$

Another important application of the hydraulic press is the use of hydraulic brakes on automobiles. Figure 10-9 explains the basic functioning of hydraulic brakes.

Figure 10-9 The hydraulic-brake system

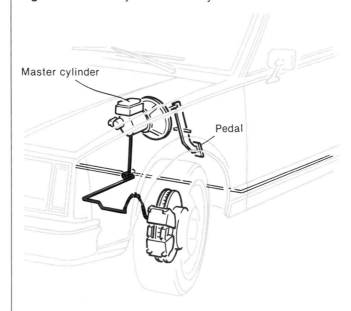

Master cylinder

Pedal

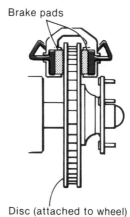

Brake pads

Disc (attached to wheel)

DID YOU KNOW?

A shock absorber on a car contains oil in an enclosed system. A piston with channels moves up and down in the absorber. As this happens, the oil squeezes through the channels, slowing down the piston's motion.

PRACTICE

21. Both gases and liquids are fluids. Why do you think it is impossible to use a gas to operate a hydraulic press?

22. Find the force applied to the cylinder of a hydraulic press if:
    (a) the pressure is 500 Pa and the area is 1.5 m²
    (b) the pressure is 6000 Pa and the area is 3.2 m²
    (c) the pressure is 8000 Pa and the area is 0.6 m²

23. The large cylinder in a hydraulic press has 3 times the surface area of the small cylinder. What force should be applied to the small cylinder to create a lifting force of 7200 N?

24. In a hydraulic-brake system, a force of 25 N can be applied to a surface area of 5.0 cm². What force can thus be exerted on each brake cylinder having an area of 100 cm²?

10.6 Buoyancy in Fluids

The force that pushes upwards on objects in fluids, causing the objects to seem lighter, is called **buoyancy**. Buoyancy helps hold a swimmer up in water and weather balloons up in air. Because buoyancy is a force, it is measured in newtons (N).

To discover why buoyancy exists, recall the results of Activity 10A. In that activity you learned that the pressure increases as the depth in the liquid increases. Consider a block of aluminum held in water as illustrated in Figure 10-10. Besides the force of gravity on the block, there are forces exerted by the water on the block. A downward force of the water occurs at surface A and an upward force at surface B. Since B is lower than A, the pressure, and therefore the force, is greater at B. The amount by which the upward force at B exceeds the downward force at A is the force of buoyancy.

Figure 10-10 Illustrating the force of buoyancy

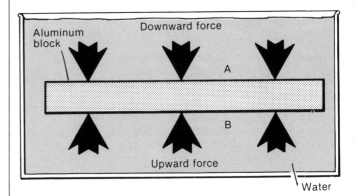

Sample Problem 6

The force of gravity on a man on the ground in 700 N. When the man lies in water, the buoyancy force is 680 N. What force would be required to keep the man from sinking?

Solution Only 20 N (700 N − 680 N) would be required.

Sample Problem 7

The force of gravity on a block of wood in air is 80 N. The block is placed in water where it floats easily. How much is the buoyancy force of the water on the block?

Solution The buoyancy force must be 80 N, enough to support the block.

In the next activity you will learn how to measure the force of buoyancy on objects that either sink or float in a liquid.

PRACTICE

25. Compare the direction of the force of gravity with the force of buoyancy in fluids.
26. A man is trying to remove a rock from the water near the shore of a lake. The buoyancy force on the rock is 200 N and the force required to lift the rock when it is completely submerged is 420 N. How much force will the man have to exert in order to lift the rock once it is in air? Do you think the man should do this task himself?
27. For an object that floats, how does the size of the force of gravity in air compare to the size of the buoyancy force on it when it is floating?

Activity 10B Measuring the Force of Buoyancy

PROBLEM ■ How does the force of buoyancy on an object in water compare to the force of gravity on the water it displaces?

APPARATUS ■ force scales (in newtons); overflow can; graduated cylinder; 2 blocks of wood that can fit into the overflow can; 2 hooked metal masses

Note: All forces in this activity must be measured in newtons. To save time in calculating the force of gravity on water, use the fact that each millilitre of water is pulled toward earth with a force of 0.01 N. That is, the force on 1.0 mL of water = 0.01 N
   the force on 10 mL of water = 0.1 N
   the force on 100 mL of water = 1.0 N, etc.
                    (Reference: Appendix F)

PROCEDURE ■

1. Make up a table for observations and calculations based on the one shown. You will use two metal masses and two wooden blocks.

Table of Observations and Calculations

Object
Force of gravity on object in air (N)
Volume of water displaced (mL)
Downward force on object in water (N)
Force of buoyancy (N)
Force of gravity on displaced water (N)

2. Fill the overflow can with water and let the excess water drip away.
3. Use the force scales to measure the force of gravity on one metal object.
4. With the graduated cylinder ready to catch the overflowing water (Figure 10-11), lower the metal object into the water and determine the:
   (a) volume of water displaced
   (b) downward force on the submerged object

Figure 10-11 Set-up for Activity 10B

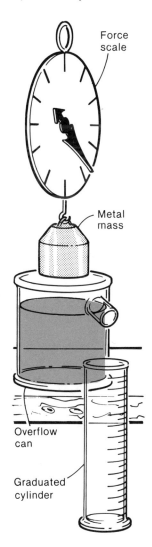

Force scale

Metal mass

Overflow can

Graduated cylinder

5. Repeat #2 to #4 using a second metal object.
6. Measure and record the force of gravity pulling down on one block of wood in air.
7. Use the overflow can and a graduated cylinder to determine how much water the block displaces when it is *gently* lowered into the water. (Do not submerge the wood.)
8. Repeat #6 and #7 using a second block of wood.

ANALYSIS ■

1. Calculate the force of buoyancy on each object placed into the water. (For objects that sink, this is the difference between the force of gravity in air and the downward force on the submerged object.) Enter the values in your chart.
2. Calculate the force of gravity on the displaced water for each object. (See the note near the beginning of the activity.) Enter the data in your chart.
3. For each object, compare the force of buoyancy with the force of gravity on the displaced water.

APPLICATIONS ■

1. How do you think the results of this activity would be affected if liquids other than water were used? Explain your answer.
2. The force of gravity on an anchor in air is 2400 N. The anchor is lowered into the water and the downward force is now 2100 N.
   (a) What is the force of buoyancy of the water on the anchor?
   (b) What is the force of gravity on the water displaced by the anchor?

10.7 Applications of Buoyancy

A famous story is told of a scientist named Archimedes who lived in Greece from about 287 BC to 212 BC. The story relates how he discovered the answer to a problem put to him by King Hiero. The king wanted to know if his crown was made out of the amount of gold he had paid for, or if some lead or silver had been dishonestly added. Melting the crown would provide the answer, but that was not a sensible solution. The problem bothered Archimedes until one day, in a public bath near his home, he stepped into a tub filled with water. As the water displaced by his body spilled onto the floor, he realized how to solve the problem. Using a piece of pure gold equal in mass to the king's crown, he could find out if the pure gold displaced the same amount of water as the crown. He was so excited by this discovery that he jumped out of the tub, and ran naked through the streets to his home yelling "Eureka!" ("I've found it!") Later he proved that the king had been cheated.

The discovery made by Archimedes can be summarized in a statement called **Archimedes' principle**:

The force of buoyancy on an object in a liquid equals the force of gravity on the liquid displaced by the object.

You observed this principle for water in Activity 10B, but it applies to all liquids.

Long before Archimedes discovered how the force of buoyancy related to the force of gravity on the displaced liquid, people were applying the concept of buoyancy in the making of ships. Their wooden ships floated easily despite the fact that they had never heard of Archimedes' ideas. However, such ships were small and weak and would not be able to serve the purposes for which we require ships nowadays.

Today's ships can be made large and strong using metal construction. Since metals are much more dense than water, why does a ship float so easily, even when loaded with cargo? The answer lies in the shape of the ship. The ship must be built so that it contains a large amount of air. The average density of the air, metal, and cargo combination is less than the density of water, so the ship floats. This also applies to the concrete boat shown at the beginning of the chapter.

Another common application of buoyancy is in the use of hydrometers. A **hydrometer** is a long, hollow tube weighted at the bottom so that it can float upright in liquids. Each hydrometer has a scale, which indicates the density of the liquid in which it is floating. As you learned in Activity 10A, the more dense the liquid the greater is the pressure. So the force of buoyancy becomes greater as the density increases. Thus, a hydrometer will sink lower in alcohol than in a more dense liquid such as water. (See Figure 10-12.)

Figure 10-12 The photograph shows a hydrometer in each of three liquids, glycerin, water, and alcohol respectively.

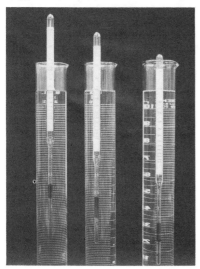

Hydrometers are used to check the densities of battery water and antifreeze in automobiles. Hydrometers also serve useful functions in the making of many liquid products such as syrup, milk, wine, perfume, and the by-products of oil.

Applications of buoyancy are also found in sea life. For example, many fish can alter their density by controlling the amount of gas in a sack called the *swim bladder*. Doing this allows them to ascend and descend in the water in their constant search for food. (The pressure of sea water increases with depth, so a fish would have to decrease the amount of gas in its bladder to go deeper.)

The principle of buoyancy is also applied in gases such as air, but only for extremely light objects. Helium balloons, for instance, are used both for fun and for sending weather-watching equipment aloft.

PRACTICE

28. A ship with a full load leaves fresh water and enters ocean water. Will the ship become higher or lower in the water, or stay at the same level? (Hint: Fresh water is less dense than sea water.)
29. How could a hydrometer be used to help determine whether or not a sample of water is pure?

10.8 Forces Acting on Liquid Particles

You learned in Chapter 6 that a force is a push or a pull. So far in this chapter, force has been studied in connection with either pressure or gravity. Now we will study forces that act on the tiny particles that make up liquids. We cannot see these forces, but we know they exist because of the way liquids act.

The forces we are concerned with here are called adhesion, cohesion, and surface tension. **Adhesion** is the force of attraction between particles that are not alike. Adhesive tape gets its name from this type of force. **Cohesion** is the force of attraction between particles that are alike. **Surface tension** is the special name given to the force of cohesion of particles at the surface of a liquid. You will learn more about these forces in the activity that follows.

Activity 10C Adhesion, Cohesion, and Surface Tension

PROBLEM ■ What factors affect the forces of adhesion, cohesion, and surface tension?

APPARATUS ■ samples of various materials (e.g., aluminum foil, paper, writing paper, and paper towel); 250 mL beaker; eye dropper; 2 paper clips; soap solution; 20 cm of copper wire; water; alcohol; pin; liquid soap

PROCEDURE ■
1. Set the samples of materials (foil and paper) on a table and be sure they are smooth. Use an eye dropper to place a drop of water gently onto each material. Describe each drop and compare the forces of adhesion and cohesion in each case.
2. Add nine more drops to each drop begun in #1 above. Describe the resulting drops and compare adhesion and cohesion. (Diagrams may help.)
3. Repeat #1 and #2, using alcohol instead of water.

4. Shape the copper wire into a loop and tie a thread loosely across the loop, as shown in Figure 10-13(a). Dip the loop into the soap solution in the beaker, then use a pin to break the soap film on one side of the thread. Draw a diagram showing the result.
5. Add water to a *clean* beaker until it is about 3/4 full. Use a paper clip made into a handle [Figure 10-13(b)] to lower another paper clip gently onto the surface of the water. Describe the water surface where the clip is resting. Save the set-up for the next step.
6. Put a small amount of liquid soap onto the tip of one finger and, as you watch very carefully, touch your finger to the surface of the water (#5 above) as far from the paper clip as possible. Describe what happens.

ANALYSIS ■

1. When a liquid is placed on a soft, porous material, which force is stronger, the cohesion of the water particles or the adhesion between the water and the material?
2. Repeat #1 for a liquid placed on a hard, shiny surface.
3. Use the concept of cohesion to explain the observations in Procedure #4.
4. Which type of force, adhesion or cohesion, is responsible for surface tension? Explain your answer.
5. What factors affect the adhesion of liquid particles to other surfaces?
6. What factors affect the cohesion of the particles of a liquid to each other?
7. What affects surface tension?

APPLICATIONS ■

1. Of the products listed below, which would require a large adhesion to water particles? Explain why.
   (a) cloth towel
   (b) floor polish
   (c) facial tissue
   (d) glass
   (e) garden soil
2. Why is it difficult to lift a flat piece of glass from a smooth table top?
3. Surface tension in water prevents water particles from getting between strands of dirty clothing. Describe how soap could help overcome this problem.

Figure 10-13

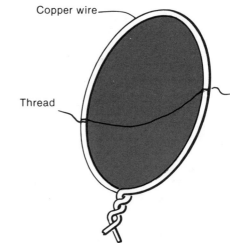

(a) Procedure #4

(b) Procedure #5

10.9 Applications of Forces on Particles of Liquids

The forces of adhesion, cohesion, and surface tension are evident in many instances in the science laboratory and our everyday lives.

A **meniscus**, the curved shape on the top of a column of liquid, occurs in a glass tube or graduated cylinder. Figure 10-14 illustrates two general shapes of curves of a meniscus. Mercury particles have low adhesion for glass but high cohesion for each other. Thus, a mercury meniscus is curved upwards in the middle. Water particles display adhesion to glass, so a water meniscus is curved downwards in the middle.

In Figure 10-14 the water appears to be crawling up the walls of the graduated cylinder. This crawling action is even more noticeable if the cylinder or tube is smaller in diameter. The term **capillary action** is used to describe the rising of a liquid up a narrow tube (capillary) due to the adhesion between the particles of the liquid and the particles of the tube. In nature, capillary action is one mechanism responsible for moving water from the ground through the stems of plants or trunks of trees to the leaves.

Surface tension is sometimes a benefit. A water strider (Figure 10-15) is an insect that can walk on water without piercing the surface. The surface tension prevents the strider's thin legs from sinking into the water.

Surface tension can also be a problem. When dirty or greasy clothes are being washed in water, the cohesion of the water particles prevents the water from getting between the fibres of the dirty clothes. The surface tension can be reduced by adding soap to the water, as you learned in Activity 10C. Then the water can seep into the places where it is needed.

PRACTICE

30. How is the operation of a wick in an oil lamp an application of the concepts in this section?
31. Why do the fibres of an artist's paint brush tend to stick to one another? Is this an advantage or a disadvantage to the artist?

Figure 10-14 The formation of a meniscus

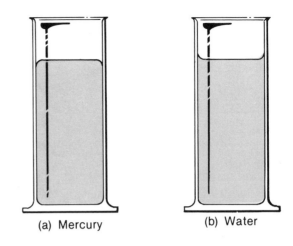

(a) Mercury   (b) Water

Figure 10-15 A water strider takes advantage of surface tension.

Words to Know

fluid	Pascal's law
pressure	buoyancy
pascal	Archimedes' principle
atmospheric pressure	hydrometer
barometer	adhesion
aneroid barometer	cohesion
altimeter	surface tension
manometer	meniscus
gauge pressure	capillary action
absolute pressure	

Chapter Objectives

Having completed this chapter, you should now be able to:

1. Define the words fluid and pressure.
2. Use the metric units of pressure.
3. Write and apply the equation for pressure in terms of force and area $\left(p = \dfrac{F}{A} \right)$.
4. Explain the cause and evidence of atmospheric pressure.
5. State the standard value of atmospheric pressure.
6. Describe how atmospheric pressure is applied in our everyday lives.
7. Describe methods whereby instruments measure pressure.
8. State the difference between gauge pressure and absolute pressure.
9. State what the pressure beneath the surface of a liquid depends on.
10. Write Pascal's law and describe its application to the hydraulic press.
11. Describe the cause of buoyancy in fluids.
12. State Archimedes' principle for objects that either sink in a liquid or float in a liquid.
13. Describe applications of buoyancy in fluids.
14. Describe the forces of adhesion, cohesion, and surface tension acting on particles of liquids.

Chapter Review

1. Define:
   (a) fluid
   (b) pressure
   (c) pascal (Pa)   (10.1, 10.2)
2. Assume that the force of gravity pulling down on a man is 800 N. If the area of the sole of his shoe is 0.02 m², how much pressure does he apply to the floor when he stands on one foot?   (10.2)
3. If the man in #2 stands on a snowshoe (area = 0.2 m²), how much pressure does he apply to the snow? (10.2)
4. Use your answers to #2 and #3 to explain why it is easier to walk on snow using snowshoes or skis than using boots.   (10.2)
5. A pressure of 200 kPa (200 000 Pa) inside a car tire is exerted over a surface area of 1.2 m². Calculate the total force on the inside of the tire.   (10.2)
6. A piece of styrofoam can withstand 30 kPa (30 000 Pa) of pressure without being crushed. A 6000 N box is to be placed on the styrofoam.
   (a) Calculate the area of the bottom of the box needed to prevent crushing the styrofoam.
   (b) If the box is placed on its side (area = 0.1 m²), will the styrofoam be crushed? Explain.   (10.3)
7. Explain what causes atmospheric pressure.   (10.3)
8. Explain how a liquid is able to rise up the tube of an eye dropper or syringe.   (10.3)
9. Figure 10-16 shows a siphon. Describe how and why a siphon works.   (10.3)

Figure 10-16

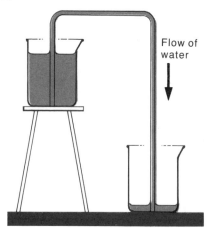

Flow of water

10. A vacuum cleaner is removing air from a hose connected to one side of a manometer. The resulting difference in height of the water columns is 72 cm. Find the difference in pressure. (10.4)

11. The gauge pressure in a truck tire is 263 kPa, and the atmospheric pressure is 102 kPa. What is the absolute pressure in the tire? (10.4)

12. The human heart exerts pressure on the blood to cause it to circulate through the body. This results in a blood pressure of between 110 kPa and 120 kPa, absolute values. If a doctor measures someone's blood pressure using a gauge, what is the approximate range of gauge pressures the doctor could expect? (Assume an atmospheric pressure of 101 kPa.) (10.4)

13. State the effect that each of the following has on the pressure beneath the surface of a liquid:
(a) decreasing the depth beneath the surface
(b) increasing the density of the liquid
(c) changing the direction from facing downward to facing upward
(d) going from a large lake to a swimming pool (at the same depth) (Act. 10A)

14. A swimmer may experience a popping sensation in the ears when diving to a depth of more than about 1 m into the water. Explain why this happens. (Act. 10A)

15. Assume that every metre increase in depth beneath the surface of water causes a pressure increase of 10 kPa. Calculate the gauge pressure at a depth of
(a) 10 m
(b) 25 m. (10.4, Act. 10A)

16. (a) State Pascal's law.
(b) Describe how Pascal's law is applied to the operation of a hydraulic press. (10.5)

17. In a hydraulic press, the pressure on the liquid is 5000 Pa. The small cylinder has an area of 0.5 m² and the large cylinder has an area of 7.0 m². Calculate the force on each cylinder. (10.5)

18. A force of 150 N is applied to a 6 cm² cylinder in a hydraulic press. How much force will be exerted on the 24 cm² larger cylinder? (10.5)

19. What is the cause of buoyancy in a fluid? (10.6)

20. The force of gravity on a human brain is about 15 N. The fluid around the brain exerts a buoyancy force of 14.5 N. What is the force exerted by the skull on the brain to keep the brain in its place? (10.6)

21. The measurements listed below were taken by a student during an experiment involving Archimedes' principle:

Force of gravity on metal block = 16 N

Volume of water displaced by the block
= 400 mL

Calculate the:
(a) buoyancy force acting on the block
(b) force pulling down on the block when it is submerged in water (Act. 10B, 10.7)

22. The force of gravity on a certain object in air is 3.0 N. The object is placed into water in an overflow can, and 300 mL of water overflow.
(a) Calculate the force of gravity on the displaced water.
(b) What is the buoyancy force acting on the object?
(c) Does the object float in water? (Act. 10B, 10.7)

23. What is the difference between cohesion and adhesion? (10.8)

24. Figure 10-17 shows a soap film in the shape of a rectangle. Draw the approximate shape of the soap film that remains after the film has been broken on the side of the thread indicated. (Act. 10C)

Figure 10-17

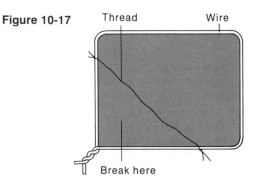

25. On what factors does the action of liquid in a capillary tube depend? (10.9)

CHAPTER 11

Fluids in Motion

One type of motion involving fluids occurs when objects travel through a fluid such as air or water. One example is shown in the photograph. Another type of motion involving fluids occurs when fluids move through a container. For example, water and natural gas are transported from one place to another through pipes.

This chapter examines both types of fluid motion. You will learn how air moving past an airplane's wings helps provide lift. You will learn why streamlining is important in the manufacturing of vehicles. And you will see how principles of fluid motion are applied in sports and other everyday activities.

Main Ideas

- Streamlining is important in nature as well as in transportation.
- The speed of motion of a fluid affects the pressure in the fluid.
- Pressure differences caused by moving fluids provide many useful applications.

11.1 Turbulence and Streamlining

Turbulence is a disturbance that results when fluids cannot move smoothly around or through objects. To observe an example of turbulence, hold a 6 cm by 6 cm piece of cardboard 4 or 5 cm from a lit candle and blow toward the cardboard, as shown in Figure 11-1(a). The candle's flame bends toward you instead of away from you. If we could see air, its motion in this demonstration might appear like that shown in Figure 11-1(b).

For a fluid travelling in a pipe, turbulence has two main causes: friction among the particles of the liquid, and friction between the liquid and the walls of the pipe. One way of reducing this type of turbulence is to inject liquid plastic into the liquid. This has been tried with success in sewage disposal systems. The plastic particles (which are biodegradable) mix with the sewage particles, reducing the turbulence of the sewage and the tendency of the sewage to stick to the walls of the sewage pipes. A similar method is used to reduce the turbulence in water ejected from fire hoses. This helps the water travel farther.

DID YOU KNOW?

Adding plastic particles to a liquid can also be done in the human bloodstream. This reduces turbulence in the blood, which helps to prevent blood stoppage.

Turbulence of moving air is a problem that often happens at the street level of high-rise buildings. It occurs when high-speed air near the top of the buildings is directed toward the bottom. Modern structures have features such as trees and overhangs at the street level to reduce this problem.

Turbulence also occurs for vehicles and other objects moving through air or water. This type of turbulence can be reduced by a process called **streamlining**. It is accomplished by making the surfaces of the objects smooth and curved. To observe a simple example of streamlining, hold a piece of paper, folded into a curve, in front of a lit candle and blow toward the flame. (See Figure 11-2.) This shape reduces turbulence greatly.

Figure 11-1 Turbulence

(a) Observing turbulence

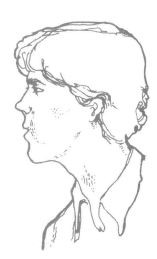

(b) Path of air in (a)

Region of turbulence

 CAUTION *Be careful with the flame, so that it does not ignite the paper.*

Figure 11-2 Simple streamlining

Smooth surfaces do not necessarily provide the best streamlining. A golf ball is an example of this. When golfing was invented, the ball was smooth. Later someone discovered that a ball with a worn surface travelled farther than a new smooth ball. Thus, the ball was changed to have a dimpled surface. A person who can drive a smooth golf ball 200 m can drive a dimpled one about 250 m.

PRACTICE

1. What shape would provide streamlining that is even better than that shown in Figure 11-2?
2. Common sense tells us that two flags close together should face the same direction when the wind blows. However, as you can see in Figure 11-3, this is not always the case. In the photograph, the wind is blowing from right to left, around the building. Explain why the flags are facing in opposite directions.

Figure 11-3

11.2   Applications of Streamlining

Streamlining helps overcome turbulence around any object that must move rapidly in a fluid. Nature has provided streamlining to animals, such as many birds and fish, that must move quickly in air or water. The transportation industry continually tries to improve streamlining of cars, trucks, motorcycles, trains, boats, airplanes, spacecraft, and other vehicles. Streamlining may improve the appearance of a vehicle, but more importantly, it improves safety and reduces fuel consumption.

Trailer-hauling trucks are good examples of the need for streamlining. Most trailers are box shaped and create much air turbulence. (Recall the turbulence illustrated in Figure 11-1.) The air resistance causes a waste of fuel, and the air patterns can be dangerous to small nearby vehicles. Figure 11-4(a) shows the pattern of turbulence around a truck. Such patterns are studied using models in water tanks or wind tunnels. Experiments using various designs of models are performed to try to improve streamlining. One streamlining design is shown in Figure 11-4(b). Refer also to Figure 11-4(c).

> **DID YOU KNOW?**
>
> A number called the drag coefficient reveals how well a vehicle passes through a fluid. An open parachute has a drag coefficient of about 1.35, and a highly streamlined car has one of about 0.3 to 0.35.

PRACTICE

3. Name four animals that are streamlined in shape.
4. Describe the features that help to reduce drag on each vehicle:
   (a) a motorcycle   (b) a spacecraft   (c) a train

Figure 11-4 Streamlining

(a) Turbulence around a truck

(b) Reduced turbulence due to streamlining

(c) This wind-generating fan (more than 13 m in diameter) is used to create wind in an aerodynamic wind tunnel to test automotive streamlining.

11.3 Bernoulli's Principle

The speed of a moving fluid has an effect on the pressure exerted by the fluid.

Consider water flowing through a pipe that is shaped like the one in Figure 11-5(a). As the water flows from the wide section to the narrow section, its speed increases. This makes sense if you think of a river. A river flows slowly when it is wide but speeds up when it passes through a narrow gorge.

Now consider Figure 11-5(b). It illustrates an apparatus that shows what happens to the pressure of the water as the speed changes. The pressure is highest where the speed is lowest, and the pressure is lowest where the speed of the water is highest.

Figure 11-5 Water flowing in a pipe

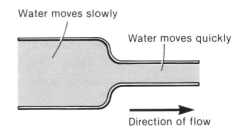

(a) The speed of the water depends on the pipe's diameter.

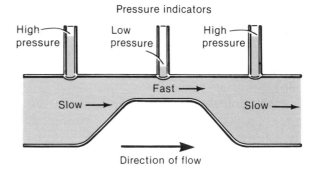

(b) The pressure of the water depends on the speed.

This concept was analysed in detail by Daniel Bernoulli (1700-1782), a Swiss scientist. His conclusion, called **Bernoulli's principle**, states that:

Where the speed of a fluid is low, the pressure is high, and where the speed of a fluid is high, the pressure is low.

The situation of water flowing in a pipe is a simple example of Bernoulli's principle. Now consider an example in which a ball is spinning as air is blowing by it. Refer to Figure 11-6. As the ball spins, it exerts a dragging force on the air near its surface. This causes the speed of the air above the ball (at A) to be greater than the speed below the ball (at C). Where the speed of the air is greater, the pressure is less (Bernoulli's principle). Thus, the pressure upward at C is greater than the pressure downward at A. The result is an upward pressure on the ball.

The concept of a spinning ball in moving air can be demonstrated as shown in Figure 11-7. The air is coming from a hose connected to the exhaust of a vacuum cleaner. The ball chosen may be a Ping-Pong ball, styrofoam ball, or tennis ball, depending on the strength of the air flow. As the air's path is slowly changed to a small angle from the vertical, the ball begins to spin in such a way that an upward pressure prevents it from falling.

PRACTICE

5. As a convertible car with its top up cruises along a highway, the top bulges outward. Explain why.
6. A fireplace "draws" better when the wind is blowing outside. Explain why.
7. Try this. Hold the short edge of a 10 cm × 20 cm piece of paper above your mouth and blow air under the paper to try to lift it. Now place the paper below your mouth, and blow again. Explain your observations.
8. Try this. Predict what will happen when a person blows air between two empty pop cans arranged as in Figure 11-8. Try it, and explain what you observe. (Hint: Recall some of the information in Chapter 10.)

Figure 11-6 A spinning ball in the path of moving air

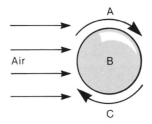

Figure 11-7 A ball in moving air

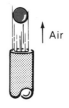

(a) Vertical path of air

(b) Air path at an angle to the vertical

Figure 11-8

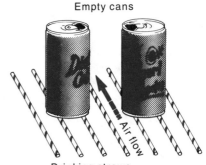

Empty cans

Air flow

Drinking straws

11.4 Applications of Bernoulli's Principle

- A *paint sprayer*, shown in Figure 11-9, applies Bernoulli's principle. Air from a pump moves rapidly across the top end of a tube, reducing the pressure in the tube. Atmospheric pressure forces the paint up the tube to be mixed with the flowing air and create a spray.

Figure 11-9 A paint sprayer

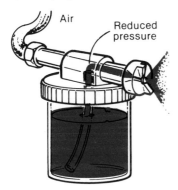

- *Airplane wings*, as illustrated in Figure 11-10, are designed to direct the air a larger distance above the wing than below. This causes the air above the wing to have an increased speed and thus a reduced pressure. The pressure below the wing is greater, exerting an upward force, or lift, on the wing. (Lift is also provided by air particles that bounce off the lower surface of the wings.)

Figure 11-10 An airplane wing

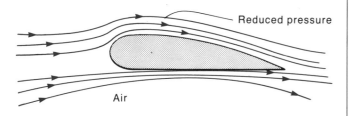

- *Throwing a curve* in baseball is another application of Bernoulli's principle. In Figure 11-11 a ball is thrown forward which means that, at least for discussion purposes, we can assume that the air is moving backward. The ball is thrown with a clockwise spin which causes air to be dragged along with the ball. To the left of the ball the speed of the air is slow, so the pressure is high. This forces the ball to curve to the right, following the path indicated in diagram (c).

Figure 11-11 Throwing a curve, as viewed from above

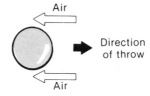

(a) No spin on a thrown ball: The motion is in a straight line.

(b) Spinning ball: Air is dragged around near the surface of the ball.

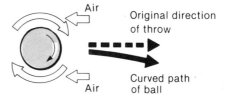

(c) Ball is thrown with a spin: The pressure to the left of the ball is greater than the pressure to the right.

> **DID YOU KNOW?**
>
> A sail boat can sail into the wind by having its jib and main sail set so that the air speed between them is greater than the air speed behind the main sail. Thus, the pressure behind the main sail is greater than ahead of it. This forces the boat forward.

• A *carburetor* in a car has a barrel in which air flow controls the amount of gasoline sent to the engine. Figure 11-12 shows air flowing by the gasoline intake. The fast-moving air has a reduced pressure, so the gasoline, under atmospheric pressure, is forced into the carburetor. There it mixes with the air and goes to the engine.

Figure 11-12   An automobile carburetor

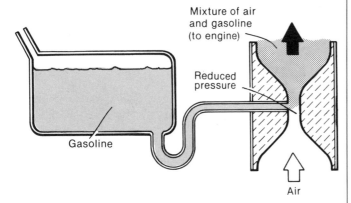

PRACTICE

9. A baseball is thrown as indicated by the broken arrow in the diagram. The ball is spinning counterclockwise. Determine the approximate direction of the path of the ball. Use diagrams to help explain your answer.

Words to Know

turbulence   Bernoulli's principle
streamlining

Chapter Objectives

Having completed this chapter, you should now be able to:
1. State the causes of and corrections for turbulence in moving fluids.
2. Describe applications of streamlining in liquids and gases.
3. State how the speed of a fluid in motion and the pressure are related (Bernoulli's principle).
4. Describe applications of Bernoulli's principle in liquids and gases.

Chapter Review

1. What causes turbulence of a fluid:
   (a) moving in a pipe?
   (b) moving around an object?   (11.1)
2. Pumping stations are needed at regular intervals along the cross-Canada natural gas pipe line. Explain why.   (11.1)
3. How can turbulence be reduced for a fluid:
   (a) moving in a pipe?
   (b) moving around an object?   (11.1)
4. In the sport of car racing, one car might be seen following the car ahead very closely. This reduces the effort needed by the car that is following. Explain why this is possible. A sketch of the turbulence may help.   (11.1)
5. Describe design features that have helped improve streamlining of modern cars.   (11.2)
6. A build-up of ice on an airplane's wings can be dangerous, even if the mass of the ice is small compared to the mass of the plane. Explain the danger. (11.2)
7. State Bernoulli's principle.   (11.3)
8. In a windstorm it is possible for the roof of a house to be lifted off while the walls remain undamaged. Use Bernoulli's principle to explain how this is possible.   (11.3, 11.4)
9. Research the meaning of "slice" and "hook" in golfing. What causes each of these? What should a golfer do to try to prevent them?
10. Research and report on a topic related to this unit. Examples of topics are hydraulic systems, pneumatic systems, streamlining, and careers that relate to fluids.

Heat

When you pour hot liquid into a mug and then hold the mug in your hands, you will soon begin to notice the mug getting hot. Heat has been transferred from the hot liquid to the mug and then to your hand. Often we want heat to be transferred, but sometimes we prefer to prevent its transfer. In the winter we want heat to be transferred from a furnace to all parts of a home, but take steps to prevent heat transferring from our homes to the outdoors.

Different materials have different capacities to absorb or release heat. This knowledge is used to better insulate our homes, produce stronger building alloys, cook our food, and operate machinery. This unit is about heat — its uses, management, and conservation.

Information gathered in this unit will be useful to you as you consider future careers in food processing and preserving, air conditioning, ventilation, insulation, and refrigeration. Building design and construction, and chemical and medical technology are also careers requiring a thorough understanding of heat management and conservation.

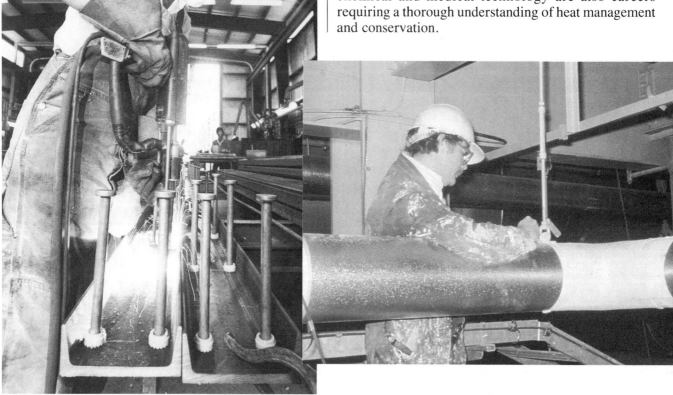

- Air conditioning is developing into one of Canada's fastest growing industries. There is a tremendous demand for specialized systems that heat, cool, humidify, circulate, filter, and purify the air around us. Workers involved in this industry require a solid knowledge of heat transfer, which materials conduct heat and which are heat resistant, and how best to conserve heat.

- Another possible career choice that requires knowledge of heat is that of an architectural technologist. One of the aspects of this career is making provisions in building projects for adequate space and design factors to ensure that the interior environment is adequately heated and ventilated.

Knowing the information in this unit will be especially useful if you plan a career in any of the areas already mentioned, as well as the following: small appliance service and repair, automobile air conditioning, and fire protection. You can find out about any of the careers mentioned by asking your local community college, university, guidance office, or counselling centre. You can also interview someone already working in a career that interests you.

CHAPTER 12

Heat: Transfer and Expansion Effects

An astronaut working in space must wear a protective outfit in order to breathe, to reduce harmful radiation from the sun, and to prevent heat transfer. The features of the outfit that prevent heat transfer are similar to the features of clothing and home insulation we are more concerned about. Much of this chapter is devoted to the study of heat transfer and how to prevent it. But other concepts, such as expansion caused by heat and the use of heat engines, will also be presented.

Main Ideas

- There is a difference between heat and thermal energy.
- There are three main ways of transferring heat.
- Heat transfer can be prevented by using insulation and other means.
- Heat causes the expansion of materials.
- Gasoline engines, diesel engines, and other types of engines require heat in order to operate.

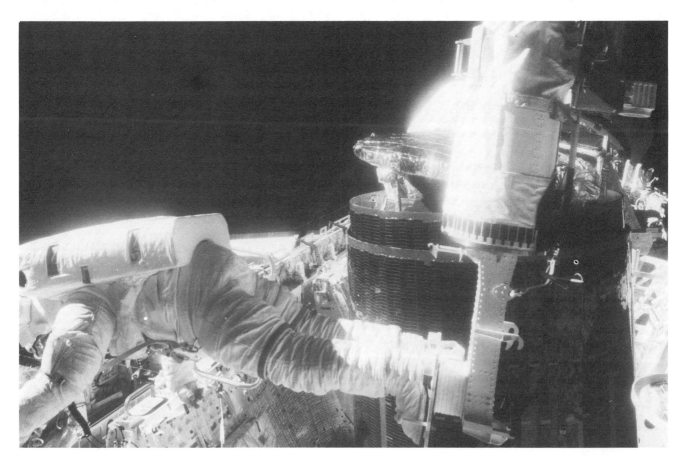

12.1 Temperature and the Kinetic Theory of Matter

The first time you ever touched a hot object with your hand you soon pulled your hand away. You learned from a young age to judge whether something is hot or cold. Later you learned that the temperature of an object denotes how hot or cold it is. For example, you may enjoy a hot chocolate drink at 70°C but would prefer a pop drink to be at about 10°C. Typical examples of temperatures in degrees Celsius are shown in Figure 12-1.

Figure 12-1 Common temperatures shown on the Celsius temperature scale

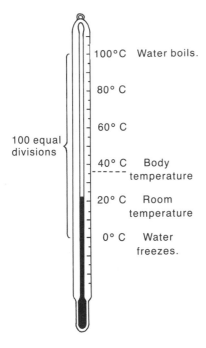

Most countries in the world use the Celsius scale, invented by Anders Celsius (1701–1744), who lived in Sweden. He chose the freezing point of water as 0°C and the boiling point of water as 100°C. Then he divided the resulting scale into 100 equal parts.

The concept of temperature and many other concepts in this unit are best understood in terms of what is called the **kinetic theory of matter**. Although you may have learned of this theory in a previous science class, it is good to review it here. The main points of this theory are:

- All matter is made of particles (called atoms and molecules) that are constantly in motion.
- If an object becomes hotter, its particles have more energy and thus move faster.
- Energy transfers from one part of an object to another by means of collisions.

Using the kinetic theory of matter we can now define **temperature**: it is a measure of the average kinetic energy (energy of motion) of the particles that make up a substance. Thus, as the average kinetic energy of the particles increases, the temperature increases. See Figure 12-2.

Figure 12-2 The average kinetic energy of air particles at 40°C is higher than at 10°C.

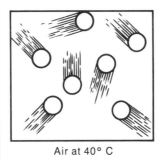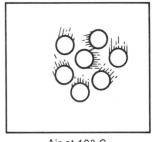

Air at 40° C   Air at 10° C

The kinetic theory also helps explain how ordinary liquid thermometers work. Such thermometers consist of a long hollow tube with a bulb containing liquid mercury or alcohol. When the bulb comes in contact with a warmer substance, the particles of the liquid gain energy, move faster, and collide more. This pushes them apart, so the liquid expands up the tube. If the bulb comes in contact with a cooler substance, the liquid contracts and moves down the tube. (More information about the expansion of materials is found in Section 12.7.)

Let us now compare two samples of water, one small and one large, at the same temperature. The particles of the two samples have the same *average* kinetic energy because the temperatures are the same. But the *total* energy of the large sample is greater than that of the small sample, simply because there are more particles. The total kinetic energy of all the particles of a substance is called the **thermal energy**. Thermal energy was one of the many forms of energy mentioned at the beginning of Chapter 7. It is important to understand the difference between thermal energy and temperature. See Figure 12-3.

Figure 12-3 The water in the cup and the kettle are at the same temperature. However, the thermal energy of the water in the kettle is greater than the thermal energy of the water in the cup.

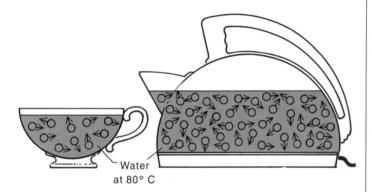

Water
at 80° C

PRACTICE

1. What is significant about these temperatures?
   (a) 100°C (b) 0°C (c) 20°C (d) 37°C
2. What does the word kinetic refer to in kinetic theory of matter?
3. Use the kinetic theory to explain the difference between the temperature and thermal energy of a metal coin.
4. List as many words as you can that start with the prefix *therm* or *thermo*. Check with a dictionary.
5. What happens to the liquid in a thermometer when the thermometer is placed into a cold liquid? Explain why this happens, using the kinetic theory.

6. A child fills a toy pail with water from a wading pool.
   (a) How do the water temperatures in the pail and in the pool compare?
   (b) How do the average kinetic energies of the particles in the pail compare to those in the pool?
   (c) How do the thermal energies compare?

12.2 Heat: The Transfer of Energy

If you are holding a mug into which you pour hot water, you soon notice that the outside of the mug feels hot. Some of the energy from inside the mug has spread throughout the mug. The transfer of energy from one object or part of an object to another is called **heat**. Heat transfers *only* from an area of high temperature (or average kinetic energy) to an area of low temperature. This is illustrated, using the mug as an example, in Figure 12-4.

Figure 12-4 Heat transfers from an area of high energy (and temperature) to an area of lower energy.

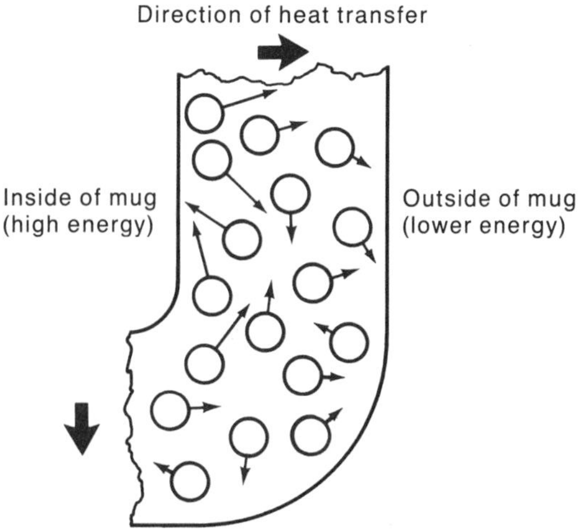

Direction of heat transfer

Inside of mug
(high energy)

Outside of mug
(lower energy)

Does heat transfer by the same method in solids, liquids, and gases? Can heat transfer where there is no substance at all? These questions and others will be explored in the next activities and sections.

PRACTICE

7. Describe the difference between heat and temperature.
8. The round end of a metal spoon is at 75°C and the handle is at 33°C. Does any heat transfer within the spoon? If so, which way does it transfer?

Activity 12A   Heat Transfer in Solids

PROBLEM ■   How does the rate of heat transfer compare in various solid rods?

APPARATUS ■   rods of equal dimensions made of various metals (e.g., aluminum, brass, copper, and iron); glass rod (one per class); aluminum foil; ruler; wax from a candle; paperclips; stopwatch; support stands and clamps; Bunsen burner; safety goggles

 CAUTION   Safety goggles should be worn for this activity. Exercise care when using an open flame. In case of an emergency, a safety blanket and fire extinguisher should be handy.

PROCEDURE ■
1. Set up a chart for data using these headings:

Type of metal	Time when clip falls (s)					
	First	Second	Third	Fourth	Fifth	Sixth
Aluminum						

2. Place small beads of wax with paperclips attached at equal intervals along the first metal rod, as shown in Figure 12-5. Support the rod horizontally at one end and place the other end where the Bunsen burner will be located. Put aluminum foil beneath the rod to catch the wax when it later melts.
3. Light the burner and start the stopwatch at the same time. Determine the time at which each clip drops from the rod. Do *not* stop the stopwatch until all the clips have dropped. Record the data in your chart.

Figure 12-5   Set-up for Activity 12A

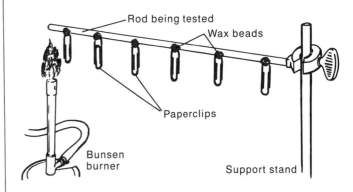

4. Repeat #2 and #3 for the other metal rods and for the glass rod. (The glass rod can be set up as a class demonstration to save time.)

 CAUTION   Do not allow the glass rod to heat to its melting point.

ANALYSIS ■
1. Plot a graph of time (along the vertical axis) against clip number for all the metal rods used in this activity. Label each line on the graph.
2. In which rod, including the glass rod, did heat transfer most quickly? most slowly?
3. How can you judge from your graph whether heat transferred along the metal rods at a constant speed?
4. Use the kinetic theory to explain how energy is transferred along a metal rod.
5. Summarize how the rate of heat transfer compares in the various solid rods.

APPLICATIONS ■
1. Why do you think the bottoms of cooking pots are often made of copper?
2. A person baking bread can choose between using a glass pan and a metal pan. Which material would be more likely to cause the bread to have a firm, brown crust? Explain your answer.

12.3 Heat Conductors and Insulators

A **heat conductor** is a material that allows heat to transfer through it easily. As you observed in Activity 12A, metals are generally good heat conductors.

A **heat insulator** is a material that does not allow heat to transfer through it readily. You observed that glass is a fairly poor conductor, which means it is a good insulator.

To understand how heat transfers through a metal rod or other material, recall the kinetic theory of matter. The rod is made of millions of moving particles. When one end of the rod is heated, the particles there gain kinetic energy and move more quickly. They collide with other particles nearby, causing them to move more quickly. This action continues along the rod, as illustrated in Figure 12-6. This process of transferring heat through a material by particle collision is called **heat conduction**.

Figure 12-6 Heat conduction: The particles near the source of heat gain energy and begin to move more quickly. They collide with other particles and transfer some energy to them.

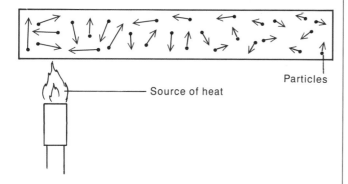

Notice in Figure 12-6 that the particles themselves do not leave the heated end of the rod and travel to the cooler end. Only the energy transfers as the particle collisions occur.

The ability of a material to conduct heat is known as *thermal conductivity*. Table 12-1 lists the thermal conductivities of several common materials, using air as a reference.

Table 12-1 Thermal Conductivities of Materials Compared to Air

Material	Conductivity
Air	1.0
Down	1.1
Cork	1.8
Asbestos	6.7
Human tissue	8.7
Water	25
Glass	35
Brick	37
Concrete	37
Lead	1 400
Iron	2 800
Brass	4 600
Aluminum	8 800
Copper	16 000
Silver	17 000

Applications of heat conduction

In some situations a good conductor helps in the heating of an object or material. For example, frying pans and pots used on stoves for cooking are made of good conductors. Conduction is also used in heat therapy to help treat physical problems such as sprains, arthritis, and back pain. Heat is transferred from a heat pack or electric heating pad to the patient's body by conduction. This treatment is effective near the surface of the body only.

In some situations it is helpful to transfer heat away from a hot object. Cold packs are used on some sprains to help reduce swelling. Car and truck engines must have heat removed constantly to prevent overheating. The cooling system consists of a liquid that circulates through the engine and then out to the radiator, which is made of a good conductor such as copper or aluminum. Heat conduction occurs from the engine to the liquid, then from the liquid to the radiator, and finally from the radiator to the air rushing past. See Figure 12-7.

Figure 12-7 An automobile radiator

(a) Basic design

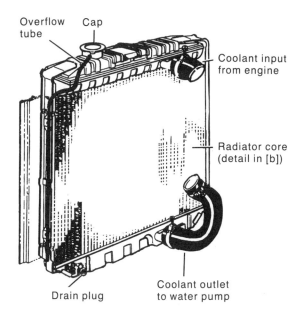

(b) Detail of one type of radiator construction: As the hot coolant passes downward through the water tubes, air rushes past the tubes and takes away heat.

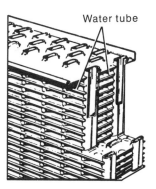

PRACTICE

9. Explain each of these situations.
   (a) Curling irons and clothes irons have plastic handles.
   (b) Cooking pots of good quality are often made with copper bottoms.
   (c) Inserting a metal skewer into a potato will decrease the amount of time required to bake the potato in an oven.
10. Is the following statement true? In heat conduction, energy is transferred but the particles themselves are not transferred. Explain your answer.
11. If air were a good conductor, you would feel cool even on a day when the air temperature is 25°C. Explain why.
12. A vacuum is a space where no particles exist. What value would you expect for the thermal conductivity of a vacuum? Consider the kinetic theory in explaining your answer.
13. What materials are commonly used to make automobile radiators? Why are these good choices?
14. Use the kinetic theory to explain why cork has a low thermal conductivity.

Activity 12B Heat Transfer in Fluids

PROBLEM ■ How does heat transfer occur in a liquid and a gas?

APPARATUS ■ two sets of convection apparatus, one for water and one for air; food colouring; Bunsen burner; support stand and clamp; candle; smoke paper; safety goggles

 CAUTION *Safety goggles should be worn. Exercise care when using an open flame.*

PROCEDURE ■
1. Set up the apparatus shown in Figure 12-8. The glass loop, which is open to the atmosphere, is filled with cold water. Predict what will occur (and why) if the bottom right corner of the loop is heated with a Bunsen burner.

Figure 12-8 Set-up for Activity 12B, Procedure #1

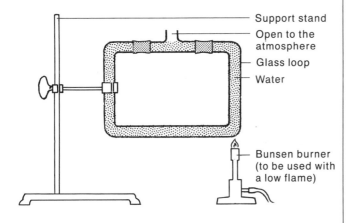

2. Add a drop or two of food colouring to the water at the top of the loop. Begin heating the corner indicated in #1 and record what you observe.
3. Set up the apparatus shown in Figure 12-9. Predict what will happen when the candle and the smoke paper are lit and the smoke paper is held first above one chimney and then above the other.
4. Verify your prediction experimentally, then record your observations.

Figure 12-9 Set-up for Activity 12B, Procedure #3

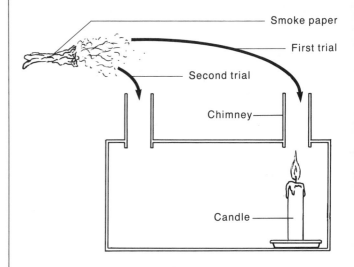

ANALYSIS ■
1. (a) In which direction, upward or downward, was the motion of the water near the source of heat?
   (b) Repeat (a) for the motion of the air.
2. Use the kinetic theory to explain the observations in this activity. In your answer, try to include as many of the following concepts as possible: particle motion, expansion, density, and rising caused by the force of buoyancy.
3. When heat is added to part of a fluid, the fluid begins to circulate in what is called a convection current. Describe as much as you can about a convection current.

APPLICATIONS ■
1. Why does smoke in a fireplace rise up the chimney?
2. Would it be better to place an electric room heater near the floor or the ceiling of a room? Explain your answer.

12.4 Heat Convection

The process of transferring heat by a circulating path of fluid particles is called **heat convection**. The circulating path is called a *convection current*. The particles of the fluid actually move, carrying energy with them. This is different from heat conduction, in which the particles transfer heat by collision, not by moving in a circulating path.

The kinetic theory helps to explain heat convection. For example, consider a room where an electric heater (without a fan) is located along one wall (Figure 12-10). The air particles near the heater gain energy and move faster. They then need more space to move as they collide more. Thus, they spread apart, causing the heated air to become less dense than the surrounding cooler air. The cooler, more dense air then exerts an upward force (the force of buoyancy, discussed in Chapter 10). Therefore, the warm air moves toward the ceiling and is replaced with the cooler air. Soon a convection current begins.

Figure 12-10 A convection current is set up in a room with an electric heater along one wall.

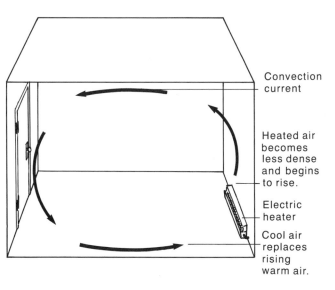

Convection current

Heated air becomes less dense and begins to rise.

Electric heater

Cool air replaces rising warm air.

Heat convection in homes and in nature

Air is a poor heat conductor, so it is better to heat the air in a home by convection than by conduction. Figure 12-11 illustrates two types of heating systems. In diagram (a), hot water circulates in a convection current, distributing energy as it moves. In diagram (b), air circulates to warm the room. In both cases, once the material releases heat to the room it becomes more dense and circulates back to the furnace to be reheated.

Figure 12-11 Convection currents in homes

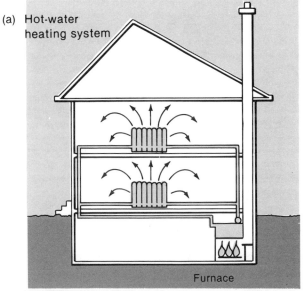

(a) Hot-water heating system

Furnace

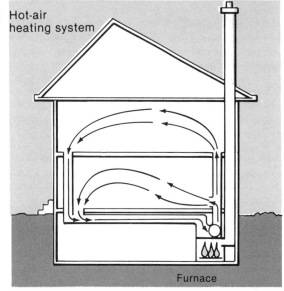

(b) Hot-air heating system

Furnace

Large convection currents of air and water are set up in nature. You may have noticed the effects of sea and land breezes near the shore of a lake or ocean. Figure 12-12 shows how a sea breeze develops on a hot, sunny day. The land warms more quickly than the water, so the air above the land also warms. Then the cooler, more dense air from above the water exerts a force (buoyancy) on the warmer air, pushing it upward. This produces a convection current of air from water to land called a sea breeze.

Figure 12-12 A sea breeze

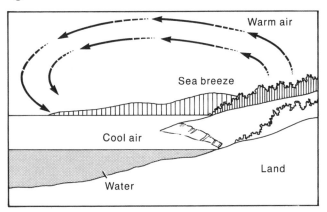

A land breeze, going from the land toward the water, is noticed at sunset. The land cools more quickly than the water. Lakes often become quite calm near the shore when a land breeze occurs.

On hot, sunny days hot air currents called *thermals* can occur over land. Gliders, hang-gliders, and some birds take advantage of these thermals. By flying from one thermal to another, hang-gliders can remain in flight for several hours (Figure 12-13).

Even larger convection currents in nature are caused by the unequal heating of air and water by the sun. Wind is really a huge convection current of air, and ocean currents are huge convection currents of water. Predominant wind currents generally follow the same directions as ocean currents. Some of the major currents in the Atlantic Ocean are shown in Figure 12-14.

Figure 12-13 Hang-gliding

Figure 12-14 The ocean currents and predominant winds follow approximately the same paths. Christopher Columbus knew about the major wind currents near the equator and used them to sail westward (with the prevailing easterlies) and then eastward (with the prevailing westerlies).

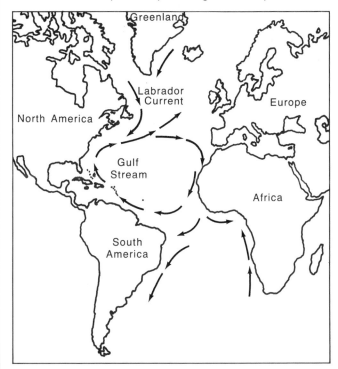

DID YOU KNOW?

Wind storms such as tornados and hurricanes can be devastating. Evidence suggests that if the air and water temperatures of the earth increase slightly, these air currents will become even more dangerous than they have been in the past.

PRACTICE

15. In what kinds of substances (solids, liquids, or gases) can heat convection occur?
16. What happens to the density of a substance when it is heated?
17. What is a *convection oven*? What circulates in this type of oven?
18. Explain the difference between a sea breeze and a land breeze.
19. By referring to Figure 12-14, state which current brings warm water to the east coast of North America, and which current brings cold water.

12.5   Heat Radiation

Both conduction and convection are methods of heat transfer that require particles. However, heat can transfer through a vacuum, which is a space that has no particles. Evidence of this is that energy reaches us from the sun after travelling through empty space. Thus, there is a third method of transferring heat, one that requires no particles. Heat and other types of energy transferred in a wave-like form are called **radiant energy**. The process of emitting radiant energy is called **radiation**. Examples of radiant energy include visible light, microwaves, radio waves, radar, X rays, and infrared rays. The last example is what is sometimes called heat radiation.

All types of radiant energy travel at the same speed in a vacuum (3.0×10^8 m/s). This is far faster than the speed of energy transfer by conduction or convection. Furthermore, radiant energy travels in a straight line. This is commonly observed for visible light. It is also observed when placing your hand close to a hot electric light bulb: only the part of your hand facing the bulb feels the heat transferred.

Heat emitted from an object in the form of radiation can be detected by an infrared photograph called a *thermograph*. A cancerous tumour is slightly warmer than its surroundings, so it is detected as a shaded region in a thermograph. One example of a thermograph is shown in Figure 12-15.

Figure 12-15   This thermograph of a small portion of a person's back was taken shortly after the person had been stung by a bee. It reveals the temperature differences at the surface of the skin.

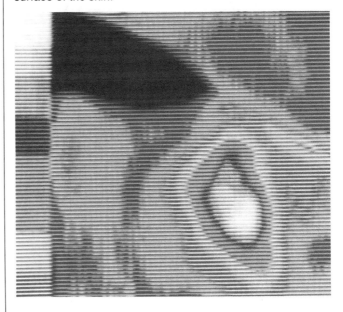

Other properties of radiation are explored in the next activity.

PRACTICE

20. List three properties of radiant energy.
21. Why is heat radiation vastly different from conduction and convection?

Activity 12C   Radiation Absorbers and Emitters

PROBLEM ■   How do different types of materials compare in their ability to (a) absorb radiation and (b) emit radiation?

APPARATUS ■   at least two metal containers with different types of surfaces (e.g., one dark dull surface, and one shiny bright surface); thermometer for each container; stirring rod for each container; 200 W lamp or flood lamp; stopwatch; support stand and clamps; source of hot water; graph paper

PROCEDURE ■

1. Make a chart of "heating data" in which you can record the temperature of at least two samples of water every minute for 12 to 15 min.
2. Set up the apparatus as shown in Figure 12-16. Make sure the lamp is the same distance from each container. Before turning on the lamp, predict what you will observe in the activity.
3. Add an equal quantity of cold water to each container. Measure and record the starting temperature of each sample of water. Then start the stopwatch and turn on the lamp at the same instant. While gently stirring the water with the stirring rod, measure and record the temperature every minute for 12 to 15 min. When you are finished, empty the containers and set them up for the cooling part of the activity.
4. Make a new chart of "cooling data" with the same headings and times as in the first chart.
5. Read the next step and predict what you will observe. Give a reason.
6. Place equal amounts of hot water into each of the containers. (Water from the hot-water tap is acceptable.) Measure and record the starting temperatures. Then start the stopwatch and measure and record the temperature every minute for 12 to 15 minutes as the samples cool. Stir gently from time to time.

Figure 12-16   Set-up for Activity 12C, Procedure #2 and #3

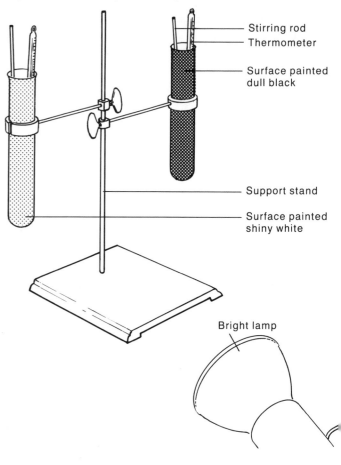

- Stirring rod
- Thermometer
- Surface painted dull black
- Support stand
- Surface painted shiny white
- Bright lamp

ANALYSIS ■

1. Plot a graph of the heating part of this activity (with temperature on the vertical axis). You should have two lines on the graph. Label them.
2. What factors affect the amount of radiation absorbed by a material?
3. Plot a graph of the cooling part of this activity.
4. Is a good absorber of radiation a poor emitter or a good emitter? Explain your answer.

APPLICATIONS ■

1. Would a person travelling by camel across a hot desert prefer black or white clothing? Why?
2. A refrigerator has a radiator to emit excess heat to the surrounding air. What colour would be best for this radiator? Why?

Activity 12D   Preventing Heat Transfer

PROBLEM ■   What are the best ways to keep a sample of hot water hot?

APPARATUS ■   small container to hold hot water (e.g., a soup can); a large container to hold the small container (e.g., a fruit juice can); thermometer; various insulating materials of your design or choice

PROCEDURE ■
1. Design a procedure to solve the problem using the apparatus suggested, or an alternative apparatus. Your design should include ways of preventing all three forms of heat transfer: conduction, convection, and radiation.

 CAUTION   Have your design checked by your teacher before you begin your procedure. There may be harmful aspects.

2. Discuss when and how your class will judge which method was most successful in preventing the heat transfer away from the hot water.
3. Carry out your procedure, then write a complete report of your activity.

APPLICATION ■   In your job at a local pizza parlour, you have the responsibility of designing two types of containers for home delivery service, one for pizzas and the other for cold drinks. Describe the features you would choose for these containers.

12.6   Controlling Heat Transfer

We often want heat to be transferred, but sometimes we want to prevent its transfer. Heat conduction can be prevented by using good insulating materials. Fur is a good insulator, so animals and humans use it to keep warm in the winter. A piece of fur may be at the same temperature as a piece of steel (e.g., −20°C), but when held to your face the fur does not feel cold. That is because it does not conduct the heat away from your face. Of course, you should not consider holding the steel to your face. The steel would conduct the heat away quickly and your skin could become frozen and bruised, especially where it is moist.

Insulating homes and other buildings is an important way to help conserve valuable energy. Proper insulation helps keep heat in during the winter and heat out during the summer. To reduce conduction, builders use materials resistant to heat conduction in the walls and ceilings of homes. The *resistance value*, or *RSI* value depends on the type of material and its thickness. Table 12-2 lists the resistance values per centimetre of thickness of several materials. (The *SI* indicates the metric resistance values.)

Table 12-2   Resistance Values of Insulating Materials

Note: The values stated are for each centimetre of thickness of the material.

Material	RSI Value
Brick	0.008
Gypsum board	0.046
Plywood	0.088
Fibreglass	0.23
Stryrofoam	0.35
Polyurethane	0.42

Table 12-2 can be used to find the total resistance values of various thickness of a material. As you will see in the sample problem, the total resistance value of a wall or ceiling is the sum of the individual resistances.

Sample Problem 1

Calculate the total resistance value of the wall of a home consisting of 10 cm of brick, 2.0 cm of plywood, 8.0 cm of fibreglass, and 1.0 cm of gypsum board.

Solution

10 cm brick	0.08
2.0 cm plywood	0.176
8.0 cm fibreglass	1.84
1.0 cm gypsum board	0.046
	2.142

Thus, the total resistance value is approximately *RSI* 2.1.

Air is an excellent insulator, but it was not included in Table 12-2 because its resistance value does not depend on thickness the way other materials do. Air acts as an insulator only if it is not in motion. (Recall that a convection current, which can be set up in air, can transfer heat readily.) A space in which air is not moving is called "dead." A dead-air space prevents not only conduction, but also convection. Dead-air spaces help provide insulation in clothing such as scarves, gloves, and thermal underwear; in down-filled objects such as ski jackets, sleeping bags, and bed covers; and in double- and triple-glazed windows. Refer to Figure 12-17.

Figure 12-17 Examples of insulation provided by dead-air spaces

(a) Fur-lined glove

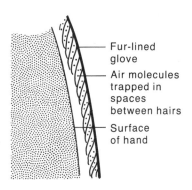

(b) Double-glazed window

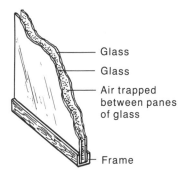

It is also possible to control the transfer of radiant energy. One way to do this is called the *greenhouse effect*, used to grow plants in glass greenhouses. Visible light from the sun can pass through the glass. Plants and their surroundings in the greenhouse absorb the light energy, which then changes into thermal energy. Now the plants have a higher temperature than before, and they emit some of their energy in the form of heat radiation (or infrared radiation). This type of energy cannot pass through the glass readily, so it reflects and becomes trapped inside the greenhouse. Thus, even in winter, the greenhouse is kept warm. See Figure 12-18.

Figure 12-18 The greenhouse effect

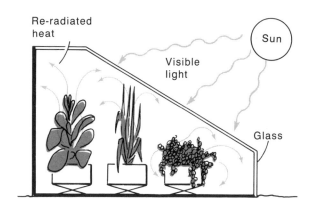

The greenhouse effect is taken into consideration by architects who design homes having *passive solar heating*. The word "passive" means that the system lets solar energy in and prevents much heat from getting out. Passive solar heating is much less expensive to install and operate than active solar heating, in which the sun's energy heats a specially designed apparatus. Figure 12-19 illustrates the basic design of a passive solar heating system. Notice the large windows on the sunny side, the overhanging roof, and the deciduous trees, which lose their leaves in the winter. The radiant energy from the sun enters the windows in the winter but not in the summer. (Active solar heating is described in Section 13.8.)

Figure 12-19 The basic design of a home with passive solar heating

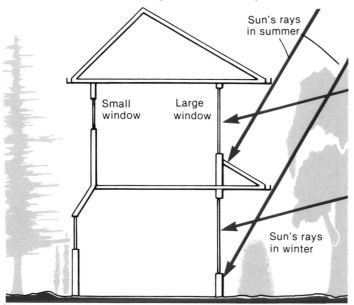

The diagram illustrates several features of a passive solar-heated home. Other features may include carpets that absorb light energy in the winter, and window shutters that are closed at night to prevent heat loss.

PRACTICE

22. Use the kinetic theory to explain why down is a good insulator.
23. Determine the *RSI* value of:
    (a) 6.0 cm of brick
    (b) 2.5 cm of plywood
    (c) 15 cm of styrofoam
24. Calculate the *RSI* value of a ceiling that consists of 3.0 cm of gypsum board and 22 cm of fibreglass insulation.
25. Explain how a double-glazed window prevents heat transfer.
26. A thermos bottle (Figure 12-20) can keep cold liquids cold and warm liquids warm. Use the information in the diagram to explain how a thermos controls conduction, convection, and radiation.
27. Refer to the photograph of the astronaut at the beginning of the chapter. Describe applications of the control of heat transfer evident in the photograph.
28. Research either passive or active solar heating, or the use of greenhouses. Then write a report or make a presentation of your findings.

Figure 12-20 A thermos bottle

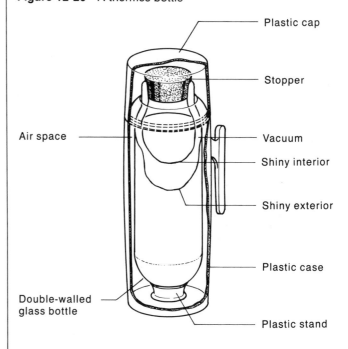

12.7 Thermal Expansion

In Section 12.1 you learned that the liquid used in thermometers expands when heated and contracts when cooled. These processes were explained by considering the motion of particles as energy is added to or removed from the liquid.

Solids and gases also expand when heated and contract when cooled. During heating, the particles gain energy, move more quickly, and have more collisions with other particles. This causes them to spread out more. The opposite occurs when the materials cool.

The expansion and contraction of metals are taken into consideration in the design and construction of bridges, high-rise buildings, and railroads. The expansion and contraction of gases are applied in the use of hot-air balloons. See Figure 12-21.

Figure 12-21 Applications of thermal expansion and contraction

(b) These hot-air balloons are drifting over a golf course at the Bow River, in Calgary, Alberta.

(a) Spaces between sections of railway tracks allow for expansion of metals in the summer.

The rate of expansion differs for different metals. Thus, when two metal strips are attached together to form a *bimetallic strip* or *compound bar*, the strip will bend when its temperature changes. Consider, for example, a bimetallic strip made of aluminum and iron. It can be shown experimentally that aluminum expands and contracts more than iron during the same temperature change. Thus, when the bimetallic strip is heated, it will bend away from the aluminum and toward the iron. The opposite occurs when the strip is cooled. See Figure 12-22.

Figure 12-22 A bimetallic strip

(a) At room temperature
(b) At a high temperature
(c) At a low temperature

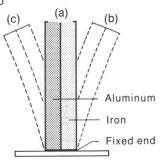

The bimetallic strip is applied in the operation of thermostats in such devices as a home furnace. One example is shown in Figure 12-23.

Figure 12-23 One type of furnace thermostat uses a bimetallic strip with a mercury switch. When the coil winds or unwinds, the glass capsule tilts. When the mercury joins the two contacts, the furnace turns on. (Mercury is an electric conductor.)

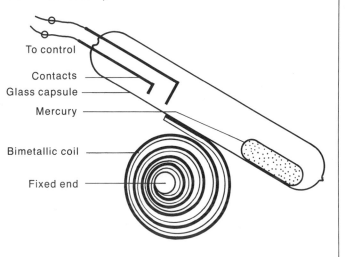

The abnormal behaviour of water

As water cools from 100°C to 4°C it contracts, just as other liquids do. However, between 4°C and 0°C, water acts differently: it expands. Thus, water at 0°C is less dense than water at 4°C, so it rises above the 4°C water. This means that as water freezes at 0°C, the ice will be at the top of the water. This explains why ice floats on water.

The abnormal behaviour of water is very important in nature. In regions where winter temperatures drop below 0°C, bodies of water begin to freeze from the top downward. The layer of ice at the top then protects the water below from the cold air temperatures. If water froze from the bottom upward, the entire body of water would freeze, and no life could survive in the winter. See Figure 12-24.

Figure 12-24 Temperatures of the water in a lake that is frozen at the top

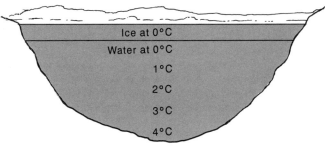

Ice at 0°C
Water at 0°C
1°C
2°C
3°C
4°C

PRACTICE

29. Use the kinetic theory to explain why a helium-filled balloon contracts when it is cooled.
30. Would you expect the gap between rails on a railroad to be larger in winter or in summer? Explain your answer.
31. A metal screw cap on a glass jar is too tight to remove. Hot water can be used to help loosen it. Explain why this would work.
32. Describe how a thermostat with a bimetallic strip could be used to control the temperature of the oven in an electric stove.
33. In what way is the expansion of water different from the expansion of other materials?
34. If a glass bottle filled with water is placed in a freezer, it is likely to burst. Explain why.
35. Why is it important to drain outside water pipes before winter in most regions in Canada?

12.8 Heat Engines

Countless devices we use depend either directly or indirectly on heat engines. You can see why simply by looking at the following list of examples of heat engines:

- gasoline engines in automobiles
- diesel engines in trucks, buses, and locomotives
- gasoline engines in lawnmowers, snowblowers, leaf blowers, chain saws, motorcycles, and outboard motor boats
- rotary engines, such as the Wankel engine, used in some cars
- jet engines in aircraft
- rocket engines in the space program
- steam turbines used to produce electricity at electric generating stations

In all of these engines a fuel is burned to produce some kind of motion. Thus, a **heat engine** is a device that changes heat available from burning fuels into kinetic energy of the moving parts of the engine. That energy is then used to operate a great variety of devices.

In this section we look at two types of gasoline engines and the diesel engine. The jet engine is mentioned in Chapter 6 (Newton's third law of motion) and steam turbines are mentioned in Chapter 21 (fossil-fuel generating stations) and Chapter 27 (nuclear powered generating stations).

The gasoline and diesel engines described here are called *reciprocating engines*. The part that reciprocates (or moves back and forth) is the piston, located in a cylinder. The reciprocating motion is changed into rotation to operate a car or other device.

Four-stroke gasoline engine

The engine most commonly used in cars is the four-stroke gasoline engine. Figure 12-25 illustrates the four strokes for one piston in the engine. (Not shown in the diagram is a rod that controls the opening and closing of the valves. It is called a camshaft. Also not shown is the engine's cooling system.)

Figure 12-25   The basic operation of a four-stroke gasoline engine

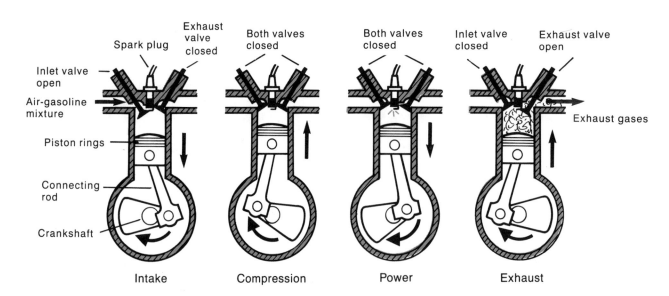

On the *intake stroke*, the piston moves downward, reducing the pressure in the cylinder. The inlet valve opens, allowing an air-gasoline mixture from the carburetor to enter the cylinder. (An engine with a fuel-injection system operates slightly differently.)

On the *compression stroke*, both valves are closed and the piston moves upward. This compresses the air-gasoline mixture.

During the *power stroke*, an electric spark jumps across the gap of the spark plug. The air-gasoline mixture explodes, forcing the piston downward.

During the *exhaust stroke*, the outlet valve opens and the piston rises, pushing the exhaust gases out of the cylinder.

Car engines have four, six, eight, or even twelve cylinders. The piston in each cylinder is connected to a rod called a crankshaft that rotates. In turn, the crankshaft is connected to a flywheel, a heavy wheel that helps keep the pistons moving when the power stroke is not on. To provide smooth operation, the pistons go through their stroke cycles at slightly different times.

DID YOU KNOW?

High-performance engines use superchargers to allow more air into the engine. Some superchargers are mechanical, and others are powered by the spare exhaust gases. The latter type is known as a turbocharger.

DID YOU KNOW?

The main exhaust gases from the burning of gasoline or other hydrocarbons are carbon dioxide and water vapour. However, other gases are also produced, including the deadly gas called carbon monoxide.

Two-stroke gasoline engine

The two-stroke gasoline engine is commonly used in small devices, such as lawnmowers. In this engine, there are ports rather than valves. The opening and closing of the ports are controlled by the positioning of the piston. This allows one cycle of operation to be complete after two strokes rather than four.

Figure 12-26 The basic operation of an air-cooled, two-stroke gasoline engine

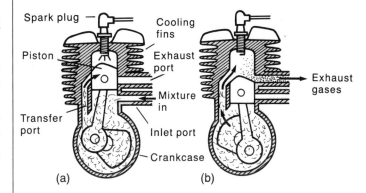

In Figure 12-26(a), the piston is shown near the top of the cylinder blocking the transfer and exhaust ports. The inlet port is open, allowing the air-gasoline mixture to enter the crankcase. The compressed air-gasoline mixture above the piston is ignited by a spark from the spark plug. This forces the piston downward.

In Figure 12-26(b), the piston is near the bottom of the stroke. The intake port is closed, but the exhaust and transfer ports are open. The new mixture of gases moves up to replace the exhaust gases. The piston is shaped to prevent the new gases from mixing with the exhaust gases. Even so, some mixing does occur, which is a disadvantage of this type of engine.

Diesel engine

The diesel engine has valves but no spark plugs. With this arrangement, the piston can complete one cycle in two strokes.

Figure 12-27(a) shows the piston moving downward in the cylinder near the bottom of the stroke. The exhaust valve has just closed and the intake valve has just opened, allowing air to enter the cylinder. Then the piston moves upward, compressing the air to a high pressure. This high compression causes the air to reach a high temperature just as the fuel is injected. The fuel ignites automatically, driving the piston downward. (If you compress the air in a bicycle pump, you can feel the air getting warmer.)

Figure 12-27 Diesel engines

(a) The cylinder design of a two-stroke engine

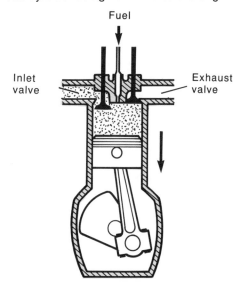

(b) Over $100 000 000 was spent in the development of the turbo-diesel engine shown here. This type of engine is used in trucks.

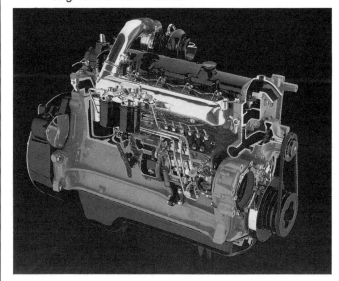

Societal effects of using heat engines

Heat engines require the use of fuel such as a fossil fuel or uranium. Although there are many advantages to using heat engines, there are also many disadvantages. Some of the disadvantages are:

- Most of the fuels available are non-renewable and our supplies are decreasing.
- Much of the energy available from the fuels is wasted as heat into the atmosphere, or bodies of water.
- Heat engines produce noise, which can be a problem.
- The exhaust gases cause air pollution (adding to the greenhouse effect in the earth's atmosphere) as well as chemicals that are harmful to all life on the earth.

What can be done to overcome these disadvantages? Some suggestions, currently being worked on, are:
- improve the efficiency of heat engines
- develop alternate sources of energy that are renewable
- promote the conservation of energy

PRACTICE

36. Name the four strokes in the operation of a gasoline engine in a car.
37. What design features allow a lawnmower engine to go through a complete cycle in two strokes rather than four?
38. How does a two-stroke diesel engine differ from a two-stroke gasoline engine?
39. Starting with chemical potential energy, trace the energy changes that occur in a gasoline engine.
40. State your opinion of our society's use of heat engines from the point of view of:
    (a) the avalablility of fossil fuels
    (b) the efficiency of heat engines
    (c) noise pollution
    (d) air pollution
41. Research and report on one or more of the heat engines named at the beginning of this section, or alternatives to those engines.

DID YOU KNOW?

The greenhouse effect occurs in the earth's atmosphere. The burning of fossil fuels increases the effect, which in turn may cause the average temperature on the earth to increase. This could be a major problem in the future.

Words to Know

kinetic theory of matter	radiant energy
temperature	radiation
thermal energy	radiation absorber
heat	radiation emitter
heat conductor	resistance value (*RSI* value)
heat insulator	greenhouse effect
heat conduction	bimetallic strip
thermal conductivity	(or compound bar)
heat convection	heat engine

Chapter Objectives

Having completed this chapter, you should now be able to:
1. Distinguish between temperature and thermal energy.
2. Apply the kinetic theory of matter to explain observations related to the topic of heat.
3. Distinguish between heat and thermal energy.
4. Define and give examples of heat conductors and heat insulators.
5. Describe and compare the three methods of heat transfer: conduction, convection, and radiation.
6. Describe examples of convection currents in nature and home heating systems.
7. Describe methods of controlling heat transfer.
8. List applications of thermal expansion.
9. Recognize and explain the advantage of the abnormal way that water cools.
10. Define heat engine, and list examples of heat engines.
11. Compare the basic operations of gasoline and diesel engines.

Chapter Review

1. Distinguish between temperature and thermal energy. (12.1)
2. Distinguish between heat and thermal energy. (12.1, 12.2)
3. A cup contains water at 70°C and a lake contains water at 15°C.
   (a) In which sample do the water particles have a greater average kinetic energy? Explain your answer.
   (b) If the water from the cup is poured into the lake, which way is heat transferred? (12.1, 12.2)
4. Do you think it would be possible for a substance to have no thermal energy whatsoever? Use the kinetic theory in your answer.
5. One morning you walk in bare feet across a rug and onto a tile floor. The rug and floor must be at the same temperature, but the floor feels much colder. Explain why. (12.3)
6. What is the most likely method of heat transfer through:
   (a) a metal?   (b) a vacuum?   (c) a liquid? (12.3 to 12.5)
7. State which method of heat transfer:
   (a) does not require particles
   (b) works because particles collide with their neighbours
   (c) travels at the speed of light
   (d) works when particles circulate in a path (12.3 to 12.5)
8. Compare the motion of particles in conduction and convection. (12.3, 12.4)
9. Use the kinetic theory of matter to explain how a hot-air thermal is set up. (12.4)
10. When down used in a ski jacket becomes wet, it loses some of its insulating ability. The insulating ability can be restored by fluffing up the jacket when it is dry. Why does this work? (12.6)
11. Sample A has an *RSI* value of 2.1 and sample B has an *RSI* value of 1.8. Which is the better insulator? (12.6)
12. Determine the total *RSI* value of a wall made of these materials: 8.0 cm of brick; 1.0 cm of gypsum board; 1.0 cm of plywood; and 6.0 cm of fibreglass. (12.6)
13. Give reasons why it would be unwise to paint the surface of a thermos bottle black rather than silver. (12.5, Act. 12C)
14. What features of a greenhouse are also found in a house with passive solar heating? (12.6)
15. (a) Describe methods that have been used in your own home to help prevent heat loss in winter.
    (b) What could be done to improve the insulating properties of your home? (12.6)
16. State a useful application of each observation:
    (a) Liquid mercury expands when heated and contracts when cooled.
    (b) Metal expands more than glass when heated.
    (c) Some metals expand more than others when heated. (12.1, 12.7)
17. Explain why an ordinary glass bowl taken from the refrigerator and placed into a hot oven is likely to break, but Pyrex probably will not. (12.7)
18. Describe how a bimetallic strip could be used to make a thermometer. How would the scale for this thermometer be made? (12.7)

19. Figure 12-28 shows a bimetallic strip in an electric iron. Describe in detail how the strip controls the temperature of the iron.   (12.7)

Figure 12-28

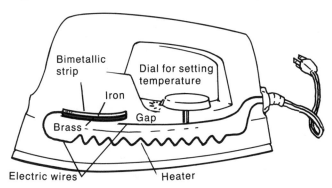

20. (a) Why is the behaviour of water as it cools called abnormal?
    (b) What is the main advantage of this abnormal behaviour?   (12.7)
21. Why can a diesel engine operate without the spark plugs required in a gasoline engine?   (12.8)
22. Figure 12-29 shows a device called Hero's engine, named after an Egyptian scientist.
    (a) Use the information in the diagram to describe how the device is forced to spin.
    (b) Which of Newton's laws of motion explains why the spinning occurs?
        (Refer to Chapter 6.)
    (c) Would you classify this device as a heat engine? Explain your answer.   (12.8)

Figure 12-29

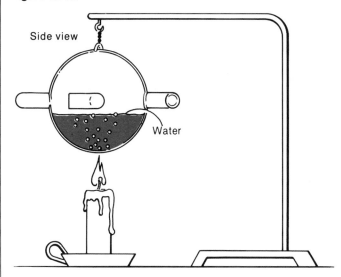

Side view

Water

Top view

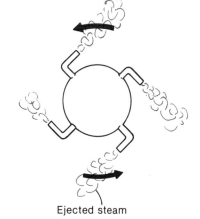

Ejected steam

CHAPTER 13

Heat Exchange and Changes of State

A tremendous amount of heat is required to cause iron to change its state from solid to liquid. Once the iron is in the molten state, it can be poured, mixed with other materials to produce alloys, and allowed to cool into special shapes. This is just one example of a process that applies an understanding of heat exchange and changes of state. Many other examples will be explored in this chapter.

Main Ideas

- Different materials have different capacities to absorb or release heat.
- When heat is transferred from one object to another under ideal conditions, no heat is lost.
- Adding heat to a substance can increase the temperature of the substance, or it can cause a change of state while the temperature remains constant.

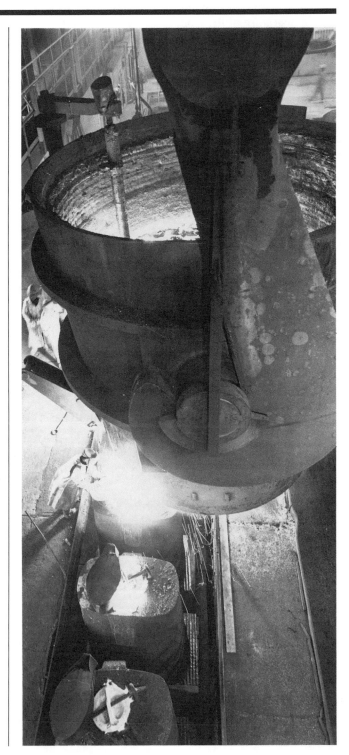

13.1 Adding Heat to a Substance

When you add water to a cooking pot and place the pot on a hot burner, heat transfers from the burner to the pot and then to the water. Obviously the water temperature will rise. But if the same mass of cooking oil is heated on the same burner for the same time, will the same temperature increase occur? And how does the mass of each liquid heated affect the temperature change? We begin this chapter by finding answers to these questions.

Activity 13A Heating Various Liquids

PROBLEM ■

(a) Do the temperatures of liquids heated under the same conditions change at the same rate, or does the rate depend on the liquid?

(b) How does the temperature change of water heated under the same conditions depend on the mass of the water?

Note: This activity may be done as a demonstration.

APPARATUS ■ 3 different liquids (e.g., water, vegetable oil, and peanut oil); balance; Pyrex beaker for each liquid tested; hot plate; beaker tongs; thermometer and stirring rod for each liquid; stopwatch or clock with second hand; graph paper

 CAUTION Do not use an open flame for this activity. Be sure the hot plate is in safe working order.

PROCEDURE ■

1. Make a chart to record the temperature of at least three samples of a liquid every 30 s for several minutes. The first reading will be at time 0.0 s.

2. Devise a method to measure out equal masses (e.g., 200 g) of each liquid used to solve problem (a). Place each liquid into its own beaker. Try to ensure that all the liquids have the same starting temperature (e.g., 22°C).

3. Set the hot-plate temperature to a medium-hot value. This value must remain constant for the entire activity. Also, be sure to use the same hot plate for all the liquids tested because some hot plates get hotter than others.

4. Measure the temperature of the first liquid to be tested. Place the beaker onto the middle of the burner and at the same instant start the stopwatch. While stirring the liquid constantly, measure and record its temperature until the temperature reaches a high but safe value (e.g., 80°C). The thermometer bulb should not touch the bottom of the beaker when readings are taken.

5. Remove the hot beaker carefully with tongs.

6. Repeat #4 for the other liquids. In each case, be sure to place the beaker at the same location on the burner.

7. Design and perform your own steps to solve problem (b).

 CAUTION Have your design checked by your teacher before you begin your procedure. There may be harmful aspects.

ANALYSIS ■

1. On a single sheet of graph paper, plot the heating curves for all the liquids used in Procedure #1 to #6. Temperature should be placed on the vertical axis. (Do you know why?) Label the lines on the graph.

2. Which liquid had its temperature increase most rapidly? most slowly?

3. Do the temperatures of liquids heated under the same conditions change at the same rate, or does the rate depend on the liquid?

4. Plot a new graph to illustrate what you learned in Procedure #7.

5. How does the temperature change of water heated under the same conditions depend on the mass of the water?

APPLICATION ■ Even during a hot summer, a large body of water such as Lake Superior or Lake Ontario takes a long time to warm up. Explain why.

13.2   Specific Heat Capacity

You have seen in Chapter 12 that heat is the transfer of energy. The amount of energy transferred cannot be measured directly, so other quantities must be found in order to calculate heat.

First, consider what you learned in Chapter 7 about energy and power. These quantities are related by the equation

power $=$ energy/time, or $P = \frac{E}{t}$, where E is measured in joules, t in seconds, and P in watts. If we rearrange this equation to find energy, we obtain

$$E = Pt$$

What this means is that a 100 W heater operating for 10 s produces (100 W)(10 s) or 1000 J of energy. Let us see how this relates to calculating heat.

Sample Problem 1

One litre (1.0 kg) of water at 12°C is placed into a 1500 W electric kettle and heated for 120 s. How much energy is given to the water?

Solution $E = Pt$
$= (1500 \text{ W}) (120 \text{ s})$
$= 180\ 000 \text{ J}$

Next, consider what you learned in the previous activity. For a given sample of a liquid, a greater temperture change resulted from a greater amount of heat added. Also, for a particular liquid, a greater mass required a greater amount of heat to increase the temperature by the same amount. If we now divide the

energy transferred to the liquid by the mass and the change of temperature, we obtain a separate quantity called the *specific heat capacity*. Thus,

specific heat capacity $=$ $\dfrac{\textbf{energy transferred}}{\textbf{(mass)(temperature change)}}$

Using the symbol c for specific heat capacity, we have

$$c = \frac{E}{m \triangle T}$$

The units of c are shown in the next sample problem where we calculate the specific heat capacity of water.

Sample Problem 2

If the temperature of the water in sample problem 1 increased to 55°C, what is the specific heat capacity of water?

Solution   The temperature change is
$55°C - 12°C = 43°C$.

Now, $c = \dfrac{E}{m \triangle T}$

$= \dfrac{180\ 000 \text{ J}}{(1.0 \text{ kg})(43°C)}$

$= 4186 \text{ J/(kg} \cdot °C)$

Thus, the specific heat capacity of water is about 4200 J/(kg·°C).

If you tried to perform an activity similar to that described in sample problems 1 and 2, your answer would likely be somewhat different. Some of the energy from the electric heater may go to the air or the kettle itself, making the measurements inaccurate.

So far we have discussed heat transferred *to* an object. But heat can also transfer *away from* an object. The same specific heat capacity still applies. Thus we can now state in words the meaning of **specific heat capacity**: it is the amount of heat transferred when the temperature of 1.0 kg of a substance changes by 1.0°C. See Figure 13-1.

Figure 13-1 The meaning of specific heat capacity, using water as the example

(a)
The specific heat capacity of water is 4200 J/(kg·C). Thus, adding 4200 J of heat to a 1.0 kg sample of water at 10°C will increase its temperature to 11°C.

(b)
If the 1.0 kg sample of water at 11°C releases 4200 J of heat, its temperature will drop to 10°C.

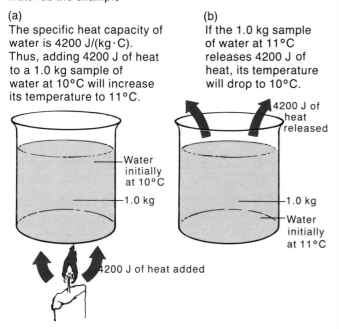

Every different substance has a different specific heat capacity. In other words, specific heat capacity is a characteristic property of substances. Table 13-1 lists the specific heat capacity of several common substances. You will need to refer to this table often in this chapter.

Table 13-1 Specific Heat Capacities of Common Substances at 25°C

Substance	Specific heat capacity [J/(kg·°C)]
Water	4200
Concrete	3000
Ethyl alcohol	2500
Ethylene glycol	2200
Vegetable oil	2000
Air	995
Aluminum	920
Glass	840
Sand	790
Iron	450
Copper	390
Brass	380
Silver	240
Lead	130

PRACTICE

1. How much heat is provided by a 200 W burner in 30 s?
2. An electric heater, rated at 80 W, adds heat to a sample of water for 2.0 min. How much energy was given to the water?
3. A heater warms 500 g of a liquid from 35°C to 55°C, as it transfers 20 000 J to the liquid.
   (a) Express the mass in kilograms.
   (b) What is the temperature change?
   (c) Calculate the specific heat capacity of the liquid.
   (d) According to Table 13-1, what is the identity of the liquid?
4. Use the information given below to determine the specific heat capacity of gold and mercury.
   (a) It takes 1300 J of heat to raise the temperature of 400 g of gold from 50°C to 75°C.
   (b) To raise the temperature of 2.5 kg of mercury from 22°C to 32°C requires 3200 J of heat.

13.3 Calculating Heat

To calculate the heat transferred to or from an object, we rearrange the equation for specific heat capacity to express energy (or heat) by itself. Thus,

$$E = mc\triangle T$$

Sample Problem 3

How much heat must be transferred to 4.0 kg of water at 3°C to increase its temperature to 5°C?

Solution The temperature change is
5°C − 3°C = 2°C.

$$\begin{aligned} E &= mc\triangle T \\ &= (4.0 \text{ kg}) [4200 \text{ J/(kg}\cdot°C)] (2.0°C) \\ &= 33\ 600 \text{ J (or } 3.4 \times 10^4 \text{ J)} \end{aligned}$$

Notice in this solution that the kg and °C cancel, leaving only J.

Sample Problem 4

Calculate the amount of heat released by a 6.0 kg iron rod as it cools from 28°C to 24°C.

Solution The temperature change is
28°C − 24°C = 4°C.

$$\begin{aligned} E &= mc\triangle T \\ &= (6.0 \text{ kg})[450 \text{ J/(kg}\cdot°C)](4°C) \\ &= 10\ 800 \text{ J (or } 1.1 \times 10^4 \text{ J)} \end{aligned}$$

This method of calculating the amount of heat gained or released will be applied in the next activity.

PRACTICE

5. Using Table 13-1 as a reference, calculate the amount of heat needed to raise the temperature of:
   (a) 10 kg of water by 5.0°C
   (b) 5.0 kg of ethyl alcohol by 6.0°C
   (c) 4.0 kg of lead by 50°C
6. Using Table 13-1 as a reference, determine the heat released when:
   (a) a 3.0 kg piece of silver cools from 90°C to 20°C
   (b) 20 kg of concrete cools from 33°C to 18°C
   (c) 200 g of water cools from 30°C to 22°C

Activity 13B Heat Transfer in Mixtures

PROBLEM ■ When hot and cold samples of water are mixed, does the heat released by the hot water equal the heat gained by the cold water?

APPARATUS ■ 2 large styrofoam cups (or alternative containers); thermometer; stirring rod; graduated cylinder; hot and cold water (water from the hot and cold taps is acceptable)

PROCEDURE ■
1. Make a chart to record observations and calculations, as shown in Table 13-2.

Table 13-2 Observations and Calculations for Activity 13B

Trial number	1	2	3	4	
Volume (mL)	100	150	50	75	Cold water
Mass (kg)	0.1				
Starting temp. (°C)					
Final temp. (°C)					
Specific heat capacity [J/(kg·°C)]	4200				
Heat gained (J)					
Volume (mL)	100	50	150	175	Hot Water
Mass (kg)					
Starting temp. (°C)					
Final temp. (°C)					
Specific heat capacity [J/(kg·°C)]					
Heat released (J)					

2. Place 100 mL (100 g) of cold water in one cup and 100 mL of hot water in the other cup. Measure and record the starting temperature of each sample of water.
3. Pour the hot water into the cold water. Stir the mixture and find the highest temperature reached. This is the final temperature of the mixture. Record it in your chart for both cold water and hot water.
4. Repeat #2 and #3 using the quantities of hot and cold water indicated in trial numbers 2, 3, and 4 of Table 13-2.
5. Calculate the temperature change and heat gained for each sample of cold water. Calculate the temperature change and heat released for each sample of hot water. Complete your chart.

ANALYSIS ■

1. For each trial, compare the heat gained by the cold water with the heat released by the hot water. Explain any differences.
2. Do you think the results would have been the same if the cold water had been poured into the hot? Explain your answer. (You may have time to verify your answer experimentally.)
3. What ways could be used to improve the accuracy of the results of this activity?
4. Use the kinetic theory of matter to explain the temperature changes observed when the water samples were mixed.
5. When hot and cold samples are mixed, does the heat released by the hot water equal the heat gained by the cold water?

13.4 The Principle of Heat Transfer

Through countless investigations, scientists have shown that when two substances at different temperatures are mixed, the amount of heat released by the hotter substance equals the amount of heat gained by the colder substance. No energy disappears; it is simply transferred from one substance to another. This observation is summarized in the **principle of heat transfer**:

> **When two substances at different temperatures are mixed, the heat released by the hotter substance equals the heat gained by the colder substance.**

In activities done in science classrooms, this principle is difficult to test without error. When two samples of water are mixed, for example, some of the energy of the hot sample is transferred to the thermometer, the stirring rod, the cold-water container, and the air. Thus, not all the energy released by the hot water is gained by the cold water. However, when errors are reduced as much as possible, the principle of heat transfer is found to apply.

The principle of heat transfer can be used to solve numerical problems involving heat exchange. The heat released by a hot substance equals the heat gained by a cold substance, so we can write

$$\text{heat released} = \text{heat gained}$$

But heat is "energy transferred", so we can write

$$E_{\text{released}} = E_{\text{gained}}$$

Since $E = mc\triangle T$, this equation becomes

$$(mc\triangle T)_{\text{hot substance}} = (mc\triangle T)_{\text{cold substance}}$$

Finally, if we use the symbols H for hot and C for cold, we have

$$m_{\text{H}}c_{\text{H}}\triangle T_{\text{H}} = m_{\text{C}}c_{\text{C}}\triangle T_{\text{C}}$$

Let us see how this equation can be used to determine the specific heat capacity of a metal.

Sample Problem 5

A piece of metal of mass 500 g is placed into boiling water at 100°C. The hot metal is then transferred quickly into a 200 g sample of water at 20°C. The final temperature of the mixture is 30°C. Determine:

(a) the specific heat capacity of the metal
(b) the probable identity of the metal

Solution

(a) The metal is the hot substance (H), and the water is the cold substance (C). The facts we know are:

$$m_H = 500\,g$$
$$\Delta T_H = 100°C - 30°C = 70°C$$
$$m_C = 200\,g$$
$$c_C = 4200\,J/(kg \cdot °C)$$
$$\Delta T_C = 30°C - 20°C = 10°C$$

We must find c_H using

$$m_H c_H \Delta T_H = m_C c_C \Delta T_C$$
$$(500\,g)(c_H)(70°C) = (200\,g)[4200\,J/(kg \cdot °C)](10°C)$$
$$c_H = \frac{(200\,g)[4200\,J/(kg \cdot °C)](10°C)}{(500\,g)(70°C)}$$
$$= 240\,J/(kg \cdot °C)$$

Thus, the specific heat capacity of the metal is 240 J/(kg·°C).

(b) According to Table 13-1, the metal is likely silver.

In the next activity, you will apply the steps described in this sample problem to find the specific heat capacity of various metals.

PRACTICE

7. Why is the principle of heat transfer difficult to prove in ordinary science activities?

8. An unknown substance at 85°C is mixed with water at 15°C. The temperature of the mixture is 35°C. If the mass of the unknown substance is 400 g and the mass of the water is 200 g, determine:
   (a) the specific heat capacity of the unknown substance
   (b) the probable identity of the substance (Refer to Table 13-1.)

9. A student heats a 70 g metal bar in boiling water (100°C), then quickly transfers the bar into a 45 g sample of water at 16°C. The highest temperature reached by the metal and water together is 28°C. Determine:
   (a) the specific heat capacity of the metal
   (b) the probable identity of the metal (Refer to Table 13-1.)

Activity 13C   Specific Heat Capacity of Metals

PROBLEM ■ How well does the principle of heat transfer apply when determining the specific heat capacity of metals?

APPARATUS ■ various metal samples (e.g., iron, brass, lead, aluminum, copper); balance; hot plate; large beaker; tongs; water; thermometer; styrofoam cup or small beaker; graduated cylinder; stirring rod

> **CAUTION**   *Be sure the hot plate is in safe working order.*

PROCEDURE ■

1. Make up a chart of observations based on Table 13-3.

Table 13-3   Observations for Activity 13C

Substance	Mass (kg)	Starting temperature (°C)	Final temperature (°C)	Temperature change (°C)
Iron		100		
Water	0.10			
Brass				
Water				

2. Half fill a large beaker with water. Place it on the hot plate and bring the water to boiling. Using tongs, gently lower the metal samples into the water. Allow them time to acquire the temperature of the boiling water (probably 100°C).
3. Place 100 mL (100 g) of cold water into the styrofoam cup or small beaker, and measure its starting temperature. Place this cold water close to the hot water bath. Use the tongs to quickly and carefully transfer one metal sample from the hot water to the cold water (Figure 13-2). Stir the water gently, then find the highest temperature it reaches. Enter the data in your chart.
4. Carefully remove and dry the metal sample. Then measure and record its mass.
5. Repeat #3 and #4 for as many different types of metal as are available.

Figure 13-2   Set-up for Activity 13C

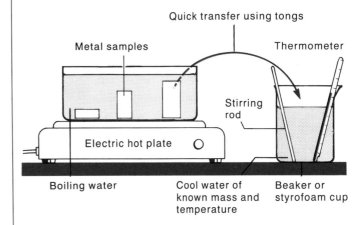

Quick transfer using tongs

Metal samples
Thermometer
Stirring rod
Electric hot plate
Boiling water
Cool water of known mass and temperature
Beaker or styrofoam cup

ANALYSIS ■

1. Use the principle of heat transfer to calculate the specific heat capacity of each metal. Refer to sample problem 5 as a guideline. Show all your calculations.
2. Compare your calculated values to the accepted values listed in Table 13-1.
3. Describe ways of improving the accuracy of the results in this activity.
4. How successful was the principle of heat transfer in helping you find the specific heat capacity of metals experimentally?
5. In general, how do the specific heat capacities of metals compare to those of liquids?

APPLICATION ■   A baked potato wrapped in metal foil is removed from a hot oven. The foil is removed from the potato, and within a few seconds it is much cooler than the potato. Explain this observation.

13.5 Changes of State

Matter may exist in one of three common states—*solid*, *liquid*, or *gaseous*. In the gaseous state, a substance is either a *gas* or a *vapour*. A vapour is a substance in the gaseous state that would be solid or liquid at room temperature (20°C). A gas is in the gaseous state at room temperature. (A fourth state of matter, called plasma, occurs only when temperatures are extremely high. For example, plasma exists in the sun.)

If heat is added to or released from a substance, its state can change. For instance, if heat is added to liquid water, the water can evaporate or boil, changing to the gaseous state. If heat is removed from the water, the water can change to the solid state, ice.

The possible *changes of state* are defined below and are illustrated in Figure 13-3.

- *Fusion* or *melting* is the change from the solid to the liquid state.
- *Vaporization* is the change from the liquid to the gaseous state. Slow vaporization is called *evaporation* and fast vaporization is called *boiling*.
- *Condensation* or *liquification* is the change from the gaseous to the liquid state.
- *Solidification* or *freezing* is the change from the liquid to the solid state.
- *Sublimation* is the change from the solid to the gaseous state or from the gaseous to the solid state. (The disappearing of frost without melting is an example of sublimation.)

You have observed that when a substance is in a given state, adding heat to it causes its temperature to rise (recall $E = mc\Delta T$). However, once the substance reaches its melting or boiling point, the added heat does not cause an increase in temperature. Rather, it causes a change of state. This is illustrated in the warming curve for the substance H_2O in Figure 13-4.

Figure 13-3 Changes of state of matter

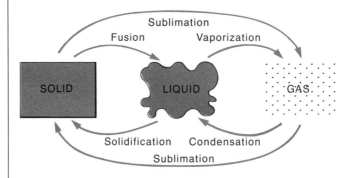

Figure 13-4 This graph shows the ideal heating curve for H_2O as it is heated first to the melting point, then to the boiling point. "Time" is plotted along the horizontal axis, but the same pattern would be observed if "heat added" were plotted there instead.

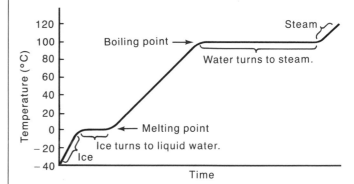

Notice in Figure 13-4 that adding heat to ice causes its temperature to increase, and adding more heat at 0°C causes the ice to melt, changing it to water. Adding heat to the water causes its temperature to rise until the boiling point of 100°C is reached. Adding even more heat causes the water to change to water vapour or steam.

Just how much heat must be added to a sample of H_2O to cause its state to change is the subject of the next two activities.

PRACTICE

10. A camper high in the Rocky Mountains is heating water in an open container over an open fire. The water begins boiling at $91\,°C$. What happens to the temperature of the water as the water is gradually boiled away? Explain your answer.

11. State whether each of the following is a solid, liquid, gas, or vapour.
    (a) steel at room temperature
    (b) mercury at room temperature
    (c) steam
    (d) air

12. Name the change of state in each case.
    (a) Molten gold releases heat to form ingots.
    (b) Unused ice cubes in a ''frost-free'' freezer gradually disappear.
    (c) Moisture forms on the outside of a glass filled with a cold drink.
    (d) Frost forms on a car's windshield during the night in winter.

13. Starting with steam at $120\,°C$, draw a cooling curve for H_2O as it releases heat. The final temperature of the H_2O is $-40\,°C$. Label as much as possible on the graph. (The cooling curve has plateaus, just as the warming curve had in Figure 13-4.)

Activity 13D   Fusion of Ice

PROBLEM ■   How much heat is required to cause a sample of ice to melt?

APPARATUS ■   styrofoam cup or alternative container; graduated cylinder; cold water; ice cubes; thermometer; stirring rod

Note: The thermometer must be accurate near the freezing point of water ($0\,°C$).

PROCEDURE ■
1. Add 150 mL (150 g) of cold water to the styrofoam cup. Measure and record the temperature of the water.
2. Add five or six average-size ice cubes to the water and stir the water-ice mixture continually as you watch the temperature. As soon as the temperature reaches $0\,°C$, remove the thermometer, the stirring rod, *and* the unmelted ice.
3. Measure the final volume of the water, and convert the answer to grams.

ANALYSIS ■
1. From your observations, determine the following:
    (a) the mass of the water before the ice was added, in kilograms
    (b) the temperature change of the water
    (c) the mass of the ice that melted, in kilograms
2. Calculate the heat released by the water as it caused the ice to melt. $E = mc\triangle T$, where m is the mass of the water before the ice was added, c is the specific heat capacity of water, and $\triangle T$ is the temperature change of the water.
3. Determine the amount of heat per kilogram required to cause the ice to melt. That is, find $\dfrac{E}{m_{ice}}$, where m_{ice} is the mass of the ice that melted in kilograms.
4. How does your value in Analysis #3 compare with the values found by other groups?
5. Describe possible sources of error in this activity.
6. State the amount of heat required to melt 1.0 kg of ice, according to the results of this activity.

Activity 13E   Vaporization of Water

PROBLEM ■ How much heat is required to cause a sample of liquid water to vaporize?

APPARATUS ■ heater of known power (e.g., a 1500 W electric kettle or a 150 W immersion heater); water; large graduated cylinder; stopwatch or clock with second hand

PROCEDURE ■
1. Add a measured quantity of water to the device in which heating will occur. (For example, if an electric kettle is used, add 500 mL of water. If a small immersion heater is used, add 100 mL of water to a Pyrex beaker.)
2. Heat the water, and as soon as it starts boiling, start the stopwatch. Measure the time needed to boil away about half the water. Record the time in seconds.

 CAUTION *Do not leave an electric water heater plugged in without sufficient water. Be careful when using hot or boiling water. Steam burns are severe.*

3. Allow the remaining water to cool somewhat, then use the graduated cylinder to find its volume. Convert the volume to mass in grams and kilograms.

ANALYSIS ■
1. Determine the heat given by the heater to the water as the water was boiling. $E = Pt$ where P is the power of the heater in watts, and t is the time of the boiling in seconds.
2. Calculate the mass in kilograms of the water that changed to steam.
3. Use your answers to Analysis #1 and #2 to determine the amount of heat per kilogram required to cause water to change to steam. That is, find $\frac{E}{m}$, where m is the mass of the water that changed to steam.
4. Describe the possible sources of error in this activity.
5. According to the results of this activity, how much heat is required to boil away 1.0 kg of water?
6. How does the heat needed to boil away 1.0 kg of water compare to the heat needed to melt 1.0 kg of ice?

13.6 Latent Heats of Fusion and Vaporization

As heat is added to a solid at its melting point, the particles of the solid gain enough energy to become free of their rigid position. This results in the change of state from solid to liquid. As you learned in Activity 13D, a large amount of heat is needed to cause this change of state. The quantity of heat needed to fuse (melt) 1.0 kg of a substance is called the **latent heat of fusion**. The word "latent" means to lie hidden, which refers to the observation that adding heat to a substance during melting does not increase its temperature. The symbol for latent heat of fusion is L_F, so the equation to find it is:

$$L_F = \frac{E}{m}$$

where E is the heat in joules and m is the mass in kilograms. The latent heat is measured in joules per kilogram (J/kg).

Sample Problem 6

A total of 4000 J of heat will cause 100 g of a certain metal to fuse at its melting point. What is the metal's latent heat of fusion?

Solution The mass is 0.1 kg.

$$L_F = \frac{E}{m} = \frac{4000\,J}{0.1\,kg} = 40\,000\ J/kg$$

$$(\text{or } 4.0 \times 10^4\ J/kg)$$

As heat is added to a liquid at its boiling point, the particles of the liquid gain enough energy to break free of the liquid. This results in the change of state from liquid to gaseous. As you discovered in Activity 13E, it takes even more heat per kilogram to cause this vaporization than to cause melting. The quantity of heat needed to vaporize 1.0 kg of a substance is called the **latent heat of vaporization**, symbol L_V. To find it, we use the equation:

$$L_V = \frac{E}{m}$$

Like L_F, L_V is measured in joules per kilogram (J/kg).

Table 13-4 lists the latent heats of fusion and vaporization of some common substances. According to the data, which requires more heat per kilogram, fusion or vaporization?

Table 13-4 Latent Heats of Fusion and Vaporization

Substance	Latent heat of fusion (J/kg)	Latent heat of vaporization (J/kg)
Aluminum	9.0×10^4	1.1×10^7
Ethyl alcohol	1.1×10^5	8.6×10^5
Iron	2.5×10^5	6.3×10^6
Lead	2.3×10^4	8.7×10^5
Silver	1.1×10^5	2.3×10^6
Water	3.3×10^5 (ice)	2.3×10^6

If the latent heats of a substance are known, they can be used to calculate the heat needed to melt or boil away certain masses of the substance. The appropriate equations are:

$$E = L_F m \quad \text{and} \quad E = L_V m$$

Sample Problem 7

How much heat is needed to change 20 kg of solid silver into liquid silver at its melting point?

Solution $E = L_F m$
$ = (1.1 \times 10^5 \text{ J/kg})(20 \text{ kg})$
$ = 2.2 \times 10^6 \text{ J}$

PRACTICE

14. (a) Calculate the latent heat of fusion if 8.4×10^5 J of heat are needed to melt 2.0 kg of a substance at its melting point.
    (b) How much heat is released by 1.0 kg of the substance in (a) as it changes back to a solid at the freezing temperature?
15. Calculate the latent heat of vaporization if 8.4×10^5 J of heat are needed to boil away 0.4 kg of a substance at its boiling point.
16. Use the data in Table 13-4 to determine the amount of heat in each case.
    (a) A mass of 4.0 kg of ethyl alcohol becomes a vapour at the boiling point.
    (b) In a factory, 500 kg of solid iron are changed into liquid iron at the melting point.
    (c) A silversmith heats 400 g of solid silver at the melting point, and the silver becomes liquid.
17. Determine the amount of heat removed by a freezer in changing 400 g of water at $0°C$ into 400 g of ice at $0°C$.

13.7 Applications of Changes of State

When you first come out of the water after a swim, you feel cool, even on a hot day. As the moisture on your body evaporates, it absorbs heat from your body and the surrounding air. Sweating involves a similar process, which helps keep the body cool. This process is called the *cooling effect of evaporation*.

Many animals use methods other than sweating to take advantage of the cooling effect of evaporation. When a dog pants, the moisture on its tongue evaporates more quickly, helping to remove heat from its body. A pig wallows in water (and mud!) to keep cool, and an elephant uses its trunk to spray water over its body.

Besides evaporation, there are two other changes of state that result in cooling — melting, and sublimation from the solid to the gaseous state. The opposite changes of state result in warming. For instance, when a gas or vapour condenses to a liquid, heat is released to the surroundings. A similar effect occurs during solidification, or during sublimation from the gaseous to the solid state. The remainder of this section presents practical examples of the cooling or heating effects of changes of state.

Refrigerators

The operation of a refrigerator is based on the vaporization and condensation cycle of a substance called a *refrigerant*. Common refrigerants are ammonia, Freon-12 (a fluorocarbon compound), and sulphur dioxide. Each of these has a boiling point well below room temperature at atmospheric pressure.

Figure 13-5 illustrates the cycle through which the refrigerant passes. The names of the components indicate their functions. The compressor compresses the refrigerant gas, and the gas condenses into a liquid in the condenser. This condensation releases heat to the surroundings, namely the air in the room. The liquid refrigerant then passes through the high-pressure part of the system, reaching the expansion valve. Here, a sudden drop in pressure occurs, and the liquid begins to vaporize. The refrigerant then passes through the evaporator coils in the low-pressure part of the system. Here, complete evaporation absorbs heat from the food and air inside the refrigerator. The gas then circulates back to the compressor, and the cycle begins again.

Air conditioners

An air conditioner operates with a refrigerant that goes through the same cycle as a refrigerator. Both home and car air conditioners release their excess heat during condensation to the outside air. Figure 13-6 shows a schematic diagram of the operation of an air conditioner. The same diagram could be applied to the refrigerator.

Figure 13-5 The operation of a refrigerator

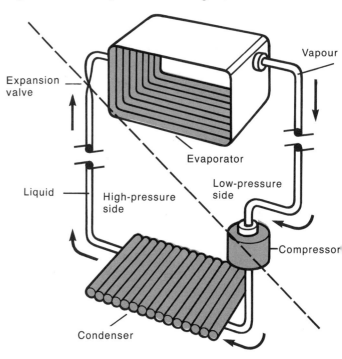

Figure 13-6 A schematic diagram of the operation of a refrigerator or air-conditioner

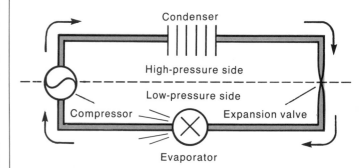

All-weather heat pumps

A *heat pump* transfers heat away from an area of low temperature to an area of higher temperature. Looked at this way, a refrigerator and an air conditioner act as heat pumps, transferring heat away from a refrigerator or a room to warmer surroundings.

Heat pumps are becoming more common for cooling a home in summer as well as heating it in winter. A single heat pump unit can accomplish both functions by being able to reverse the direction of the refrigerant during different seasons.

Figure 13-7 shows a schematic diagram of the operation of a heat pump. In summer, the refrigerant evaporates inside the home, absorbing heat there. Then it condenses outdoors, releasing heat there. In winter, the refrigerant flows in the opposite direction. It evaporates outdoors, absorbing heat there. Then it condenses indoors, releasing heat where it is needed.

Figure 13-7 A schematic diagram showing the basic operation of a heat pump

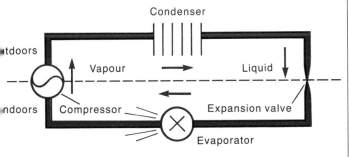

(a) In summer, evaporation occurs indoors to absorb heat; condensation occurs outdoors to release the heat.

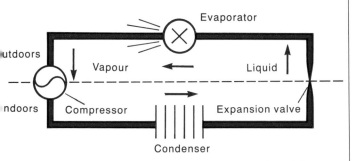

(b) In winter, evaporation occurs outdoors to absorb heat; condensation occurs indoors to release the heat.

Cooling spacecraft by ablation

When a spacecraft must travel through the earth's atmosphere, it experiences a large amount of friction with the air. This friction causes a great increase in temperature on the surface of the craft, and could result in serious melting or a fire. A process used to remove some of the excess heat on the surface of the craft is called **ablation**. A special ceramic material on the surface of the craft melts, and then evaporates after it melts. These changes of state require heat, which is absorbed from the surface of the craft. This cools the craft somewhat. The ablation continues as the craft travels through the atmosphere.

PRACTICE

18. Try this. Add room-temperature ethyl alcohol to one beaker and room-temperature water to a second beaker. Place your left index finger into the alcohol and your right index finger into the water. Then hold your fingers in the air.
    (a) Which finger feels cooler?
    (b) Which liquid evaporates more quickly?
    (c) Explain why one finger is cooled more than the other.
19. Explain each of the following observations in terms of changes of state and latent heats.
    (a) A block of ice is useful in a camping cooler.
    (b) A steam burn can be much more severe than a hot-water burn. (This is particularly true when the steam is under high pressure.)
    (c) Water in an unglazed clay jug remains fairly cool, even on a hot day. (Clay is a porous material.)
20. What do refrigerators, air conditioners, and heat pumps have in common?
21. Do you think it would be possible to cool your kitchen by leaving the refrigerator door open? Explain your answer.
22. Research the use of heat pumps or other applications related to this section. Prepare a written report or a video on your findings.

13.8   Energy in Our Society

Countless ways of using energy have provided us with a high standard of living. Almost all the sources of energy involve heat either directly or indirectly. This is certainly true of energy from the sun or from fossil fuels. Futhermore, most uses of energy involve heat in the form of waste energy. Thus, an understanding of heat is important in improving ways of using and conserving energy.

Several comments about the use of energy in our society have been mentioned earlier in this unit and in other parts of this book. Let us consider a few more observations, especially related to heat.

Energy consumption

North Americans consume more energy per person than any other group of people in the world. Furthermore, the energy used per person continues to increase, as does our population. This high consumption means we are using up energy resources more and more quickly.

Non-renewable energy resources

An energy resource is called *non-renewable* if it cannot be replaced in a normal human lifespan. The most common non-renewable resources are uranium and the fossil fuels—coal, crude oil, and natural gas. The fossil fuels took millions of years to form, and once we use them up, they will be gone forever.

The worldwide supply of non-renewable fuels is decreasing. Predictions are that the crude oil and natural gas supplies will be used up first. About 70% of the energy consumed in Canada comes from these sources. See Figure 13-8.

Figure 13-8   Canada's main sources of energy

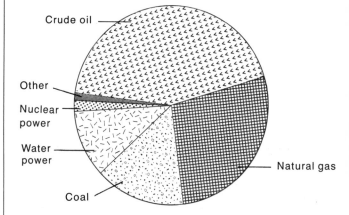

Renewable energy resources

An energy resource is called *renewable* if it renews itself in a normal human lifespan. Society's challenge is to find ways of changing the energy from these resources into useable energy.

Solar energy, or radiant energy from the sun, can be used in a variety of ways. It can produce small amounts of electrical energy when it strikes photovoltaic cells. These cells are used in satellites, small instruments such as calculators, and may be used to charge batteries in solar-powered cars (Figure 13-9).

Figure 13-9 These experimental cars use solar energy. Much research will have to be done before such cars can be used in a practical way.

Solar energy can also be used to heat buildings and swimming pools directly. Passive solar heating, described in some detail in Chapter 12, refers to building a structure to take advantage of the sun's energy at all times of the year. For example, some homes have a concrete wall or floor that absorbs radiant energy during the day, and then re-emits some of the stored energy at night. As you can see in Table 13-1 (repeated below), concrete has a fairly high specific heat capacity, so it can retain its thermal energy well after receiving the solar energy.

Table 13-1   Specific Heat Capacities of Common Substances at 25°C

Substance	Specific heat capacity [J/(kg·°C)]
Water	4200
Concrete	3000
Ethyl alcohol	2500
Ethylene glycol	2200
Vegetable oil	2000
Air	995
Aluminum	920
Glass	840
Sand	790
Iron	450
Copper	390
Brass	380
Silver	240
Lead	130

DID YOU KNOW?

Another way of using solar energy in a passive system is through the use of a heat pack. This device contains a solution of special salts in water. The melting point of the solution is 20°C. In the daytime, the solution absorbs heat and melts. At night, the solution gradually solidifies and releases its latent heat of fusion to warm the surrounding area.

Active solar heating converts solar energy into other forms of energy as well as heat. The word "active" means that the heating system is designed so that as much solar energy as possible is absorbed by a material, which is then distributed around the building. Figure 13-10 shows one design of an active solar system. One possible feature not shown is an array of solar cells (on a south-facing roof) to convert light energy into electrical energy.

Notice in Figure 13-10 that the solar collector has a liquid that absorbs heat as it passes through the pipes. The advantage of using water for this liquid is that it has a high specific heat capacity. This means it releases the stored thermal energy slowly, allowing the heat to be available much later. The disadvantage of using water is that it freezes at a fairly high temperature. Thus, the liquid chosen is a mixture of water and another liquid that prevents freezing.

Figure 13-10 Active solar heating

(a) Basic operation of an active solar-heating system

(b) An example of solar collector design

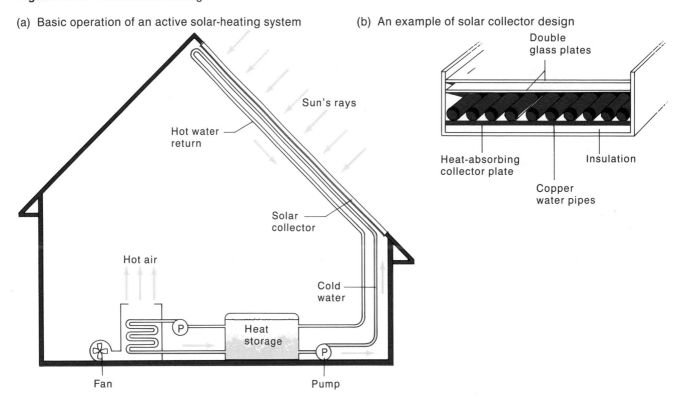

Other renewable forms of energy are listed below. Most of them are described elsewhere in the text. Any one of these would provide an appropriate topic of research.

- *Wind energy*, caused indirectly by solar energy, can operate wind generators.
- *Hydraulic energy*, or the qravitational potential energy of water, can be converted into electrical energy.
- *Tidal energy* is available where the ocean tides are large.
- *Waves* on oceans have energy that can be converted into electrical energy.
- *Biomass energy* is the chemical energy stored in plants and animal wastes. It can be released by burning.
- *Geothermal energy* is thermal energy available within the earth.
- *Nuclear fusion* provides energy stored in the nuclei of atoms. Vast amounts of this energy may be available in the world's water supplies.

Pollution

Much of the energy we consume is wasted in the form of heat transferred to the atmosphere or bodies of water. This wasted heat is called *thermal pollution*. Other types of pollution that result from our use of energy include noise pollution, chemical pollution caused by the burning of fossil fuels, and radioactive wastes produced at nuclear generating stations.

Many of our pollution problems can be reduced if and when we learn to use alternative energy resources appropriate to the situation.

Energy conservation

Conserving energy (i.e., not wasting it) is an important goal of everyone in our society. Governments, industries, and individuals must cooperate to achieve this goal.

There are dozens of ways to conserve energy. Only a few will be described here.

- Governments provide incentives for people to improve home insulation.
- Industries are finding ways of improving the efficiency of devices that use energy.
- People are being urged to turn off lights and appliances when they are not in use.
- People are being reminded of the benefits of exercise rather than relying on machines to do all our work. For example, it is better to walk or cycle short distances than to take the car, and it is better to rake leaves in the fall than blow them with a noisy, energy consuming machine.

Conserving energy not only slows the pace at which we are using our natural resources; it also helps reduce the major problems of pollution.

PRACTICE

23. Which renewable energy resources would be appropriate in your region?
24. List ways that energy conservation can be improved:
    (a) in your home
    (b) in your school
    (c) in the transportation system in your community
25. The "wise use of energy" is an excellent subject for research and/or discussion. Choose a specific aspect of this subject (e.g., biomass energy) and research it. Then write a report, participate in a class discusssion, or make a video of your findings.

Words to Know

specific heat capacity   energy conservation
principle of heat transfer   non-renewable energy
changes of state   resource
latent heat of fusion   renewable energy
latent heat of vaporization   resource
heat pump   active solar heating
ablation   thermal pollution

Chapter Objectives

Having completed this chapter, you should now be able to:

1. Determine the energy provided by a heater of known power for a measured amount of time $(E = Pt)$.
2. Define specific heat capacity.
3. State and use the SI unit of specific heat capacity.
4. Calculate the specific heat capacity of a substance knowing the heat given to the substance as well as the mass and change of temperature $\left(c = \dfrac{E}{m\Delta T}\right)$.

5. Calculate the heat transferred to or from an object that experiences a temperature change $(E = mc\Delta T)$.
6. Determine the exchange of heat when hot and cold water are mixed together.
7. State the principle of heat transfer.
8. Apply the principle of heat transfer to determine the specific heat capacities of metals.
9. Name the possible changes of state of matter.
10. Define latent heat of fusion (L_F) and latent heat of vaporization (L_V), and describe how to find them for water $\left(L = \dfrac{E}{m}\right)$.
11. State and use the SI unit of latent heat.
12. Describe applications of the changes of state of matter.
13. Recognize the difference between non-renewable and renewable energy resources, and name examples of each.
14. Appreciate the need for energy conservation in our society.

Chapter Review

1. State the SI unit used to measure:
   (a) mass
   (b) heat
   (c) power
   (d) specific heat capacity
   (e) temperature change
   (f) time
   (g) latent heat of fusion
   (h) latent heat of vaporization

2. Explain why a hot water bottle can keep a bed warm for up to several hours. (Act. 13A, 13.2)
3. You are at a beach on a clear, hot day.
   (a) During the day, which becomes warm faster, the sand or the water?
   (b) Which cools down more rapidly at night?
   (c) Relate your answers in (a) and (b) to the specific heat capacities of water and sand (Refer to Table 13-1.) (13.2)

4. A 1200 W electric frying pan warms a liquid sauce for 4.0 min (240 s). How much heat is given to the sauce? (13.2)

5. A student performs an activity to find the specific heat capacity of liquid L using a 200 W immersion heater. The student heats 0.2 kg of the liquid from 25°C to 75°C. The heating takes 120 s.
   (a) Find the heat given by the immersion heater to liquid L.
   (b) Calculate the specific heat capacity of liquid L.
   (c) What might liquid L be? (13.2, Table 13-1)

6. Calculate the heat gained or released in each case. (Specific heat capacities are given in Table 13-1.)
   (a) 5.0 kg of ethyl alcohol are warmed from 15°C to 25°C
   (b) 3.0 kg of brass are cooled from 100°C to 60°C
   (c) 2.5 kg of glass are heated from 90°C to 110°C
   (d) 500 g of iron are cooled from 80°C to 0°C (13.3)

7. In an activity with "ideal" results, a sample of hot water is mixed with a sample of cold water. The hot water releases 2.0 × 10⁴ J of heat.
   (a) According to the principle of heat transfer, how much heat does the cold water gain?
   (b) What factors would prevent such ideal results in a science laboratory? (Act. 13B, 13.4)

8. 230 g of water at 15°C are used to cool 200 g of a substance having a starting temperature of 140°C. The temperature of the mixture is 35°C.
   (a) Determine the specific heat capacity of the unknown substance.
   (b) Use Table 13-1 to identify the substance. (13.4)

9. Describe in detail how you would determine the amount of heat needed to warm the water used to fill your bathtub at home. Use estimated values of mass and temperatures to perform the calculations. (13.3, 13.4)

10. Try this. Gently heat a small amount of salol (phenyl salicylate) on a glass slide. Watch closely as the liquid cools, forming a crystallized solid. Use the kinetic theory of matter to explain what you observe. (13.5)

11. Is it possible to add heat to a material without changing its temperature? Explain your answer. (13.5, 13.6)

12. Calculate the latent heat of fusion in each case:
    (a) 3.3 × 10⁴ J of heat will melt 0.1 kg of ice
    (b) 8.0 × 10⁴ J of heat are needed to melt 2.0 kg of a substance (13.6)

13. Calculate the latent heat of vaporization in each case:
    (a) 3.0 × 10⁶ J of heat boil away 1.5 kg of a liquid
    (b) 2.3 × 10⁵ J of heat boil away 100 g of water (13.6)

14. Determine the amount of heat needed to change:
    (a) 2.0 kg of solid iron into liquid at the melting point
    (b) 3.0 kg of liquid silver into a vapour at the boiling point (13.6, Table 13-4)

15. Calculate the heat that must be released from 10 kg of water at 0°C to allow it to change to 10 kg of ice at 0°C. (13.6, Table 13-4)

16. Use the kinetic theory of matter to explain why sweating helps cool the human body. (13.7)

17. Describe why evaporation and condensation are important in the operation of a refrigerator. (13.7)

18. Describe ways that North Americans can use radiant energy from the sun both directly and indirectly to provide useful energy. (13.8)

Waves, Sound, and Music

Everyone is familiar with the waves created when a pebble is dropped into water. A wave is a travelling disturbance which carries energy from place to place. The dropped pebble disturbs the water and starts the wave, which travels outward in a ripple effect. There are many different kinds of waves. Familiar terms are microwaves, radio waves, light waves, and sound waves. A sound wave is a particular kind of wave created by a vibrating object and transmitted through some material, such as air. This unit is about different kinds of vibrations and waves, noise, and the characteristics of musical sounds.

If you are considering a career in radio, television, or music (as a musician or a sound technician), the information in this unit will be useful to you.

• One of the employment opportunities open to an electronics technologist is as an audio-system designer. The television and radio broadcasting industries have ongoing needs for top quality audio systems. The design, maintenance, and operation of such systems are also necessary in theatres and concert halls for dance and musical productions. An understanding of waves, sound, and music is essential for a career in these fields.

- An instrument used to test people's hearing is called a audiometer. An audiometric technician is a person who performs hearing tests in clinics, private industry, and government inspections. Laws in each province are being introduced to limit the level of noise to which a worker may be exposed. As more is understood about hearing damage, audiometric technicians are increasingly in demand. Detailed knowledge of waves and sound is necessary to become an audiometric technician.

Knowing the information in this unit will be especially useful if you plan a career in any of the areas already mentioned, as well as the following: the recording industry, dance, medical technology, acoustics, audio-visual technology, or environmental noise pollution. Look into any career possibility mentioned: interview someone working in that area, contact your local community college, university, guidance office, or ask at a counselling centre for more information on training for the career of your choice.

CHAPTER 14

Vibrations and Waves

A trapeze artist vibrates back and forth before letting go of the swing and flying through the air. The wings of birds and insects vibrate. A guitar string vibrates, producing sound. These are examples of vibrations that can be seen. Often, vibrations set up waves that travel through a material or space. Visible waves are easily studied using ropes, coils, and water waves. What you learn about vibrations and waves in this chapter will help you understand vibrations that cause sound, and waves that transfer it.

Main Ideas

- There are three main types of vibrations.
- Vibrations cause waves, which in turn transfer energy.
- Regular vibrations have a period and frequency that can be measured.
- The speed of a travelling wave can be calculated.
- Pulses and waves can interfere with each other.
- Waves can bend when they meet an obstacle.
- Resonance is a natural vibration that results in a large vibration.

14.1 Vibrations

A **vibration** is a back-and-forth motion. The main types of vibration are shown in Figure 14-1.

A **transverse vibration** occurs when the object vibrates at right angles to its line of rest (e.g., a child swinging on a swing).

A **longitudinal vibration** occurs when the object vibrates parallel to its line of rest (e.g., a coil spring supporting a car).

A **torsional vibration** occurs when the object twists around its line of rest (e.g., a string supporting an object can be twisted and the object will vibrate around and back).

To study transverse vibrations we will use a pendulum. (If you have performed Activity 1B, you are familiar with the pendulum.) Consider Figure 14-2. Diagram (a) illustrates the mass and line of rest of a pendulum as well as two quantities, length and amplitude, which may be measured. The **length** of a pendulum is the distance from its top to the middle of the mass. The **amplitude** (A) is the largest distance (in one direction) the mass moves from its rest position. Diagram (b) shows that a **cycle** is a complete vibration of the pendulum.

Figure 14-2   The pendulum

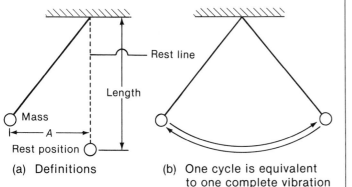

(a) Definitions

(b) One cycle is equivalent to one complete vibration

Figure 14-1   Types of vibration

(a) Transverse vibration

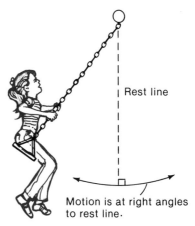

Rest line

Motion is at right angles to rest line.

(b) Longitudinal vibration

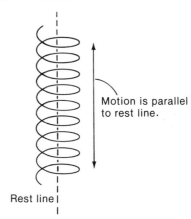

Motion is parallel to rest line.

Rest line

(c) Torsional vibration

Rest line

Motion twists around rest line.

Sample Problem 1

A child is swinging on a swing. The amplitude of vibration is constant at 1.0 m. Through what total horizontal distance does the child move in:
(a) each cycle?   (b) 3 cycles?

Solution
(a) The child moves 4.0 m in each cycle.
(b) In three cycles the child moves
    3×4.0 m $= 12.0$ m.

Figure 14-4 Torsional vibrations occur on this type of clock, called an anniversary clock.

To study longitudinal vibrations we will consider a mass hung on the end of a spring, as shown in Figure 14-3. Diagram (a) shows the spring and mass at rest. In diagram (b) the mass has been lifted up. The amplitude (*A*) is the greatest distance from the rest position. Then the mass is released and drops to its lowest position in diagram (c). The cycle is complete when the mass returns to its top position, as in diagram (d).

Torsional vibrations can be viewed on the type of clock shown in Figure 14-4. The central shaft rotates first in one direction, then in the opposite direction. This motion is repeated in uniform periods of time.

Figure 14-3 The spring

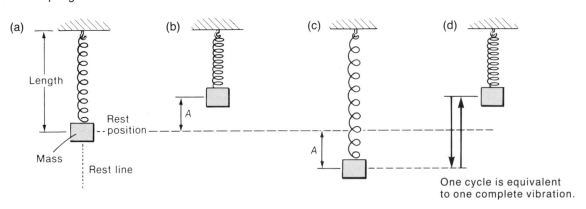

One cycle is equivalent to one complete vibration.

PRACTICE

1. State the type of vibration in each case.
   (a) A diving board vibrates momentarily after a diver jumps off.
   (b) A woodpecker's beak pecks a tree trunk.
   (c) The shock absorbers on a motorcycle vibrate as the bike travels over a rough road.

2. For the pendulum shown in the diagram, state the:
   (a) type of vibration   (b) amplitude

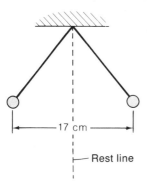

Rest line

3. The diagrams show a mass at rest on a spring and then vibrating. State the:
   (a) type of vibration   (b) amplitude

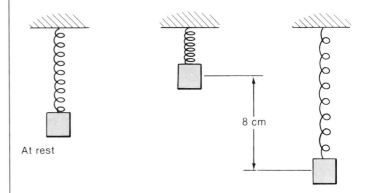

At rest

8 cm

4. The amplitude of a certain pendulum is 10 cm. How far horizontally does the mass move in five cycles?

5. The amplitude of vibration of a mass on a spring is 3.0 cm. How far vertically does the mass move in two cycles?

14.2   Producing Pulses and Waves

Imagine you are holding one end of a rope and the other end is caught around a tree stump. Rather than walking over to the tree stump to untie the rope, you flick your wrist, producing a pulse (⌒‾ or ‿⌄), which is a disturbance that travels along the rope. If you're lucky, the rope will become free of the stump.

If you make a complete vibration by swinging the rope back and forth with your wrist, a double-sided pulse, or a wave (⌒‿), will be created. Thus, a

wave is a disturbance caused by a vibration. The vibration caused by the rope is a transverse one, so the wave is also transverse. Transverse waves can also be produced on a spring coil, as Figure 14-5(a) and (b) show.

A longitudinal wave can be produced by a longitudinal vibration. Longitudinal waves cannot be produced on a rope, but they can be produced on a spring coil, as illustrated in Figure 14-5(c).

Some of the properties of pulses will be explored in the activity that follows. The properties of waves are similar to the properties of pulses.

Figure 14-5   Waves on a rope and spring coil

(a) Transverse wave on a rope

(b) Transverse wave on a coiled spring

(c) Longitudinal wave on a coiled spring

Activity 14A Pulses Travelling Along a Coiled Spring

PROBLEM ■ What are the properties of pulses that travel along a coiled spring?

APPARATUS ■ coiled spring (such as a Slinky toy); piece of masking tape; piece of paper; stopwatch; metre stick

 CAUTION Do not overstretch the springs and do not let go of a stretched spring.

Note: The distances indicated in the instructions are meant for short springs. If long ones are used, double all distances.

PROCEDURE ■

1. Attach the masking tape to a coil near the middle of the spring. Stretch the spring along a smooth surface (the floor) to a length of 2.0 m. With one end of the spring held rigidly, use a rapid sideways jerk to create a transverse pulse at the other end. See Figure 14-6(a). Describe the motion of the particles of the spring. (Hint: Watch the tape attached to the spring.)
2. With the same set-up as in #1, use a rapid forward push to create a longitudinal pulse along the spring. Refer to Figure 14-6(b). Again describe the motion of the particles of the spring.
3. Stand a folded piece of paper on the floor close to the middle of the spring, as shown in Figure 14-6(c). Use energy transferred by a transverse pulse to knock the paper over. Describe where the energy came from and how it got to the paper.

Figure 14-6 For Activity 14A

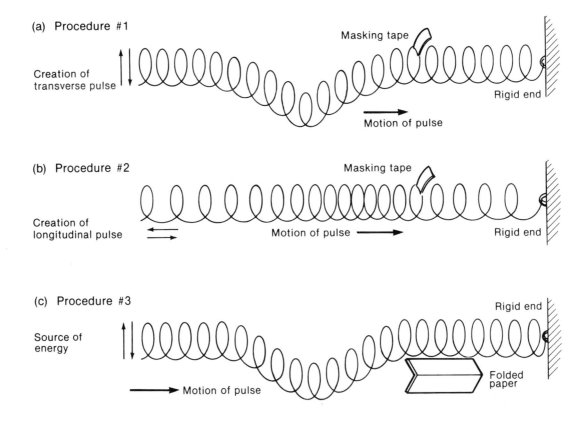

(a) Procedure #1

Creation of transverse pulse

Masking tape

Rigid end

Motion of pulse

(b) Procedure #2

Creation of longitudinal pulse

Masking tape

Motion of pulse

Rigid end

(c) Procedure #3

Source of energy

Rigid end

Motion of pulse

Folded paper

4. Stretch the spring to a length of 1.0 m. Measure the time for a transverse pulse to travel from one end of the spring to the other *and back again*. Repeat the measurement several times for accuracy while trying to keep the amplitude constant. Calculate the speed of the transverse pulse along the spring $\left(v = \dfrac{d}{t}\right)$.

5. Determine whether the speed of the pulse in #4 depends on the size of the pulse.
6. Predict what will happen to the speed of the pulse when the spring is stretched more. Check your prediction by using a stretch of 2.0 m, then 3.0 m.
7. If different types of springs are available, find the speed of a transverse pulse along them.

ANALYSIS ■
1. Based on the observations in this activity, discuss whether the following statements are true or false.
   (a) The function of a pulse or wave is to transfer energy from one place to another.
   (b) Energy may move from one end of a spring to the other.
   (c) The particles of a spring move from one end of a spring to the other with the energy.
2. Choose which factors listed below affect the speed of a pulse in a material.
   (a) type of material
   (b) condition of the material (e.g., stretching a spring changes its condition)
   (c) size of the pulse
3. Summarize the properties of pulses or waves travelling along a coiled spring by answering these questions.
   (a) For a *transverse* pulse or wave, how does the motion of the particles compare to the motion of the wave?
   (b) Repeat (a) for a *longitudinal* pulse or wave.
   (c) What is the function of a pulse or wave?
   (d) What does the speed of a pulse or wave depend on?

14.3 Frequency and Period

A vibrating object has a frequency and period. The **frequency** (f) is the number of cycles that occur in a specific amount of time.

$$f = \frac{\text{number of cycles}}{\text{total time}}$$

In the SI, frequency is measured in cycles per second or hertz (Hz).

The **period** (T) is the amount of the time required for one cycle of vibration.

$$T = \frac{\text{total time}}{\text{number of cycles}}$$

The SI unit of period is seconds per cycle, or simply seconds.

Since frequency is measured in cycles per second and period in seconds per cycle, they are reciprocals of each other.

$$T = \frac{1}{f} \quad \text{and} \quad f = \frac{1}{T}$$

(Sample problems and practice questions involving frequency and period are found in Section 1.2. Before doing the practice questions here, it would be wise to look back at that section.)

PRACTICE

6. A trapeze artist completes 8.0 vibrations in 20 s. Determine the frequency and period of the vibration.
7. A baby's heart beats with a frequency of 2.4 Hz. What is the period of the heartbeat?
8. An electric drill rotates with a period of 0.040 s. Determine the frequency of rotation of the drill.

14.4 Periodic Waves

Periodic waves are created by a source of energy vibrating at constant frequency. As you have learned, the function of a wave is to transfer energy from one place to another.

Figure 14-7 indicates the important parts of a transverse wave. Figure 14-8 shows the corresponding parts of a longitudinal wave. A transverse wave consists of a **crest** above the rest line and a **trough** below the rest line. A longitudinal wave consists of a **compression** where the particles are close together and a **rarefaction** where the particles are spread apart or rarefied. The **amplitude** (*A*) is the largest distance (in one direction) from the rest line or rest position. The **wavelength** (λ) is the length of one wave. (The symbol λ is taken from the Greek alphabet. It is spelled lambda.) As shown in the diagrams, there are several ways of measuring wavelength.

Figure 14-7 Transverse waves

(a) Crest and trough of a single wave

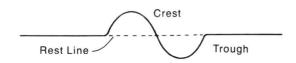

(b) Amplitude (*A*)

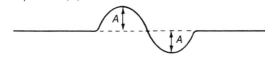

(c) A series of waves showing examples of wavelength (λ)

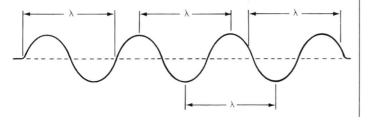

Figure 14-8 Longitudinal waves

(a) Compression and rarefaction

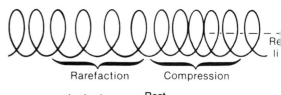

Rarefaction   Compression

(b) Amplitude (*A*)

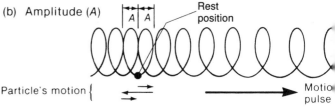

Particle's motion

(c) A series of waves showing examples of wavelength (λ)

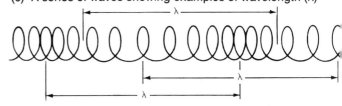

Sample Problem 2

Draw a set of two transverse waves such that *A* = 1.0 cm and λ = 2.0 cm.

Solution

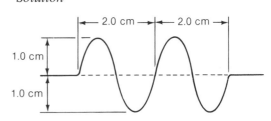

Periodic waves are caused by vibrations. A vibrating source of waves has a frequency and a period, as you learned in Section 14.3. If the frequency of the vibration increases, the wavelength decreases. This can be demonstrated using a rope, a coiled spring, or a wave machine.

PRACTICE

9. Measure the amplitude and wavelength of the periodic transverse waves in Figure 14-7(c).
10. Measure the wavelength of the periodic longitudinal waves in Figure 14-8(c).
11. Draw a set of two transverse waves such that $A = 0.5$ cm and $\lambda = 4.0$ cm.
12. What happens to the wavelength of a periodic wave if the frequency decreases?

14.5 The Universal Wave Equation

You learned in Activity 14A that the speed of a pulse or wave depends on the material and the condition of the material. For a pulse on a spring, the speed can be found using $v = \dfrac{d}{t}$. For a periodic wave, however, another equation should be derived.

Consider diagram (a) in Figure 14-9. It shows a set of train cars travelling to the right. If each car is 20 m long and takes 4.0 s to pass point X, then the train's speed is

$$v = \frac{d}{t}$$
$$= \frac{20\,\text{m}}{4.0\,\text{s}}$$
$$= 5.0\,\text{m/s}$$

Figure 14-9 Comparing train cars and waves

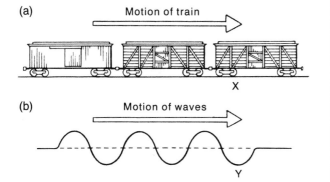

(a) Motion of train

X

(b) Motion of waves

Y

Now compare the train cars to the periodic wave in diagram (b). If each 20 m wave was created in a period of 4.0 s, then the speed of the periodic wave past point Y is the ratio of the wavelength to the period.

$$v = \frac{d}{t}$$
$$= \frac{\lambda}{T} \quad (\text{because } d = \lambda \text{ and } t = T)$$
$$= \frac{20\,\text{m}}{4.0\,\text{s}}$$
$$= 5.0\,\text{m/s}$$

This equation for speed $\left(v = \dfrac{\lambda}{T}\right)$ may also be written $v = \left(\dfrac{1}{T}\right)\lambda$. Since $f = \dfrac{1}{T}$, we can now write an equation for speed in terms of frequency and wavelength.

$$v = f\lambda$$

This last equation is called the **universal wave equation**. It is used to find the speed of all periodic waves whose frequency and wavelength are known. Units involving the universal wave equation are shown in the example that follows.

Sample Problem 3

Find the speed of a wave in water if $f = 4.0$ Hz and $\lambda = 2.5$ m.

Solution
$$v = f\lambda$$
$$= 4.0\,\text{Hz} \times 2.5\,\text{m}$$
$$= 4.0\,\frac{\text{cycles}}{\text{s}} \times 2.5\,\frac{\text{m}}{\text{cycle}}$$
$$(\text{see note below})$$
$$= 10.0\,\text{m/s}$$

Note: If frequency is stated in cycles per second and wavelength in metres per cycle, you can see how the cycles divide, leaving metres per second, the correct unit of speed.

Sample Problem 4

A periodic source of waves creates a wave of $\lambda = 3.2$ cm every 0.5 s. Calculate the:
(a) frequency of the waves
(b) speed of the waves

Solution

(a) $f = \dfrac{1}{T}$

$\quad = \dfrac{1}{0.5\,\text{s}}$

$\quad = 2.0\,\text{Hz}$

(b) $v = f\lambda$

$\quad = 2.0\,\text{Hz} \times 3.2\,\text{cm}$

$\quad = 6.4\,\text{cm/s}$

PRACTICE

13. Calculate the speed in each situation:
    (a) $f = 12$ Hz, $\lambda = 2.5$ m
    (b) $f = 60$ Hz, $\lambda = 0.05$ m
    (c) $f = 200$ Hz, $\lambda = 0.4$ m
14. Calculate the speed if:
    (a) $T = 3.0$ s, $\lambda = 12$ m
    (b) $T = 0.4$ s, $\lambda = 8.0$ m
    (c) $T = 0.02$ s, $\lambda = 1.6$ m
15. Rearrange the equation $v = f\lambda$ to solve for:
    (a) frequency
    (b) wavelength
16. Calculate the unknown quantity in each case:
    (a) $v = 300$ m/s, $\lambda = 0.50$ m, $f = $? Hz
    (b) $v = 20$ m/s, $f = 400$ Hz, $\lambda = $? m
17. A 3.5 m sound wave is moving with a speed of 350 m/s. Calculate the:
    (a) frequency of the sound
    (b) period of vibration of the source of the sound
18. A wave machine creates water waves in a tank with a frequency of 7.5 Hz. If the waves are travelling at a speed of 45 cm/s, calculate the wavelength of the waves.

Activity 14B   Pulses Meeting Pulses

PROBLEM ■   What happens when pulses travelling in opposite directions meet each other?

APPARATUS ■   coiled spring (such as a Slinky toy)
Note: This activity can be demonstrated using a specially designed wave machine.

   CAUTION   Do not overstretch the coil.

PROCEDURE ■
1. With a student at each end of the coil, stretch the coil an appropriate amount. Call one side of the coil the trough side, and the other the crest side. One student should send a crest at the same instant the other student sends an equal-sized trough. Observe what occurs before, during, and after the pulses meet. You may have to try this more than once before recording your observations.
2. Repeat #1, this time using two crests.
3. Repeat, this time using two troughs.

ANALYSIS ■
1. What happens to the amplitude of a disturbance when:
   (a) a crest meets a trough?
   (b) a crest meets a crest?
   (c) a trough meets a trough?
2. When two pulses meet, under what conditions can the amplitude of a disturbance increase?
3. Under what condition(s) can the amplitude decrease?

14.6   Interference of Pulses

If a pulse moving in one direction meets a pulse moving in the opposite direction, the pulses interfere with each other. This interference lasts for only an instant. After the interference is over, the pulses travel in their original directions. The interference of transverse pulses can be observed using a spring or wave machine. Interference also occurs for longitudinal pulses but is not as easily observed.

Two types of interference can occur. **Destructive interference** occurs when a crest meets a trough. If the crest and trough are equal in size, they destroy each other for an instant, then continue in their original directions. The point where total destruction occurs is called a **nodal point** or **node**. Figure 14-10(a) illustrates destructive interference for transverse pulses. A node is produced with longitudinal pulses where a compression meets a rarefaction of equal size.

Constructive interference occurs when pulses build each other up to a larger size. This can occur if a crest meets a crest causing a **supercrest**, or a trough meets a trough causing a **supertrough**. Figure 14-10(b) shows a supercrest resulting when two transverse crests meet. Constructive interference can also occur for longitudinal pulses.

PRACTICE

19. State whether the interference is constructive or destructive:
    (a) a crest meets a trough
    (b) a supertrough is formed
    (c) a compression meets a compression
    (d) a node is produced
20. Draw a series of diagrams, similar to those in Figure 14-10(b), showing the creation of a supertrough when two transverse pulses meet. Draw each trough 2.0 cm wide with an amplitude of 1.0 cm.

Figure 14-10 Interference of transverse pulses

(a) Destructive interference

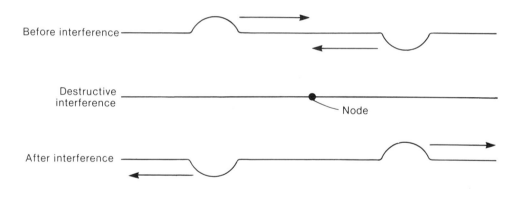

(b) Constructive interference

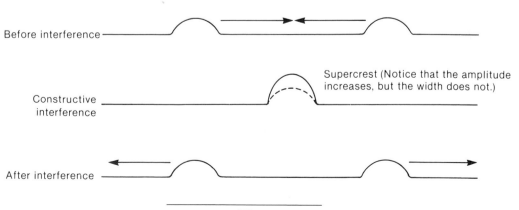

14.7　Viewing Waves on Water

Viewing pulses on coiled springs is a good way to start the topic of waves. However, a spring has only one dimension, length. A surface of water has two dimensions, length and width, so investigating water waves is the next step. This will help in the study of sound waves travelling in three-dimensional air. (Air spaces have length, width, and depth.)

Figure 14-11　The ripple tank

(a) Ripple tank set-up

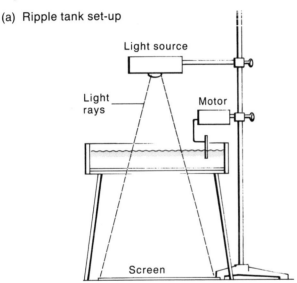

(b) Light travelling through waves

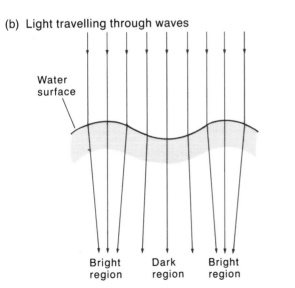

A **ripple tank**, shown in Figure 14-11(a), is a device used in science laboratories to study waves in water. It is a raised, shallow tank with a glass bottom. For most experiments the tank is level and contains water to a depth of about 10 mm.

A light source is used to allow the transverse water waves to be easily seen. The light source, held by a stand above the water, sends light through the water to a screen below the tank. The crest of each wave acts like a magnifying glass, focussing the light to a bright region. The trough of each wave spreads the light out, making a dark region. The bright and dark regions appear on the screen.

In a ripple tank, periodic straight waves are produced by a wave generator connected to a straight bar. See Figure 14-11(b) and (c).

One use of a ripple tank is to observe what happens when waves meet a barrier. When this happens, a process called diffraction is observed. **Diffraction** is the bending effect of a wave as it passes through an opening or by a barrier. You will observe the diffraction of water waves in the next activity.

(c) Straight waves

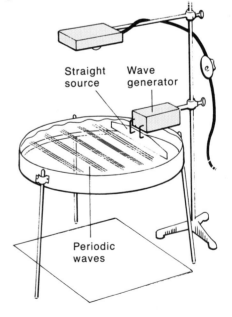

Activity 14C The Diffraction of Water Waves

PROBLEM ■ How does the diffraction of waves depend on their wavelength?

APPARATUS ■ ripple tank and related apparatus; ripple-tank motor; support stands and clamps; wax barriers; pencil or dowel

CAUTION *Keep all electric leads, plugs, and outlets away from any water. Do not touch electric equipment with wet hands.*

PROCEDURE ■
1. Place water in the ripple tank to a depth of about 10 mm. Make sure the tank is level.
2. Set up the motor to provide a source of straight waves. Place a straight wax barrier about 3 cm in front of the source, as illustrated in Figure 14-12(a). Operate the motor at a fairly high frequency to produce waves of short wavelength. Observe the diffraction pattern around the edge of the barrier. Draw the pattern.

Figure 14-12 Barrier arrangements for Activity 14C

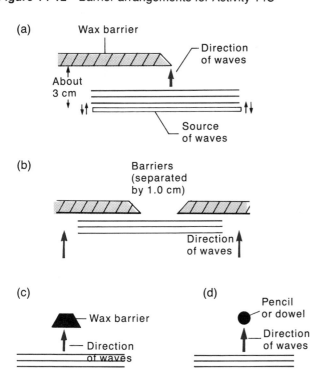

3. Gradually reduce the frequency used in #2 and describe the effect on the pattern. Draw a diagram of the diffraction at long wavelength (low frequency).
4. Predict the shape of the diffraction pattern when waves of short and long wavelength meet the various barriers placed as shown in Figure 14-12(b), (c), and (d). Check your predictions experimentally, and draw a diagram of each pattern.
5. Empty the tank and dry it completely.

ANALYSIS ■
1. Which type of waves, short wavelength or long wavelength, appear to diffract more when they meet an opening or a barrier?
2. How does the diffraction of waves depend on their wavelength?

APPLICATION ■ Which type of sound waves, high frequency or low frequency, do you predict will diffract better around corners? Explain your answer.

14.8 Mechanical Resonance

Any object that vibrates will do so with its largest amplitude if it is vibrating at its own natural frequency. The natural or **resonant frequency** is the frequency at which a vibration occurs most easily. A small force repeated at this resonant frequency will cause a large amplitude of vibration. When the vibration is mechanical the natural vibration is called **mechanical resonance**. If you understand the examples of mechanical resonance that follow, you should be able to understand resonance of sound waves discussed in the next two chapters.

A pendulum of a certain length has its own resonant frequency (Section 14.3). A playground swing, which acts like a long pendulum, also has its own resonant frequency. If you are pushing someone on a swing, the amplitude of vibration can be built up by pushing at the correct instant in each cycle. In other words, your pushing frequency equals the resonant frequency of the swing.

If a car is stuck in snow, it can be rocked back and forth at the resonant frequency of the system. This motion builds up the amplitude, helping the car get out of the snow.

Another example of resonant frequency was discovered by military leaders in previous centuries. If the soldiers in an army marched across a small bridge in unison, the amplitude of vibration of the bridge built up. If the frequency of the soldiers' steps was the resonant frequency of the bridge, the vibration could possibly break the bridge. To prevent this, the soldiers were told to "break step" as they crossed bridges.

Figure 14-13 The Tacoma Narrows Bridge

(a) The centre span of the bridge is shown vibrating torsionally before collapse.

DID YOU KNOW?

The human body also has resonant frequencies. Experiments have shown that the entire body has a mechanical resonant frequency of about 6 Hz, the head of between 13 Hz and 20 Hz, and the eyes of between 35 Hz and 75 Hz. Large amplitude vibrations at any of these frequencies could irritate or even damage parts of the body. In occupations such as transportation and road construction, efforts are made to reduce the effects of mechanical vibrations on the human body.

A spectacular example of mechanical resonance was the disaster that caused the collapse of a bridge in the state of Washington, U.S.A., in 1940. A bridge called the Tacoma Narrows Bridge was suspended by huge cables across a valley. On a windy day soon after its opening, the bridge began vibrating at its resonant frequency. At first the bridge vibrated as a transverse wave. Then one of the suspension cables came loose and the entire 850 m centre span of the bridge vibrated torsionally. The vibrations were so great that the bridge collapsed. Refer to Figure 14-13.

(b) The vibrations caused the bridge to collapse.

DID YOU KNOW?

If you were working in a restaurant and had to carry a flattish bowl of soup you would find it difficult to do, without spilling. The reason is that the resonant frequency of the soup slopping back and forth is close to the frequency of walking. This causes a large amplitude of the soup wave.

PRACTICE

21. Describe two examples of mechanical resonance other than those given in this section.

(c) This is a view of the rebuilt bridge. What structural changes have been made to the new bridge?

Activity 14D A Demonstration of Resonance

Class demonstration: Set up the apparatus shown in Figure 14-14. Place the support stands about 50 cm apart. Connect the stands with a tight string. Suspend two pendulums of equal length (about 30 cm) and equal mass (50 g). Set one pendulum swinging at right angles to the horizontal string. Watch carefully for several minutes. Explain in detail what you observe.

Repeat the activity, using two pendulums of equal mass and different lengths.

Figure 14-14 Set-up for Activity 14D

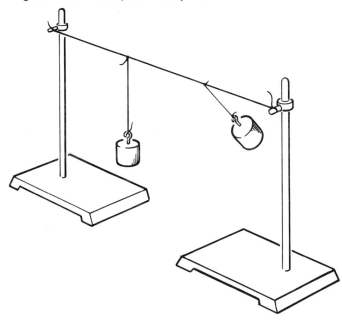

14.9 Standing Waves—A Special Case of Both Interference and Resonance

If periodic transverse waves travel in opposite directions on a spring, rope, or wave machine, a standing-wave pattern can be set up. The pattern has supercrests, supertroughs, and nodes. The nodes stay standing in the same position, so the formation is called a **standing-wave pattern**. (Standing waves produce the sound in wind instruments, as you will learn in Chapter 16.)

A standing-wave pattern is an example of both interference and resonance. To understand why, set up such a pattern yourself. Tie one end of a long rope to a rigid support. Send periodic waves toward the rigid end. Those waves will reflect back and *interfere* with the ones you are sending. This interference causes nodes and antinodes. An **antinode** is a position of largest amplitude. It is actually a combination of a supercrest and supertrough.

Try to create patterns having the shapes shown in Figure 14-15. As you are creating the patterns, notice that there is only one frequency that produces each shape. That frequency is the **resonant frequency** of the system. Try producing patterns with three, four, or more nodes between the ends.

Assume that in Figure 14-15 the distance from the rigid end to the source of vibrations is 3.0 m. The standing wave in diagram (b) is one wavelength long, so its wavelength is 3.0 m.

Figure 14-15 Standing waves

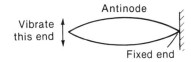

(a) Low frequency; long wavelength; zero nodes between the ends

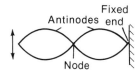

(b) Medium frequency; shorter wavelength; one node between the ends

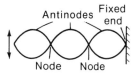

(c) Higher frequency; still shorter wavelength; two nodes between the ends

Sample Problem 5

What are the wavelengths of the standing waves in diagrams (a) and (c) of Figure 14-15?

Solution

(a) The standing wave is half a wavelength:

$$\frac{1}{2}\lambda = 3.0 \text{ m}$$

$$\lambda = 6.0 \text{ m}$$

(c) The standing wave is $1\frac{1}{2}$ wavelengths:

$$\frac{3}{2}\lambda = 3.0 \text{ m}$$

$$\lambda = 2.0 \text{ m}$$

From these examples, we can conclude that the distance from one node to the next in a standing-wave pattern is $\frac{1}{2}\lambda$. Check this fact in Figure 14-15. We can also conclude that for a given length of rope only certain wavelengths and frequencies create standing waves. These ideas will be discussed further in the study of sound waves.

PRACTICE

22. What is the wavelength of the standing waves shown in the diagram?

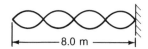

━━━ 8.0 m ━━━

23. In a certain standing-wave pattern, the distance from one node to the next is 2.0 m. What is the wavelength of the standing waves?

Words to Know

vibration	amplitude of a wave
transverse vibration	wavelength
longitudinal vibration	universal wave equation
torsional vibration	destructive interference
amplitude of vibration	node (or nodal point)
cycle of vibration	constructive interference
wave	supercrest
frequency	supertrough
period	diffraction
crest	resonant frequency
trough	standing-wave pattern
compression	antinode
rarefaction	

Chapter Objectives

Having completed this chapter, you should now be able to:

1. Define transverse, longitudinal, and torsional vibrations.
2. Define cycle and amplitude of a vibration.
3. State the function of a wave.
4. State factors that affect the speed of a wave.
5. Define period and frequency and understand how they are related.
6. Given one of period or frequency, calculate the other.
7. Describe these parts of a transverse wave: rest line, crest, trough, wavelength, and amplitude.
8. Describe these parts of a longitudinal wave: rest position, compression, rarefaction, wavelength, and amplitude.

9. Use the universal wave equation ($v = f\lambda$) to find the speed of a wave, knowing its frequency and wavelength.

10. Describe how constructive interference and destructive interference occur.

11. Define diffraction of waves, and describe how diffraction depends on the wavelength of the waves.

12. State what is meant by mechanical resonance.

13. Describe examples of mechanical resonance.

14. Draw the shape of a standing-wave pattern, and from the shape find the wavelength of the waves.

Chapter Review

1. State whether the vibration indicated is transverse or longitudinal:
   (a) a tree sways in the wind
   (b) a sewing-machine needle moves up and down
   (c) a child bounces on a pogo stick   (14.1)

2. A pendulum mass moves 16 cm in one cycle. What is the amplitude of vibration?   (14.1)

3. Name the type of wave that results when the particles of an object vibrate:
   (a) parallel to the rest line
   (b) at right angles to the rest line   (14.2)

4. What is the main function of a wave?   (Act. 14A, 14.4)

5. Name two factors that affect the speed of a wave in a material.   (Act. 14A, 14.5)

6. Calculate the period of each of these motions:
   (a) a child, while skipping, jumps off the ground 80 times in 120 s
   (b) a pulse beats 25 times in 15 s
   (c) a man shovels at a rate of 15 shovelsful per minute   (14.3)

7. Calculate the frequency of the following:
   (a) an automatic gun fires 10 bullets at a target every 0.5 s
   (b) a tuning fork vibrates 21 times in 0.1 s
   (c) a recording timer creates 3600 dots in one minute   (14.3)

8. How are frequency and period related to each other?   (14.3)

9. Calculate the period if the frequency is:
   (a) 5.0 Hz   (b) 500 Hz   (14.3)

10. Calculate the frequency if the period is:
    (a) 10 s   (b) 0.25 s   (14.3)

11. Measure the amplitude and wavelength of the waves shown in the diagram.   (14.4)

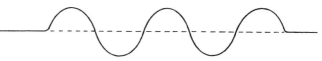

12. What is the universal wave equation?   (14.5)

13. A source of sound sends 500 Hz sound waves through water. The wavelength of the waves is 3.0 m. What is the speed of the sound in the water?   (14.5)

14. The wavelength of a certain sound is 0.3 m. If the speed through a certain material is 240 m/s, calculate the frequency of the sound waves.   (14.5)

15. What is the wavelength of a sound that travels at a speed of 340 m/s if its frequency is 510 Hz?   (14.5)

16. Under what conditions can a node occur during the interference of:
    (a) transverse pulses?   (b) longitudinal pulses?
    (14.6)

17. What happens to the frequency of a periodic wave if the wavelength decreases?   (14.4, Act. 14C)

18. Straight water waves of low frequency are sent toward an opening between two barriers.
    (a) What happens to the waves as they pass through the opening?
    (b) Describe what occurs as the frequency is gradually increased.   (Act. 14C)

19. Describe in your own words the meaning of mechanical resonance.   (14.8)

20. A 6.0 m rope is used to create standing waves. Draw a diagram of the shape of the standing wave when it has a wavelength of:
    (a) 12.0 m   (b) 6.0 m   (c) 3.0 m   (14.9)

CHAPTER 15

Sound Energy and Hearing

Aircraft that travel faster than the speed of sound, like the one shown, could cause windows and eardrums to shatter if they were too near. How fast does an aircraft have to travel to go faster than sound? How does sound reach our ears through air? How do our ears function? These questions and many others will be explored in this chapter.

Main Ideas

- Sound is a form of energy that is produced by vibrations and is transmitted by waves.
- The speed of sound in air can be measured experimentally.
- The speed of sound is not constant. It is different in different materials or at different temperatures.
- Sound waves can interfere with each other.
- The human ear is a sensitive and important instrument, well worth taking care of.
- Sounds with frequencies that we cannot hear often have useful applications.
- Frequencies of sounds appear to change when the source of sound or the listener are in motion.

15.1 The Production of Sound Energy

Sounds we hear are described in many ways. Leaves rustle, lions roar, babies cry, birds chirp, corks pop — the list is long. The energy that creates those sounds comes from vibrating objects.

Some vibrations that make sound can be seen. If you pluck a guitar string or strike a low-frequency tuning fork, vibrations are observed. If you watch the low-frequency woofer of a loudspeaker system, you can see it vibrating.

Some vibrations that create sound cannot be seen. When you speak, for example, parts of your throat vibrate. When you make a sound by blowing into an empty pop bottle, the air molecules in the bottle vibrate.

All sound energy is produced by vibrations, both visible and invisible. Definitions and ideas related to vibrations were studied in Chapter 14.

PRACTICE

1. State what vibrates to produce the sound from a:
   (a) banjo   (b) drum   (c) coach's whistle

15.2 The Transmission of Sound Energy

In an electric bell, sound is created by a vibrating metal arm striking a metal sounder. Such a bell is shown in a jar in Figure 15-1. The jar is connected to a vacuum pump. As the pump sucks the air out of the jar, sound from the bell becomes more difficult to hear. If all the air is taken out, no sound can be heard, even though the metal arm may be seen to vibrate. Thus, sound energy needs a material to travel through. It cannot travel in a vacuum.

Air is the most common material that transmits sound energy to our ears. Sound energy travels through air by means of longitudinal waves. (Remember in the

Figure 15-1   Bell in a vacuum

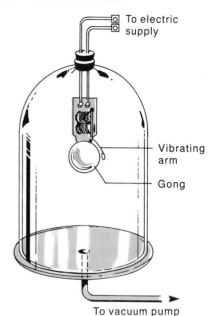

coiled-spring experiment, Activity 14A, that the energy from your hand was transmitted by wave action along the spring.) Longitudinal waves have compressions where the molecules are close together and rarefactions where the molecules are spread apart. (See Section 14.4.)

Although air molecules are invisible, the effect of their motion can be seen. Figure 15-2 shows a way of demonstrating compressions and rarefactions of air. A piece of cardboard, in line with a set of lit candles, is waved back and forth. Compressions force the flames away from the cardboard and rarefactions force the flames toward the cardboard.

Figure 15-2   Illustrating compressions and rarefactions of air molecules

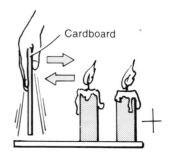

In a physics laboratory a common source of sound energy is a tuning fork, illustrated in Figure 15-3. A tuning fork has two prongs. When one prong is struck from the side with a rubber hammer, both prongs move together, as shown in diagram (a). This causes a compression of air molecules between the prongs, as shown in diagram (b). At the same instant there are rarefactions outside the prongs.

At the next instant, as shown in diagram (c), the prongs are spreading apart. This causes a rarefaction between the prongs and compressions outside them. The air molecules vibrate back and forth at the same frequency as the tuning fork. They transfer the sound energy from the source to the listener by colliding with each other as shown in diagram (d).

Diagram (e) shows how longitudinal sound waves can be represented by transverse waves. Transverse waves are often used in diagrams because they are easier to draw than longitudinal waves.

The transmission of sound in air is fast. But you know from experience that sound does not travel as fast as light. For example, during a thunder storm, lightning is noticed first. Several seconds later, thunder is heard. A similar phenomenon occurs at track meets when the timer of a 100 m sprint stands at the finish line and watches for a puff of smoke from the starter's pistol. Shortly after the smoke is seen, the sound of the gun is heard. The light travels very fast (3.0×10^8 m/s), but the sound travels slowly enough to have its speed measured experimentally, as described in the next activity.

Figure 15-3 The tuning fork and longitudinal waves

(a) Side view of a tuning fork

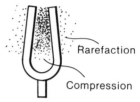

(b) Prongs coming together

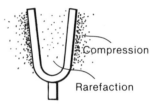

(c) Prongs spreading apart

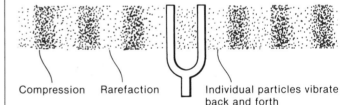

(d) Longitudinal waves coming from a tuning fork

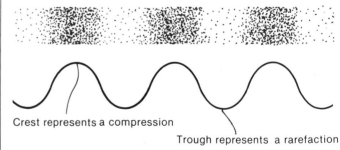

(e) Longitudinal waves represented by transverse waves

PRACTICE

2. Describe what happens to air molecules during:
   (a) compression   (b) rarefaction
3. Why is sound unable to travel in a vacuum?
4. Measure the approximate wavelength of the longitudinal waves shown in Figure 15-3(d).
5. Describe at least one example (other than those given in this section) of proof that sound travels more slowly than light.

Activity 15A Measuring the Speed of Sound in Air

PROBLEM ■ What difficulties are involved in measuring the speed of sound in air?

APPARATUS ■ tape measure; 2 blocks of wood; stopwatches; thermometer; sound-reflecting wall; ear protection

PROCEDURE ■
1. Choose a location outdoors a large distance (at least 150 m) away from a flat wall of a building. Measure the distance.
2. Measure and record the air temperature. This value will be used in Section 15.3.
3. Have one student create a loud sound by banging the two wooden blocks together. Find the total time it takes the sound to travel to the wall and back to the source.

 CAUTION *When producing the sound, make sure that you are not near your own, or anyone else's, unprotected ears.*

4. Repeat #3 several times to find an average value.

ANALYSIS ■
1. Calculate the speed of sound in air using the equation $v = \frac{d}{t}$, where d is the total distance the sound travels and t is the time for the round trip.
2. List possible sources of error in this activity.

APPLICATIONS ■
1. A pistol is used to start a 500 m race along a straight track. A puff of smoke is seen and 1.5 s later the sound is heard at the finish line. What is the speed of the sound?
2. Assume that during a storm, thunder was heard 8.0 s after lightning was seen. If the speed of sound in air was 350 m/s, what was the distance from the lightning to the observer? (Hint: Rearrange the equation $v = \frac{d}{t}$ to solve for distance.)

15.3 Temperature and the Speed of Sound in Air

The speed of sound in air is 332 m/s at 0°C. If the air temperature increases, the speed increases because the air molecules move more rapidly. (The speed of sound in air depends on other factors that will not be mentioned here.)

For every degree Celsius rise in temperature, the speed of sound in air increases by 0.6 m/s. Thus, at 1°C, the speed of sound is 332 m/s + 0.6 m/s = 332.6 m/s. In general, the speed of sound in air can be found using the equation:

$$v = 332 \text{ m/s} + (0.6\,T) \text{ m/s}$$ where T is the air temperature in °C

Sample Problem 1

Calculate the speed of sound in air when the temperature is 16°C.

Solution
$$\begin{aligned} v &= 332 \text{ m/s} + (0.6\,T) \text{ m/s} \\ &= 332 \text{ m/s} + (0.6 \times 16) \text{ m/s} \\ &= 332 \text{ m/s} + 9.6 \text{ m/s} \\ &= 341.6 \text{ m/s} \quad \text{or} \quad 342 \text{ m/s} \end{aligned}$$

If the temperature drops below 0°C, the speed of sound in air is less than 332 m/s.

PRACTICE

6. Calculate the speed of sound in air when the temperature is:
   (a) 3°C   (b) 20°C   (c) −2°C
7. (a) Plot a graph to show how the speed of sound in air depends on the temperature from −10°C to +30°C. (Since speed is the dependent variable, it should be placed on the vertical axis.)
   (b) Find the slope of the line on the graph. Relate the answer to the equation for the speed of sound in air.

8. In Activity 15A you recorded the outside air temperature. Use that temperature to calculate the speed of sound in the air. Compare this value with the one found in the activity.

15.4 The Speed of Sound in Various Materials

Children at play sometimes discover that sound travels very easily along a metal fence. Swimmers notice that they can hear a distant motor boat better with their ears under the water than in the air. In both cases, sound is travelling in a material other than air.

Sound travels most rapidly in certain solids. It travels less rapidly in many liquids, and quite slowly in most gases.

Table 15-1 lists the speed of sound in various materials. Scientists use these values to study the structure of the earth, search for oil and minerals, and locate objects beneath the surface of the sea. (This will be discussed further in Section 15.8.)

Table 15-1 The Speed of Sound in Common Materials

State	Material	Speed (m/s)
Gas	Carbon dioxide	258 (at 0°C)
(at atmospheric	Oxygen	317 (at 0°C)
pressure)	Air	332 (at 0°C)
	Helium	927 (at 20°C)
Liquid	Alcohol	1240
	Sea water	1470 (varies)
	Fresh water	1500
Solid	Pine wood	3300
	Maple wood	4100
	Steel	5000
	Aluminum	5100

PRACTICE

9. Try this. Hold a ticking stopwatch about 1 m from your ear. Listen. Then touch a metre stick to one ear and have your partner hold the ticking stopwatch to the other end. Describe what happens and why.

10. A 21-gun salute is about to be given by a navy ship anchored 3000 m from shore. A swimmer near shore sees a puff of smoke from the gun, quickly pops her head under water, and listens. In 2.0 s she hears the sound of the gun and then lifts her head above the water. In another 6.6 s (total time, 8.6 s) she hears the sound that has come through the air from the same shot. Find the speed of the sound in the:
(a) water   (b) air

Activity 15B   Careful Listening

PROBLEM ■ Does everyone hear the same thing when listening to the same sounds or combinations of sounds?

APPARATUS ■ unmounted tuning fork; two identical tuning forks mounted on resonance boxes; rubber hammer or stopper; two strong elastic bands

PROCEDURE ■

1. Strike a tuning fork with a rubber hammer or on a rubber stopper. Hold the fork vertically near your ear and *slowly* rotate it. Listen carefully for loud and soft sounds. Have your partner help you locate the positions of the loud and soft sounds. Repeat until you are certain of your results.

 CAUTION Do not touch your ear with the vibrating tuning fork. The edges could cause abrasions.

2. Compare your results in #1 with the results of other groups. If the results are different, repeat the procedure until everyone is in agreement.

3. Place two mounted tuning forks close to and facing each other. Wrap an elastic band tightly around a prong of one of them (Figure 15-4). Use a rubber hammer to sound the two forks. Describe the resulting sound.

4. Repeat #3 using two elastic bands on the same prong. Compare the sound to what you heard in #3.

5. One of the tuning forks in #4 has a lower frequency than the other. Decide which by listening to their sounds. Does everyone agree on the choice?

6. Remove the elastic bands from the prong and sound the forks together again. Describe what you hear.

Figure 15-4 Mounted tuning forks

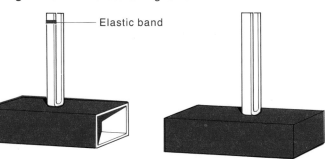

Elastic band

ANALYSIS ■

1. Figure 15-5 shows the top view of a tuning fork with eight positions labelled. When the fork is vibrating, state the positions at which you hear (a) loud sounds (b) soft sounds.

Figure 15-5 Top view of a tuning fork

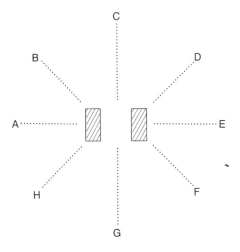

2. Do you think that the frequency of a tuning fork increases or decreases when elastic bands are wrapped around a prong? Explain your answer.
3. Does everyone hear the same thing when listening to the same sounds or combinations of sounds?

APPLICATION ■ Suggest a way to determine if a person is tone deaf, and thus would be unwise to choose a career in music.

15.5 Interference of Sound Waves —Beats

If sound is transmitted by waves, it should display the same interference effects noticed for other waves (Section 14.6). Under normal conditions, most people do not notice sound interference. However, under certain circumstances, sound interference is easy to hear.

We will examine two ways of producing sound interference, both of which you heard in Activity 15B.

Consider first the sound from a single tuning fork. Recall from Section 15.2 that longitudinal waves spread out from the prongs of a tuning fork. A view of these waves travelling outward from the prongs is shown in Figure 15-6. The waves travel outward not only from the sides of the prongs, but also from between the prongs. The sounds in these four directions are loud. Now notice that wherever there is a compression from the sides of the prongs there is a rarefaction from between the prongs. At each of the four corners of the set of prongs a compression always meets a rarefaction. This results in destructive interference. Thus, a soft sound is heard at the four corners.

Figure 15-6 Top view of a tuning fork, showing longitudinal sound waves spreading out from the prongs

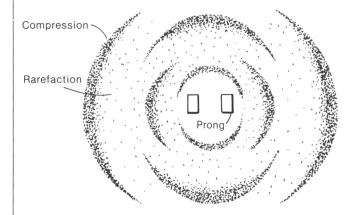

Next consider what occurs when two sounds of nearly the same frequency are heard together. In this case, both constructive and destructive interference occur, resulting in loud and soft sounds. The pattern of

loud and soft sounds that is produced when two sounds have nearly the same frequency is called the production of **beats**. This is what you heard in Activity 15B when two tuning forks of different frequencies were sounded together.

Beat frequency is the number of beats heard per second. It is found by subtracting the lower frequency from the higher frequency. For example, if a 256 Hz tuning fork is heard with a 250 Hz note from an electronic frequency generator, the beat frequency is 256 Hz − 250 Hz = 6 Hz.

Sample Problem 2

Two 384 Hz tuning forks are sounded together and no beats are heard. Then a metal clip is attached to a prong of one fork and again the forks are sounded together. This time a beat frequency of 4 Hz is heard. What is the new frequency of the fork with the clip?

Solution   The frequency of the fork must be either 4 Hz higher or 4 Hz lower than 384 Hz. Adding extra mass to a tuning fork makes it more difficult for the prongs to vibrate, so the frequency must be 4 Hz lower. Thus, it is 380 Hz.

An application of beats is the tuning of a musical instrument such as a piano. A note on the piano is sounded with the corresponding tuning fork. The tension in the piano strings can be adjusted until no beats are heard.

PRACTICE

11. Explain how Activity 15B helps to prove that sound energy travels by means of waves. (Hint: What property of waves was discussed in Section 14.6?)
12. State the beat frequency when the following pairs of frequencies are heard together:
    (a) 202 Hz, 200 Hz   (b) 341 Hz, 347 Hz
    (c) 1003 Hz, 998 Hz

13. A 512 Hz tuning fork is sounded with a second tuning fork and a beat frequency of 7 Hz is heard. State two possible frequencies of the second tuning fork.

15.6   Resonance in Sound

No doubt you have heard the high-pitched squeal produced when a person runs a moist finger around the lip of a long-stemmed glass. The frequency of such a sound is the natural frequency for the glass. That natural frequency is called **resonant frequency**, as you learned in Section 14.8. The resonant frequency of a long-stemmed glass can be changed by adding water to the glass. Also, if a nearby sound with the same frequency as the resonant frequency is loud enough, the glass may shatter (Figure 15-7).

Figure 15-7   The energy of amplified sound waves having the resonant frequency of this wine glass causes the glass to shatter.

Sound resonance, like mechanical resonance, occurs when a small force is repeated at the resonant frequency of the vibrating object. This can be demonstrated using two tuning forks having the same resonant frequency. Obtain two 256 Hz tuning forks. Strike one and hold it close to the other, as shown in Figure 15-8. After about 15 s, stop the first fork from vibrating and listen to the second one. It is vibrating because it has picked up the vibration from the first fork, which has the same resonant frequency. The small force of the air molecules is repeated at the resonant frequency. If the forks are of different resonant frequencies, the transfer of energy does not occur. The demonstration is more effective if mounted tuning forks of equal frequency are used.

Figure 15-8 Demonstrating resonance in sound

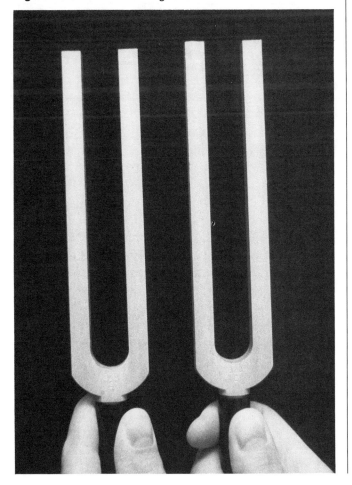

Transfer of energy at resonant frequencies can also be shown if a piano is available. Suppress the right (sustaining) pedal to free all the strings in the piano. Sing a certain note loudly into the piano. Listen for the sound of the strings that vibrate in resonance with your voice.

Resonance of sound in musical instruments will be studied in more detail in Chapter 16.

PRACTICE

14. (a) What happens to the resonant frequency of an object when its length increases?
    (b) On what facts do you base your answer to (a)?

15.7 Hearing and the Human Ear

Hearing is an important sense that we often take for granted. Understanding what and how we hear helps us appreciate and care for this precious sense.

Our ears are very important and sensitive organs. They react to a wide range of frequencies. With the proper equipment your teacher can check the frequency response for everyone in the class. A frequency generator is connected to a loudspeaker. The frequencies of sound may range from quite low to more than 25 000 Hz (25 kHz), depending on the speaker.

All the frequencies you can hear make up your **audible range**. Most students have an audible range of about 25 Hz to 20 000 Hz. The ear is most sensitive to frequencies between 1000 and 3000 Hz.

Often older people are unable to hear high frequencies. Young people who expose their ears to loud sounds for long periods of time also may reduce their audible range.

The human ear is complex, but a short description of it will help you understand how we hear. The human ear consists of three parts—the outer ear, middle ear, and inner ear. Refer to Figure 15-9(a) (overleaf).

Figure 15-9 The human ear

(a) The three main parts of the human ear

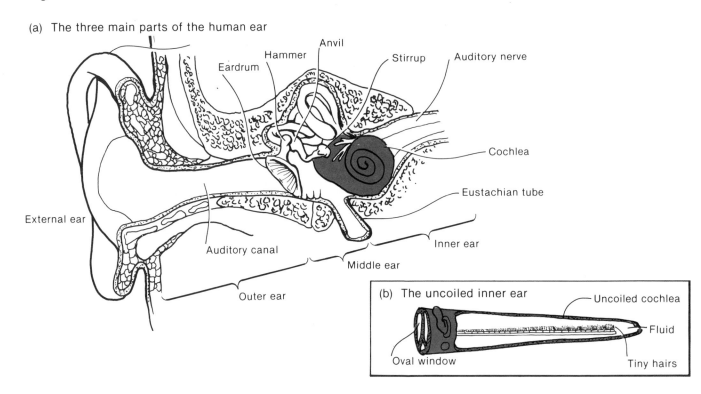

The **outer ear** consists of the **external ear** that we can see, and the **auditory canal**. The external ear funnels the sound waves into the auditory canal. The auditory canal directs the longitudinal sound waves to the **eardrum**. The eardrum, which is about the thickness of a hair, connects the outer ear to the middle ear.

The **middle ear** consists of three tiny bones called the hammer, anvil, and stirrup. The vibrating eardrum transfers its energy to these tiny bones. The bones act like a system of levers to transfer energy to the **oval window**. The oval window joins the middle ear to the inner ear.

The **eustachian tube** joins the middle ear to the throat. It allows air pressure to become equal on both sides of the eardrum. Your ears "pop" when the air pressure equalizes whenever you are ascending or descending in elevators or aircraft.

The **inner ear** consists of a coiled tube called the **cochlea** and the **auditory nerve**. The cochlea is filled with fluid and has thousands of tiny hairs of varying lengths. See Figure 15-9(b). Vibrations from the oval window force special hairs to vibrate. Different lengths of hair have different resonant frequencies. The vibrating hairs change energy of vibrations into electrical energy. The electrical energy is transferred through the auditory nerve to the brain. The brain then records what you have heard.

DID YOU KNOW?

The stirrup is the smallest bone in the human body. It is only 3.6 mm long.

DID YOU KNOW?

Some popular entertainers have hearing that is damaged due to prolonged exposure to loud music. They are trying to persuade music lovers to protect their hearing by reducing the loudness of the sounds they listen to.

It is estimated that about one person in 20 in North America is either deaf or hard of hearing. Deafness may be caused if signals cannot travel through the auditory nerve to the brain. There is no cure for such deafness.

Deafness may also be caused by damage to the eardrum or the middle ear. This problem may be solved by an operation or by the use of a hearing aid. A hearing aid transmits energy through the skull to the inner ear. The inner ear then acts in the normal manner. Yet another type of deafness is caused by an impaired cochlea. This problem may be overcome in the future by using a tiny electronic device placed in the cochlea.

PRACTICE

15. The tiny hairs in the cochlea have different lengths. Which lengths (short or long) vibrate at high frequencies? Explain why you think so.

15.8 Infrasonics, Ultrasonics, and Echo Finding

The average human audible range is from about 25 Hz to 20 000 Hz. Frequencies lower than 25 Hz are called **infrasonic**. (Infra means lower than.) If we could hear frequencies lower than 25 Hz, we would often be bothered by sounds in and around us. For example, some sounds inside the body have a frequency of about 10 Hz. You can imagine how annoying it would be to hear the sounds of muscles every time they were activated.

Frequencies higher than 20 000 Hz are called **ultrasonic**. (Ultra means higher than.) A dog whistle creates sound that is ultrasonic. Dogs' ears are sensitive to frequencies higher than we can hear. Dogs are not the only animals that hear ultrasonic sounds. Several others are listed in Table 15-2.

Table 15-2 Audible Ranges

Animal	Audible Range (Hz)
Human	25 to 20 000
Dog	15 to 50 000
Cat	60 to 65 000
Bat	1000 to 120 000
Porpoise	150 to 150 000
Robin	250 to 210 000

Some animals, such as some types of bat, navigate and hunt using ultrasonics. The bat sends out high-frequency sounds that reflect off objects. The reflected sounds return to the bat and allow it to tell what is in the way. This explains why the bat can navigate in darkness as well as in light.

Equipment is available that uses reflection of ultrasonic sounds in water. A process called echo finding is used to determine the depth of water below a ship, or to locate a school of fish. Ultrasonic sounds are sent from the ship, as shown in Figure 15-10. They reflect off the object and return to the ship. An instrument measures the time for the signal to return. Then the equation $v = \frac{d}{t}$ can be used to find either the speed of the sound or the distance it travelled.

Figure 15-10 Echo finding using ultrasonics

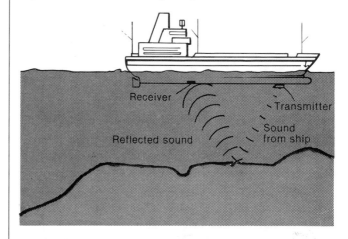

Sample Problem 3

A ship is anchored where the depth of water is 120 m. A sound signal is sent to the bottom of the lake and returns in 0.16 s. What is the speed of the sound in water?

Solution   The distance travelled by the sound is 240 m.

$$v = \frac{d}{t}$$

$$= \frac{240\,\text{m}}{0.16\,\text{s}}$$

$$= 1500\,\text{m/s}$$

Ultrasonic sounds have several other applications. They can help find flaws in metal products. They are used in burglar alarms as well as to clean electronic parts of watches and surgical instruments. In medicine they are used to analyse body organs such as the brain and kidneys (Figure 15-11). They are also used to study the growth of unborn babies. Ultrasonic sounds are much less dangerous than high-energy X rays for these medical applications.

Figure 15-11   Ultrasonic sound is used to analyse body organs. One mode of viewing the results of the analysis is to display the scan on a monitor, as shown. In this case, the scan of a kidney is being traced with a light pen which will yield useful information.

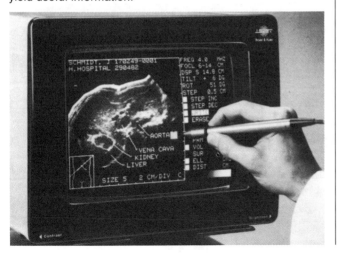

PRACTICE

16. Ultrasonic sound is sent to the ocean floor 360 m below a submarine. The sound reflects back to the submarine in 0.5 s. Find the speed of the sound in water.
17. The speed of sound in a fresh-water lake is 1500 m/s. Ultrasonic sound is sent from the surface of the water to the bottom of the lake. It returns in 0.2 s. How deep is the lake? (Hint: $d = vt$)

15.9   The Doppler Effect and Supersonic Speeds

An observer is standing by the side of a race track as a racing car approaches. The noise of the engine appears to become higher in frequency. Suddenly the car passes by the observer, and the frequency appears to drop noticeably. The apparent changing frequency of sound due to an object's motion is called the **Doppler effect**. It is named after Christian Doppler (1803-1853) from Austria. He was the first to analyse this phenomenon. Likely you have heard the Doppler effect from train whistles, car horns, or sirens on emergency vehicles.

To understand why the Doppler effect occurs, study Figure 15-12. The first diagram shows circles that represent sound waves travelling outward from a source that is standing still. The second diagram shows the source of sound travelling to your left. As the sound waves approach observer A, they are closer together than they would be if the source were not moving. Thus, observer A hears a sound of higher frequency. Observer B, however, hears a sound of longer wavelength because the source is travelling away. This produces a lower-frequency sound. Similar situations occur when the source of sound is standing still and the observer is moving toward or away from the source.

The Doppler effect has various applications. Medical technicians use the effect at ultrasonic frequencies to determine the rate of blood flow of a patient. They

Figure 15-12 The Doppler effect

(a) The source is stationary. Both observers, A and B, hear the same frequency of sound.

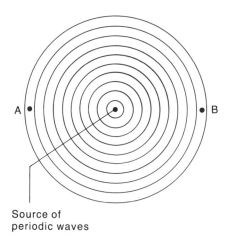

Source of
periodic waves

(b) The source is moving to the left. Observer A hears a higher frequency and Observer B hears a lower frequency than the observers in (a).

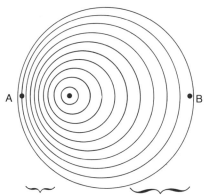

Shorter wavelength;   Longer wavelength;
higher frequency   lower frequency

also use the effect to view the heartbeat of unborn babies. Police take advantage of the Doppler effect when they reflect radar waves off a vehicle to determine its speed (Figure 15-13).

Figure 15-13 The Doppler effect is applied in the use of radar to determine the speed of vehicles on a highway. The radar system in a moving police cruiser can determine the speed of a car ahead or behind, travelling in the same direction or the opposite direction.

(a) Same direction

Police cruiser

(b) Opposite direction

Police cruiser

The effect shown in Figure 15-12(b) applies if the source is travelling at less than the speed of sound. However, some aircraft can reach **supersonic speeds**, which are speeds faster than the speed of sound. As an aircraft approaches the speed of sound, the sound waves it produces pile up, creating a region of high air pressure called the **sound barrier**. To go faster than the speed of sound, extra thrust is needed until the aircraft "breaks through" the sound barrier. Only specially constructed aircraft can withstand the vibrations caused in breaking through the sound barrier.

When an object travels at supersonic speeds, it produces what is known as a **shock wave**. The source of sound actually overtakes its own waves, causing the compressions to overlap one another. The overlapping waves form a shock wave "cone" that spreads outward from the source (Figure 15-14). If a shock wave from a supersonic aircraft reaches the ground before its energy is weakened, it produces a **sonic boom**. This boom sounds like thunder and can do much damage to ears and buildings. To prevent injury-causing sonic booms, supersonic aircraft are required to travel at very high altitudes. (The photograph at the beginning of the chapter shows a supersonic aircraft.)

Figure 15-14 A shock wave

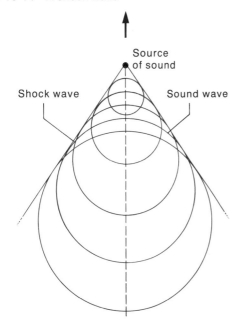

PRACTICE

18. State whether the apparent frequency is higher or lower in each case.
    (a) The listener is standing still and the source is approaching.
    (b) The listener is standing still and the source is moving away.
    (c) The source is standing still and the listener is approaching.
    (d) The source is standing still and the listener is moving away.
19. Discuss the advantages and disadvantages of supersonic air travel:
    (a) near large cities
    (b) over rural areas
    (c) over the oceans

Words to Know

beats	echo finding
beat frequency	Doppler effect
sound resonance	supersonic speeds
audible range	sound barrier
infrasonic	shock wave
ultrasonic	sonic boom

Chapter Objectives

Having completed this chapter, you should now be able to:

1. State what produces sound energy.
2. Describe how sound energy is transmitted from one place to another.
3. Determine the speed of sound in air experimentally.
4. Given the temperature of air, find the speed of sound in air [$v = 332$ m/s $+ (0.6\ T)$ m/s].
5. List factors that affect the speed of sound in various materials.
6. Describe what is heard when listening to the interference of sound waves.
7. Calculate the beat frequency when sounds of two different frequencies are heard together.
8. Describe how beats can be used to tune musical instruments.
9. Describe examples of resonance in sound.
10. Explain how a human ear transmits sound to the brain.
11. Define audible range and recognize its average value for human hearing.
12. Define infrasonic and ultrasonic frequencies.
13. Describe applications of ultrasonic frequencies.
14. Describe the Doppler effect and explain how it is caused.
15. Recognize applications of the Doppler effect.
16. Know the meaning of supersonic speed.
17. Describe how a shock wave and sonic boom are produced.

Chapter Review

1. State what produces sound energy. (15.1)
2. What vibrates to produce the sound from:
   (a) an acoustic guitar?
   (b) an electric doorbell?
   (c) a stereo system? (15.1)
3. Describe how sound energy is transferred from one place to another. (15.2)
4. There is no air on the moon. Discuss how astronauts on the moon can hear each other speak.
5. At a certain instant a tuning fork is creating compressions outside the prongs. What is being created between the prongs? (15.2)
6. At a baseball game a physics student with a stopwatch sits behind the centre-field fence marked 136 m. He starts the watch when he sees the bat connect with the ball. He stops the watch when he hears the resulting sound. The time is 0.4 s. How fast is the sound energy travelling? (Act. 15A)
7. At a speed of 345 m/s in air, how far can sound travel in 6.0 s? (Act. 15A)
8. State the speed of sound in air when the temperature is: (a) 25°C (b) 8°C (c) −10°C (15.3)

9. Explain why sound energy travels faster in warm air than in cold air. (Hint: Consider the motion of the individual air molecules.) (15.3)
10. State in which type of substance (solid, liquid, or gas) sound seems to travel:
    (a) fastest (b) slowest (15.4, Table 15-1)
11. Sound in a certain substance travels 3750 m in 2.5 s.
    (a) What is the speed of the sound in the substance?
    (b) According to Table 15-1, what is the substance? (15.4)
12. How far can sound travel in steel in 1.5 s? (15.4)
13. Describe the sound heard when beats are produced. (15.5)
14. Find the beat frequency when the following pairs of frequencies are sounded together:
    (a) 256 Hz, 261 Hz (b) 512 Hz, 508 Hz (15.5)
15. What are the possible beat frequencies when these tuning forks are available: 256 Hz, 259 Hz, 251 Hz? (15.5)
16. Explain how the production of beats could be used to tune a guitar string. (15.5)

17. Describe two examples of resonance in sound. (15.6)
18. State the meaning of:
    (a) human audible range
    (b) ultrasonic
    (c) infrasonic (15.7, 15.8)
19. State your own audible range. (15.7)
20. Describe how a bat uses sound energy to find its way around. (15.8)
21. Reflecting sound is used to find the speed of sound in water. A signal is sent from a ship to the floor of the ocean 420 m below the ship. The reflected signal is received 0.6 s later. What is the speed of the sound in the water? (15.8)
22. Ultrasonic sound is used to locate a school of fish. The speed of sound in the ocean is 1450 m/s and the reflection of sound reaches the ship 0.1 s after it is sent. How far is the school of fish from the ship? (15.8)

23. What is the Doppler effect? What causes it? (15.9)
24. What is meant by supersonic speeds? (15.9)
25. How is a shock wave caused? (15.9)
26. Estimate how fast the end of a whip would have to travel to produce a sonic boom in your classroom. Show your reasoning. (15.3, 15.9)
27. Choose one or more of the topics of study listed below. Research the topic and report on your findings.
    (a) the human ear (e.g., deafness, causes of hearing loss, hearing aids, careers related to human hearing)
    (b) uses of ultrasonic sound (ultrasound) (e.g., medical imaging, industrial uses)
    (c) sonar
    (d) radar
    (e) supersonic air travel

CHAPTER 16

Music, Musical Instruments, and Acoustics

Rooms that reflect a lot of sound would be poor to use to record music. However, specially designed rooms, such as the recording studio shown here, ensure that the recorded sound is as high in quality as possible. To appreciate the design of such rooms and auditoriums used for music, we will first study the characteristics of musical sounds and musical instruments. This study is based on the concepts of vibrations, waves, and sound presented in the previous two chapters.

Main Ideas

- Musical sounds have various characteristics that can be analysed scientifically.
- The human ear is sensitive to a huge range of loudnesses.
- Much can be learned by watching the waveform of a sound while listening to that sound.
- The frequency of a note produced by a musical instrument depends on factors that can be measured.
- Each family of musical instruments produces sound in a different way.
- The design of a room affects the sounds in it.

16.1   Noise and Music

Noise is sound that is unpleasant or annoying. **Music** is sound that is pleasant and harmonious.

The difference between noise and music depends somewhat on the judgment of the individual. However, there is also a scientific difference.

In order to study noise and music, we use our ears as well as an instrument called an oscilloscope, which is illustrated in Figure 16-1. Longitudinal sound waves in air can be changed to electrical signals which are changed to traces of waves on the oscilloscope screen. If you listen to a sound as you watch its wave, you will learn how the pleasantness of a sound corresponds to the shape of the wave.

Figure 16-1   Using an oscilloscope to "see" sound

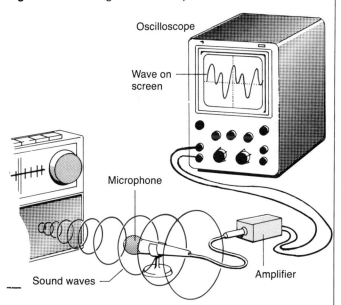

Figure 16-2 illustrates the possible shapes of waves that appear on an oscilloscope screen when various sounds are heard. Diagram (b) shows that the shape of noise waves is not smooth or regular.

Figure 16-2   Shapes of sounds on an oscilloscope screen

(a) Pure sound from a tuning fork

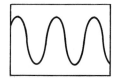

(b) Random noise

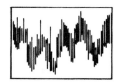

(c) "oooooo" sound of a high falsetto

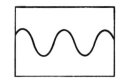

(d) "eeeee" sound

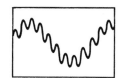

(e) "awwww" sound

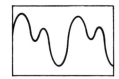

The next three sections discuss in detail the three main characteristics of musical sounds — pitch, loudness, and quality. Oscilloscope displays of the waves of sound from musical instruments will help you distinguish noise from music scientifically.

16.2 Pitch and Musical Scales

If you are near a pond on a summer evening, you might hear crickets chirping and bullfrogs croaking. The sounds are easy to distinguish. Sound from crickets has a high pitch, and sound from bullfrogs has a low pitch.

A pitch wheel, shown in Figure 16-3, is a device that shows how pitch depends on the frequency of vibration. It consists of a set of three or four equal-sized wheels. Each wheel has a different number of teeth. As the wheels spin, a piece of paper is held up to each wheel in turn. The paper vibrates with the lowest frequency when it touches the wheel with the least teeth. This creates the sound of lowest pitch. The other wheels create sounds of higher pitch. Thus, *pitch increases as frequency increases*.

Figure 16-3   The pitch wheel

As the pitch of a sound changes, the sound wave also changes. This can be illustrated using an audio frequency generator connected to an oscilloscope. Resulting waves are shown in Figure 16-4. It is clear that *as the pitch increases the wavelength decreases*.

Figure 16-4   Oscilloscope displays of pitch and wavelength

(a) Low frequency, low pitch, long wavelength

(b) High frequency, high pitch, short wavelength

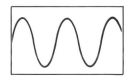

There are two main musical scales that we will study. One scale, which we will call the **scientific scale**, is used in science laboratories. Tuning-fork frequencies are often named using this scale. For example, 256 Hz is the note "middle C" and 512 Hz is "high C". Table 16-1 lists eight common frequencies on the scientific scale.

Table 16-1   Some Frequencies on the Scientific Scale

Note	C	D	E	F	G	A	B	C
Frequency (Hz)	256	288	320	341	384	427	480	512

In Table 16-1, notice that 512 Hz is exactly twice the frequency of 256 Hz. The two frequencies sound pleasant when heard together. They are exactly one **octave** apart. If one note is an octave above another, its frequency is twice as high as the first note. For instance, a frequency of 1024 Hz is one octave above 512 Hz.

The other musical scale, which we will call the **musicians' scale**, is based on a frequency of 440 Hz. That frequency is the note A above middle C on the piano. An octave below that A has a frequency of 220 Hz and an octave above has a frequency of 880 Hz. Figure 16-5 shows part of the piano scale, including the notes and their frequencies. This is the scale used to tune most musical instruments with fixed frequencies.

The standard frequency of A = 440 Hz is used in many countries throughout the world. To allow the public to check for that frequency, government agencies broadcast it by telephone and radio. For example, if you dial the telephone number 1-303-499-7111 (at your own expense!) you will be given the standard time in Greenwich, England, and a standard frequency broadcast at intervals of exactly 1.0 s.

Figure 16-5   The musicians' scale illustrated on a piano keyboard

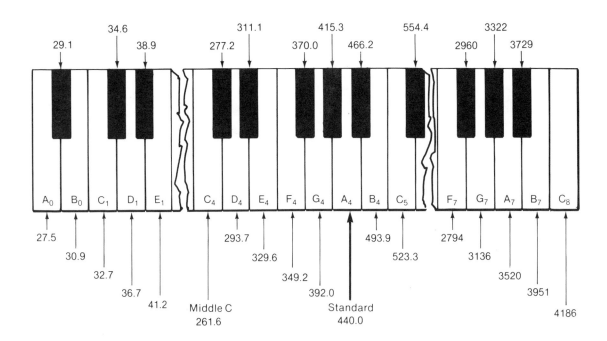

PRACTICE

1. On what does the pitch of a musical sound depend?
2. State the frequency of a note one octave above a note of:
   (a) 200 Hz   (b) 320 Hz   (c) 580 Hz
3. State the frequency of a note one octave below a note of:
   (a) 200 Hz   (b) 320 Hz   (c) 580 Hz
4. State the frequency of a note two octaves above a note of:
   (a) 300 Hz   (b) 1000 Hz   (c) 256 Hz

16.3 Loudness and Intensity Level of Sounds

Of course there is a difference in loudness between a soft whisper and the roar of nearby thunder. The loudness we hear depends on several factors. The most important factor is the intensity of the sound that reaches our ears.

The intensity of a sound is a measure of how much energy per second strikes a certain area. (Recall from Chapter 7 that energy per second—or energy per time—is power. Thus, intensity can also be stated as power/area, measured in watts per square metre, W/m^2.) However, there is a problem in expressing the intensity of some sounds because our ears are sensitive to a huge range of intensities. In fact, the loudest sounds we can tolerate have an intensity about a million million times greater than the softest sounds we can hear. The problem of using such large numbers to express the intensity of sound is overcome by defining another term called intensity level. **Intensity level** is the intensity of a sound measured in bels or decibels. The decibel, dB, is more common than the bel, B (1 dB = 0.1 B). These units are named in honour of Alexander Graham Bell (Figure 16-6) who invented the telephone. Bell was born in Scotland in 1847. He worked in Canada and the United States, and died in Nova Scotia in 1922.

To appreciate the convenience of using intensity level measured in decibels, refer to Table 16-2. The first column lists the intensities of sounds in watts per square metre. The second column lists the same sounds, this time using intensity level in decibels. The third column lists the number of times the intensity is greater than the intensity at 0 dB. The final column provides examples of sounds for each intensity level given.

The lowest intensity level that a healthy teenage ear can detect is about 4 dB. This is called the *threshold of hearing*. Very loud sounds, often experienced when listening to music, cause sensations of feeling in the ear. An intensity level of 120 dB is called the *threshold of feeling*. An even higher level of 130 dB is called the *threshold of pain*.

Figure 16-6 Alexander Graham Bell (1847-1922) is shown making the famous phone call inaugurating the line linking Chicago and New York City.

Table 16-2 Intensity Levels of Sounds

Intensity (W/m^2)	Intensity level (dB)	Ratio of intensity to the intensity at 0 dB	Example
10^{-12}	0	1	Formerly defined as the threshold of hearing
10^{-11}	10	10	Empty church on quiet street
10^{-10}	20	100	Average whisper, at 1 m
10^{-9}	30	1000	Library reading room
10^{-8}	40	10 000	Inside a car with engine on
10^{-7}	50	100 000	Quiet restaurant
10^{-6}	60	1000 000	Conversation, at 1 m
10^{-5}	70	10 000 000	Machinery in factory
10^{-4}	80	100 000 000	Noisy street corner
10^{-3}	90	1000 000 000	Loud hi-fi in average room
10^{-2}	100	10 000 000 000	Rock concert
10^{-1}	110	100 000 000 000	Jet taking off, at 60 m
10^{0}	120	1000 000 000 000	Threshold of feeling
10^{1}	130	10 000 000 000 000	Threshold of pain

DID YOU KNOW?

In some regions it is against the law to have a car's audio system so loud that it can be heard on the street outside the car.

Figure 16-7 Ground personnel working near airplanes must have ear protection.

Listening to loud sounds for long periods of time can cause hearing loss. We use the term **noise pollution** to describe the effect of excess noise in our modern society. Governments try to prevent noise pollution by setting standards of noise levels on streets and in places of work. Also, ear protection must be provided for people who work where the loudness is greater than about 80 dB (Figure 16-7). Much research is conducted to determine the effects of noise pollution. For example, in one experiment, chinchillas were blasted with loud sounds of certain frequencies for a long time. This caused hairs in the cochlea sensitive to those frequencies to become blunted and permanently damaged.

PRACTICE

5. On what main factor does the loudness of a sound depend?
6. State the number of times the first sound is higher in intensity than the second. (Use Table 16-2.)
   (a) 40 dB, 30 dB   (c) 100 dB, 70 dB
   (b) 80 dB, 60 dB   (d) 120 dB, 80 dB
7. A 50 dB sound is increased in intensity 1000 times. What is the new intensity level? (Refer to Table 16-2.)

16.4   Quality of Musical Sounds

Assume you hear the note middle C equally loudly from a piano, a violin, and a trumpet. The three sounds have equal pitch and equal loudness. However, they sound different. The difference is in their quality.

A beginning music student will create poor-quality sound on a musical instrument. An experienced player using the same instrument will create high-quality sound. A small portable radio produces sound of poor quality compared to sound from an expensive high-fidelity sound system. Thus, the quality of musical sounds can differ greatly.

The **quality** of a sound means how pleasant the sound is. Scientifically the quality depends on the shape of the sound waves. This can be demonstrated on an oscilloscope using sound waves from various musical instruments. Figure 16-8 shows sound waves of different quality. The pure tone in diagram (a) is a boring sound. The other diagrams show waves of higher quality.

Figure 16-8   Quality of sound displayed on an oscilloscope

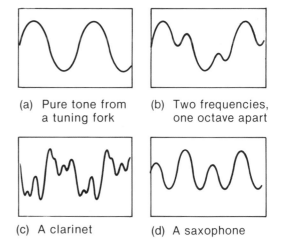

(a) Pure tone from a tuning fork

(b) Two frequencies, one octave apart

(c) A clarinet

(d) A saxophone

PRACTICE

8. On what does the quality of a musical sound depend?
9. Try this. If the equipment is available to your class, view the oscilloscope traces of various musical sounds as you listen to them. Draw diagrams of the wave traces you observe.

Activity 16A   The Pitch of Vibrating Strings

PROBLEM ■ How does the pitch of a vibrating string depend on its length, tension, and diameter?

APPARATUS ■ sonometer with 2 or more strings (see Figure 16-9); metre stick

Note: A guitar or other convenient stringed instrument could be used instead of a sonometer. If possible, measure the frequency of the string in each step.

Figure 16-9 A sonometer

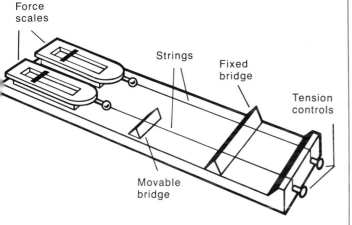

Force scales
Strings
Fixed bridge
Tension controls
Movable bridge

Figure 16-10

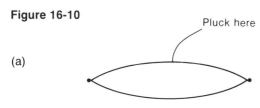

(a)   Pluck here

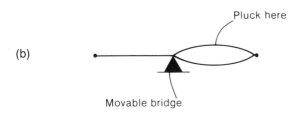

(b)   Pluck here
Movable bridge

(c)   Pluck here
Movable bridge

PROCEDURE ■

1. Adjust the tension in the thin wire to a convenient value, such as 30 N. Pluck the string as shown in Figure 16-10(a). Listen to the pitch produced.

  CAUTION   Do not adjust the tension too tightly or pluck the string violently. If the string were to break, the recoil could be dangerous.

2. Place the movable bridge midway between the ends of the string. Pluck the string as shown in Figure 16-10(b). Compare the pitch of this shorter string to the pitch heard in #1.

3. Place the bridge at a position one quarter of the way along the wire as shown in Figure 16-10(c). Again pluck the string and compare the pitch to that in #1 and #2.

4. Using the full length of the string and the tension used in the previous steps, pluck the string and listen. Now increase the tension, listen to the sound, and compare the two pitches. Use other tensions and compare the sounds.

5. Set all the strings on the sonometer to equal lengths and tensions. Compare the diameters of the strings. Pluck the strings and compare their pitches.

ANALYSIS ■

1. If you were able to measure the frequency of the string, plot a graph of the frequency (vertical axis) against the length of the string for Procedure #1, 2, and 3. If you did not measure actual frequencies, use these data to plot the graph.

length (cm)	20	40	60	80
frequency (Hz)	800	400	270	200

2. Plot a graph of the frequency against the tension in the string for a constant length (Procedure #4). If frequencies were not found, use these data.

tension (N)	20	40	60	80
frequency (Hz)	220	320	390	450

3. Do the graphs from #1 and #2 correspond to what you heard in the activity? Explain your answer.

4. How does the pitch of a vibrating string depend on its length, tension, and diameter?

APPLICATION ■ A note sounded on a guitar is flat; in other words, its frequency is lower than it should be. What must be done to increase the frequency?

16.5 Stringed Instruments

Stringed instruments consist of two main parts — the **vibrator** and the **resonator**. The vibrator is the string. The resonator is the case, box, or sounding board that the string is attached to. A string by itself does not give a loud or pleasant sound. It must be attached to a resonator to improve its loudness and quality. Even a tuning fork has a louder and better sound if its handle is touched to a desk or a wall.

Stringed instruments can be played by plucking, striking, or bowing. The quality of sound is different in each case. The quality also depends on what part of the string is plucked, struck, or bowed. For example, a string plucked in the middle has a pure sound, as shown in Figure 16-11(a). Plucking at other positions changes the shape of the wave and thus the quality. This is illustrated in diagrams (b) and (c).

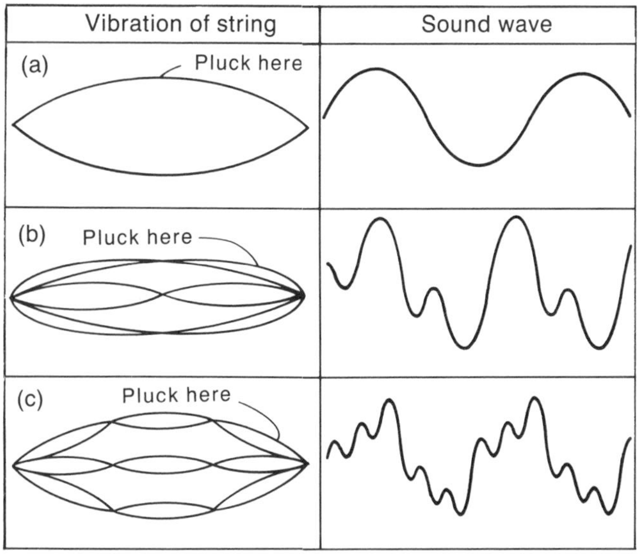

Stringed instruments that are *plucked* include the harp, banjo, guitar, mandolin, and ukulele. The harp is a complex instrument. It has 46 strings. The other stringed instruments are all similar to each other. They have 4 to 8 strings as well as frets to guide the placing of fingers. The lower notes have thick wires with low tension. The higher notes have thin wires with more tension.

The main stringed instrument that is *struck* is the piano. A piano key is connected by a system of levers to a hammer that strikes the string or strings of a certain note. (See Figure 16-12.) A modern piano has 88 notes with a frequency range from 27.5 Hz to 4186 Hz. The

Figure 16-12 Inside an upright piano

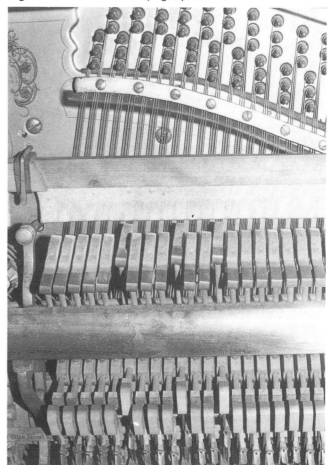

Figure 16-11 Changing the quality of sound of a vibrating string

Vibration of string	Sound wave
(a) Pluck here	
(b) Pluck here	
(c) Pluck here	

short, high-tension wires produce high-pitch notes. The long, thick wires produce low-pitch notes. The sounds from the strings are increased in loudness and quality by the wooden sounding board of the piano.

Stringed instruments that are usually *bowed* belong to the violin family. This family consists of the violin, viola, cello, and bass. The bows are made with dozens of fine fibres that are rubbed with rosin to increase friction between them and the strings. Each instrument has four strings and wooden sounding boards at the front and back of the case. The members of the violin family have no frets. Thus, the pitch can be changed gradually, not necessarily in steps as in the guitar family. (The only other instrument capable of changing pitch gradually is the trombone.) Again, the smallest instrument has the highest-pitch sounds and the largest has the lowest-pitch sounds.

Stringed instruments do not give out a great amount of energy. That is why a large number of violins are needed in an orchestra compared with the number of drums or trumpets.

16.6 Vibrating Columns of Air

A sound can be made by blowing into an empty pop bottle. The air inside the bottle vibrates, creating sound. When water is added to the bottle, the pitch of the sound changes. The shorter the column of vibrating air, the higher the frequency. The frequency of the vibrating air is its natural or *resonant frequency*.

Resonance occurs in a column of air when a standing wave fits neatly into the column. Standing waves result from interference. (See Section 14.9.) A device that illustrates resonance of sound in a column of air is shown in Figure 16-13. The flask can be raised or lowered to adjust the level of water in the tube. This changes the length of the air column. If a tuning fork, say 512 Hz, is sounded and held near the open end of the air column, resonant sounds will be noticed as the length of the air column changes.

Figure 16-13 Resonance apparatus

To understand how resonant sounds are caused by standing waves, consider Figure 16-14. It shows waves of sound in a column of air that is open at one end. (The waves shown are transverse only because they are easier to draw.) The air molecules in the tube cannot vibrate easily at the closed end, where the water is located. Thus a node exists there. At the open end, air molecules vibrate easily, so an antinode occurs there. Resonance occurs only when a wave of sound fits into the tube so that a node occurs at the closed end and an antinode at the open end.

Figure 16-14 Standing-wave patterns in columns of air closed at one end

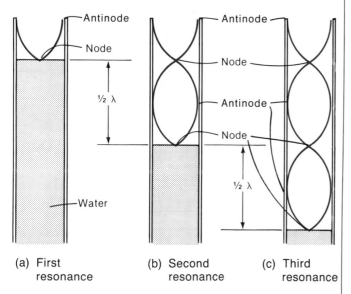

(a) First resonance
(b) Second resonance
(c) Third resonance

In Figure 16-14 the second column, (b), is half a wavelength longer than the first column. Also, the third column is half a wavelength longer than the second column. This means that the distance from one maximum sound to another in an air column is one-half the wavelength $\left(\frac{1}{2}\lambda\right)$ of the sound. The distance from one node to another is also $\frac{1}{2}\lambda$. (This was also true for standing waves on ropes, studied in Section 14.9.)

Sample Problem 1

A vibrating tuning fork is held near the mouth of a column filled with water. The water level is lowered until the first loud sound is heard. Then the water level is lowered another 18 cm and a second loud sound is heard. What is the wavelength of the sound from the tuning fork?

Solution $\frac{1}{2}\lambda = 18$ cm

$\lambda = 36$ cm or 0.36 m

A similar calculation can be made for columns of air that are open at both ends. Figure 16-15 shows why the distance from one maximum to the next is again $\frac{1}{2}\lambda$. In these columns antinodes occur at both ends because air molecules vibrate easily there.

Figure 16-15 Standing-wave patterns in columns of air open at both ends

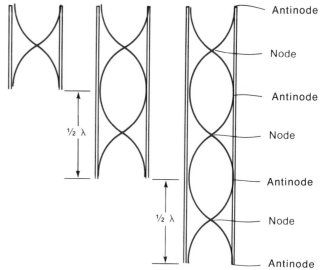

(a) First resonance
(b) Second resonance
(c) Third resonance

These ideas will be applied to an activity involving columns of air. Then they will be used to explain wind instruments, which create sound because of vibrating air in columns.

PRACTICE

10. What vibrates to create sound in a column of air?
11. In an air column closed at one end the distance from one loud sound to the next is 22 cm. What is the wavelength of the sound producing resonance?
12. In an air column open at both ends the distance between loud sounds is 60 cm. What is the wavelength of the sound?
13. Try this. Listen to the sound of water being added to a graduated cylinder. What happens to the pitch of the sound as the water is added? Explain why.

Activity 16B Measuring the Wavelength of Sound in a Column of Vibrating Air

PROBLEM ■ How can resonance be used to determine the wavelengths of sounds?

APPARATUS ■ 3 tuning forks of known frequency (between 384 Hz and 2000 Hz); resonance apparatus (Figure 16-13); rubber stopper; thermometer; metre stick; column of air open at both ends

  CAUTION Do not allow the vibrating metal tuning fork to touch the glass tube because it will shatter easily.

PROCEDURE ■
1. Adjust the water level in the long glass tube by raising the supply flask by hand until the water is near the top of the tube.
2. One person should strike the first tuning fork and hold it close to the mouth of the tube. Remember the **Caution**. Another person should slowly lower the level of the water. When the first resonant sound occurs, a third student should mark the level of the water. Then raise and lower the water around that level until you are sure of it. Then measure and record the length of the air column.
3. Repeat #2 for the second resonant sound and a third if there is one.

4. Repeat the entire procedure, using tuning forks of different frequencies.
5. Repeat the procedure, using a column of air open at both ends, if one is available.
6. Measure and record the air temperature in the classroom.

ANALYSIS ■
1. Use the data from Procedure #2 and #3 to calculate an average value of the wavelength of the sound from the tuning fork.
2. Use the air temperature of your classroom to find the speed of sound in the air around you:
   $[v = 332\,\text{m/s} + (0.6T)\,\text{m/s}]$. This value is needed in the next question.
3. Use the universal wave equation $(v = f\lambda)$ in the form $\lambda = \dfrac{v}{f}$ to find another value for the wavelength of the sound from the tuning fork.
4. Compare the wavelengths you found in Analysis #1 and #3. If the values are close, the experiment was a success.
5. Repeat the above Analysis steps for the other situations in this activity.
6. Describe how resonance can be used to determine the wavelength of sounds.

APPLICATIONS ■
1. Do low-frequency sounds require short or long columns of air for resonance? Explain your answer.
2. How do you think your answer in #1 applies to the sounds produced by wind instruments, which use air to produce sounds?

16.7 Wind Instruments

All wind instruments have columns of vibrating air molecules. The frequency of vibration of the air molecules depends on the length of the column and whether the column is open or closed at the ends. As is the case with all vibrating objects, the large instruments create low-frequency sounds and the small instruments create high-frequency sounds.

In some wind instruments the length of each air column is fixed. This is true of a pipe organ. However, in most wind instruments, such as the trombone, the length of the air column can be changed.

To cause the air molecules to vibrate, something else must vibrate first. There are four general ways of causing air molecules to vibrate in wind instruments.

(1) **Air reed instruments:** Air is blown across or through an opening. The moving air sets up a turbulence inside the column of the instrument. Examples are the pipe organ, flute, piccolo, recorder, and fife. The flute and piccolo have keys that are pressed to change the length of the air column. The recorder and fife have side holes that must be covered with fingers to change the length of the air column.

(2) **Single-membrane reed instruments:** Moving air sets a single reed vibrating. This in turn sets the air in the instrument vibrating. Examples include the saxophone, clarinet, and bagpipe. Again, the length of the air column is changed by holding down keys or covering side holes.

(3) **Double-mechanical reed instruments:** Moving air causes a set of two reeds to vibrate against each other. These vibrations cause air in the instrument to vibrate. Examples include the oboe, English horn, and bassoon. Keys are pressed to change the length of the air column.

(4) **Lip reed instruments** (also called **brass instruments**): The player's lips function as a double reed. They vibrate, causing air in the instrument to vibrate. The air does not escape through side holes as in the other wind instruments. The air must travel all the way through the brass instrument. Examples are the bugle, trombone, trumpet, French horn, and tuba. The length of the air column is changed by pressing valves or keys that add extra tubing to the instrument.

DID YOU KNOW?

Many musicians agree that the oboe and French horn are among the most difficult instruments to learn how to play.

PRACTICE

14. From the pairs of instruments listed, choose the one that would have a higher pitch. (It will be helpful to discuss in class the sizes of the instruments.)
    (a) piccolo, flute
    (b) oboe, English horn
    (c) bassoon, English horn
    (d) tuba, trumpet

Activity 16C   An Airy Concert

In a large group, design and carry out an activity to play a musical tune using pop bottles as wind instruments. Each pop bottle can contain water at a different level and can be "played" by blowing air across the mouth. There are various ways of tuning the bottles. One suggestion is to use a portable synthesizer as a reference.

16.8   Percussion Instruments

Percussion means the striking of one object against another. Percussion instruments are usually struck by a firm object such as a hammer, bar, or stick. These were the first musical instruments invented because they are fairly easy to make. (Even doctors use percussion when they tap a patient's ribs and listen for sounds that indicate either clear or congested lungs.)

Percussion instruments can be put in the following categories:

(1) **Indefinite pitch:** These instruments are meant for special effects or to keep the beat of the music. Examples include the triangle, bass drum, and castanets.

(2) **Definite pitch:** These instruments have bars or bells of different sizes. When struck, the bars or bells produce their own resonant frequencies. Examples are the tuning fork, orchestra bells, marimba (Figure 16-16), xylophone, and carillon.

Some instruments, such as the accordion and harmonica, are difficult to classify as one type of instrument. The accordion and harmonica use moving air to set reeds into vibration. However, they do not have resonating columns of air, so they are not usually called wind instruments. They are better classified as percussion instruments in which air knocks against reeds, causing them to vibrate.

Figure 16-16 The marimba

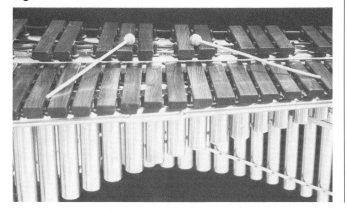

16.9   The Human Voice

The human voice is a fascinating instrument. The main parts of the body that help create sound are shown in Figure 16-17(a). Diagram (b) shows how the flow of air from the lungs causes sound.

The voice consists of three main parts:
(1) the **source** of air (lungs)
(2) the **vibrators** (vocal folds)
(3) the **resonators** (lower throat or pharynx, mouth, and nasal cavity)

To create most sounds, air from the lungs causes the vocal folds to vibrate. The vocal folds are two bands of skin that act like a double reed. The loudness is controlled by the amount of air. The frequency is controlled by muscular tension as well as the size of the vibrating parts. As usual, the larger instruments have lower resonant frequencies, so, in general, male voices are lower in frequency than female voices. Refer to Table 16-3 (overleaf).

Figure 16-17 The human voice

(a)

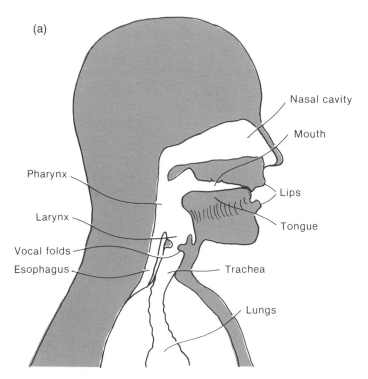

(b)

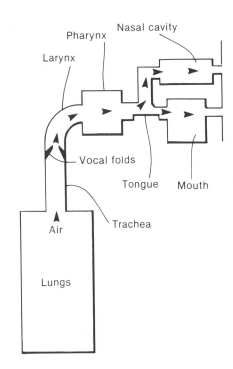

Table 16-3 Approximate Frequency Ranges of Voices

Type of voice	Frequency range (Hz)
Bass	82– 294
Baritone	110– 392
Tenor	147– 523
Alto	196– 698
Soprano	262–1047

The quality of sound from the voice is controlled by the parts in the resonating cavities such as the lips, tongue, mouth, and nasal cavity. You can see an interesting demonstration of this by holding a microphone to your throat and then to your mouth while making the same sound. If the signals are viewed on an oscilloscope screen, the effect of the resonating cavities can be seen.

Of course, the quality of sound may also be improved by proper training. Good singers can control such effects as vibrato and tremolo. **Vibrato** is a slight changing of frequency and **tremolo** is a slight changing of amplitude.

PRACTICE

15. Try this. If the computer hardware and software are available, obtain a printout of your voice.

16.10   Electric Instruments

Electric instruments are made of three main parts — a **source** of sound, a **microphone**, and a **loudspeaker**. At hockey or football games the announcer's voice directs sound energy into a microphone. The microphone changes sound energy into electrical energy. The electrical energy then causes vibrations in a loudspeaker.

Many of the musical instruments discussed in the previous sections can be made into electric instruments by adding a microphone and a loudspeaker. This is often done with stringed instruments that normally give out low amounts of energy. A microphone can be attached directly to the body of the instrument. In some cases the design of the instrument is changed. An electric guitar, for example, may have a body that is solid rather than hollow.

Loudspeakers are important in determining the quality of sound from an electric instrument. A single loudspeaker does not have the same frequency range as our ears. A set of two or three loudspeakers must be used to obtain both quality and frequency range. Table 16-4 lists three common sizes of loudspeakers used in electric sound systems.

Table 16-4 Loudspeakers

Name	Approximate size (cm)	Frequency range (Hz)	Wavelength range (cm)
Woofer (low-range)	25–40	25–1000	34–1400
Squawker (mid-range)	10–20	1000–10 000	3.4–34
Tweeter (high-range)	4–8	3000–20 000	1.7–11

The final column of Table 16-4 indicates that the sound waves from the tweeter have much shorter wavelengths than those from the woofer. Long wavelengths are diffracted easily through doorways and around furniture and people. However, the short waves from a tweeter are not diffracted around large objects, so their sound tends to be directional. As a result, a listener must be in front of the tweeter to get the full sensation of its sound, especially in the very-high-frequency range. (The diffraction of waves was examined in Activity 14C.)

16.11 Electronic Instruments

Electronic instruments produce vibrations using electronics rather than the normal sources which stringed, wind, and percussion instruments use. The electronic parts that create the vibrations are called transistors and resistors.

An electronic instrument consists of four main parts:
(1) The **oscillator** creates the vibrations.
(2) The **filter circuit** selects the frequencies that are sent to the mixing circuit.
(3) The **mixing circuit** adds various frequencies together to produce the final sound.
(4) The **amplifier and speaker system** makes the sound loud enough to be heard.

Synthesizers and electronic organs are common electronic instruments. They can control the shape of their sound waves. Thus, sound can be produced to resemble the sound of almost any musical instrument. The basic shapes of waves that are used to make other waves are shown in Figure 16-18.

Figure 16-18 The waves shown can be used to create various other waves.

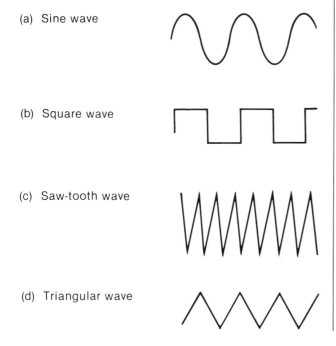

(a) Sine wave

(b) Square wave

(c) Saw-tooth wave

(d) Triangular wave

Figure 16-19 Control patterns

(a) Attack patterns

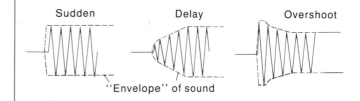

Sudden   Delay   Overshoot

"Envelope" of sound

(b) Decay patterns

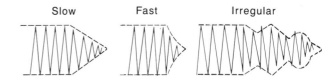

Slow   Fast   Irregular

Synthesizers and electronic organs can also control the **attack** and **decay** properties of the sound. When a sound is first heard, its attack may be sudden, delayed, or overshot. Refer to Figure 16-19(a). When a sound comes to an end, its decay may be slow, fast, or irregular. See Figure 16-19(b).

16.12 Acoustics

Some people claim that their singing voices are better in the shower than anywhere else. If that is true, it is because of all the reflections of sound in a small room.

The qualities of a room that determine how well sound is heard in the room are called **acoustics**.

The acoustics of a room depend on the shape of the room, what is in the room, and what is on the walls, ceiling, and floor. Sounds in a large, empty room are hollow and poor in quality. When rugs and furniture are added to the room, the acoustics improve.

Figure 16-20 This 2300-seat concert hall is in the National Arts Centre in Ottawa, Ontario. The design takes into consideration both acoustics and beauty.

In auditoriums and theatres, special designs must be used to help improve acoustics, especially for listening to music. The walls and ceiling must be designed to provide a good balance of reflection and absorption of sound. Figure 16-20 shows an auditorium with many features to improve acoustics.

Sometimes construction is needed for special purposes. This is shown in Figure 16-21. Diagram (a) shows the design of a recording or sound-testing studio. Diagram (b) shows a band shell in a park directing sound to an outdoor audience.

This is only the beginning of the fascinating topic of sound — an important type of energy that surrounds us at all times.

DID YOU KNOW?

The concave shape used in a band shell is the basis of the curved reflectors used to gather sounds of birds or of play-ers on sports fields. Sounds from the sources reflect off the concave surface to a microphone located at the focal point.

Figure 16-21 Special acoustics effects

(a) A recording or sound-testing studio is designed to absorb sound.

(b) The Hollywood Bowl in California is designed to direct sound from the stage to the audience. This outdoor theatre seats over 18 000 people.

Activity 16D   Sound Absorption

PROBLEM ■

(a) What are the features of a device that is successful at *absorbing* a specific sound?

(b) Repeat (a) for a device that *reflects* the sound.

APPARATUS ■   audio frequency generator or portable synthesizer; sound level meter (in decibels); construction materials (e.g., wood, cloth, egg cartons, aluminum foil)

PROCEDURE ■

Design and carry out an activity (perhaps as a contest) to determine the best design of devices that will (a) absorb and (b) reflect a single-note sound (e.g., A = 440 Hz) from an instrument. Some clues for designing such structures may be found in the photographs in this chapter. Figure 16-22 provides a suggested way of testing the devices.

Figure 16-22   Testing the intensity level of reflected sound

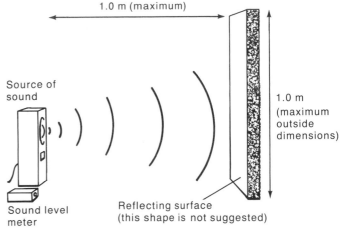

Notice in Figure 16-22 that even without the reflected sound, the sound level meter will record a value. This does not hinder a comparison of the reflecting ability of the object being tested. The distances suggested should be decided before starting the construction.

ANALYSIS ■   Discuss the features of the best and worst designs for absorbing and reflecting sound.

APPLICATION ■   Describe the features of your home and its furnishings that provide good absorption of sound.

Words to Know

noise
music
pitch
scientific scale
musicians' scale
intensity level
noise pollution

quality (of musical sound)
stringed instruments
wind instruments
percussion instruments
electric instruments
electronic instruments
acoustics

Chapter Objectives

Having completed this chapter, you should now be able to:

1. Describe the scientific differences between noise and music.
2. State the three characteristics of musical sounds and describe what each characteristic depends on.
3. Describe the two main musical scales.
4. Given the frequency of one musical note, calculate the frequency of a note one octave from it.
5. State the units used to measure the intensity level of sound.
6. Describe the dangers of loud sounds.
7. Describe how changing the shape of a sound wave changes the quality of the musical sound.
8. State how tension, length, and diameter affect the frequency of a vibrating string.
9. State the two main parts of stringed instruments.
10. List various types of stringed instruments.
11. Describe how resonance of sound is created in vibrating columns of air.
12. Calculate the wavelength of a sound that resonates in an air column, knowing the distance from one loud sound to another.
13. Calculate the speed of sound in air given the frequency and wavelength ($v = f\lambda$).
14. State four ways of making air in wind instruments vibrate.
15. List various types of wind instruments.
16. List various types of percussion instruments.
17. Describe the functions of the main parts of the human voice.
18. Describe the difference between electric and electronic instruments.
19. Describe how certain factors affect the acoustics of rooms and auditoriums.

Chapter Review

1. Which of the following descriptions best suits each oscilloscope display shown: pure sound; noise; high-quality sound? (16.1)

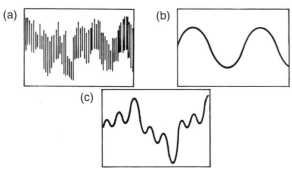

(a)   (b)

(c)

2. (a) Name the three characteristics of musical sounds.
   (b) State what each characteristic depends on. (16.1 to 16.4)

3. List the following frequencies in order of decreasing pitch:
   512 Hz, 768 Hz, 384 Hz, 256 Hz, 420 Hz   (16.2)
4. Which sound has the higher pitch?   (16.2)

(a) 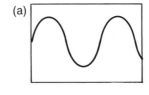   (b)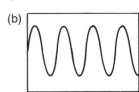

5. What is the frequency of middle C on the:
   (a) scientific scale?
   (b) musicians' scale?   (16.2)
6. Use Table 16-1 and Figure 16-5 to calculate the frequency of a note one octave above:
   (a) F on the scientific scale
   (b) B on the scientific scale
   (c) C_1 on the musicians' scale
   (d) G_4 on the musicians' scale   (16.2)

7. A certain note has a frequency of 1000 Hz. Calculate the frequency of a note:
   (a) one octave above it
   (b) one octave below it
   (c) two octaves above it
   (d) two octaves below it   (16.2)

8. One person has a threshold of hearing of 10 dB and another has a threshold of hearing of 30 dB. Which person has better hearing?   (16.3)

9. How many times higher in intensity is a 70 dB sound than a 40 dB sound?   (16.3)

10. Describe practical ways to reduce noise pollution at a busy intersection in a city.   (16.3, especially Table 16-2)

11. Compare the qualities of the sounds shown in the diagrams.   (16.4)

(a) 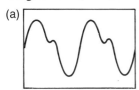   (b)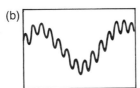

12. State what happens to the frequency of a vibrating string when:
    (a) the tension increases but the length remains constant
    (b) the length increases but the tension remains constant   (Act. 16A)

13. What are the two main parts of stringed instruments?   (16.5)

14. Give an example of a stringed instrument that:
    (a) has frets   (b) has no frets   (c) is struck   (16.5)

15. Describe two ways of changing the quality of sound of a stringed instrument.   (16.5)

16. The distance from one loud sound to another in a column of air is 0.27 m. What is the wavelength of the sound?   (16.6)

17. The frequency of the sound resonating in the air column in #16 is 650 Hz. Calculate the speed of the sound in air.   (Act. 16B)

18. (a) Name four methods of getting air to vibrate in wind instruments.
    (b) State an example of an instrument that uses each method in (a).   (16.7)

19. What is an example of a percussion instrument that has:
    (a) an indefinite pitch?   (b) a definite pitch? (16.8)

20. In Section 16.5 a piano was described as a stringed instrument. Do you think it could also be described as a percussion instrument? Why or why not?

21. Discuss in class whether the human voice might be classified as a stringed, wind, or percussion instrument.   (16.9)

22. Electric and electronic instruments have different sources of vibrations. Explain the difference.   (16.10, 16.11)

23. Give an example of an:
    (a) electric instrument
    (b) electronic instrument   (16.10, 16.11)

24. Discuss in class the acoustics of both your physics classroom and the school's auditorium. In each case consider:
    (a) what has been done to provide good acoustics
    (b) what could be done to improve the acoustics   (16.12)

25. To review the most important concepts in the topics of sound, answer these questions:
    (a) What is needed to cause sound?
    (b) By what means does sound energy get transferred from one place to another?
    (c) If the frequency of a sound wave increases, what happens to its wavelength?
    (d) What is the universal wave equation?
    (e) Given the temperature of air, how do you find the speed of sound in air?
    (f) How is interference of sound waves produced?
    (g) What is the human audible range?
    (h) What are the characteristics of musical sounds and what do they depend on?
    (i) How does the size of a musical instrument relate to its frequency range?

26. Choose one or more of the topics listed below. Research and report the topic.
    (a) musical scales (e.g., the equitempered scale)
    (b) noise pollution
    (c) a musical instrument
    (d) acoustics (e.g., in theatres, halls, or homes)
    (e) careers associated with music and/or acoustics

Electricity and Electro-magnetism

It is possible that your entire working life may be very closely tied to applications of electricity and electromagnetism. Applications of electricity take advantage of the ease with which electrical energy can be transferred from its source to many devices via transformers and conducting wires. Clocks, sound systems, computers, appliances, motors, and lights are only a few of the devices operated by electricity.

Magnetic fields are used to produce electricity. Magnetic fields are utilized in large generators to produce electricity for home and industrial use, as well as in cassette decks to control electrical signals that are sent to the rest of the audio-system for amplification and conversion into sound. This unit is about electricity, types of electrical currents, and the relationship between electricity and magnetism.

An understanding of electricity and electromagnetism is essential if you are thinking about a career in electric motor or generator design and maintenance, telecommunications, or electrical contracting. This understanding is also important if you are considering careers in audio-visual technology, instrumentation technology, or robotics.

- The rapidly expanding field of robotics requires knowledge of electricity and electromagnetism. Robots that perform routine mechanical tasks are used widely in many production lines that manufacture everything from bottled liquids to automobiles. Of course, knowledge of electricity and electromagnetism is vital in the design, manufacture, operation, and maintenance of robots.

Knowing the information in this unit will be especially useful if you plan a career in any of the areas already mentioned, as well as the following: appliance manufacture and repair, auto mechanics, pollution control, electric power distribution, computers, astronomy, microelectronics, or optoelectronics. To find out more about any career possibility mentioned, interview someone already on that career path. If it still appeals to you, contact your local community college, university, guidance office, or counselling centre for more information on training.

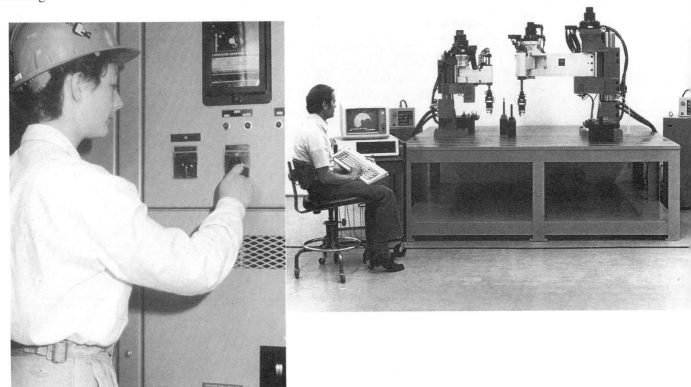

CHAPTER 17

Static Electricity

Lightning is a spectacular example of an electric discharge. Tall buildings tend to be struck by lightning numerous times each year. These buildings, and others, can be protected from lightning by applying concepts learned in this chapter. The chapter begins with an examination of the force of electricity and the meaning of "static" in static electricity. Through various activities and examples of applications, you will realize just how common static electricity is.

Main Ideas

- Electric sparks and lightning are examples of electric discharge.
- Electric charges either attract or repel other electric charges, depending on the types of charges.
- Some materials are excellent electric conductors; many materials are not.
- Although static electricity can be a nuisance, it also has many useful applications.

17.1   The Force of Electricity

Everyone has felt little electric shocks from touching certain objects after walking across a rug. Everyone has also seen a lightning bolt during a thunderstorm. Both the electric shock and lightning result when a build-up of electric charge is transferred from one place to another. The rapid transfer of charge is called a **discharge**. Refer to Figure 17-1.

Figure 17-1   Static-electricity discharge in the classroom. The device on the left creates a build-up of electric charge. The charge then jumps to the sphere on the right.

The build-up of electric charges on an object is called **static electricity**. The word static means at rest. Thus, static electricity is not the type of electricity that flows through a wire. Rather it builds up on an object and may then discharge (i.e., jump to another object).

The electric charge that builds up and causes shocks and lightning also creates a force that is easily observed. If you rub a balloon with a cloth, the balloon will stick to a wall or ceiling. If you stroke a brush through clean, dry hair, the hair is attracted to the brush. If you remove clothes from a hot dryer, the clothes stick together. The force caused by electric charges is called the **force of electricity**.

The force of electricity was first studied and described in Greece about 600 B.C. by a man named Thales. He used a substance called amber, a hard, yellowish resin from dead trees. He rubbed the amber with fur and discovered that the amber attracted feathers and pieces of straw. Because the Greek word for amber is *elektron*, modern words related to electricity stem from that discovery.

In the seventeenth century scientists finally advanced the study of electricity by experimenting. One of the most famous scientific experiments was performed by an American inventor, Benjamin Franklin (Figure 17-2). He wanted to discover if lightning was similar to the static electricity created by rubbing a piece of amber. During a thunderstorm he connected a kite to one end of a long rope and a large metal key to the other end. He held onto the rope using a silk cloth and flew the kite in the storm. He discovered that lightning had the same effect as static electricity in the laboratory, except it was strong enough to knock him over. If he had not used the silk cloth as insulation against electricity, he likely would have been killed!

Figure 17-2   Benjamin Franklin (1706-1790)

It was Benjamin Franklin who introduced the idea of positive and negative electric charges. He called the charge on amber rubbed with fur *negative*, and we still use that term today.

Since the time of Franklin, much has been discovered about electricity. Today so much of what we do depends on electricity that we tend to take this amazing force for granted.

PRACTICE

1. List four examples of static electricity given in this section.
2. List two examples of static electricity other than those given in this section.

Activity 17A   Properties of Electric Charges

PROBLEM ■ How do electric charges on different objects affect each other?

APPARATUS ■ support stand with clamp and support; 2 vinyl and 2 acetate strips (or their alternatives); wool cloth; cotton cloth; comb; plastic pen

Notes:
1. Acetate is clear plastic; vinyl is white plastic.
2. This activity is best done on a dry winter day.

Figure 17-3 Set-up for Activity 17A

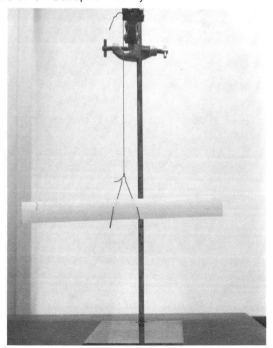

PROCEDURE ■

1. Suspend the vinyl strip as shown in Figure 17-3. Hold the suspended strip in the middle and charge it by rubbing both ends with wool. Rub one end of the second vinyl strip with wool so it attains the same type of charge as the suspended strip. Now hold the charged end of the second strip close to the suspended strip. Try this a few times. Record what you observe.

2. For this step assume that the charge acquired by the vinyl rubbed with wool is *negative*. Rub both ends of the suspended vinyl with wool. Now hold the part of the wool that you just used for rubbing close to one end of the vinyl. Describe what happens. Does the wool appear to have the same type of charge as the vinyl (negative), or the opposite type of charge (positive)? Explain your answer.

3. Recharge the suspended vinyl with wool. Charge one end of an acetate strip by rubbing it with cotton. Hold the charged end of the acetate close to the suspended, negatively charged vinyl. Describe the effect. What type of charge is on the acetate?

4. Suspend an acetate strip from the stand, and charge it at both ends with cotton. Charge one end of a second acetate strip with cotton and hold this strip close to the suspended one. Describe what you observe.

5. Suspend the vinyl strip once again from the stand. Charge it negatively, so it can be used to test other charges. Determine the size (small, medium, or large) and type (positive or negative) of charge on the following:
   (a) a plastic comb run through your hair
   (b) a plastic pen rubbed on a piece of clothing
   (c) various objects rubbed on a material of your choice

ANALYSIS ■

1. What evidence in this activity proves that two like charges repel each other?
2. What evidence from this activity proves that two opposite charges attract?
3. State the type of charge that results on each of the following:
   (a) vinyl rubbed with wool
   (b) the wool used to rub the vinyl
   (c) acetate rubbed with cotton
   (d) the cotton used to rub the acetate

APPLICATION ■ When you pull the plastic cover off a new record jacket or other container, the plastic cover is attracted back to the container. Why does this attraction occur?

DID YOU KNOW?

Clothes removed from a dryer often cling to each other. You can reduce this static cling by adding a special product to the clothes washer during the rinse cycle, or to the dryer.

17.2 The Laws of Electric Charges

The force of electricity can be either a repulsion or an attraction. Repulsion means repelling or pushing apart. It is the opposite of attraction.

As you observed in the previous activity, there are two opposite types of electric charges, negative and positive. No overall charge is called *neutral*. Two objects having the same type of charge (i.e., either negative and negative or positive and positive) repel each other. Two objects with opposite charges (positive and negative) attract each other. These observations can be summarized in the following two statements, called the **laws of electric charges**.

(1) **The law of repulsion: Like charges repel one another.**
(2) **The law of attraction: Unlike charges attract one another.**

These laws can be applied to determine the types of charges on objects. A device with a known charge used to determine other charges is called an **electroscope**. A simple form of an electroscope is a suspended strip that has a known charge. For example, the negatively charged strip used in the last step in Activity 17A was an electroscope. Other types of electroscopes are shown in Figure 17-4.

Figure 17-4 Examples of simple electroscopes

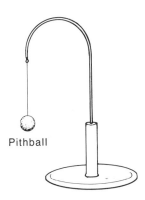

(a) A pithball electroscope: Metallic paint covers a lightweight ball of pith, which comes from the centres of some plants.

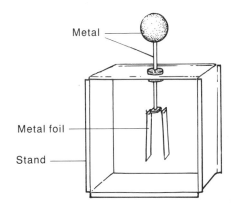

(b) A leaf electroscope: Two pieces of metal foil are joined together and connected to a piece of metal. The metal does not come in direct contact with the stand.

The laws of electric charges will be applied in other situations in the remainder of this chapter.

PRACTICE

3. A balloon is rubbed on a sweater and brought close to a suspended negative strip. The strip is observed to be repelled from the balloon. What type of charge is on the balloon? Explain how you know.

17.3   The Theory of Atoms

By the early 1900s scientists had developed a theory that matter is made of tiny particles called atoms. An atom consists of a dense central part called a **nucleus**, surrounded by much smaller particles called **electrons**. These electrons move in regions around the nucleus at extremely high speeds. The nucleus, in turn, is composed of particles called **protons** and **neutrons**. All atoms of a particular element have the same number of protons. For example, all atoms of helium have two protons and all atoms of oxygen have eight protons. Diagrams representing atoms of these two elements are shown in Figure 17-5.

Figure 17-5   Atoms of two common elements

(a) Helium

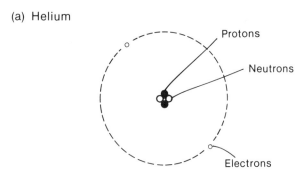

(b) Oxygen

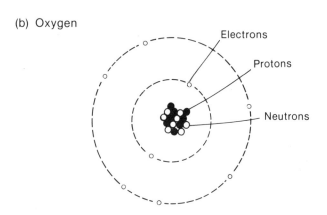

Scientists have discovered that electrons have the same type of charge as a piece of amber rubbed with fur. Thus, *electrons have a negative charge*. Electrons

are kept in their paths around the nucleus by a force of attraction (the electric force). Since opposite charges attract, it is logical to conclude that the nucleus must have a positive charge. Again, after conducting experiments, scientists have found that *protons have a positive charge*. The neutrons are left with no charge. Thus, the *neutrons are neutral*.

The mass of an electron is almost 2000 times smaller than the mass of a proton or a neutron. Also, an electron is more free to travel than a proton or a neutron. Thus, electron motion is important in electricity; it can account for many observations. For example, consider a single atom of oxygen. When it is neutral it contains eight protons and eight electrons. Now if two nearby electrons become part of the atom, there are eight protons and 10 electrons. Thus, the atom has an overall negative charge.

PRACTICE

4. State the type of charge on each of the following:
   (a) a proton
   (b) a neutron
   (c) an electron
   (d) a nucleus
   (e) an atom having an equal number of protons and electrons
   (f) an atom having more electrons than protons
5. A piece of amber rubbed with fur becomes negatively charged. What particles must have been deposited on the surface of the amber?

17.4   Transferring Electric Charge by Friction

The theory of atoms can be used to explain the effects observed in static electricity experiments. For example, in Activity 17A you obtained a negative charge on a strip of vinyl (or similar material) by rubbing it with wool. The reason this occurred is illustrated in Figure 17-6 and explained in the next paragraph.

Before rubbing occurs, the vinyl has an equal number of electrons and protons, so it is neutral. The wool is also neutral. The vinyl atoms have a stronger attraction for electrons than the wool atoms do. When the wool and vinyl are rubbed together, there is a large area of contact between the wool and vinyl atoms. The vinyl attracts some electrons, resulting in *extra* electrons. This gives it an overall negative charge. The wool has lost some electrons, so it has a *lack* of electrons. This gives it an overall positive charge. When the charged vinyl and wool are held close together, they attract one another. This occurs because opposite charges attract.

Figure 17-6 Charging vinyl and wool: Each positive and negative sign could represent millions of charged particles.

(a) Neutral charges before rubbing

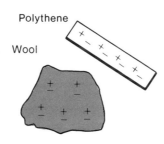

(b) Rubbing causes electrons to go from the wool to the vinyl.

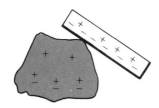

(c) Opposite charges attract.

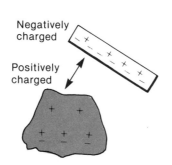

The atoms of different substances have different abilities to attract electrons. For example, rubber atoms attract electrons more than wool or fur atoms do. Table 17-1 lists several substances in the order in which their atoms attract electrons. The list is called the **static-electricity series**.

Table 17-1 The Static-Electricity Series: A material will lose electrons when rubbed with a material lower in the list.

+	
Cat's Fur	Atoms have a poor attraction for electrons.
Acetate	
Glass	
Wool	
Silk	
Cotton	
Vinyl	
Rubber	
Amber	Atoms have a large attraction for electrons.
−	

Sample Problem 1

What types of charges result on cotton and rubber when they are rubbed together?

Solution According to Table 17-1, rubber atoms have a larger attraction for electrons than cotton atoms. Thus, the rubber will become negatively charged and the cotton positively charged.

PRACTICE

6. When acetate and wool are rubbed together, the acetate becomes positively charged.
   (a) What type of charge is on the wool?
   (b) Do the electrons escape from the acetate to the wool, or from the wool to the acetate?
7. State the types of charges that result when each pair of substances is rubbed together:
   (a) rubber, silk   (c) glass, cotton
   (b) silk, glass   (d) cat's fur, amber

17.5 Electric Conductors and Insulators

All matter is composed of atoms that contain electrons. But not all atoms have electrons that can move easily from one atom to the next. A material whose electrons do not travel easily is called an **electric insulator**. The opposite kind of material, an **electric conductor**, allows the transfer of electrons easily.

A simple test can be made to determine whether a substance is a conductor or an insulator. Figure 17-7 shows an object to be tested with one end touching a simple electroscope that has a negative charge. Another negative charge is brought close to the opposite end of the test object. If the material is a conductor, its electrons will be repelled toward the electroscope and the electroscope will swing away. If the material is an insulator, nothing will happen.

Table 17-2 lists several conductors and insulators. Notice that metals are good electric conductors.

Table 17-2 Electric Conductors and Insulators (in alphabetical order)

Conductors	Insulators
Aluminum	Air (dry)
Copper	Amber
Gold	Glass
Iron	Paper
Nickel	Rubber
Silver	Silk
	Wool

To deposit a charge on a metal conductor, the conductor must be insulated from its surroundings. The metal sphere in Figure 17-8(a) is resting on an insulating stand. Such a sphere can be charged negatively or positively. In diagram (b) it has a negative charge. Once it is charged, you can discharge it by touching it with your hand. The charge travels from the sphere through your body to the earth. The process of conducting a charge to the earth is called **grounding** (⏚). See diagram (c). Grounding a small metal sphere may be compared to pouring a cup of water into the ocean. It makes a lot of difference to the cup but no difference to the ocean.

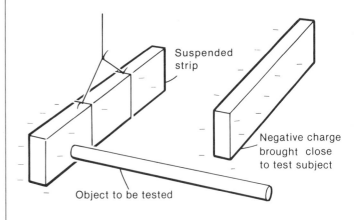

Figure 17-7 Testing for conductors and insulators

Suspended strip

Negative charge brought close to test subject

Object to be tested

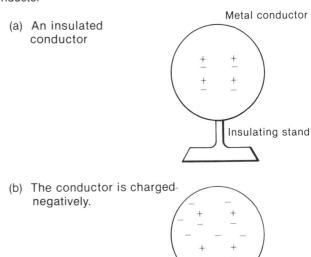

Figure 17-8 Charging and discharging an insulated conductor

(a) An insulated conductor

Metal conductor

Insulating stand

(b) The conductor is charged negatively.

(c) The conductor is grounded and becomes neutral.

An important application of grounding is used during aircraft refuelling, when there is a danger that a static electricity spark may cause the fuel to explode. To prevent this danger, the aircraft and the fuel-hose nozzle are grounded before refuelling begins. See Figure 17-9.

Figure 17-9   An airplane must be grounded during refuelling to prevent a static-electricity discharge.

PRACTICE

8. Were the materials you used in Activity 17A insulators or conductors?

9. What kind of charge results on an insulated conductor that is grounded?

17.6   Distribution of Charges on Insulators and Conductors

If one end of a vinyl strip is rubbed with wool, only that end of the vinyl becomes charged. Vinyl is an insulator, so the electrons do not spread throughout it. Rather they stay piled up at one location, as shown in Figure 17-10.

Figure 17-10   Charge distribution on an insulator

This end was rubbed with wool.

Vinyl

Figure 17-11   Charge distribution on metal conductors

(a) Spherical shape

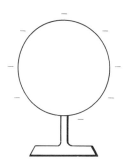

(b) Pear shape

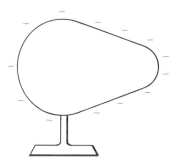

(c) Pointed shape

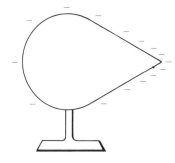

Charges act differently on conductors. If a metal sphere is charged negatively, the electrons spread evenly over the outside surface of the sphere. If the conductor has a pointed shape, the electrons tend to repel each other toward the point. Negative charges on various shapes of conductors are shown in Figure 17-11.

In Figure 17-11(c) the electrons could easily be repelled off the pointed end. In general, a pointed conductor is very useful in allowing a charge to pass to or from an object. An important application of this principle is the **lightning rod**.

A lightning rod helps prevent lightning from striking a house or barn. The rod is a pointed metal conductor, placed higher than any other part of the building. (See Figure 17-12.) Whether the charge travels from the ground to the clouds or from the clouds to the ground, it can drain quickly through the conductor. This prevents the lightning from starting a fire. Highrise buildings are connected to the ground by their steel frames or by special metal conductors.

Figure 17-12 The lightning rod

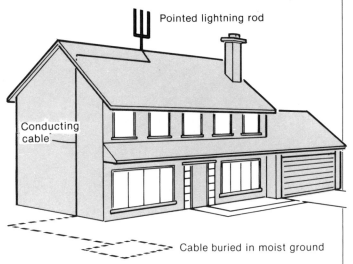

PRACTICE

10. From which object listed below would electrons jump most easily? Why?
    (a) a pointed insulator
    (b) a spherical insulator
    (c) a pointed conductor
    (d) a spherical conductor

17.7 Charging Conductors

There are two ways of depositing a charge on an insulated conductor—by conduction and by induction.

To *charge by conduction*, all you have to do is touch a charged object to the conductor. Two examples are shown in Figure 17-13. Each metal sphere is on an insulating stand and is originally neutral. In (a), a strip with a negative charge is touched to the sphere. The extra electrons on the charged strip repel one another. This causes some of the electrons to move to the sphere, giving it a negative charge. In (b), a strip with a positive charge is touched to the metal sphere. The positive charge attracts electrons from the sphere. This causes the sphere to have an overall positive charge.

Figure 17-13 Charging by conduction

(a) Creating a negative charge

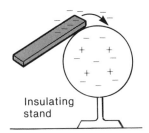

Insulating stand

(b) Creating a positive charge

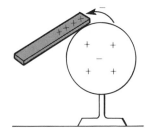

Notice in Figure 17-13 that when charging by conduction, the final charge on the conductor is the same type as the charge on the original strip. Notice also that only the electrons (the negative charges) actually move.

The other method of charging a conductor, called induction, does not involve contact. **Induction** is the movement of charged particles within a substance, caused by another nearby charge. Two examples are illustrated in Figure 17-14. In diagram (a), a negatively charged strip is brought close to a neutral conductor. Electrons on the conductor are forced (induced) to the far end of the conductor. In diagram (b) a positively charged strip attracts the electrons in a neutral conductor. Notice again that it is the electrons that move in a conductor.

Figure 17-14 Induction

(a) Electrons are repelled.

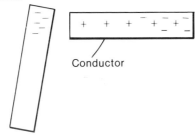

Conductor

(b) Electrons are attracted.

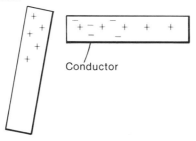

Conductor

PRACTICE

11. A conductor is charged by conduction using a positive strip. What type of charge results on the conductor?

Activity 17B Induction and Charging by Induction

PROBLEM ■

(a) Can induction of charge occur in water?

(b) What ways can be used to charge an electric conductor by induction?

APPARATUS ■ 2 vinyl strips; 1 acetate strip; support stand and clamp; wool cloth; cotton cloth; stream of water; 2 metal spheres mounted on insulating stands; electrophorus set (Figure 17-16)

PROCEDURE ■

1. Charge a vinyl strip negatively by rubbing it with wool. Hold it close to a smooth stream of water from a tap. Describe what happens.
2. Repeat #1, using an acetate strip charged positively by rubbing it with cotton. Again describe what happens.
3. Suspend a vinyl strip from the support stand. Charge the strip to act as an electroscope. What type of charge is on the electroscope?
4. Place two metal spheres together and neutralize them by touching them with your hand. Bring a charged vinyl strip close to one end of the pair as shown in Figure 17-15(a). Remove the sphere that is farthest from the vinyl strip. Predict the type of charge on each sphere. Check your prediction using the charged electroscope. This is one way of charging conductors by induction.
5. Charge a vinyl strip and bring it close to a neutralized mounted sphere. Ground the sphere as shown in Figure 17-15(b). Predict the type of charge remaining on the sphere. Check your prediction using the charged electroscope. This is another way of charging conductors by induction.

Figure 17-15 Charging by induction

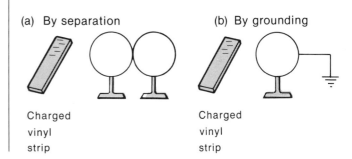

(a) By separation

Charged
vinyl
strip

(b) By grounding

Charged
vinyl
strip

Figure 17-16 The electrophorus

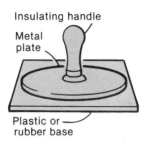

6. An electrophorus set is shown in Figure 17-16. Rub the base of the electrophorus with wool. Place the metal plate on the charged base. Touch the metal very briefly. Predict the type of charge on the metal plate. Check your prediction using the charged electroscope. A spark may result if you ground the electrophorus plate.

ANALYSIS ■
1. Can induction of charge occur in water?
2. In Procedure #1 and 2, why do you think water acted the way it did? (Hint: Water molecules have both positive and negative particles.)
3. Draw a series of diagrams to explain how charging by induction occurred in Procedure #4.
4. Describe ways that can be used to charge an electric conductor by induction.

17.8 Using Diagrams to Explain Charging by Induction

In Activity 17B, Procedure #5, you charged a metal conductor by induction starting with a negatively charged vinyl strip. The charge that resulted on the metal was positive. We will use diagrams to explain how the conductor became positively charged.

Consider Figure 17-17. In diagram (a) the metal sphere is neutral, having an equal number of positive and negative charges. In diagram (b) the negative vinyl is brought close to the sphere. Electrons on the surface of the conductor are repelled far away. The conductor is then grounded in diagram (c). Some electrons leave the conductor and are repelled to the ground. Finally, in diagram (d), the result is a positive charge on the conductor. We say the metal has been charged positively by induction.

Figure 17-17 Charging a metal sphere by induction

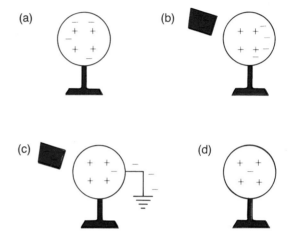

Notice in Figure 17-17 that the charge on the conductor is opposite to the charge on the vinyl strip. If the original charge had been positive, the final charge on the conductor would be negative. Thus, when charging a single conductor by induction, the final charge on the conductor is opposite to the type of the original charge.

Several other observed results may be explained using a series of diagrams similar to Figure 17-17.

PRACTICE

12. A conductor is charged by induction using a positively charged strip. What type of charge results on the conductor?
13. Draw a series of diagrams to show how to charge a single metal sphere by induction starting with a positively charged strip. (Hint: Only the electrons move. When the sphere is grounded, electrons travel *from* the ground *to* the conductor.)
14. Draw a series of diagrams illustrating how the electrophorus was charged in Activity 17B, Procedure #6.

17.9 Static-Electricity Generators

A static-electricity generator is a device that creates a large build-up of charge. The charge can be used for demonstrations and practical purposes.

A common type of static-electricity generator is called the Van de Graaff generator, named after its designer. Refer to Figure 17-18. The source of charge at the bottom of the machine gives energy to millions of electrons to free them from atoms. The electrons are carried by a rubber belt (an insulator) to the top of the machine. The electrons are distributed rapidly and evenly over the outside surface of the metal conductor.

The Van de Graaff generator or a similar device can be used to demonstrate many phenomena in static electricity.

 CAUTION *Anyone with heart problems should not go near a Van de Graaff generator. It should always be left unplugged and neutralized.*

Figure 17-18 The Van de Graaff generator

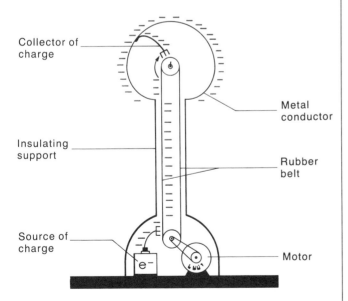

One example is shown in Figure 17-19. A person with clean, dry hair stands on an insulating stand and holds onto the generator. The electrons are discharged through the hair, and the repulsion of like charges causes the hair to stand up.

Figure 17-19 Flying hair

Artificial lightning produced by a large static-electricity generator can be used to test cars. Tests verify that a car is a safe place to be during a lightning storm.

PRACTICE

15. What type of charge ends up on the outside of the Van de Graaff generator described in this section?

17.10 Applications of Static Electricity

Static electricity is often harmful and sometimes useful. This section tells how to reduce the unwanted effects of static electricity. Then it presents useful applications that have not yet been mentioned.

Static electricity can be a nuisance. For example, it may cause clothes to cling to the body, and it may cause scratchy sounds during the playing of a record. Sprays and antistatic "guns" have been developed to reduce this type of static. Adding moisture to the air also helps.

Explosions and fires may be caused by a static-electricity discharge. In hospital operating rooms explosive gases (anesthetics) are sometimes needed. To prevent spark discharges, the floor and the footwear worn by the doctors and nurses must be good conductors of electricity.

Static electricity can also be a help. One simple use is in the wrapping of food. Static-electricity forces help plastic wrap cling to food. This keeps the food fresh longer.

Many large industries use static electricity to help prevent air pollution. A device called a precipitator (Figure 17-20) works as follows. A metal electrode is negatively charged. Polluted gases pass by the electrode. Particles in the gases become charged negatively by induction. They are then attracted to the grounded wall of the precipitator, called the collector. If the particles are liquid, they simply drain off. If the particles are solid, the collectors must be shaken once in a while to force the particles to fall down.

Figure 17-20   The static-electricity precipitator

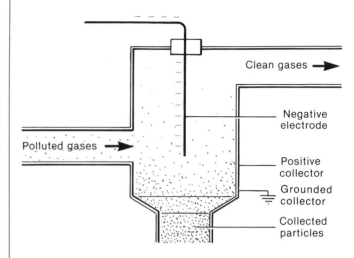

The following is a list of some important applications of static electricity:

- cleaning air in homes
- separating minerals from ores
- separating unwanted particles from grain seeds
- separating shells from nuts
- applying certain spray paints
- coating short fibres on rugs and the insides of musical instrument cases
- making expensive sandpaper
- spraying insecticides on plants
- photocopying
- studying living cells
- making microphones with high-frequency response
- arc welding

It is obvious that static electricity is important. However, its applications are not as common as the applications of current electricity, discussed in the next chapter.

PRACTICE

16. Explain why the conducting floor and footwear of doctors and nurses in an operating room help prevent sparks.
17. Research and report on applications of static electricity (also called electrostatics).

Words to Know

discharge
static electricity
force of electricity
laws of electric charges
theory of atoms
nucleus
proton
neutron

electron
static-electricity series
electric insulator
electric conductor
grounding
lightning rod
induction

Chapter Objectives

Having completed this chapter, you should now be able to:
1. Define and give examples of static electricity.
2. Define and give examples of the force of electricity.
3. State and prove the laws of electric charges.
4. Use an electroscope having a known charge to find the type of charge on an object.
5. Describe the structure of the atom.
6. State the type of charge on a proton, neutron, and electron.
7. Explain how rubbing two objects together causes a build-up of static-electricity charges.
8. Use the static-electricity series to find out what types of charges occur on objects that are rubbed together.
9. Explain the difference between an electric conductor and an electric insulator.
10. Describe how charges are distributed on conducting objects of different shapes.
11. Explain how a charged object can be used to charge another object by conduction and induction.
12. Describe applications of static electricity.

Chapter Review

1. Define and give two examples of the force of electricity. (17.1)
2. What is meant by static-electricity discharge? (17.1)
3. Describe a method to prove the law of:
   (a) repulsion
   (b) attraction (Act. 17A, 17.2)
4. Draw a diagram of an atom having three protons, three neutrons, and three electrons. (Show two electrons close to the nucleus and the third electron farther away.) (17.3)
5. What kind of charge does the atom in #4 have? (17.3)
6. (a) Which particle is the most important in explaining static-electricity events?
   (b) What kind of charge does that particle have? (17.3)
7. Objects A and B are rubbed together. Object A loses electrons to object B.
   (a) What kind of charge is on A?
   (b) What kind of charge is on B?
   (c) What happens if A is brought close to a negatively charged electroscope? (17.2, 17.3)
8. When hard rubber and wool are rubbed together, the rubber becomes negatively charged. Explain how this happens, starting with neutral pieces of rubber and wool. (17.4)
9. What kind of charge results on each substance when the following pairs of substances are rubbed together? (Refer to Table 17-1, 17.4.)
   (a) amber, rubber
   (b) wool, rubber
   (c) vinyl, silk

10. What is the difference between electric conductors and electric insulators? (17.5)

11. What is meant by the term ''grounding'' in static electricity? (17.5)

12. The diagrams below show insulated metal conductors that are charged negatively. Show how electrons are distributed on the conductors. (17.6)

(a)

(b)

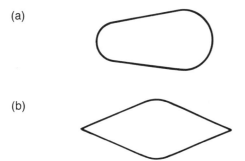

13. The diagram below shows a neutral metal conductor. A negatively charged strip is brought close to the right end of the conductor. Draw a diagram in your notebook, showing the distribution of charges on the conductor. (17.7)

+	+	+	+	+	+	+	+
−	−	−	−	−	−	−	−

14. State the final charge on a conductor that is:
    (a) charged by conduction using a negative strip
    (b) charged by conduction using a positive strip
    (c) charged by induction using a negative strip
    (d) charged by induction using a positive strip
    (17.7)

15. The diagrams below show a step-by-step procedure for charging two metal conductors by induction. Redraw the diagrams in your notebook, showing the distribution of charges in each case. (17.7, 17.8)

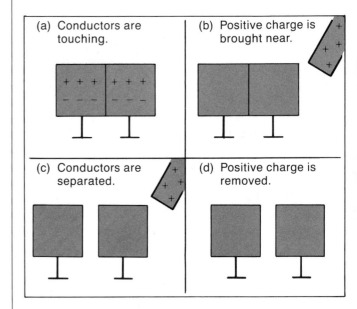

16. Static electricity shocks are noticed more in the dry winter months than in the moist summer months. What can be done to the air to reduce shocks in the winter? (17.10)

17. Research and report on careers that relate to static electricity (or electrostatics). Possible careers include the control of static electricity in the textile industry, the manufacture of electronic components, the manufacture and maintenance of photocopiers, and pollution control.

CHAPTER 18

Current Electricity

This chapter presents many of these fundamental concepts.

The electric circuit boards of devices such as computers and musical synthesizers appear to be very complex. However, the design of these complex circuits is based on some fundamental concepts of current electricity.

Main Ideas

- Current electricity is different from static electricity, and has many more uses.
- Components can be connected together (in series, or in parallel) to make an electric circuit.
- Three quantities often measured in electric circuits are current, potential difference (voltage), and resistance.

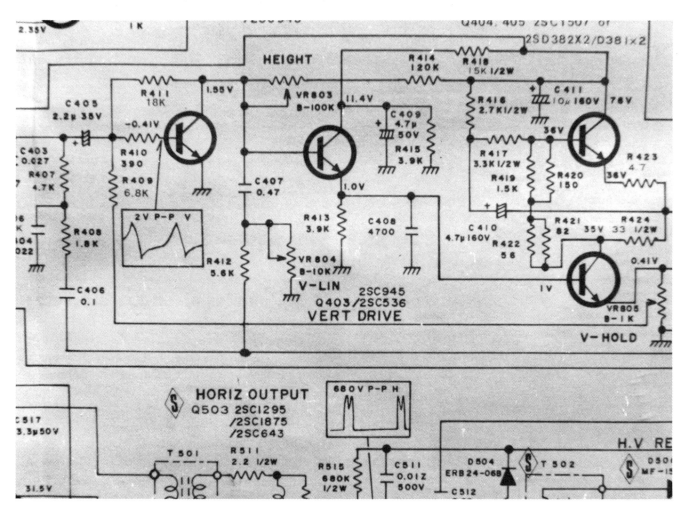

18.1 Electric Charges in Motion

The study of current electricity began about 200 years ago when an Italian doctor experimented with the legs of dead frogs. The doctor, named Luigi Galvani (1737-1798), noticed that the frog's legs jerked when they were touched with two different metals at the same time. He thought that something inside the legs had created electricity, which had caused the jerking movement.

Another Italian, a scientist named Count Alessandro Volta (1745-1827), heard about Galvani's experiments and began his own research. Volta proved it was the metals, not the frog's legs, that created the electricity. He was able to create electricity by simply placing two different metals into a fruit and connecting the metals with a wire. Such a set-up, now called a *voltaic cell* in his honour, is shown in Figure 18-1. The instrument that indicates the flow of electrons is called a *galvanometer*. It was named after Luigi Galvani.

Figure 18-1 A simple voltaic cell

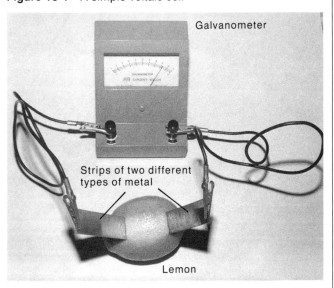

The type of electricity created by a voltaic cell is called current electricity. **Current electricity** is a continuous movement of charged particles in a path. This is different from static electricity (studied in Chapter 17) in which the charges do not flow in a set path. (In this book the charged particles we are concerned with are the negative electrons that move freely in conductors. Some scientists, especially those studying chemistry and electronics, are also concerned with the motion of positive charges.)

The electrons that move in current electricity get energy from some source. Then they repel each other through a path, such as a wire, and give their energy to some object. Of course, there are thousands of devices that use electrical energy. Our lives would be very different without this important type of energy.

PRACTICE

1. Describe the difference between static electricity and current electricity.
2. What type of charge is on the particles that move in a metal conductor?

18.2 Sources of Electrical Energy

People have learned how to change several kinds of energy into electrical energy. The source of energy depends greatly on what the electricity is used for. The electricity may be used to start a car, listen to a portable radio, operate computers on a satellite, heat a home, and so on.

Following is a description of five types of energy that can be changed into electrical energy. Scientists are constantly searching for new ways to perform this important task.

(1) **Chemical energy:** A chemical reaction can give energy to electrons to free them from atoms. When a wire is connected to a source, the electrons have a path through which to travel. We will mention two kinds of cells that change chemical energy into electrical energy. Two or more cells connected together form a battery of cells, or simply a *battery*.

   (a) **The primary cell or dry cell:** This source consists of two different metals and a chemical paste. Electrons repel each other from one metal (the negative electrode) through a conductor to the other metal. The electrons give energy to whatever is in the path. A primary cell cannot be recharged, but it is convenient because it contains no liquid and it can be made small. Primary cells are used to operate portable devices such as radios, electric toys, and flashlights. Miniature primary cells are used in quartz watches, hearing aids, musical greeting cards, microprocessor memory back-ups, as well as in pacemakers, which control the heartbeat of people with heart problems.

   (b) **The secondary cell or storage cell:** Again, this source has two different metals and a chemical substance. The important advantage of the secondary cell is that it can be recharged. This is done by using an outside source of electricity. Secondary cells that use acid and two types of lead are used in cars, trucks, and boats. Secondary cells that use other types of metal, such as nickel/cadmium cells, are used in camera flash sets, video cameras, and other portable devices.

(2) **Light energy:** When light strikes certain metal surfaces, electrons may be freed from the atoms near the surface. The electrons repel each other through the wire and give their energy to some device. Spacecraft, satellites, calculators, and camera light meters use photocells to change light energy into electrical energy. Refer to Figure 18-2.

(3) **Thermal energy:** Two wires made of different metals may be used to change thermal energy into electrical energy. The wires must be joined at one end and there must be a temperature difference between the joined end and the other ends of the wires. Such a device has several applications, including the measurement of very high and very low temperatures.

(4) **Mechanical energy:** Most of our electricity comes from spinning generators that change the mechanical energy of motion into electrical energy. The generators are forced to spin by the use of running water or by steam pressure. Electrons in the wires of the generators gain energy that is then distributed to homes, offices, and industries. This source of energy will be discussed in more detail later in the book.

(5) **Geothermal energy:** Electric generators can be run by using steam produced by thermal energy inside the earth. See Figure 18-3.

Figure 18-2 A spacecraft uses thousands of solar cells to create electricity.

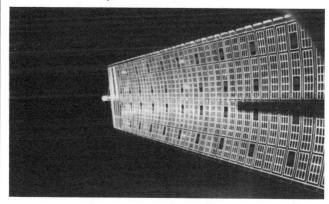

Figure 18-3 This geyser generating station is located in California, U.S.A.

PRACTICE

3. Name an electric device that receives energy from:
   (a) a primary cell or battery
   (b) a secondary cell or battery
   (c) the sun
   (d) falling water
4. State the difference between:
   (a) a cell and a battery
   (b) a primary cell and a secondary cell
5. Discuss in class how the following may be used to create electrical energy:
   (a) wind   (c) ocean waves
   (b) ocean tides   (d) biomass

Activity 18A   Portable Electric Devices

PROBLEM ■   What can be learned by comparing several devices that use electricity?

APPARATUS ■   several examples of electric devices that can be operated without being plugged into an electric outlet

PROCEDURE ■

1. Examine the electric devices available, and answer the following questions about them.
   (a) What types of sources provide energy for the devices?
   (b) For devices that use cells or a battery, which require only one cell or battery?
   (c) For devices that use more than one cell, how are the cells connected together: positive to negative, or positive to positive and negative to negative?
   (d) Are any of the cells or batteries rechargeable? If so, what are they made of?
   (e) Is there a way that the device can be operated by plugging it into an electrical outlet? If so, how is this accomplished?
   (f) What information about electricity is labelled on each device?
   (g) What information is labelled on the cells found in some of the devices?
2. List other observations about the devices or others you are familiar with.

ANALYSIS ■
1. List properties that portable electric devices have in common.
2. List properties that portable electric devices do not have in common.

18.3   Electric Current

In this chapter we will study three important electrical quantities: current, potential difference, and resistance.

Electric **current** is a measure of how many electrons pass through a wire or other electric device each second. The symbol for current is *I*. Its unit of measurement is the ampere or amp (A). This unit is named in honour of André-Marie Ampère, a French physicist who lived from 1775 to 1836.

An instrument used to measure electric current is called an **ammeter**. It must be connected directly into the path of the moving electrons. This kind of connection is called a **series connection**. Figure 18-4 shows the correct way of doing this. Follow the path of the electrons (e⁻) in that diagram. They leave the negative terminal of the battery. Then they enter the negative terminal of the ammeter, causing the needle to swing to the right. As they pass through the light bulb they give energy to the bulb. Then they are attracted back to the positive terminal of the source where they gain more energy.

Figure 18-4   Measuring electric current

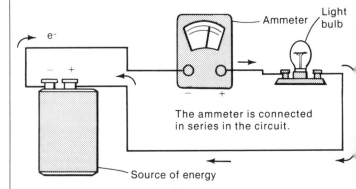

Figure 18-5   Reading an ammeter

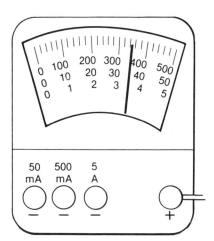

You will use an ammeter in activities later in this chapter. Some ammeters have a digital display, while others have a scale, or set of scales. One type, with three different scales, is shown in Figure 18-5. If you are required to change milliamps (mA) to amps, remember that milli means 1/1000. Thus, 1 A = 1000 mA.

Sample Problem 1

What does the ammeter in Figure 18-5 read if the wire is connected to the:
(a) 0–50 mA scale?
(b) 0–500 mA scale?
(c) 0–5 A scale?

Solution
(a) 35 mA or 0.035 A
(b) 350 mA or 0.35 A
(c) 3.5 A

PRACTICE

6. In a series connection, what is the maximum number of paths available for electron movement?
7. Change to amps:
   (a) 600 mA   (b) 80 mA   (c) 4000 mA

8. State the current in amps for the ammeter in Figure 18-6 when the wire is connected to the:
   (a) 0–500 mA scale
   (b) 0–5 A scale
   (c) 0–25 A scale

Figure 18-6

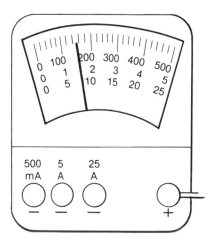

18.4   Electric Potential Difference

The purpose of electricity is to take energy from a source and deliver it to a useful device called a **load**. The source of electric current gives energy to the electrons it sends out. Electric **potential rise** is a measure of the amount of energy given to a group of electrons that leave the source. When the energetic electrons reach a load, they give their energy to it. Electric **potential drop** is a measure of the amount of energy given by a group of electrons to a load. An electric **potential difference** is either a potential rise or a potential drop.

Both potential rise and potential drop have the symbol V and are measured in **volts** (symbol V). This unit is named after Alessandro Volta, mentioned in Section 18.1. Because of this unit, electric potential difference is often called *voltage*. (In a similar fashion, current is sometimes called amperage.)

An instrument used to measure potential difference is called a **voltmeter**. To measure potential rise, the voltmeter must be connected across the source. To measure potential drop, the voltmeter must be connected across the load. This kind of connection is called a **parallel connection**. It is illustrated in Figure 18-7. Compare this parallel connection to the series connection for ammeters in Figure 18-4.

Notice in Figure 18-7 that the electrons leave the negative terminal of the source and enter the negative terminal of each voltmeter. This causes the needle in each voltmeter to swing to the right.

Figure 18-7 Measuring potential rise and potential drop

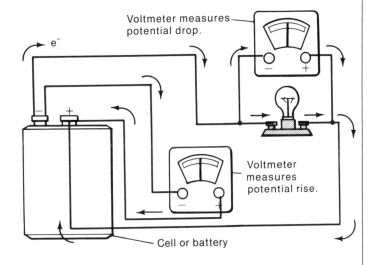

Voltmeter measures potential drop.

Voltmeter measures potential rise.

Cell or battery

Reading a multi-scale voltmeter is similar to reading a multi-scale ammeter, as you will discover in Practice #10.

PRACTICE

9. In a parallel connection, what is the minimum number of paths available for electron movement?

10. What is the voltage reading on the voltmeter in Figure 18-8 when the wire is connected to the:
    (a) 0–5 V scale?   (b) 0–15 V scale?
    (c) 0–300 V scale?

Figure 18-8

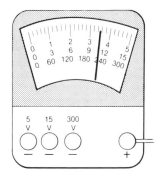

18.5 Electric Resistance

Electric conductors and insulators were discussed in Section 17.5. Conductors allow electrons to move more freely than do insulators. Electric **resistance** is a measure of how much a conductor fights the flow of electrons through it. The greater the resistance, the greater the amount of energy the electrons give up as they pass through a conductor.

An ordinary light bulb operates on this idea. Figure 18-9 shows the inside of such a bulb. The thick outside wires have low resistance and gain little energy from electrons. The very thin, coiled wire strung across the top has a high resistance to electron flow. Thus it gains much energy from the electrons, becomes hot, and gives off light. If the thin wire were replaced with straight copper wire, the bulb would not become hot.

The resistance of an electric conductor depends on four factors:
(1) **Length:** The longer the conductor, the greater the resistance.
(2) **Cross-sectional area:** The smaller the area, the greater the resistance.
(3) **Type of material:** Silver, copper, and gold have very low resistance; aluminum and tungsten have slightly higher resistance; iron has an even higher resistance.

Figure 18-9 Resistance wire in an electric light bulb

(4) **Temperature:** As the temperature drops, the resistance of most metals becomes lower. At low enough temperatures, the resistance of some materials drops to zero. These materials are called *superconductors*. Such materials would be very efficient in transporting electrical energy or operating ultra-fast computers. There are different materials, called *semiconductors*, whose resistance increases when the temperature drops. These materials are used in making electronic parts.

The symbol for resistance is R. Its unit of measurement is the **ohm** (symbol Ω, the Greek letter *omega*). This unit is named in honour of Georg Simon Ohm, 1787-1854, a German physicist. Resistance may be measured using an ohmmeter (see Practice #26). Rather than measuring it directly at the beginning, however, we will be using calculations to find resistance (Activity 18B).

Resistors are devices that have a known resistance. They are often used in electric and electronic devices, and in science laboratories. Two common materials used to make resistors are wire and granulated carbon. Figure 18-10 illustrates three resistors, a wire-wound resistor of constant or fixed value, a carbon resistor of fixed value, and a wire-wound variable resistor called a *rheostat*.

Figure 18-10 Three types of resistors

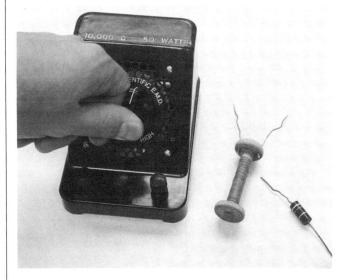

PRACTICE

11. If you were designing an electric toaster, would you use wire of high resistance or extremely low resistance? Why?
12. What happens to the resistance of an electric conductor when its:
    (a) length is decreased?
    (b) cross-sectional area is decreased?
13. Research and report on the use of either superconductors or semiconductors.

18.6 Electric Circuits

An electric **circuit** is a path through which electric charges may flow. It consists of three main parts:
(1) the source of energy (cell, battery, etc.)
(2) the transporter of energy (wires)
(3) the user of energy, or load (light bulb, etc.)

A circuit may also have switches and measuring instruments such as ammeters and voltmeters to determine current, potential difference, and resistance. Figures 18-4 and 18-7 show examples of circuits.

Figure 18-11 shows another simple but complete electric circuit. The voltmeter connected across the cell measures how much energy the cell gives to groups of electrons. The negatively charged electrons (e⁻) leave the cell and pass through an ammeter, which counts how many groups of electrons travel through the circuit each second. Then the electrons pass through the light bulb, giving their energy to it. The voltmeter across the bulb registers how much energy the groups of electrons give to the bulb. Finally the electrons are attracted back to the cell where they gain more energy.

So far we have seen circuits with only one load (a single light bulb). If a circuit has more than one load,

the energy from the electrons must be shared. This is presented in more detail later in the chapter.

The circuit in Figure 18-11 is a **closed circuit**. This means that electrons have a path they can follow. An **open circuit** results when the electron path is broken. For example, cutting the wire at point ''a'' in Figure 18-11 would cause an open circuit.

An electric circuit such as the one in Figure 18-11 is time-consuming to draw. Thus, symbols shown in Figure 18-12 are used to draw simpler diagrams of electric circuits. You should learn these symbols.

Figure 18-12 Symbols for drawing electric circuits

(a) Voltmeter

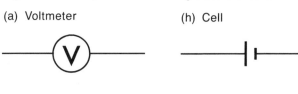

(h) Cell

(b) Ammeter

(i) Cells in series

(c) Resistor

(j) Battery of cells in series

(d) Incandescent light bulb

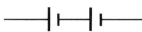

(k) Battery of cells in parallel

(e) Single-pole switch (open)

(l) Galvanometer

(f) Button switch (open)

(m) Fuse

(g) Ground

(n) DC power supply

(o) Rheostat

Figure 18-11 A simple electric circuit

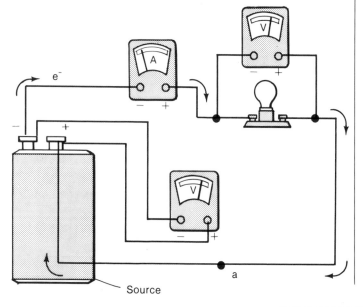

e⁻

a

Source

The advantage of using symbols in circuit diagrams is evident in Figure 18-13. Diagram (a) shows an electric circuit and diagram (b) shows the same circuit using symbols.

Figure 18-13 Circuit diagrams

(a) An electric circuit

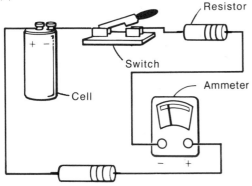

(b) The circuit in (a) using symbols

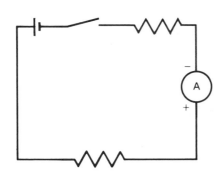

PRACTICE

14. In an electric circuit, what is the function of each of the following?
    (a) battery   (d) ammeter
    (b) wires   (e) voltmeter
    (c) load
15. Use symbols to draw a diagram of the circuit shown in:
    (a) Figure 18-4 (b) Figure 18-7 (c) Figure 18-11

16. Try this. Determine the potential rise of series and parallel cells in a circuit. You will need a voltmeter, two or three cells, connecting wires, and a load (for example, a 25 Ω resistor). Measure the potential rise of each cell connected to the load. Then arrange the cells in series and parallel and find the potential rise in each case. See Figure 18-14.

⚠ **CAUTION   Have your teacher check each circuit before you close the switch.**

Figure 18-14

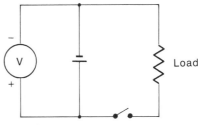

(a) Single cell

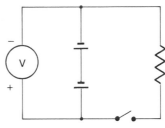

(b) Cells in series

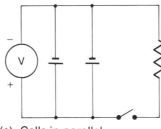

(c) Cells in parallel

17. What is the total potential rise for a series connection of these cells?
    (a) 2.0 V, 5.0 V
    (b) 2 V, 3 V, 4 V
    (c) 50 V, 100 V, 70 V

18.7 Ohm's Law

It was the German scientist, Georg Simon Ohm, who discovered one of the most important laws of physics. Ohm's law describes how electric current, potential difference, and resistance are related. It states that:

The ratio of the potential difference across a resistor to the current through it is constant, if we neglect the effect of temperature.

This ratio of potential difference to current is what we call resistance, R (Section 18.5). Thus, Ohm's law can be written in equation form.

$$R = \frac{V}{I}$$

Since potential difference is measured in volts and current in amps, resistance is measured in volts per amp or ohms (Ω).

To have consistent units, current readings in milliamps should be changed to amps before calculations are made.

Sample Problem 2

A heating coil on an electric stove draws 25 A of current from a 240 V circuit. What is the coil's resistance?

Solution $R = \frac{V}{I}$

$$= \frac{240 \text{ V}}{25 \text{ A}}$$

$$= 9.6 \,\Omega$$

The coil's resistance is 9.6 Ω.

PRACTICE

18. Calculate the value of the resistance in each case:
    (a) $V = 20$ V, $I = 4.0$ A
    (b) $V = 120$ V, $I = 8.0$ A
    (c) $V = 8.0$ V, $I = 0.50$ A
    (d) $V = 10$ V, $I = 400$ mA

19. Rearrange the equation $R = \frac{V}{I}$ to express:
    (a) V by itself   (b) I by itself

20. The current through a 50 Ω resistor is 2.5 A. What is the potential drop across the resistor?

21. The potential drop across a 20 Ω resistor is 10 V. What is the current through the resistor?

Activity 18B   Testing Resistors

PROBLEM ■   How can graphing be used to check Ohm's law?

APPARATUS ■   3 fixed resistors of different values (e.g., 100 Ω, 50 Ω, and 25 Ω); 3 dry cells or a variable power supply; voltmeter; ammeter; connecting wires

 CAUTION *Never leave an electric circuit connected longer than necessary because overheating may result.*

 CAUTION *Do not exceed the electric potential rise prescribed by your teacher.*

PROCEDURE ■
1. Connect the circuit as shown in Figure 18-15 using the first resistor (R_1) and a low potential rise. Record the labelled resistance of R_1 in a table based on Table 18-1.
2. Measure the current through the resistor and the potential drop across it. Record your observations.

3. Repeat #2 using the same resistor but a higher potential rise.
4. Repeat #2 using a third, still higher potential rise.
5. Repeat #1 to #4 using a second resistor (R_2) and finally a third resistor (R_3).

Figure 18-15

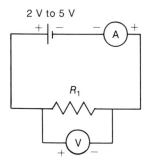

2 V to 5 V

R_1

Table 18-1 For Activity 18B

R (ohms)	V (volts)	I (amps)
R_1 =		

SAMPLE

ANALYSIS ■

1. On a single graph of potential rise (vertical axis) against current (horizontal axis), plot the results of the activity. Draw three separate straight lines of best fit, one for each resistor. Label the lines.
2. Calculate the slope of each straight line. Include units.
3. Compare the slopes to the values of the labelled (known) resistances of the resistors.
4. Comment on how well the activity worked out. (Hint: Consider both #3 and the points on the graph.)

18.8 Series and Parallel Circuits

There are two different methods of connecting resistors. In a **series circuit** all the electrons that leave the source must follow the same path [Figure 18-16(a)]. In a **parallel circuit** the electrons leave the source and come to a junction or dividing point. At that point the electrons must choose which path to take [Figure 18-16(b)]. Circuits may have both series and parallel connections, as shown in Figure 18-16(c).

Figure 18-16 Series and parallel circuits

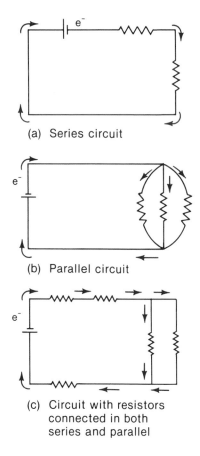

(a) Series circuit

(b) Parallel circuit

(c) Circuit with resistors connected in both series and parallel

To analyse the currents and potential differences in various parts of circuits, two convenient symbols will be introduced.

The symbol I_a means the current through the wire at point "a". The symbol V_{bc} means the potential drop (or rise) from point "b" to point "c". These are illustrated in Figure 18-17.

Figure 18-17

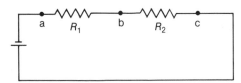

(a) Circuit with points a, b, and c

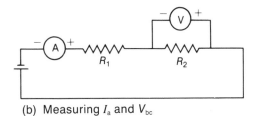

(b) Measuring I_a and V_{bc}

Activity 18C   Resistors in Series

PROBLEM ■ What are the properties of a series circuit?

APPARATUS ■ 2 fixed resistors of different size (e.g., 100 Ω and 50 Ω); dry cells or a variable power supply; voltmeter; ammeter; connecting wires

Figure 18-18

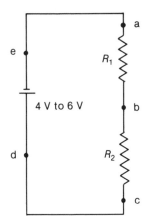

PROCEDURE ■
1. Set up the series circuit shown in Figure 18-18 but place an ammeter at "a" to measure I_a. Record the current in amps.

 CAUTION Do not exceed the electric potential rise prescribed by your teacher.

2. Using the same basic circuit and potential rise, measure I_b and I_c. Compare these values to I_a.
3. Using the same circuit, measure V_{ed}, V_{ab}, and V_{bc}. Compare the potential rise (V_{ed}) to the sum of the potential drops across the resistors ($V_{ab} + V_{bc}$).

ANALYSIS ■
1. How does the current in one part of a series circuit compare with the current in another part?
2. How does the potential rise (given by the source) compare with the sum of the potential drops (used by the loads)?
3. Use Ohm's law to calculate the total resistance of the circuit $\left(R_T = \dfrac{V_{ac}}{I}\right)$.
4. Use the same law to calculate $R_1 = \dfrac{V_{ab}}{I}$ and $R_2 = \dfrac{V_{bc}}{I}$.
5. Find the sum of R_1 and R_2, and compare it to R_T.
6. How does the total resistance in a series circuit compare with the sum of the individual resistances?
7. In a series circuit, will the current continue to flow if one resistor is suddenly removed? Explain your answer.

Activity 18D   Resistors in Parallel

PROBLEM ■ What are the properties of a parallel circuit?

APPARATUS ■ as in Activity 18C

Figure 18-19

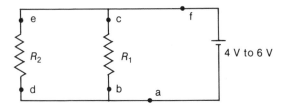

PROCEDURE ■

1. Set up the parallel circuit shown in Figure 18-19, but place an ammeter at "a" to measure the total current (I_a) coming from the power supply.
2. Alter the circuit to measure first I_b and then I_d. What does the sum $I_b + I_d$ represent? (This is the most difficult experimental procedure in the chapter. Have your teacher check the results before you proceed to #3.)
3. In the same circuit measure the potential drops V_{bc} and V_{de}. What do you observe?

ANALYSIS ■

1. In a parallel circuit, how does the total current coming from the source compare with the sum of the currents through the individual resistors?
2. In a parallel circuit, how does the potential drop across one resistor compare with the potential drop across the other resistors?
3. Use Ohm's law to calculate the total resistance of the circuit $\left(R_T = \dfrac{V}{I_a} \right)$.
4. Use the same law for $R_1 = \dfrac{V_{bc}}{I_b}$ and $R_2 = \dfrac{V_{de}}{I_d}$.
5. How does R_T compare with either R_1 or R_2?
6. How does the total resistance in the parallel circuit compare with the individual resistances?
7. In a parallel circuit, will the current continue to flow if one resistor is suddenly removed? Explain your answer.

18.9 Calculations Involving Electric Circuits

When resistors are connected in series, the total resistance (R_T) is the sum of the individual resistances. This can be summarized in the following equation.

$$R_T = R_1 + R_2 + R_3 + \ldots$$
where R_1, R_2, and R_3 . . . are individual resistances connected in series

When resistors are connected in parallel, the total resistance (R_T) can be found using the following equation.

$$\frac{1}{R_T} = \frac{1}{R_1} + \frac{1}{R_2} + \frac{1}{R_3} + \ldots$$
where R_1, R_2, and R_3 . . . are individual resistances connected in parallel

The derivations of these resistance equations are found in Appendix F at the back of the book.

Sample Problem 3

Find the total resistance when 5 Ω, 10 Ω, and 30 Ω are connected in:
(a) series
(b) parallel

Solution

(a) series $R_T = R_1 + R_2 + R_3$
$ = 5\,\Omega + 10\,\Omega + 30\,\Omega$
$ = 45\,\Omega$

(b) parallel $\dfrac{1}{R_T} = \dfrac{1}{R_1} + \dfrac{1}{R_2} + \dfrac{1}{R_3}$

$\dfrac{1}{R_T} = \dfrac{1}{5} + \dfrac{1}{10} + \dfrac{1}{30}$

$\dfrac{1}{R_T} = \dfrac{6}{30} + \dfrac{3}{30} + \dfrac{1}{30}$

$\dfrac{1}{R_T} = \dfrac{10}{30}$

therefore $R_T = \dfrac{30}{10} = 3\,\Omega$

Notice in sample problem 3 that the total resistance (3 Ω) is less than any of the resistances connected in parallel. You also observed this for two resistors in Activity 18D. The reason it occurs is that the electrons have more than one path to take, so the resistance actually decreases.

The remainder of this section is devoted to solving circuit problems by applying Ohm's law and the information in Table 18-2 (overleaf).

The equations for total resistance as well as other properties of series and parallel circuits are summarized in Table 18-2.

Table 18-2 Series and Parallel Circuits

Type of circuit	Series	Parallel
Example	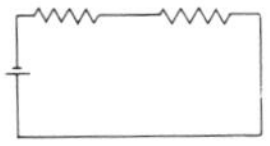	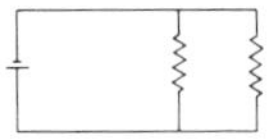
Current	Current is constant throughout the entire circuit.	Individual currents add up to the total current.
Potential Difference	Individual potential drops add up to the total potential drop.	Potential difference is constant across all parts of the circuit.
Resistance	$R_T = R_1 + R_2 + \ldots$	$\frac{1}{R_T} = \frac{1}{R_1} + \frac{1}{R_2} + \ldots$

Sample Problem 4

Given: $V_{ab} = 20$ V;
$R_1 = 10\ \Omega$;
$I_a = 2$ A

Find: (a) I_b
(b) V_{bc}
(c) R_T
(d) R_2

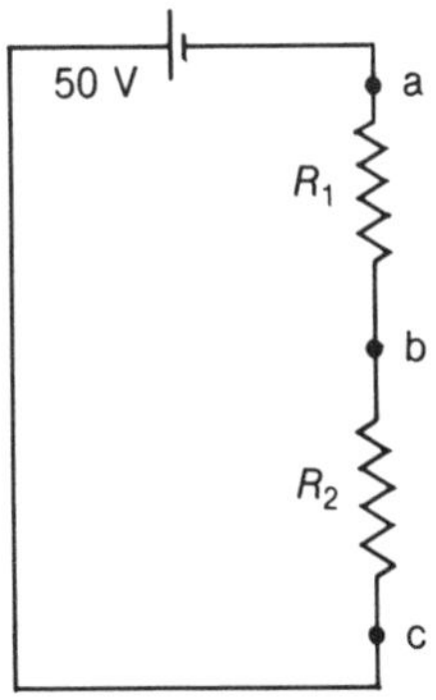

Solution

(a) I_b = 2 A because the current is constant in a series circuit.

(b) V_{bc} = 50 V − 20 V
= 30 V because the total potential drop is the sum of the individual potential drops.

(c) $R_T = \frac{V_T}{I}$
$= \frac{50\text{ V}}{2\text{ A}}$
$= 25\ \Omega$

(d) $R_2 = 25\ \Omega - 10\ \Omega$
= 15 Ω because the total resistance is the sum of the individual resistances.

Sample Problem 5

Given: $V_{ab} = 20$ V;
$I_a = 4$ A;
$I_c = 1$ A

Find: (a) V_{cd}
(b) I_e

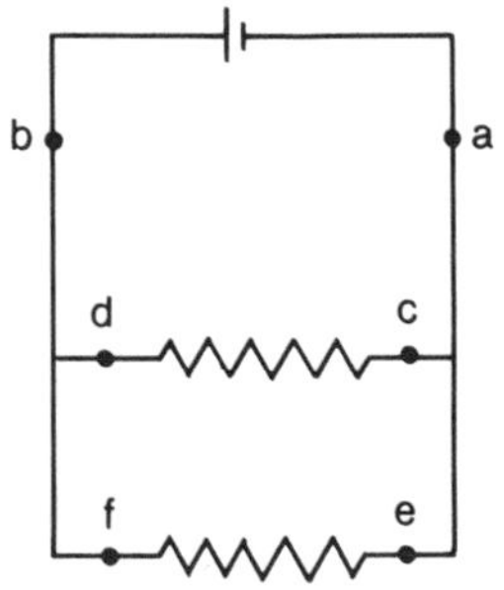

Solution

(a) V_{cd} = 20 V because the potential difference is constant in a parallel circuit.

(b) I_c = 4 A − 1 A
= 3 A because the total current equals the sum of the individual currents.

PRACTICE

22. Find the total resistance when the following resistors are connected in series:
    (a) 2.2 Ω, 5.5 Ω
    (b) 80 Ω, 320 Ω, 800 Ω
    (c) 1 Ω, 10 Ω, 100 Ω, 1000 Ω
23. Find the total resistance when the following resistors are connected in parallel:
    (a) 8 Ω, 8 Ω
    (b) 30 Ω, 30 Ω, 30 Ω
    (c) 15 Ω, 60 Ω, 60 Ω
24. In the circuit diagram, $V_{ab} = 4$ V, $I_a = 2$ A, and $R_1 = 2$ Ω
    Find   (a) I_c (b) V_{bc} (c) R_T (d) R_2

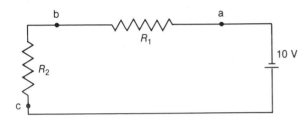

25. In the circuit diagram, $I_b = 2$ A and $I_c = 3$ A.
    Find   (a) V_{bd} (b) I_a (c) R_T

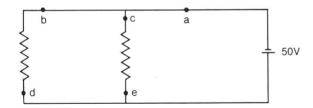

26. Try this. Obtain an ohmmeter and two or three resistors of unknown resistances. Measure each resistance using the ohmmeter. Use the data to determine what the total resistance would be if these resistors were connected in parallel. Then connect them in parallel and use the ohmmeter to check your calculations.

Words to Know

current electricity	resistance
current	ohm
ammeter	resistor
amps	circuit
potential difference	closed circuit
potential rise	open circuit
potential drop	Ohm's law
volt	series circuit
voltmeter	parallel circuit

Chapter Objectives

Having completed this chapter, you should now be able to:

1. State the difference between static electricity and current electricity.
2. List sources of electrical energy.
3. Define electric current and measure it using an ammeter.
4. Define electric potential difference and measure it using a voltmeter.
5. State the difference between potential rise and potential drop.
6. Define electric resistance and state the factors that affect the resistance of an electric conductor.
7. Draw diagrams of electric circuits using correct symbols.
8. Set up electric circuits using equipment available in the laboratory.
9. Describe how to connect cells in series and calculate the resulting potential rise.
10. State Ohm's law in equation form $\left(R = \dfrac{V}{I} \right)$ and prove it experimentally.
11. Given the potential difference across a resistor and the current through it, calculate its resistance in ohms.
12. Calculate the total resistance for resistors connected in series or in parallel.
13. Analyse electric circuits for resistors connected either in series or in parallel.

Chapter Review

1. Describe the difference between static electricity and current electricity. (18.1)
2. Name a common device that changes chemical energy into electrical energy. (18.2)
3. State one advantage of a:
   (a) primary cell
   (b) secondary cell (18.2)
4. What is our most common source of electrical energy? (18.2)
5. Write the symbol for each of the following:
   (a) current
   (b) potential difference
   (c) resistance
   (d) amps
   (e) volts
   (f) ohms
   (g) milliamps
   (h) kilovolts
   (18.3-18.5)
6. Name the instrument used to measure:
   (a) electric current
   (b) electric potential difference (18.3, 18.4)
7. Change the following to amps or volts:
   (a) 350 mA (c) 905 mV
   (b) 42 mA (d) 1050 mV (18.3, 18.4)
8. State the kind of connection (series or parallel) for:
   (a) an ammeter
   (b) a voltmeter (18.3, 18.4)
9. What is the difference between potential rise and potential drop? (18.4)
10. State four factors that affect the resistance of an electric conductor. (18.5)
11. Why is copper a good choice for electric wiring? (18.5)
12. Describe the difference between a closed circuit and an open circuit. (18.6)
13. Use proper symbols to draw a diagram of the following series circuit. Two cells are connected to a switch, a light bulb, an ammeter, and two resistors. Include a voltmeter to measure the potential drop across the light bulb. (18.6)
14. What is the total potential rise when four 2.5 V cells are connected in series? (18.6)
15. State Ohm's law in equation form. (18.7)

16. Calculate the resistance of each of the following appliances:
    (a) an electric toaster draws 10 A of current from a 120 V circuit
    (b) an electric razor operates at 0.25 A when the potential difference is 5.0 V
    (c) a clothes dryer, operating at 240 V, draws 12 A of current (18.7)
17. Calculate the unknown quantities: (18.7)
    (a) $R = 70\ \Omega;\ I = 0.30\ \text{A};\ V = \ ?\text{V}$
    (b) $R = 24\ \Omega,\ V = 12\ \text{V};\ I = \ ?\text{A}$
18. If 0.8 A of current flow through a 75 Ω resistor, what is the potential drop across the resistor? (18.7)
19. A certain fuse used in a 120 V circuit has a resistance of 8.0 Ω. What is the current rating of the fuse? (18.7)
20. Redraw the circuit shown here in your notebook.

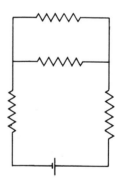

    (a) Indicate the direction of the flow of electrons in all parts of the circuit.
    (b) State the purpose of the cell. (18.6, 18.7)
21. Calculate the total resistance when 100 Ω, 200 Ω, and 600 Ω are connected in:
    (a) series
    (b) parallel (18.9)

22. In the circuit shown, $R_1 = 20\ \Omega$.
The potential drop across R_1 is 10 V and across R_2 is 20 V.

(a) What type of circuit is shown?
(b) What is the total potential drop across both resistors?
(c) What is the potential rise given by the source?
(d) Calculate the total resistance in the circuit if the current is 0.50 A.
(e) Find the value of R_2. (18.9)

23. In the circuit shown, $I_a = 2.0$ A and $I_c = 0.50$ A. The potential rise given by the source is 3.0 V.
(a) What type of circuit is shown?
(b) What is the potential drop across R_1?
(c) What is the potential drop across R_2?
(d) What is the value of I_b?
(e) Calculate the total resistance of the circuit. (18.9)

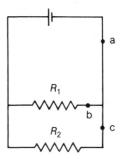

24. Write a story of how your lifestyle would be different if all vehicles in North America used rechargeable batteries rather than fossil fuels.

CHAPTER 19

Using Electrical Energy

Every year numerous homes and other structures are partially or totally burned by fires started by electrical problems. Electrical energy is very useful, but only if it is used wisely and safely. This chapter emphasizes the use of electrical energy in the household. It concludes with a look at electrical safety and the conservation of electrical energy.

Main Ideas

- Both direct and alternating electric currents have specific uses.
- Household electric circuits apply the advantages of parallel connections.
- The cost of current electricity can be found by knowing the amount of energy consumed and the cost rate of the energy.
- It is important to use electrical energy wisely by exercising both safety and conservation.

19.1 Direct and Alternating Currents

Current electricity is a flow of electric charges; in metal conductors it is the flow of electrons. If the electrons flow continuously in a path without reversing direction, the current is called **direct current** or **DC**. Battery-operated devices, such as flashlights, electrical systems in cars, and portable radios, use direct current. The activities performed in Chapter 18 also used direct-current circuits (Figure 19-1).

Figure 19-1 A DC circuit

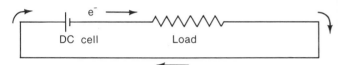

Electrons repel each other through the circuit without reversing direction.

If the electrons in a circuit are forced to reverse their direction periodically, the current is called **alternating current** or **AC**. This type of current is created by our huge electric generators. The generators force nearby electrons back and forth in the wires. Those electrons repel other electrons almost immediately back and forth through the entire circuit. Most of our industries and most of our appliances use alternating current. See Figure 19-2. (Electric generators are discussed in greater detail in Chapter 21.)

Figure 19-2 An AC circuit

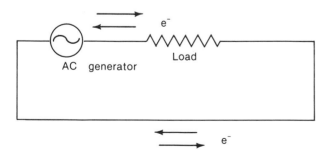

Electrons are repelled back and forth in the circuit. (Notice the new symbol introduced in the circuit diagram.)

The AC generators in North America force the electrons to repeat their back-and-forth motion 60 times per second. Thus, our AC is rated at a frequency of 60 Hz. (Some countries, including those in Europe, use a frequency of 50 Hz.) Our eyes cannot tell that lights are flashing on and off 60 times each second. At lower frequencies, say around 20 Hz to 25 Hz, we can see a flickering.

The reason AC is used in our electrical systems is that, with our present technology, AC is easier to transmit than DC. Electrical energy produced by generators can be transmitted large distances by great networks of power lines and transformers. (Transformers are discussed in Chapter 21.)

The electricity available in most outlets in homes and schools is 120 V (AC). That potential difference can be changed into some other value using a device called an adaptor. Figure 19-3 shows an adaptor that can operate an instrument such as a calculator. The adaptor changes alternating current (120 V, 60 Hz) into direct current (9 V, 100 mA). In this case the instrument can also be operated with a 9 V (DC) battery.

Figure 19-3 An adaptor can change AC into DC.

PRACTICE

1. Describe how electrons move in:
   (a) a direct-current circuit
   (b) an alternating-current circuit
2. State which type of current (AC or DC) is used to operate:
   (a) a refrigerator
   (b) a portable radio
   (c) an automobile cigarette lighter
   (d) an incandescent light bulb

19.2   Uses of Current Electricity

Anyone who has experienced an electrical "blackout" can appreciate how much we rely on electricity. Electricity provides comfort, convenience, and entertainment, and does a great amount of work for us.

Section 18.2 described how chemical, thermal, light, and mechanical energies can be changed into electrical energy. Once the electrical energy is distributed to the user, it can be changed back into other types of energy.

Electrical energy is easily changed into light and thermal energy. Light energy is one of the most common uses of electricity. Thermal energy is used to cook food, iron clothes, and heat car engines on winter nights in cold regions.

Electrical energy can be changed into chemical energy, creating special chemical reactions. One process uses electrical energy to separate certain metals, such as aluminum, from their ores. Another process uses electrical energy to electroplate one metal onto another. For example, steel bumpers on cars are covered with thin layers of copper, nickel, and chromium.

Electrical energy is often turned into mechanical energy or energy of motion. This occurs in devices such as egg beaters, drills, lathes, and many other tools.

Perhaps the most versatile electric tool is the computer, which, of course, requires electrical energy to function. Computers are found in control systems in cars, airplanes, and spacecraft. They are used to help design cars, boats, and buildings; operate mechanical robots in industry; run instant banking systems; guide devices that help handicapped people to live independently; compose/enhance music, drawings, and so on.

Because the human body has its own electrical system, electrical energy also has many medical uses. Injuries, especially bone fractures, heal faster with increased electrical activity. If this increase is not provided from inside the body, it can be supplied from outside the body. As another example, some people have abnormal heartbeats, and need a device — a pacemaker — to regulate this, and so lead a normal life. (Pacemakers were mentioned in Section 18.2.)

Of course, there are hundreds of other uses of current electricity, too numerous to mention here.

PRACTICE

3. Name two devices, other than those mentioned in this section, that change electrical energy into:
   (a) thermal energy   (b) mechanical energy
4. Sound energy was not mentioned in this section. Name two devices that change electrical energy into sound energy.

19.3   Current Electricity in the Home

Figure 19-4 shows the basic electrical wiring entering an ordinary household. Electrical energy is delivered to homes either through underground cables or from utility poles. Three wires are fed into a meter and then into a fuse box or circuit-breaker box. Two wires, covered with red insulation (R) and black insulation (B), are called "hot" or "live". The third wire, usually bare or covered with white insulation (W), is called neutral. (Green insulation may also be used to cover the neutral wire.)

Several other things can be seen in Figure 19-4. The neutral wires are connected to the neutral bar. They have a direct path to the ground because they are not connected to any fuses. The black and red wires pass through large cartridge fuses. Then they are directed,

again through cartridge fuses, to a circuit for large appliances. The potential difference between the black wire and the red wire is 240 V. This is the amount needed for major appliances such as a clothes dryer, stove, water heater, and air conditioner.

The black wire in Figure 19-4 is also shown connected through plug fuses to two 120 V circuits. The potential difference between B and W is 120 V. This amount is used for most lights, outlets, and small appliances. The 120 V circuits may also be connected between R and W, although this is not shown in the diagram.

The broken lines in Figure 19-4 are grounding wires, which are included for extra safety.

A **fuse** is a device used to protect against overheating. A fuse has a wire that burns if the current exceeds a certain limit, such as 15 A. This causes an open circuit and the electrons no longer flow. Then the fuse must be replaced.

Figure 19-4   Electricity delivered to the home

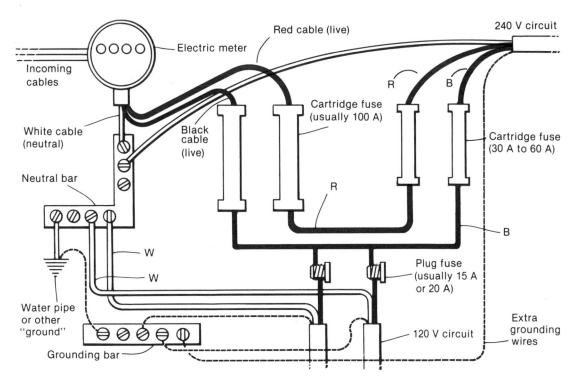

Circuit breakers have the same function as fuses, but are more convenient. One type of circuit breaker has a bar made of two strips of different metals. The metals expand at different rates when heated, causing the bar to bend. If a circuit overheats, the bar bends far enough to trip a switch. The switch must then be reset. (The compound bar was discussed in Chapter 12.)

In each household there are several 120 V circuits connected either to B-W or R-W. A simple 120 V circuit is shown in Figure 19-5(a). It consists of two lights, two single outlets, and a plug fuse to the black or red wire. Diagram (b) shows the same circuit with grounding added. Diagram (c) shows a three-prong plug and receptacle. Notice in all three parts of Figure 19-5 that the left side of the plug is longer than the right side. This type of "polarized" plug ensures that the correct part of the circuit of each appliance is attached to the live wire in the circuit.

In Figure 19-5 the loads are connected in parallel.

Figure 19-5 A simple 120 V circuit

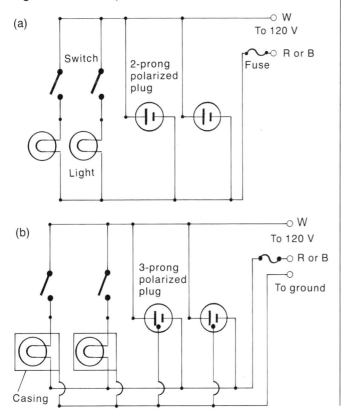

(c)

As you learned in Activities 18C and 18D, this type of connection has an advantage over a series connection. In a series connection, if one load is burned out or removed, the other loads do not work. In a parallel connection each load can work without the other loads.

PRACTICE

5. What potential differences are possible in household circuits?
6. In a household electric circuit, what is the function of each of the following?
   (a) the electric meter   (c) grounding wires
   (b) a fuse or circuit breaker   (d) a switch

19.4 Electric Power

Power is the rate of using energy. (See Section 7.6.) Its equation is:

$$\text{power} = \frac{\text{energy}}{\text{time}} \quad \text{or} \quad P = \frac{E}{t}$$

Energy is measured in joules (J), time in seconds (s), and power in joules per second or watts (W).

The equation $P = \frac{E}{t}$ can be used to derive an equation for electric power in terms of potential difference and current. That equation, derived in Appendix F, is:

$$\text{electric power} = \text{potential difference} \times \text{current}$$
$$\text{or} \qquad P = VI$$

Potential difference is measured in volts (V), current in amps (A), and power in watts (W). A watt is a small unit, so power is often stated in kilowatts (1 kW $= 10^3$ W), or megawatts (1 MW $= 10^6$ W).

Sample Problem 1

A small colour television, connected to a 120 V outlet, draws 1.5 A of current. Calculate its power rating.

Solution $P = VI$
$\qquad\quad = 120 \text{ V} \times 1.5 \text{ A}$
$\qquad\quad = 180 \text{ W}$

PRACTICE

7. Calculate the power rating of each appliance:
   (a) a 120 V electric sander draws 3.0 A of current
   (b) an electric can opener, used in a 120 V circuit, operates at 2.2 A
   (c) an electric handsaw operates at 9.5 A when connected to 120 V
   (d) a portable radio, using four 1.5 V cells in series, draws a current of 0.6 A
8. Rearrange the equation $P = VI$ to express:
   (a) V by itself
   (b) I by itself
9. Calculate the potential difference across a 0.9 W calculator that draws a current of 0.1 A.
10. What is the current used by a 1200 W electric kettle in a 120 V household circuit?

19.5 The Cost of Current Electricity

Whether we use electrical or other forms of energy, the cost is important in our daily lives. To learn how power companies charge customers for energy, we shall begin with the equation for power expressed in terms of energy and time, $P = \frac{E}{t}$. If that equation is rearranged to express E by itself, we have:

$$\text{energy} = \text{power} \times \text{time} \quad \text{or} \quad E = Pt$$

Thus, if we know the power rating (in watts) of an appliance and the time (in seconds) it is used, we can find the energy consumed (in joules).

After the energy has been calculated, it can be used in another equation to find the cost of the electricity. That equation is:

$$\text{cost} = \text{rate} \times \text{energy}$$

The rate is expressed in some convenient unit, as you will learn in the sample problems that follow.

In sample problem 2, assume that a power company charges 1.6¢ for each one million joules (1.0 MJ) of energy consumed. In other words, the rate is 1.6¢/MJ.

Sample Problem 2

A 500 W hair dryer is used for 5 min (300 s). Calculate the:
(a) energy consumed (in joules and megajoules)
(b) cost of the energy

Solution
(a) $E = Pt$

$$= 500 \text{ W} \times 300 \text{ s} \qquad \left(\text{W} = \frac{\text{J}}{\text{s}}\right)$$

$$= 150\ 000 \text{ J or } 0.15 \text{ MJ}$$
(Move the decimal six places.)
(b) cost = rate × energy

$$= 1.6 \frac{\text{¢}}{\text{MJ}} \times 0.15 \text{ MJ}$$

(Note the division of units.)

$$= 0.24\text{¢}$$

DID YOU KNOW?

The cost of electrical energy increased an average of about 3% per year for the 10 years prior to the writing of this text. This is less than the average increase of most things in our society; it is much less than the average increase in the cost of energy used to power automobiles.

In many regions, power companies calculate energy in units other than megajoules. Thus, in the equation $E = Pt$, if power is measured in kilowatts (kW) and time in hours (h), then energy is stated in kilowatt hours (kW·h).

In sample problem 3, assume that the rate charged by a power company is 5.5¢/(kW·h).

Sample Problem 3

A 100 W (0.10 kW) light bulb is turned on for 4.0 h. Calculate the
(a) energy consumed (in kilowatt hours)
(b) cost of the energy

Solution
(a) $E = Pt$

$$= 0.10 \text{ kW} \times 4.0 \text{ h}$$

$$= 0.40 \text{ kW·h}$$
(b) cost = rate × energy

$$= 5.5 \frac{\text{¢}}{\text{kW·h}} \times 0.40 \text{ kW·h}$$

(Note the division of units.)

$$= 2.2\text{¢}$$

An electric meter is used to determine how much energy (in megajoules or kilowatt hours) is consumed by a household each month. Figure 19-6(a) shows a typical electric meter having four dials. The dials are read from left to right and the reading is multiplied by 10. Meters with five dials do not require the multiplication factor of 10. In Figure 19-6(b) the reading is $2418 \times 10 = 24\ 180 \text{ kW·h}$.

Sample Problem 4

(a) What is the meter reading in Figure 19-6(c)?
(b) Assume that one month elapsed between the readings in (b) and (c), Figure 19-6. How much energy was used in the month?
(c) At a rate of 6.0¢/(kW·h), how much did the electrical energy cost?

Solution
(a) 24 530 kW·h
(b) 24 530 kW·h − 24 180 kW·h = 350 kW·h
(c) cost = rate × energy

$$= 6.0 \frac{\text{¢}}{\text{kW·h}} \times 350 \text{ kW·h}$$

$$= 2100\text{¢ or } \$21.00$$

Figure 19-6   Reading an electric meter

(a) Notice that the dials on this typical electric meter have pointers which move (reading left to right) counterclockwise, then clockwise, then counterclockwise, and finally clockwise.

(b) March 1 reading   kilowatt hours

multiply by 10

(c) April 1 reading   kilowatt hours

multiply by 10

PRACTICE

11. For each appliance listed calculate the *energy* consumed (in megajoules) and the *cost* of the energy. Assume a rate of 2.0¢/MJ.
    (a) a 50 W stereo is operated for 15 h (54 000 s)
    (b) a 200 W air conditioner is run for 10 h (36 000 s)
    (c) a 1500 W coffee-making machine is left on for 2 h (7200 s)

12. For each appliance listed calculate the *energy* consumed (in kilowatt hours) and the *cost* of the energy. Assume a rate of 6.0¢/(kW·h).
    (a) a 300 W drill (0.3 kW) is used for 0.5 h
    (b) a 1500 W oven (1.5 kW) is operated for 2 h
    (c) an 800 W car engine heater (0.8 kW) is used for 8.0 h

13. The diagrams show meter readings two months apart. The electricity costs 5.0¢/(kW·h).

May 1      × 10

July 1      × 10

(a) How much energy was used during the two months?
(b) Calculate the cost of the energy.

DID YOU KNOW?

In a home that has a furnace with an electric fan, the fan consumes about 1/8 of all the electrical energy used in the home.   To maintain the efficiency of the fan, it is important to keep the furnace filters clean.

Activity **19A**   Home Energy Consumption

Read the electric meter in your home, or the home of a friend, at about the same time each day for a predetermined amount of time, such as two weeks. Make up a table summarizing your readings. By subtraction, determine the energy consumed each day. Then use the local cost rate to find the cost of the energy each day.

 CAUTION   Do not touch the meter, or any wires attached to the meter.

Write a report that includes the following:
- the observations and calculations suggested above
- a description of factors that may have affected the electrical energy consumption during the time of the activity
- a discussion of ways the use of electrical energy in your home could be reduced

Activity **19B**   Appliance Energy Consumption

Choose several electric appliances or other devices whose power rating is indicated on a label plate.

 CAUTION   Disconnect the appliance first.

For each device chosen, estimate as closely as possible the amount of time it would be in use in one year. Then calculate the electrical energy consumed *and* the cost of that energy for each device for one year. (Use the cost rate charged by your local electric power company.) Write a report of your findings.

19.6   Electrical Safety

Each year many lives are lost and properties damaged due to the careless use of electricity. Electricity can be a hazard and must be treated wisely.

If a fuse blows, it should be replaced with a fuse of the correct size. Overheating causes fuses to blow, so the reason for overheating should be found and corrected. The reason may be too many appliances connected to one circuit, a frayed cord, or a faulty appliance. Similar precautions apply to the use of circuit breakers.

Wherever there is water or moisture, electricity should be avoided. For example, a telephone or electric radio should not be used near a bathtub. Impure water is a good conductor of electric current, and household currents are large enough to kill a person.

> **DID YOU KNOW?**
>
> **A** current of only 20 mA (AC) can cause human muscles to become paralysed. If a person grabs a bare wire that is live and receives this small amount of current, it would be impossible to let go of the wire. A current of about 100 mA (AC) causes the heart to begin beating out of control. Death soon follows.

Extension cords can be a fire hazard. Often they can carry no more than 7 A of current safely. Thus, only low-power appliances should be connected to ordinary extension cords. For example, the maximum power for a 7 A cord is $P = VI = 120 \text{ V} \times 7 \text{ A}$ or 840 W. If a 1200 W kettle is plugged into the cord, overheating will result. A 15 A fuse will not provide safety in such a circumstance.

PRACTICE

14. Why would it be dangerous to replace a burned-out fuse with a copper penny?

19.7 Conserving Electrical Energy

North Americans are among the highest users of energy in the world. We have more electric appliances and gadgets than even science-fiction writers could have imagined just 30 years ago.

Electrical energy has brought us comfort, convenience, and much leisure time. It has helped increase our store of knowledge and our ability to communicate. If we wish to continue enjoying these benefits, we must take care not to waste our resources. Everyone must do his or her part to conserve electrical energy.

DID YOU KNOW?

A consumer intending to buy a new appliance should consider the information regarding energy consumption on the "Energuide" label carefully. A wise selection can save the consumer hundreds of dollars worth of energy over the lifetime of each major appliance.

Words to Know

direct current (DC)	fuse
alternating current (AC)	circuit breaker

Chapter Objectives

Having completed this chapter, you should now be able to:

1. State the difference between direct current and alternating current.
2. Name ways of changing electrical energy into other types of energy.
3. Describe how a three-wire system can create 240 V and 120 V circuits in a home.
4. State the advantage of using parallel connections for electric circuits in homes and commercial buildings.
5. Given the potential drop across an electric device and the current through it, find its electric-power rating ($P = VI$) in watts.
6. Given the power of an electric device and the amount of time it is used, calculate the energy consumed ($E = Pt$) in joules, megajoules, or kilowatt hours.
7. Given the cost rate of electricity and the energy consumed, calculate the total cost of the electrical energy (cost = rate × energy).
8. Explain the need for safety when dealing with current electricity.
9. Describe the function of fuses and circuit breakers.
10. Give reasons for the need for the safe use and conservation of electrical energy.

Chapter Review

1. Describe the difference between alternating current and direct current.   (19.1)
2. What is the frequency of AC in North America? (19.1)
3. Name the type of energy created by electrical energy in each of the following:
   (a) an oven   (c) an electric sander
   (b) a doorbell   (19.2)
4. State the potential difference between these pairs of wires in a household circuit:
   (a) black and white   (c) red and white
   (b) black and red   (19.3)
5. What is the advantage of connecting appliances in parallel in a household circuit?   (19.3)

6. Calculate the power rating of each device:
   (a) an electronic toy, using a 9 V battery, draws 0.2 A of current
   (b) a 240 V water heater draws 20 A of current
   (c) a computer printer operates at 0.9 A and 120 V (19.4)

7. Calculate the unknown quantities:
   (a) $P = 6.0$ W; $I = 0.50$ A; $V = ?$ V
   (b) $P = 40$ W; $V = 8.0$ V; $I = ?$ A   (19.4)

8. An electric clock uses 2.4 W of power in a 120 V circuit. What is the current through the clock? (19.4)

9. A 30 W stereo tape-deck uses 2.5 A of current. What is the potential difference across the tape-deck? (19.4)

10. A 2000 W stove burner is used for 30 min (1800 s). The rate of electricity is 1.5¢/MJ. Calculate the:
    (a) energy consumed (in megajoules)
    (b) cost of the energy   (19.5)

11. Many light bulbs are planned to burn out after about 3000 h of operation. Assume a 100 W (0.10 kW) light bulb is left on for 3000 h (about four months), and that the rate of electricity is 5.0¢/(kW·h). Find the:
    (a) energy consumed (in kilowatt hours)
    (b) cost of the energy consumed   (19.5)

12. Read the meters in the diagram and find the cost of the electricity, assuming the rate is 6.0¢/(kW·h). (19.5)

13. What is the purpose of a fuse or circuit breaker? (19.6)

14. Calculate the maximum power available to each circuit:
    (a) a 15 A fuse is used in a 120 V circuit
    (b) a 60 A fuse is used in a 240 V circuit
    (c) a 6 A extension cord is used in a 120 V circuit (19.4, 19.6)

15. List three ways that could be used to conserve electrical energy in your:
    (a) school
    (b) home

16. Make lists of the advantages and disadvantages of developing more uses of electrical energy in our society. Discuss your lists in class.

CHAPTER 20

Magnetism and Electromagnetism

An electric current can be used to produce magnetism. An application of this is the electromagnetic lift used to move metal, as shown on the photograph. Other applications are found in audio tapes, computer storage systems, burglar alarms, loudspeakers, electric motors, and many other devices. This chapter begins with a review of magnetism, which you probably studied in a previous science class. Then you will examine concepts related to the interaction of electricity and magnetism.

Main Ideas

- Magnetism occurs for only a small number of materials.
- A compass and iron filings can be used to observe the properties of magnetic fields.
- An electric current can produce magnetism.
- Electromagnets have several uses.
- Electric motors operate due to the interaction of two magnetic fields.

20.1   The Force of Magnetism

Every student probably knows something about magnets and compasses. The force that attracts nails to a magnet or causes a compass to point north is called the **magnetic force** or **force of magnetism**.

The early Greeks knew about the force of magnetism. They discovered a mysterious metal they named lodestone in a district called Magnesia. This mineral attracted iron and some other substances. The force of attraction was called magnetism (after Magnesia).

You have likely experimented with magnetism in previous science classes. The first three sections of this chapter will review activities involving magnetism.

Figure 20-1 shows three suspended objects: a chunk of lodestone, a magnet, and the needle of a compass. All three have come to rest in a north-south direction. They are influenced by the earth's magnetic force. Even the Greeks realized that one end of a suspended piece of lodestone always faces toward the North Star in the sky. That star was called the leading or "lode" star, thus the name "lodestone".

In Figure 20-1 the end of each object that faces north is called the **north-seeking pole** and has the symbol N. The opposite end is called the **south-seeking pole** and has the symbol S. Every magnet has an N-pole and an S-pole.

If the N-pole of one magnet is brought close to the N-pole of another magnet, they repel each other. Also, the S-pole of one magnet repels the S-pole of another magnet. However, if N- and S-poles are brought close together, they attract each other. (See Figure 20-2.) These facts are summarized by the **laws of magnetic poles**:

(a) **Like poles repel.**
(b) **Unlike poles attract.**

Figure 20-1   Objects influenced by the earth's force of magnetism

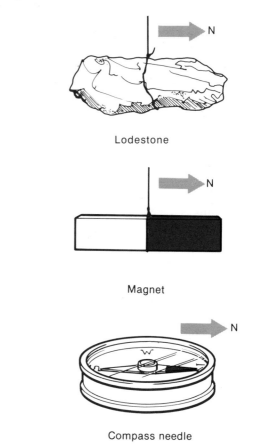

Lodestone

Magnet

Compass needle

Figure 20-2   The laws of magnetic poles

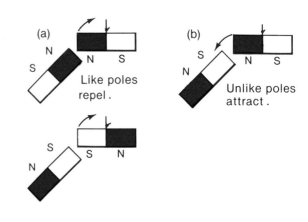

(a) Like poles repel.

(b) Unlike poles attract.

PRACTICE

1. Compare the laws of magnetism to the laws of electric charges (Section 17.2).
2. Is the south magnetic pole of the earth south-seeking or north-seeking? Explain your answer.

20.2   A Theory of Magnetism

If a magnet is brought close to paper, there is no magnetic action. If a magnet is brought close to an iron wire, the wire is attracted to the magnet. Iron is a substance that can be influenced by the force of magnetism. Such a substance is called a **magnetic substance**. Iron, nickel, and cobalt are important magnetic substances. Alloys of these substances are also magnetic. For example, steel is an alloy consisting of iron with a small amount of carbon. It is magnetic. Most other substances, such as paper, are **non-magnetic**.

Scientists believe that magnetic substances have sets of atoms that are lined up like little magnets. This is illustrated in Figure 20-3. If the sets of atoms are arranged so that many of them face the same direction, a weak magnet results, as shown in diagram (b). If all the sets of atoms face the same direction, a strong magnet results, as in diagram (c). If this arrangement lasts for a long time, the magnet is called a **permanent magnet**.

One way to make a magnetic substance into a magnet is to stroke it with another magnet. For example, a steel needle becomes a magnet after being stroked several times with a strong magnet. See Figure 20-4(a). If the needle is suspended, as in diagram (b), it will line up in the north-south direction.

Figure 20-3   A magnetic substance can become a magnet.

(a) A magnetic substance

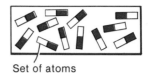

Set of atoms

(b) A weak magnet

Several sets face the same direction .

(c) A strong magnet

All sets face the same direction .

Figure 20-4   Making a needle into a magnet

(a) Stroking the needle

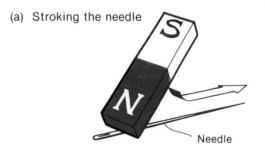

Needle

(b) Testing the magnetic needle

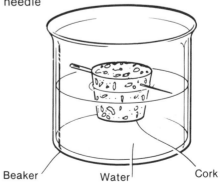

Beaker   Water   Cork

Another way to make a magnetic substance into a magnet is to hold it close to a permanent magnet. An iron wire becomes a magnet when held close to a magnet, as shown in Figure 20-5. This procedure is called **induction**, because touching is not necessary. In this case the wire is a **temporary magnet**. When the wire is moved away from the magnet, it loses its magnetism. If the wire were made of steel instead of iron, it would keep its magnetism longer.

Figure 20-5   Making a temporary magnet by induction

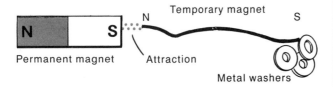

If a permanent magnet is broken in two, each part of the original magnet becomes a new magnet with its own N- and S-poles, as shown in Figure 20-6(a). The breaking process can continue with similar results, as shown in diagram (b). This helps prove the scientists' theory that a magnet has many sets of atoms that face the same direction.

Figure 20-6   Breaking a permanent magnet

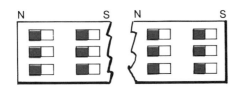

(a) One break

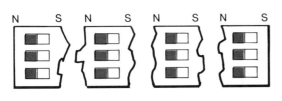

(b) Several breaks

PRACTICE

3. (a) What two main elements are used in making steel?
   (b) Which one is responsible for the magnetic properties of steel?
4. Describe how you could use a compass to determine which end of the needle in Figure 20-4 is the N-pole.
5. In the diagram, which end of the needle becomes the north-seeking pole?

6. Try this. Magnetize a steel needle (or a large steel paper clip that has been straightened out) by stroking it with the N-pole of a magnet, as shown in Figure 20-4(a). Use a compass to discover which end of the needle (or clip) becomes the N-pole.

20.3   Magnetic Fields

A baseball field is a space in which a baseball game is played. A **magnetic field** is a space in which a magnetic force exists.

In science laboratories there are two common ways to observe the properties of a magnetic field. One is with a compass and the other is with small particles of a magnetic substance, such as iron filings. Figure 20-7(a) shows several compasses in the magnetic field around a permanent bar magnet. Diagram (b) shows iron filings sprinkled on paper over the same magnet. Diagram (c) illustrates how we draw lines representing the magnetic field. These lines are called **magnetic field lines** and are simply a way of drawing the field.

By referring to Figure 20-7, we can discover three important **characteristics of magnetic field lines**.
(1) The lines do not cross each other.
(2) The lines are concentrated at the poles.
(3) The lines leave N and proceed to S outside the magnet. (You can remember this by the order of the letters in the alphabet: N comes before S.) This direction can be tested with the N-pole of a compass.

Figure 20-7 The magnetic field around a bar magnet

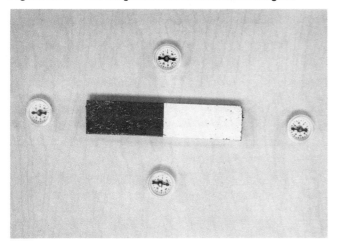

(a) Using compasses

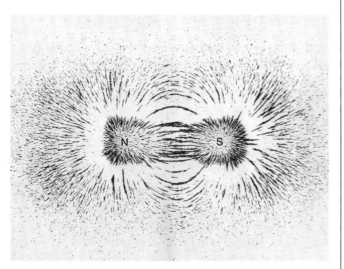

(b) Using iron filings

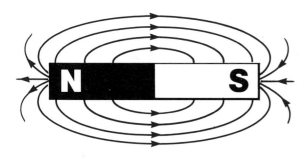

(c) Magnetic field lines

It is interesting to view the shape of the magnetic field near other types of magnets. For example, Figure 20-8(a) uses iron filings to show the magnetic field near a horseshoe magnet. Diagram (b) shows what happens to that field when an iron bar, called a **keeper**, joins the poles. The keeper sustains the magnetism when the magnet is not in use.

Figure 20-8 A horseshoe magnet

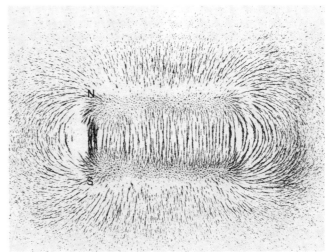

(a) Without a keeper

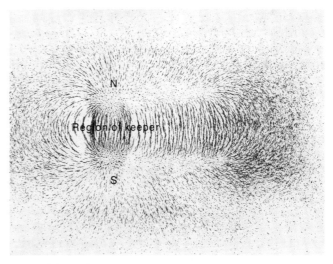

(b) With a keeper

Iron filings are also useful to illustrate the magnetic fields near pairs of magnets. In Figure 20-9(a) two like poles are repelling each other. In diagram (b) two unlike poles are attracting each other.

Figure 20-9 Magnetic fields near pairs of magnets

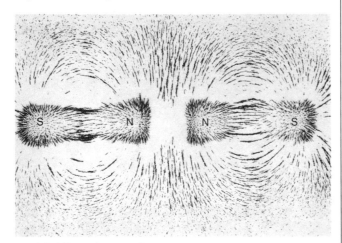

(a) Like poles repel.

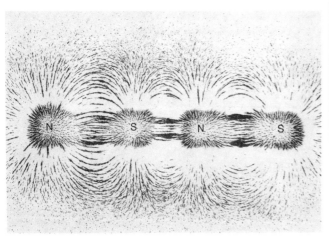

(b) Unlike poles attract.

An orienteering compass works because the earth has a magnetic field around it. In that field a compass needle points toward the magnetic north pole (actually a south-seeking or S-pole) of the earth. The magnetic north pole of the earth is not located at the geographic North Pole. Thus, for most locations the compass needle does not point toward true north. See Figure 20-10.

Figure 20-10 The earth's magnetic field

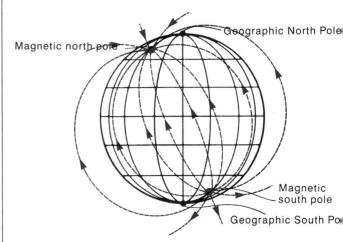

PRACTICE

7. In the diagrams below each circle represents a compass. Draw the diagrams and show the direction of the needle in each compass.

(a)

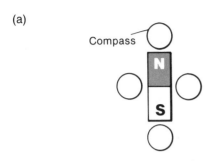

Compass

(b)

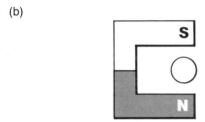

(c)

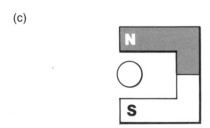

8. Draw a diagram, similar to Figure 20-7(c), showing the magnetic field lines near a horseshoe magnet. Include the directions of the field lines.

9. Are the north magnetic pole of the earth and the N-pole of a magnet the same? Explain your answer.

20.4 The Magnetic Effects of Electricity

The study of how electricity and magnetism interact is called **electromagnetism**. Electromagnetism was first observed almost 200 years ago, in 1819.

In the next activity, you will observe the effects discovered at that time. To help explain your observations, it will be useful to draw diagrams using the following symbols:

(X) This represents a wire with electrons going away from you, into the page. (Imagine the tail of an arrow travelling away from you.)

(•) This represents a wire with electrons coming toward you, out of the page. (Imagine the tip of an arrow travelling toward you.)

Activity 20A   The Magnetic Field Near a Straight Conductor

PROBLEM ■ What are the properties of the magnetic field near a straight conductor?

APPARATUS ■ dry cell or DC power supply; magnetic compass; switch; connecting wires

Note: Iron filings may also be used in this activity, especially for demonstration purposes.

 CAUTION
To prevent overheating, do not leave the switch closed for very long at any one time.
If a DC power supply is used, a 5 Ω or 10 Ω resistor should be connected in series in the circuit.

PROCEDURE ■

1. Check the compass to be sure it is facing north, not south. If it is not working properly, let your teacher know.

Figure 20-11   Set-up for Activity 20A

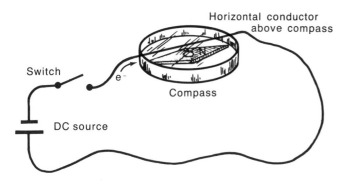

2. Set up a table of observations with the titles shown in Table 20-1. (The last two columns will be completed in the Analysis.)

Table 20-1   Observations for Activity 20A

Procedure number	Observed result	View from the "south end"	LHR
3			
4			
5			
6			

3. Set up the apparatus shown in Figure 20-11 so that the electrons flow *north*, parallel to the compass needle. The wire should be above the compass. Close the switch for a moment, and determine the final direction the needle faces. This is the direction of the magnetic field lines beneath the conductor. Open the switch. Enter the result in the table.
4. Repeat #3, this time with the compass above the wire.
5. Reverse the connections to the energy source so the electrons flow above the compass in the horizontal conductor. In other words, the electron flow is opposite in direction to the compass needle. Predict the final direction of the compass needle when the switch is closed for a moment. Check your prediction.

6. Predict what would happen to the strength of the magnetic field if the current through the conductor were increased. Add a second cell in series, and check your prediction.
7. What do you think happens to the strength of the magnetic field as the distance from the conductor increases? Check your answer experimentally.

ANALYSIS ■

1. To complete the third column of your observation table, assume that you are looking along the horizontal conductor from south to north. Draw diagrams of the results observed in Procedures #3 to #6 using the appropriate symbols (ⓧ ⊙). (Step #3 is already done for you.)
2. A useful rule to use is the **left-hand rule (LHR) for straight conductors**. It helps you to remember the direction of the magnetic field lines. *Point the thumb of your left hand in the direction of the electron flow. The fingers wrapped around the conductor point in the direction of the magnetic field lines.* (See Figure 20-12.) Use this LHR to check your results in Procedures #3 to #6, and complete the last column in your table. (Again, Step #3 is already done.)

Figure 20-12   The LHR for straight conductors

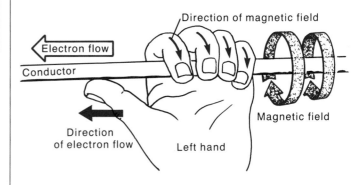

3. How does the strength of the magnetic field depend on:
   (a) the amount of current through the conductor?
   (b) the distance from the conductor?

APPLICATIONS ■

1. Each empty circle represents a compass. Show the direction of the needle of each compass.

(a)

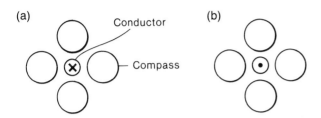

Conductor

Compass

(b)

2. Each empty circle represents a conductor with a magnetic field around it. State whether there should be a dot or an × in each empty circle.

(a)

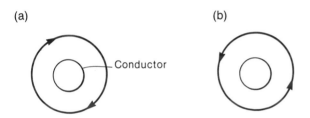

Conductor

(b)

20.5 Coiled Conductors

The magnetic field around a straight conductor is rather weak. To make the field stronger, the conductor can be wound around and around to create a coil.

A **galvanoscope**, suggested for the next activity, is a device with two or three sets of coils. Each set has a different number of windings. Refer to Figure 20-13(a).

If a commercial galvanoscope is not available, you can make your own. Simply wind about 50 turns of fine, insulated copper wire around a toilet-paper roll or a beaker. See Figure 20-13(b).

Symbols can make diagrams easier to draw. Figure 20-14 shows two common ways of illustrating a coiled conductor with electrons travelling through it.

Figure 20-13 Galvanoscopes

(a) A commercial galvanoscope

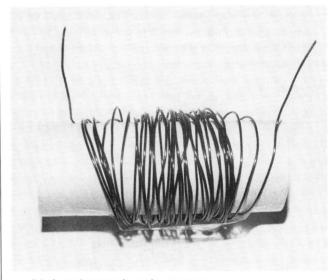

(b) A student-made galvanoscope

Figure 20-14 Symbols for coiled conductors

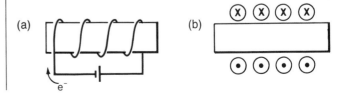

(a)

(b)

Activity 20B   The Magnetic Field In and Near a Coiled Conductor

PROBLEM ■   What are the properties of the magnetic field in a coiled conductor?

APPARATUS ■   dry cell or DC power supply; magnetic compass; galvanoscope; switch; connecting wires

 CAUTION *Check the insulation on the galvanoscope wires. Any bare wires could short-circuit and become very hot.*

PROCEDURE ■
1. Check the compass to be sure it faces north.
2. Set up the apparatus as shown in Figure 20-15. (Remember to add a small resistor in series if a DC power supply is used.) Be sure that the compass needle points in the same direction as the wires of the coil. Determine which direction the electrons will be flowing in the coil when the switch is closed.

Figure 20-15

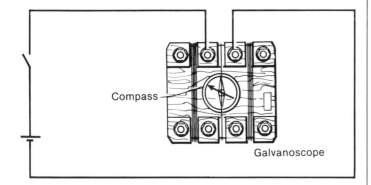

3. Close the switch for an instant and determine the *final direction* of the compass needle. This indicates the direction of the field.
4. Reverse the terminals so the electrons flow in the opposite direction. Repeat #3.

5. Relate the observations in #3 and #4 to the following **left-hand rule for coiled conductors**: *Wrap the fingers of your left hand around the coil in the direction of the electron flow. Then the thumb points in the direction of the magnetic field inside the coil.* The compass needle should also point in this direction. Thus, your thumb shows where the N-pole of the compass should be. Check to see if this is the case.
6. Predict what happens to the strength of the magnetic field inside the coiled conductor when you:
   (a) increase the current (by adding another cell in series)
   (b) increase the number of windings
   If possible, check your predictions.

ANALYSIS ■
1. If the electrons in the top part of a coiled conductor are travelling toward you, in which direction (left or right) does the magnetic field in the coil face?
2. On what factors does the strength of a magnetic field in a coiled conductor depend?

APPLICATION ■   Each empty circle represents a compass near one end of a coiled conductor. Label the ends of the coils as N or S. Show the direction of the needle of each compass.

(a)

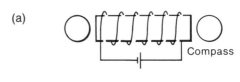

(b)

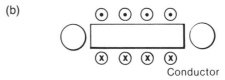

(c)

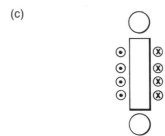

20.6   Electromagnets

Both permanent magnets and electron-carrying conductors exert a magnetic force. A permanent magnet attracts magnetic objects, such as iron washers and nails. An **electromagnet** is an electron-carrying conductor that attracts magnetic objects.

The straight conductor and coiled conductor used in the previous two activities had weak magnetic fields. To make a strong electromagnet, an iron core is placed inside a coiled conductor. This concentrates the magnetic field lines.

In the next activity, you will explore the properties of an electromagnet. If a manufactured coil and core set is not available, you can make your own by wrapping a fine insulated wire many times around an iron bar or a large steel nail.

Activity 20C   The Properties of an Electromagnet

PROBLEM ■   What are the properties of an electromagnet?

This is an ideal activity for you to design on your own. Begin by listing the Apparatus and the Procedure steps you think are appropriate. After these are approved by your teacher, carry out your procedure and write a report of the activity. The following hints may be helpful.

- Do not keep the switch closed for more than about 10 s at a time.
- Qualitative observations can involve a switch, an iron core, and a compass.
- Quantitative observations can be made. (Recall what you did in Activity 20B.)
- Applications can be researched in reference books and described. Electromagnets are used in doorbells, loudspeakers, electric meters, relays, electromagnetic lifts, solenoids, monorail trains, and other devices.

20.7   Applications of Electromagnets

Several devices make use of the force created by an electromagnet. The electromagnetic lift, the door chime, and the audio tape-recorder will be described here. Other applications include the electromagnetic relay, the telephone earpiece, and the recording timer used in activities in Chapters 4 and 5.

The electromagnetic lift

Huge electromagnets are used to lift or move scrap iron or iron sheets as shown at the beginning of this chapter. Some electromagnets can lift more than 20 000 kg of metal.

One way of making an electromagnetic lift is shown in Figure 20-16. When the switch is closed, the device becomes a powerful magnet. The core passes through the coil and almost completely surrounds it. When the switch is opened, the magnetism no longer exists and the load drops.

Figure 20-16   Design of a powerful electromagnetic lift

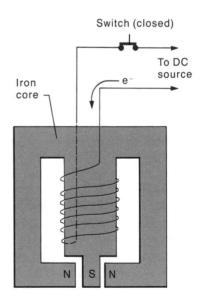

Figure 20-17 Basic structure of a door chime

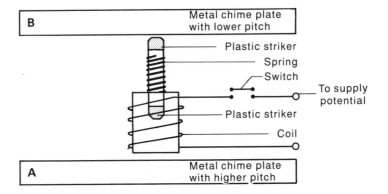

The door chime

The basic design of a door chime is shown in Figure 20-17. When the switch is closed the coil becomes an electromagnet, pulling the iron rod down. The rod strikes the metal chime plate (A), and remains down until the switch is opened. Then the current stops and the spring forces the rod up quickly, and the rod strikes the other metal chime plate (B). The sound produced is the "ding-dong" sound heard at the front door of many homes.

The audio tape-recorder

The tape used in an audio tape-recorder has millions of magnetic particles made of iron oxide that can be lined up using an electromagnet. The process works as follows.

A microphone receives sound signals of various frequencies and amplitudes. Those signals are changed into electric signals, which are sent to an electromagnet called the recording head. The magnetic field of the electromagnet changes according to the electric signals. As a tape is pulled past the electromagnet, the magnetic field causes the iron oxide particles to form certain patterns. Those patterns will remain on the tape.

To produce the recorded sound, the tape, now having its own magnetic field, must be pulled past the electromagnet. Electric signals are then changed back into sound signals.

PRACTICE

10. The diagram shows one way of making a U-shaped electromagnet. Use the LHR for coiled conductors to determine which pole is N and which is S.

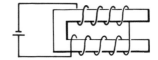

11. It is better to use plastic scissors than steel scissors when repairing a broken magnetic tape from a tape recorder. Why?

> **DID YOU KNOW?**
>
> Any device on which information has been stored using electromagnetism must be protected from strong magnetic fields. If a magnetic tape or disk is brought too close to a strong magnet, the stored information can be destroyed.

20.8 The Interaction of Magnetic Forces

After the discovery in 1819 that a current moving in a conductor produces a magnetic field around the conductor, many scientists experimented with electricity and magnetism. For example, an English scientist named Michael Faraday (1791-1867) discovered that the magnetic field of a permanent magnet can interact with the magnetic field of an electron-carrying conductor. Faraday's discovery is called the **motor principle** because it is the basis of the operation of an electric motor.

Consider Figure 20-18, which explains how the motor principle works. Diagram (a) shows the magnetic field of a permanent U-shaped magnet. Diagram (b) shows the magnetic field around a conductor with electrons flowing away from you. (Remember the LHR for straight conductors.) Diagram (c) shows the two sets of fields together. To the right of the conductor the field lines are opposite in direction, so they tend to cancel. The field lines are concentrated to the left of the conductor and reinforce each other, pushing the conductor to the right, as seen in diagram (d).

An interesting example of the interaction of electricity and magnetism can be seen if a showcase bulb is available. Hold a permanent magnet close to the bulb without the light on. Notice the effect. Now turn the light on and again hold the magnet close to it.

PRACTICE

12. Redraw this diagram, then:
    (a) draw the field lines for the magnet and the conductor
    (b) show where the cancellation of field lines occurs
    (c) determine the direction of motion of the conductor

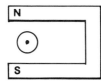

Figure 20-18 The motor principle

(a) Magnetic field of the permanent magnet

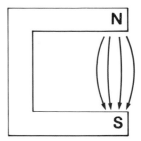

(b) Magnetic field of the electron-carrying conductor

(c) Shape of the magnetic field when the fields in (a) and (b) are superimposed

Concentration of field lines

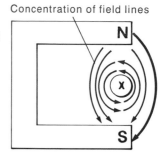

(d) The direction of the force on the conductor is away from the region of concentrated field lines.

Force on conductor

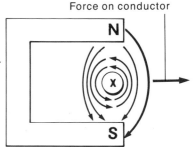

Activity **20D** The Motor Principle

PROBLEM ■ Is the motor principle theory successful in predicting the direction of the force on a conductor in a magnetic field?

APPARATUS ■ U-shaped magnet(s); dry cell(s); switch; connecting wires

PROCEDURE ■
1. Set up the apparatus as shown in Figure 20-19 with the S-pole resting on the bench top. Leave the switch open while you determine the direction of motion of the electrons. Use the theory from Section 20.8 to predict which way the conductor will be pushed.

Figure 20-19

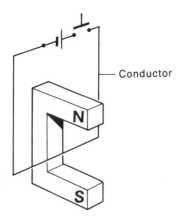

2. Check your prediction by closing the switch for a few seconds. If your prediction was correct, proceed to #3. If your prediction was wrong, find out why and try again.

 CAUTION Do not leave the circuit complete for more than a few seconds. It is a short circuit.

3. Reverse the magnet so the N-pole is resting on the bench. Repeat #1 and #2.
4. Reverse the wires on the cell so the electrons flow in the opposite direction. Repeat #1, #2, and #3.
5. Predict what factors affect the force on the conductor in this activity. If possible, check your prediction experimentally.

ANALYSIS ■
1. Is the motor principle theory successful in predicting the direction of the force on a conductor in a magnetic field?
2. What happens to the force pushing the conductor if the:
   (a) magnet is made stronger?
   (b) current through the conductor is increased?

APPLICATION ■ Determine the direction of motion of the conductor in each case. Use a diagram to explain each answer.

(a)

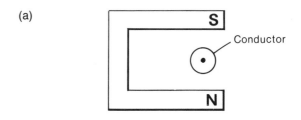

(b)

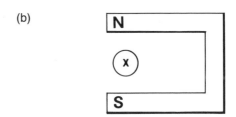

20.9 Applying the Motor Principle

The motor principle is used in the design of several devices, including ammeters, voltmeters, galvanometers, loudspeakers, and electric motors. Only the latter two will be discussed in detail here.

The loudspeaker

The purpose of a loudspeaker is to change electric signals into sound vibrations quickly and accurately. The components of a loudspeaker are shown in Figure 20-20. A movable coil is attached to a paper cone. It is placed over the central shaft of a permanent magnet. Variable currents from a radio or record player experience forces caused by the field of the permanent magnet. The coil is forced to vibrate according to the frequency and amplitude of these variable currents. The paper cone vibrates with the coil, sending sound waves into the surrounding air.

Figure 20-20 The loudspeaker

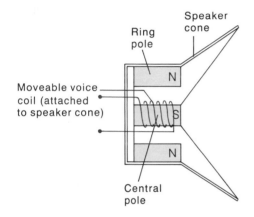

The electric motor

In Activity 20D, the conductor simply swings back and forth. If the conductor can somehow be made to rotate around and around, the result is called an electric motor.

An **electric motor** is a device that changes electrical energy into mechanical energy. It consists of two main parts: a magnet and an electron-carrying conductor. The easiest way to see how a motor works is to follow a set of diagrams step by step.

Figure 20-21 shows how we can apply the motor principle to a conducting loop. Diagram (a) has a conductor with electrons coming toward you. Use the motor principle to prove to yourself that the force on the conductor is downwards. Diagram (b) shows a conductor with the force upwards. Diagrams (a) and (b) are combined to obtain (c). Then in diagram (d) we have a three-dimensional view of the loop of wire. Prove to yourself that (d) is the same as (c) in Figure 20-21.

In Figure 20-21(d) the loop of wire is experiencing a clockwise force. After making half a turn, the loop would be forced counterclockwise. This would not allow a constant rotation of the motor. This problem is solved by an important invention called a commutator.

Figure 20-21 Applying the motor principle to a loop of wire

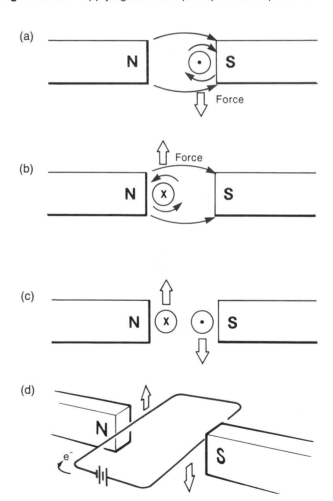

A **commutator** is a metal ring split into two parts. It allows a loop in a DC electric motor to continue rotating in one direction. Its operation is shown in Figure 20-22. Diagram (a) shows a commutator made of two parts, R_1 and R_2. The parts touching the split ring are called **brushes**, B_1 and B_2. They are connected to a DC battery.

Figure 20-22   Creating a force in a clockwise direction

(a)

(b)

(c)

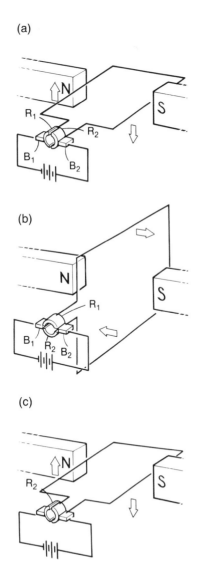

Figure 20-22(a) shows the same situation as Figure 20-21(d). The force on the loop is clockwise. In Figure 20-22(b) the loop has swung to its vertical position. Here the electrons stop flowing for an instant because the brushes do not touch the split ring. However, the loop keeps moving because it is already in motion. In diagram (c), R_2 is contacting B_1. This situation is similar to diagram (a) in which R_1 is touching B_1. Thus, the force on the loop is again clockwise. This process continues as the electrons reverse directions in the loop every half turn of the loop. Try to understand Figure 20-22 before you proceed to the next section.

PRACTICE

13. The conductors represent a loop in a magnetic field. Determine whether the force on the loop is clockwise or counterclockwise.

14. For the instant shown in the diagram, is the force on the loop clockwise or counterclockwise?

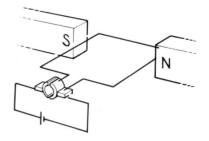

15. State two possible ways of forcing the loop in Figure 20-22 to rotate counterclockwise.

20.10 Constructing and Using Electric Motors

Although Section 20.9 describes how an electric motor operates, it does not show the actual construction. To make the motor strong enough to be useful, some additions must be made. First, instead of using a single loop, a set of several loops can be added. In a motor this set of loops is called the **armature**. An iron core is also added inside the armature. This helps increase the magnetic force, as you learned in the electromagnet activity. The result is a motor strong enough to operate some device.

To help students understand the parts of a motor, special motors are available. One such motor, called a St. Louis motor, is shown in Figure 20-23(a). You can see the armature, commutator, and metal brushes. The permanent magnets are called **field magnets** because they create the magnetic field.

In Figure 20-23(b) and (c) follow the flow of electrons from the source and through the coil. Use the LHR for coiled conductors to see why one end of the armature is N and the other S. The force on the armature is clockwise because N repels N and S repels S. If a St. Louis or similar motor is available, use it to learn firsthand how an electric motor operates.

The field magnets in the motors described have been permanent magnets. It is also possible to use electromagnets as field magnets. This will be the case when you build your own motor in the next activity.

Up to this point, the description of how a motor works has been limited to DC motors. AC motors are actually more common. They work in much the same manner as DC motors. The main difference between an AC motor and a DC motor is in the commutator arrangement.

Electric motors range in size from tiny to huge. Small motors are used in toys and ripple tanks. Larger motors are used for electric tools and machines. Very large motors are used in subway trains and electric locomotives.

Figure 20-23 The St. Louis motor

(a) General construction of the motor

(b) Top view

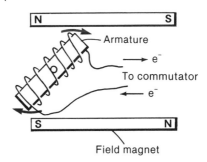

Armature

e⁻

To commutator

e⁻

Field magnet

(c) End view

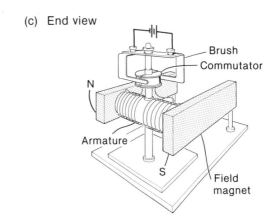

Brush

Commutator

N

Armature

S

Field magnet

PRACTICE

16. State the function of each of the following parts of a DC motor:
    (a) commutator   (c) armature
    (b) brushes   (d) field magnets

Activity 20E   Making a DC Electric Motor

Notes:
1. There are several ways to build an electric motor, depending on the materials available. Instructions could fill many pages. To prevent wordy instructions, diagrams and suggestions will be used. You will have to decide on the details.
2. The motor you build will have electromagnets for the field. Only one DC circuit is needed to operate both the field magnets and the armature. A well-built motor will be self-starting using only 1.5 V as the source. A poorly built motor will need a push to get started and may need up to 6 V. A useless motor will not spin at all.

PROBLEM ■   What difficulties must be overcome to build a DC electric motor that works?

APPARATUS ■
(a) **Materials required to build one motor:**
   1 pine or plywood board, about
   12 cm × 6 cm × 2 cm; 5 common nails, about 8 to 10 cm long; 1 piece of glass tubing, about 5 to 6 cm long and large enough in diameter to fit over a nail; 12 m of #18 insulated copper magnet wire; 2 pieces of thin copper sheeting, about 2.5 cm × 1.5 cm; 2 thumbtacks; 1 DC cell, 1.5 V

(b) **Apparatus needed to help construct the motor:**
   hammer; knife; solder; soldering iron; sandpaper; file; masking tape; glue; Bunsen burner; heat-insulating board

CAUTION Exercise care when using a soldering iron and a Bunsen burner. Hair should be tied back. Do not wear loose clothing.

PROCEDURE ■
1. Read all the instructions and look at all the diagrams before you start building your motor.
2. Put together the parts of the motor using the steps shown in Figure 20-24. The following suggestions may help:
   (a) Sand or file down the tip of the nail that acts as a pivot.
   (b) When cooling the glass tubing, press the sealed end against a heat-insulating board to flatten the end.
   (c) From the 12 m of wire you need three pieces. You must decide on the length of each piece.
   (d) When you make the electromagnets or the armature, wrap the wire in only one direction. It might be interesting to count the number of windings in each case.
   (e) Wherever an electrical contact is needed, the insulation must be sanded off the wire.
   (f) Be sure the field magnets are wound so that one is N and the other S. (You can check the poles with a compass.)
3. Try your motor.
4. If you wish, try to design changes to improve your motor.

ANALYSIS ■
1. In Figure 20-24 which field magnet is N and which S?
2. Describe the features of the motor that worked best.
3. If you were to start the project over again, what changes would you make?

APPLICATIONS ■
1. Use a reference book to discover how electric motors are used in common devices such as hair dryers, electric razors, food processors, sewing machines, garage-door openers, and electric drills.
2. Compare the operation of the motor built in this activity with that of a motor researched in #1.

Figure 20-24 Steps in making a DC electric motor

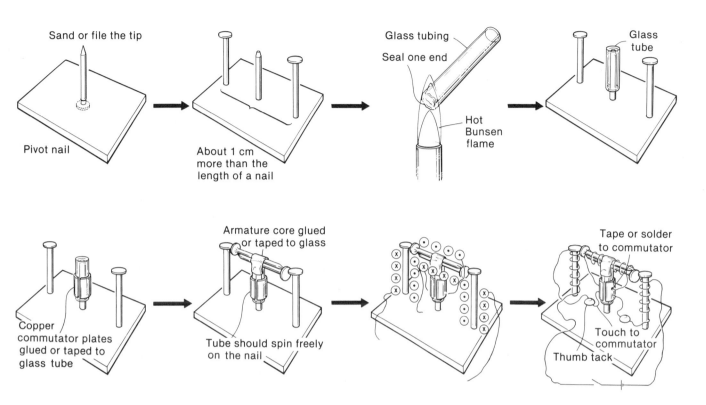

Sand or file the tip

Pivot nail

About 1 cm more than the length of a nail

Glass tubing

Seal one end

Hot Bunsen flame

Glass tube

Copper commutator plates glued or taped to glass tube

Armature core glued or taped to glass

Tube should spin freely on the nail

Tape or solder to commutator

Touch to commutator

Thumb tack

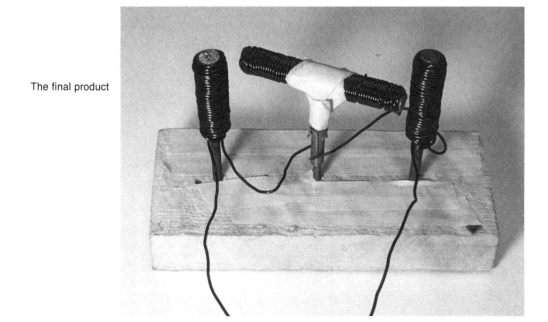

The final product

Words to Know

magnetic force
north-seeking pole
south-seeking pole
laws of magnetic poles
magnetic substance
permanent magnet
induction (magnetic)
temporary magnet
magnetic field
magnetic field lines

keeper
electromagnetism
left-hand rule for a
   straight conductor
left-hand rule for a coiled
   conductor
electromagnet
motor principle
motor (electric)
commutator

Chapter Objectives

Having completed this chapter, you should now be able to:

1. State the meaning of magnetic N-poles and S-poles.
2. State the laws of magnetic poles.
3. Compare magnetic and non-magnetic substances.
4. Describe how to make a magnetic substance into a magnet by either stroking or induction.
5. Define magnetic field.
6. Describe how iron filings and a compass are used to find the shape of the magnetic field around a magnet.
7. List three characteristics of magnetic field lines.
8. Draw diagrams showing field lines around permanent magnets.
9. Describe the earth's magnetic field.
10. Define electromagnetism.
11. State and apply the left-hand rule for straight conductors.
12. State and apply the left-hand rule for coiled conductors.
13. Make an electromagnet and state what factors affect its strength.
14. Describe applications of the electromagnet.
15. Use the motor principle to determine the direction of the force on an electron-carrying conductor in a magnetic field.
16. In an electric motor locate the field magnets, armature, commutator, and brushes.
17. Explain the operation of a DC electric motor.
18. Make a simple DC electric motor.

Chapter Review

1. State the laws of magnetic poles.   (20.1)
2. Describe the difference in the structure of magnetic and non-magnetic substances.   (20.2)
3. What is the difference between a magnet and a magnetic substance?   (20.2)
4. An iron bar is held close to a magnet, as shown in the diagram on the right.
   (a) Which end of the bar becomes N?
   (b) What is the name of the process that makes the bar a temporary magnet?   (20.2)
5. List three characteristics of magnetic field lines. (20.3)

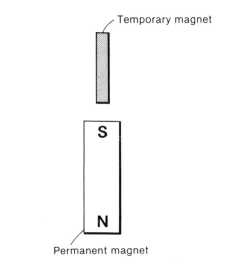

Temporary magnet

S

N

Permanent magnet

6. In your notebook, draw the diagrams shown, then draw the shape of the magnetic field in each case. Include the direction of the magnetic field lines. (20.3)

(a)

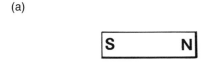

(b)

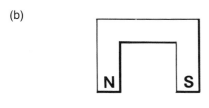

(c)

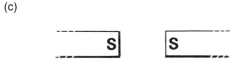

7. In each case determine which end of the permanent magnet is N and which is S. (20.3)

(a)

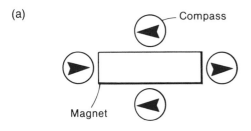

(b)   (c)

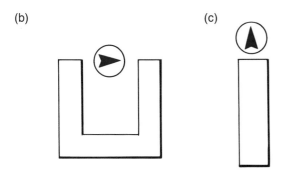

8. Define electromagnetism. (20.4)
9. State the left-hand rule for:
   (a) straight conductors   (b) coiled conductors
   (Act. 20A, Act. 20B)
10. State whether the magnetic field lines are clockwise or counterclockwise when the electrons in a conductor are travelling:
    (a) toward you   (b) away from you   (Act. 20A)
11. Each empty circle represents a compass near one end of a coiled conductor. Draw the diagrams, in your notebook.
    (a) Label the ends of the coils as N or S.
    (b) Show the direction of the needle of each compass. (Act. 20B)

(i)

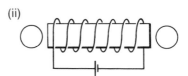

(ii)

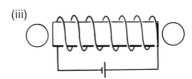

(iii)

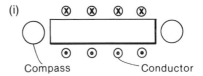

12. The small circles represent conductors around a coil. Determine which circles should have a dot and which an ×. (Act. 20B)

(a)   (b)

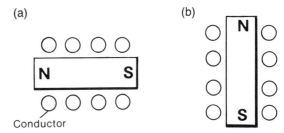

13. If you were making an electromagnet, what would you do to improve its strength? (20.6, Act. 20C, 20.7)

14. The diagrams show electromagnets. Determine which poles are N and which are S. (20.5 to 20.7)

(a)

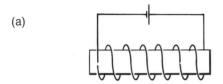

(b)

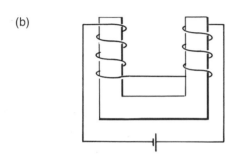

(c)

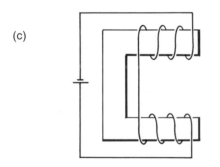

15. In the diagram a current-carrying conductor is in the magnetic field of a U-shaped magnet. With the aid of a diagram, explain why the conductor experiences an outward force. (20.8)

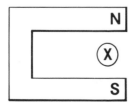

16. In each case, draw the diagram in your notebook, then determine the direction of the force on the conductor. (20.8)

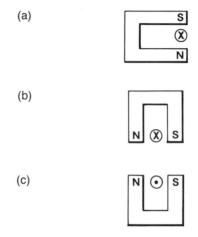

(a)

(b)

(c)

17. The diagram represents a single loop in an electric motor. Determine whether the force on the loop is clockwise or counterclockwise. (20.9)

18. Refer to the diagram of the St. Louis motor.
    (a) List the names of the parts of the motor labelled A, B, C, and D.
    (b) Determine which end of the coil is N.
    (c) In which direction will the armature spin? (20.10)

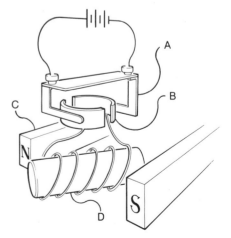

19. Use a ''how it works'' reference book to find out how electromagnetism applies to the operation of one or more of these devices: electric guitar, quartz clock, car temperature gauge, cruise control, burglar alarm, car horn, aircraft autopilot, metal detector, coin tester, traffic light detector (embedded in the road), airport security checks, and video recorders. Write a brief report of your findings.

CHAPTER 21

Electromagnetic Induction

Our society uses vast amounts of electrical energy. Most of that energy is produced at huge electric generating stations. One type of generating station changes the energy of falling water into electrical energy. We don't have many large waterfalls, so we make artificial ones by building dams, like the one shown in the photograph. We then control the flow of the water to produce electrical energy. This chapter discusses how magnetism is used to generate current electricity. Both the advantages and the disadvantages of electric generating stations are examined. This chapter also presents the way in which electrical energy is distributed to consumers.

Main Ideas

- Under certain circumstances, a magnetic field can create an electric current in a conductor.
- Electric generators use a magnetic field to convert some form of energy into electrical energy.
- A transformer can be used to increase or decrease potential differences.
- Transformers provide the key to distributing electrical energy in our society.

21.1 Using Magnetism to Induce Electric Current

In Chapter 20 it was shown that current electricity causes magnetism. In this chapter you will study how magnetism can create electric current. Magnetism and electricity are closely related. Thus, as you study this chapter, try to recall facts from the previous chapter.

In order for a magnetic field to produce electricity, some kind of change in the field must occur. This is shown by an experiment using the set-up in Figure 21-1(a). A conductor is held between the poles of a U-shaped magnet. A galvanometer is connected to the conductor to indicate current. The three arrows, X, Y, and Z, show three ways the conductor can be moved in the magnetic field. Diagrams (b), (c), and (d) indicate what happens for each motion.

Notice in Figure 21-1(b) and (c) that the conductor does not cross any lines in the magnetic field. In other words, as far as the conductor is concerned, the magnetic field is not changing. No current flows in the conductor.

In diagram (d), however, the conductor cuts across the magnetic field lines. Thus, as far as the conductor is concerned, the magnetic field is changing and current flows in the conductor. We say the current has been **induced**. Therefore, **electromagnetic induction** means the creation of an electric current caused by a changing magnetic field.

In the example given, the conductor was moved to cause the magnetic field around it to change. A second way to create a changing magnetic field is to hold the conductor still and move the magnet in the appropriate direction. A third way is to change the size of the magnetic field around a stationary conductor. This is done with an electromagnet rather than a permanent magnet.

It was Michael Faraday (Section 20.8) who discovered in 1831 that a changing magnetic field can cause electricity. In fact, the **law of electromagnetic induction** is named after him. Faraday's law states that:

Whenever the magnetic field in the region of a conductor changes, electric current is induced in the conductor.

Figure 21-1 One way to create electricity using a magnetic field

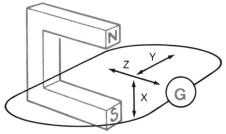

(a) Experimental set-up to show how magnetism can create electricity

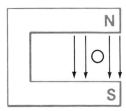

(b) Motion in the direction of X: The conductor is moved vertically, parallel to the magnetic field lines. No current is produced in the conductor.

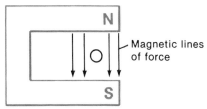

(c) Motion in the direction of Y: The conductor is moved parallel to itself. Again, no current is produced in the conductor.

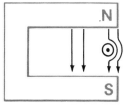

(d) Motion in the direction of Z: The conductor is moved horizontally, cutting across the magnetic field lines. In this case, current is produced in the conductor. (If the conductor is moved to the left, the electrons flow in the opposite direction.)

Faraday's law helped change the industrial world. Most of the electricity we use is created and transmitted using electromagnetic induction. How we create and transmit electricity is the topic of the remainder of this chapter.

PRACTICE

1. What conditions are necessary for a magnetic field to induce a current in a conductor?
2. In each case state which way(s) the conductor must move in order to have a current induced in it.

(a)

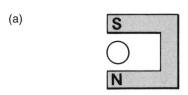

(b)

(c)

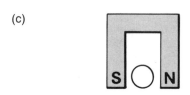

3. Based on the concepts studied in Chapter 20, predict ways of increasing the current induced in a conductor by a changing magnetic field.

Activity 21A Inducing Current in a Coiled Conductor

Note: The examples of electromagnetic induction given in Section 21.1 used a single conductor. In that case the current is very small. Therefore, in this activity, a coiled conductor is used to create a larger current.

PROBLEM ■
(a) How can an electric current be induced in a coiled conductor?
(b) How can the size of the induced current in a coiled conductor be increased?

APPARATUS ■ galvanometer; set of 2 coils with different numbers of windings (say 50 and 100); 2 bar magnets (one stronger than the other); connecting wires

PROCEDURE ■
1. Connect the coil with the smaller number of windings to the galvanometer, as shown in Figure 21-2. Move one end of the magnet into the coil. Describe what happens.

Figure 21-2

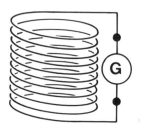

2. Determine what happens to the current when the magnet is held still in the coil.
3. Move the magnet out of the coil. Describe what happens.
4. Hold the magnet still and move the coil in various directions. Describe the effects.
5. Determine how the factors listed below affect the size of the current induced in a conductor by a changing magnetic field:
   (a) number of turns of the coil (use two different coils)
   (b) speed of motion of the magnet (use fast, medium, and very slow speeds)
   (c) strength of the magnetic field (use a strong magnet and a weak magnet)

ANALYSIS ■
1. Is the electric current you generated AC or DC? Explain your answer.
2. Compare what you observed in this activity to the law of electromagnetic induction.
3. How can an electric current be induced in a coiled conductor?
4. How can the size of the induced current in a coiled conductor be increased?

APPLICATION ■ Assume you are asked to make a "generator" of electricity. Based on this activity, what conditions would you use to obtain a large current?

Activity 21B The Direction of Induced Current

PROBLEM ■ How can the direction of an induced current in a coiled conductor be determined?

APPARATUS ■ galvanometer; coiled conductor; magnet; connecting wires

PROCEDURE ■
1. Examine the coil carefully to determine which way the wire is wound. Connect the coil to the galvanometer.
2. Plunge the N-pole of the magnet downward into the coil. Answer the following questions.
   (a) Does the galvanometer needle swing left or right?
   (b) When viewed from above, is the electron flow in the coil clockwise or counterclockwise? (Hint: In a galvanometer, the needle swings in the same direction as the electron flow.)
   (c) Does the top of the coil become N or S as the N-pole of the magnet approaches it? (Hint: Use the LHR for coiled conductors.)
   (d) Does the magnetic field of the coil help or hinder the motion of the magnet?

Before you proceed, have your teacher check your answers to these questions.

3. To see if you can predict the direction of an induced current, answer these questions. Assume the N-pole of the magnet is being pulled out of the coil.
   (a) Will the galvanometer needle swing left or right?
   (b) When viewed from above, will the electron flow in the coil be clockwise or counterclockwise?
   (c) Will the top of the coil be N or S as the magnet is moving outward?
   (d) Will the motion of the magnet be helped or hindered by the coil's magnetic field?
4. Verify your answers in #3 experimentally.
5. Repeat #3 and #4 with the S-pole of the magnet moving *into* the coil.
6. Repeat #3 and #4 with the S-pole of the magnet moving *out of* the coil.

ANALYSIS ■
1. Did the induced magnetic field in the coiled conductor assist or oppose the action of the field of the permanent magnet?
2. Assume that the N-pole of a magnet is pushed into a coiled conductor. List the steps you would take to predict the direction of the current induced in the conductor.

21.2 Lenz's Law

In 1834, Heinrich Lenz (1804-1864), a German physicist working in Russia, first explained the direction of a current induced by a changing magnetic field. He showed that when a force is exerted, nature opposes that force. Let us see how this applies to a magnet moving near a coil.

Figure 21-3(a) shows the N-pole of a magnet being pushed into a coil. As the N-pole approaches the coil, the magnetic field near the conductor increases. This changing magnetic field induces a current in the conductor. (Remember Faraday's law.)

Figure 21-3 Pushing the N-pole of a magnet into a coil

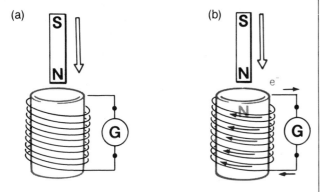

In this example, there are only two directions the induced current can flow, clockwise or counterclockwise, when viewed from above. Consider what would happen if the electrons went counterclockwise. The top of the coil would become an S-pole. (Recall the LHR for coils.) This S-pole would attract the N-pole of the magnet, thus increasing its speed. This would increase the current and electrical energy would be produced with no effort. However, since this cannot happen, we conclude that the electrons must flow clockwise.

If the electrons in the same coil flow clockwise, the top of the pole becomes an N-pole as the magnet moves downward. The N-pole of the coil *opposes* the N-pole of the magnet. Thus, the induced magnetic field opposes the field that produces it. See Figure 21-3(b). This is what you observed in Activity 21B.

A similar discussion can be used to predict what happens if the magnet is pulled upward, out of the coil.

In Figure 21-4, the N-pole of the magnet is being pulled out of the coil. In this case the top of the coil becomes an S-pole to try to prevent the magnet from leaving. Thus, the electrons flow in a direction opposite to that in Figure 21-3.

Figure 21-4 Pulling the N-pole of a magnet out of a coil

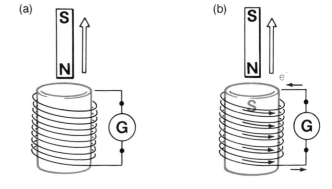

Heinrich Lenz summarized these ideas in a statement now called **Lenz's law**. It states:

For a current induced in a conductor by a changing magnetic field, the current is in such a direction that its own magnetic field opposes the change that produced it.

Lenz's law is applied in the operation of electric generators and transformers, presented later in the chapter.

PRACTICE

4. In each case state which end of the coil is N and find the direction of the electron current.

(a)

(b)

(c)

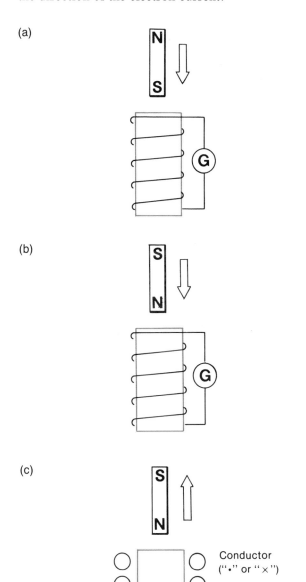

Conductor
("•" or "×")

21.3 Electric Generators

In performing Activities 21A and 21B, you were acting as a generator of electricity. You converted mechanical energy (energy of motion) into electrical energy. A device that changes some form of energy into electrical energy is called an **electric generator**.

Manufactured generators are almost identical to motors. To understand how a generator works, all you have to do is relate Lenz's law to motors.

Consider Figure 21-5. It shows a St. Louis generator, which resembles a St. Louis motor. The motor was connected to a DC source, but the generator is connected to a galvanometer. A mechanical push on the armature causes electrons to flow.

Figure 21-5 A St. Louis generator used to produce direct current

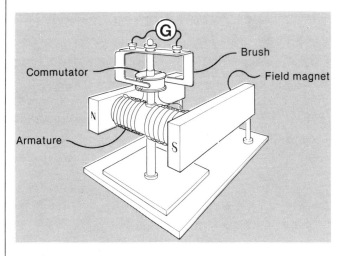

To discover which way the electrons flow in the DC generator, we use the same procedure used in Activity 21B. In Figure 21-6 the left end of the armature coil is being pushed toward an N-pole. Thus the left end of the armature becomes N. (Remember from Lenz's law that the fields must oppose each other.)

Now applying the LHR for coils, we can find the direction of the electron flow. This is shown in Figure 21-6(b).

Figure 21-6   Finding the direction of current in a generator

(a)

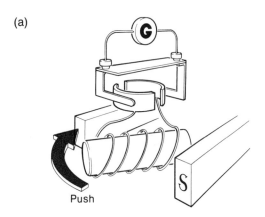

(b)

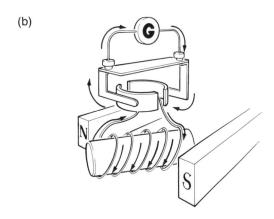

If a St. Louis generator is available, connect it to a galvanometer and check your understanding of these ideas.

Most electric generators create AC electricity rather than DC. As is the case with motors, the main difference between an AC generator and a DC generator is that the brushes are connected to two slip rings rather than a split-ring commutator. A St. Louis generator used to produce AC is shown in Figure 21-7.

Figure 21-7   A St. Louis generator with slip rings produces AC.

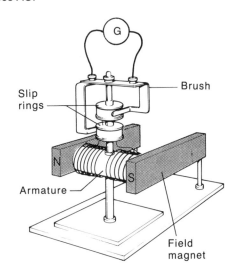

Commercial generators are more complex than St. Louis generators, in that they use several sets of armature windings to help create a current that has a nearly constant value.

Huge AC generators create the electricity that we use in our homes, buildings, and industries. These generators are forced to spin either by falling water or the pressure of steam. Figure 21-8 shows how the kinetic energy of falling water is changed into electrical energy. The photograph at the beginning of the chapter showed an actual dam. Figure 21-9 (overleaf) shows how thermal energy from burning coal is changed into electrical energy. The energy to boil water in this type of generator can also be obtained from natural gas, oil, or nuclear reactions. (Nuclear generating stations are discussed in Section 27.3.)

Figure 21-8 A hydro-electric generating plant

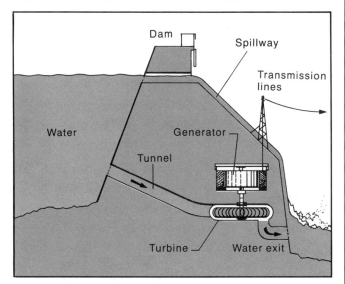

(a) At the top of the dam, the water has gravitational potential energy. The falling water gains kinetic energy which causes huge turbines to spin. The generator changes the mechanical energy of spinning into electrical energy.

(c) Construction of a water tunnel leading to the turbines

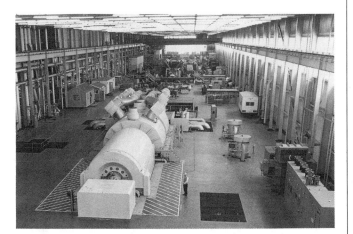

(b) A commercial AC generator

(d) Interior view showing the construction of the generators

There are problems associated with our large generating stations. Our supplies of fossil fuels are declining, in some cases at a fast rate. Burning fossil fuels causes unwanted pollution. The wastes from nuclear generating stations are difficult or impossible to dispose of. Dams cause great changes to the local ecosystem. And often the generating stations are a long distance from the consumers, so huge transmission systems must be built. These occupy much land and present possible hazards to nearby people and animals.

Figure 21-9   A thermal-electric generating plant

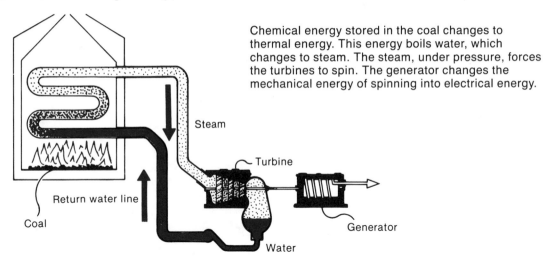

Chemical energy stored in the coal changes to thermal energy. This energy boils water, which changes to steam. The steam, under pressure, forces the turbines to spin. The generator changes the mechanical energy of spinning into electrical energy.

Steam

Turbine

Return water line

Coal

Generator

Water

Figure 21-10   Generating electricity using energy from nature

(a) These solar panels collect light energy from the sun and convert this energy into electrical energy.

(b) This vertical-axis wind generator can rotate no matter which way the wind is blowing. It is part of Canada's continuing effort to develop energy resources.

Electricity is extremely useful and common, and we won't stop using it. This means that we, as a society, must find ways of solving the problems we have created in producing electricity. One important step is in con-serving electrical energy. Another is in the designing of devices that take advantage of energy available from nature, for example, energy from the sun or the wind. (See Figure 21-10.)

PRACTICE

5. The diagram shows a DC St. Louis generator. A push is exerted on the armature as indicated.

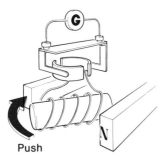

Push

(a) Determine which end of the armature becomes N.
(b) Find the direction of the flow of electrons in the circuit.
6. Natural gas can be used in a generating station to create electricity. Describe how the chemical energy stored in natural gas is changed into electrical energy.

21.4 Using Electricity to Create Electricity

From Section 21.1 we know that a changing magnetic field near a conductor will induce a current in the conductor. This fact has been illustrated several times so far in this chapter. We will illustrate it once more using a device with a different shape.

Figure 21-11 Another example of electromagnetic induction

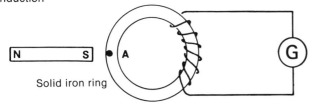

Solid iron ring

Refer to Figure 21-11, which shows a solid iron ring with a conductor coiled around part of the ring. When a magnet is suddenly touched to point A, the magnetic field in the ring changes. This induces a current in the coil for an instant. The current is indicated by the galvanometer.

When the magnet is held still at A, the magnetic field does not change. Thus, no current flows in the coil.

Then when the magnet is suddenly pulled away from A, the magnetic field in the ring changes. Current is again induced in the coil for an instant.

Instead of using a magnet touched to point A, we could use current electricity. This was first discovered by Michael Faraday who designed a device now called Faraday's ring. This device is illustrated in Figure 21-12. There are two parts attached to the ring, a primary circuit and a secondary circuit. When the switch in the primary circuit is suddenly closed, the magnetic field in the ring changes. A current is induced in the secondary circuit for an instant.

As long as the switch remains closed, the magnetic field does not change, so no current flows in the secondary circuit.

Then when the switch is suddenly opened, the magnetic field in the ring changes. Again a current is induced in the secondary circuit for an instant.

Figure 21-12 Faraday's ring

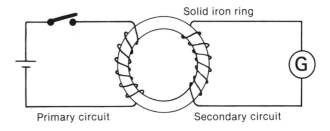

Solid iron ring

Primary circuit   Secondary circuit

In Faraday's ring it is not easy to open and close the switch every time current is needed in the secondary circuit. A better way is to use AC electricity. That way, every time the electrons in the primary circuit change direction, the magnetic field in the ring changes. Then a current is induced in the secondary circuit. Thus, 60 Hz (AC) electricity in the primary circuit creates 60 Hz (AC) electricity in the secondary circuit.

In the next two sections you will learn why these ideas are important.

PRACTICE

7. Choose the statement that best summarizes the operation of Faraday's ring:
   (a) a magnetic field induces current in a conductor
   (b) electricity creates magnetism
   (c) a changing magnetic field induces current in a conductor
   (d) magnetism creates electricity

21.5   Transformers

The idea of Faraday's ring has been applied to a very useful, important electrical device—the transformer. A **transformer** is a device that changes electricity at one potential difference to electricity at a different potential difference.

A transformer has two circuits, a **primary** and a **secondary**. The primary circuit has the source of electricity. The secondary circuit has the load that uses the electrical energy. Each circuit has a different number of windings. This allows the potential difference in one circuit to be different from the potential difference in the other circuit.

Consider Figure 21-13. It shows that a transformer is similar to Faraday's ring. In this example the primary coil has three turns and the secondary coil has nine turns. If the potential difference in the primary is 10 V then the potential difference in the secondary is 30 V. The secondary coil has three times as many windings as the primary, so it steps up the potential difference three times. This type of transformer is called a **step-up transformer**.

If the primary circuit has more turns than the secondary circuit, then the transformer is a **step-down transformer**. This is illustrated in Figure 21-14.

In Figure 21-14 there are four times as many windings in the primary as there are in the secondary. Thus the primary potential difference is four times as much as the secondary potential difference. Therefore the potential difference in the secondary is 5 V.

Figure 21-13   A step-up transformer

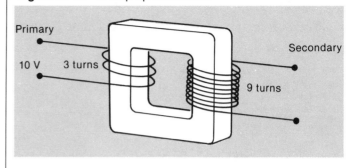

Figure 21-14   A step-down transformer

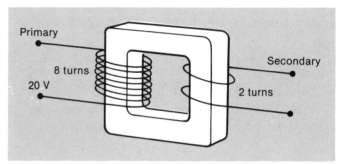

In both these examples the ratio of the secondary potential difference to the primary potential difference equals the ratio of the secondary windings to the primary windings. This can be written in equation form:

$$\frac{\text{secondary potential difference}}{\text{primary potential difference}} = \frac{\text{secondary windings}}{\text{primary windings}}$$

or

$$\frac{V_s}{V_p} = \frac{N_s}{N_p}$$

where V means potential difference, N means the number of windings, s means secondary, and p means primary.

This equation can be used to find any one quantity if the other three quantities are known. For example, to find the secondary potential difference:

$$V_s = \frac{V_p N_s}{N_p}$$

Sample Problem 1

Prove that the secondary potential difference in the transformer in Figure 21-13 is 30 V.

Solution

$$V_s = \frac{V_p N_s}{N_p}$$

$$= \frac{10\,\text{V} \times 9\,\text{turns}}{3\,\text{turns}}$$

$$= 30\,\text{V}$$

In sample problem 1, 10 V from the source in the primary circuit gives 30 V to the secondary circuit. It appears as if we have received something for nothing. But nature does not allow this to happen. Actually, the current in the secondary circuit is only $\frac{1}{3}$ of that in the primary. In other words, in a transformer, if the potential difference increases, the current decreases.

If the proper equipment is available, a demonstration of an AC transformer can be shown. Figure 21-15 shows a set-up to determine if the ratio of $N_s:N_p$ is the same as the ratio of $V_s:V_p$.

Figure 21-15   A demonstration AC transformer

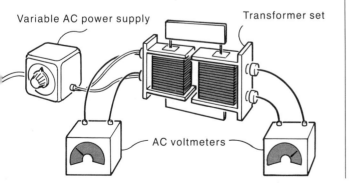

Variable AC power supply

Transformer set

AC voltmeters

PRACTICE

8. For each transformer shown:
   (a) state whether it is a step-up or step-down transformer
   (b) calculate the secondary potential difference

(i)

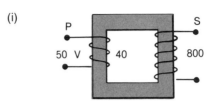

(ii)

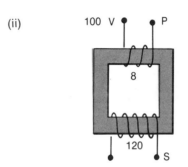

(iii)

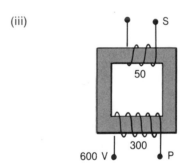

9. Alter the equation $\dfrac{V_s}{V_p} = \dfrac{N_s}{N_p}$ to express:
   (a) N_s by itself   (b) N_p by itself
   (c) V_p by itself

10. Calculate the unknown quantities:
    (a) $N_p = 250\,\text{turns}$; $N_s = 1000\,\text{turns}$;
        $V_s = 960\,\text{V}$; $V_p = ?\,\text{V}$
    (b) $N_p = 50\,\text{turns}$; $V_p = 12\,\text{V}$; $V_s = 3600\,\text{V}$;
        $N_s = ?\,\text{turns}$
    (c) $N_s = 80\,\text{turns}$; $V_p = 240\,\text{V}$; $V_s = 4.0\,\text{V}$;
        $N_p = ?\,\text{turns}$

21.6 Using Transformers to Distribute Electrical Energy

Electric generating stations are almost always built far from where most of the electricity is used. Thus the electrical energy must be transmitted over long distances.

Generating stations produce AC electricity with potential differences of about 20 kV (20 000 V) as well as high currents. If this electricity is transmitted over long distances, much energy is lost due to heating of the wires.

It has been found that less energy is lost if the potential difference is increased and the current decreased. The device that increases potential difference and at the same time decreases current is the transformer. Therefore, to transmit electricity long distances, we must use transformers connected to high-potential difference, low-current lines. This keeps heat loss to a minimum.

Figure 21-16 shows one possible transformer arrangement used to distribute electrical energy. First the potential difference is stepped up from the generating station to the main transmission line. Then it is stepped down in stages and finally used in the home. Notice that the electrons in a home circuit do not come from the generating station. They just move back and forth in the very last circuit. Refer also to Figures 21-17 and 21-18.

Figure 21-16 Distributing electrical energy

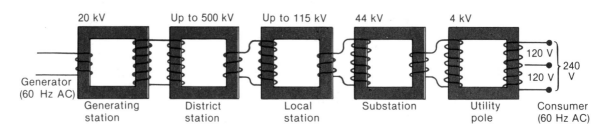

Figure 21-17 A local transformer station

Figure 21-18 A utility-pole transformer

21.7 Electromagnetic Waves

You have studied how charged particles, namely electrons in metal conductors, move back and forth in an alternating current. The electrons gain energy and speed up. Then they slow down, stop, and change direction. Each time they slow down they lose energy. Some of that energy is given off by the electrons in the form of a wave. Such a wave, which originates with the acceleration of a charged particle, is called an **electromagnetic wave**.

There is an entire set of electromagnetic waves. Those caused by 60 Hz (AC) have a frequency of 60 Hz. You may have noticed the interference effects of such waves on a car radio as the car passes under a high-potential difference transmission line.

Waves such as radio waves and radar waves are also electromagnetic. They have frequencies between 10^4 Hz and 10^7 Hz. Another type of electromagnetic wave is called light. It is the topic of the next four chapters.

DID YOU KNOW?

Electric power transmission lines produce hazards for people living nearby. Electric charges induced on farm machinery can result in a spark discharge, which could cause an explosion. Long-term effects on the human body are not known for certain yet. Until more is known about such hazards, it is wise to avoid being close to transmission lines.

Words to Know

induced current
electromagnetic induction
law of electromagnetic
  induction
  (Faraday's law)
Lenz's law
electric generator

transformer
primary circuit
secondary circuit
step-up transformer
step-down transformer
electromagnetic wave

Chapter Objectives

Having completed this chapter, you should now be able to:

1. State the conditions needed for magnetism to induce electricity.
2. Define electromagnetic induction.
3. State the factors that affect the size of a current induced in a conductor by a changing magnetic field.
4. Apply Lenz's law to find the direction of an induced current in a coiled conductor.
5. Describe how an electric generator transforms other energy into electrical energy.
6. Describe how an electric current in one part of a transformer creates an electric current in another part of the transformer.
7. Define step-up transformer and step-down transformer.
8. Given the number of windings in the primary and secondary coils of a transformer and the potential difference of the primary coil, find the potential difference of the secondary coil $\left(V_s = \dfrac{V_p N_s}{N_p} \right)$.
9. Explain why transformers are needed to transmit electrical energy over long distances.
10. State the origin of 60 Hz electromagnetic waves.

Chapter Review

1. Suppose you were given a straight conductor and a U-shaped permanent magnet. Describe how you could induce a current in the conductor when the:
   (a) magnet is held still
   (b) conductor is held still   (21.1)
2. Define electromagnetic induction.   (21.1)
3. In each diagram an arrow shows the direction of motion of a conductor. State whether or not a current is induced in the conductor and explain why. (21.1)

(a)

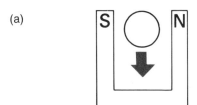

(b)

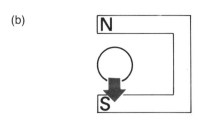

(c)

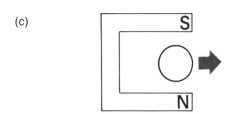

4. Assume you are using a bar magnet to induce a current in a coiled conductor. What happens to the current when you:
   (a) increase the number of windings of the coil?
   (b) increase the speed of motion of the magnet?
   (c) use a stronger magnet?
   (d) stop the magnet?   (Act. 21A)

5. Determine the direction of the electron flow in each coiled conductor.   (21.2)

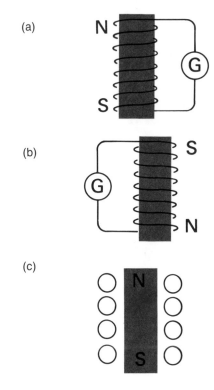

6. Use Lenz's law to decide which end of each coil is N. Then determine the direction of motion of the electrons in the coil.   (21.2)

(a)

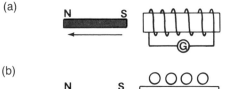

(b)

(c)

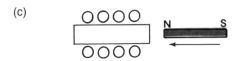

7. What is the purpose of an electric generator? (21.3)

8. In the DC generator in the diagram, the armature is pushed as shown.

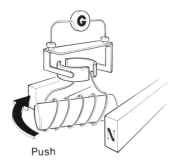

Push

(a) Which end of the coil is N?
(b) Which way do the electrons flow? (21.3)

9. Assume you live in a log cabin on a hill far away from any source of electricity. How could you use the wind to generate electricity to operate lights inside the cabin? (21.3)

10. In a Faraday's ring apparatus, a DC source and a switch are connected in the primary circuit. Under what conditions is a current induced in the secondary circuit? (21.4)

11. In a transformer, why is it better to use AC electricity than DC electricity? (21.5)

12. Describe the construction of:
(a) a step-up transformer
(b) a step-down transformer (21.5)

13. A transformer is needed to operate a fluorescent light fixture. The primary coil has 240 windings and the secondary has 60. If the primary coil is connected to a 120 V household circuit, what is the potential difference that operates the light? (21.5)

14. A model electric train requires 8.0 V to operate. A transformer with a primary coil of 900 windings is plugged into a 120 V wall circuit. How many windings does the secondary coil have? (21.5)

15. An induction coil in an automobile acts like a transformer. It changes 12 V from the primary into perhaps 24 kV (24 000 V) in the secondary. If the number of windings in the secondary is 4.0×10^5 (400 000), find the number of windings in the primary. (The 12 V circuit in a car works on DC. In order to make the induction coil work, the DC must be turned off and on quickly. This is controlled by the car's distributor.) (21.5)

16. An electric doorbell uses a transformer to obtain 6.0 V. If the primary coil has 840 turns and the secondary coil has 42 turns, what is the primary potential difference? (21.5)

17. Choose the condition that best prevents heat loss when transmitting electrical energy long distances:
(a) low potential difference, high current
(b) low current, high potential difference
(c) high current, high potential difference (21.6)

18. Determine at least two electric devices in your home or school that use a transformer. In each case state whether the transformer increases or decreases the potential difference.

19. What is the origin of 60 Hz electromagnetic waves? (21.7)

20. Make a list of jobs and careers that apply the principles of current electricity and electromagnetism described in Chapters 18 to 21. (Some examples are listed at the beginning of this unit.)
(a) Which do you think are likely to remain in high demand for the next 40 or 50 years?
(b) Which are likely to become more in demand in the future?

Light and Colour

The sense of sight is extremely important to you, since it provides a great deal of the information about people and the immediate environment. By entering your eyes, light energy makes it possible for you to see. You can perceive colour in an object because part of the light that strikes it is absorbed by the object and the rest is reflected into our eyes. Microscopes, cameras, and telescopes are examples of optical instruments that utilize mirrors and lenses to control light and produce images for specific purposes. This unit is about light, optical instruments, and the properties of light which cause different colours to be seen.

Information gained in this unit will be useful to you as you consider future careers in an unusually large number of fields. Video technology, photography, television, camera manufacturing and service, lens making, optical dispensing, and telescope and microscope technology are careers that require a thorough knowledge of light, optical instruments, and colour. This knowledge is equally essential should you be considering a career in fashion design or consulting, interior decorating, or communications.

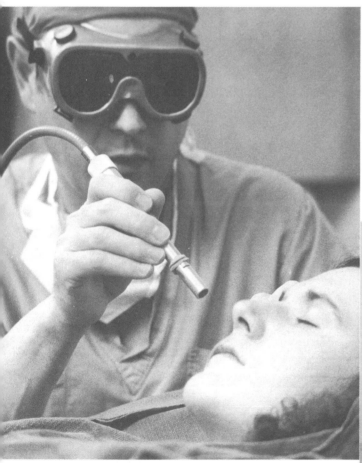

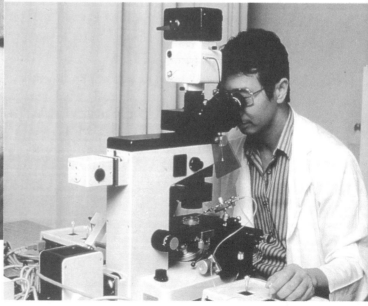

- A telescope or microscope technologist is highly trained in the design, manufacture, and uses of optical devices. There are dozens of types of both microscopes and telescopes with widely different purposes. Thorough knowledge of lenses and the refraction (or bending) of light is essential to a technologist specializing in this field.

- Due to the rapidly expanding uses to which lasers are being applied, laser technologists are enjoying broad areas of employment. Laser technology is used to perform delicate eye surgery, weld automobile frames together, transmit telephone conversations, and reproduce music in compact disc players. Before he or she can begin training, a laser technologist must understand the principles of light and colour.

Knowing the information in this unit will be especially useful if you plan a career in any of the areas already mentioned, as well as the following: theatre, holographic technology, occupational health and safety technology, astronomy, or forensic technology. You can find out about jobs in any of the areas mentioned by talking to someone employed in, or training for, a career that interests you. Contact your local community college, university, guidance office, or counselling centre for more information.

CHAPTER 22

The Nature and Reflection of Light

The sun gives off tremendous amounts of energy, much of which is light energy, spreading out in all directions. (This spectacular photograph, taken with ultraviolet light, shows a solar flare that is equal in size to about fifty earth diameters.) A small amount of the sun's total energy reaches the earth. That energy provides light for us to see, helps plants grow, and ensures that the temperature on earth is suitable for life. This chapter examines various sources of light, including the sun. It also describes how light reflects off various types of mirrors.

Main Ideas

- Light energy can be produced from a variety of sources.
- Eclipses are produced by shadows in the solar system.
- The way light reflects off an object depends on the nature of the object.
- The images produced by a mirror depend on whether the mirror is flat or curved.

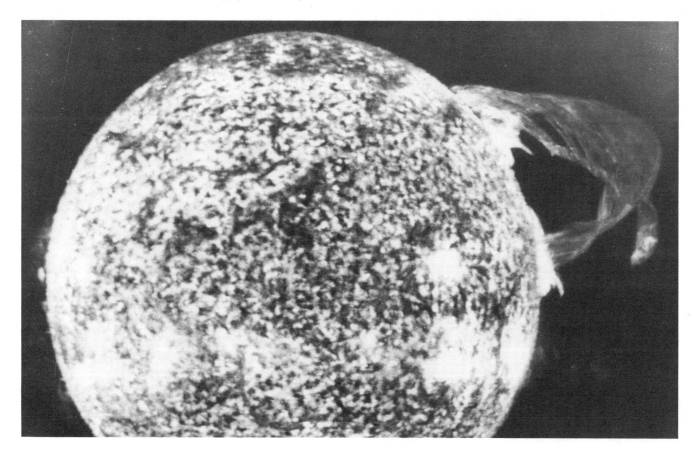

22.1 Sources of Light Energy

Humans have always wondered about light. Today we know quite a lot about light, and we certainly know how to use it. But we don't know all there is to know. A definition that is acceptable is that **light** is a form of energy visible to the eye. That energy can come from a variety of sources. An object that gives off its own light is called **luminous**.

Objects that are luminous because they have a high temperature are called **incandescent**. They are the most common sources of light. Examples of incandescent objects are fires, incandescent light bulbs, and the sun. Another example is shown in Figure 22-1.

Figure 22-1 This molten iron being poured in a steel manufacturing plant is emitting light because of its high temperature.

Substances that are luminous only when they are struck by high-energy waves or electrons are called **fluorescent**. Gases used in fluorescent and neon lights react this way.

Phosphorescent materials become luminous when struck by high-energy waves or electrons and remain luminous for a time. Luminous dials on some watches and clocks give off light for several hours after they absorb energy. An oscilloscope screen gives off light for a short time after the oscilloscope is turned off.

Chemicals that react to produce light with little change in temperature are called **chemiluminescent**. Fireflies, certain fish, and some safety lights give off light energy in this manner.

Certain sources of light have specific uses. For example, an electronic stroboscope (or strobe), used to analyse moving objects, emits short bursts of light at regular intervals. In Figure 22-2, the hand is visible only when light from the strobe bounces off it. The strobe is a luminous object; the hand is not. Another special light source, the laser, will be discussed in Chapter 25.

Figure 22-2 A stroboscope is a special light source that can be used to analyse motion.

PRACTICE

1. List three reasons why light is important to us. (Refer to the chapter introduction.)
2. Is the earth luminous? Explain your answer.
3. What is the main difference between a fluorescent source and a phosphorescent source?
4. Listed below are examples of luminous objects. State whether each should be called incandescent, fluorescent, phosphorescent, or chemiluminescent.
   (a) white-hot molten iron
   (b) material on a Halloween outfit that gives off light
   (c) television screen
   (d) liquid light (Two chemicals are added together to produce a faint glow in the dark.)
   (e) headlight of a car
   (f) lights in your classroom

Figure 22-3 Shadows

(a) Point source

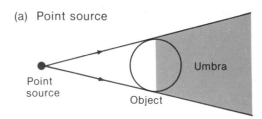

(b) Larger source

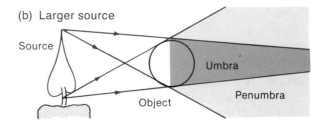

Figure 22-4 This ray box produces both rays and beams.

 CAUTION *Some ray boxes have external power packs. Take care to set the power packs to the potential difference that does not cause the bulbs to blow.*

22.2 Shadows

If light from a source is blocked by an object, a shadow is created behind the object. If the light comes from a source that appears small, the shadow is entirely dark and is called an **umbra**. See Figure 22-3(a).

If light comes from a larger source, or from two sources, the shadow has more than one part. The umbra is the part where no light falls. The **penumbra** is the part where some light falls. Refer to Figure 22-3(b).

In Figure 22-3 the coloured lines represent paths of light that are part of the entire beam coming from the source. We call these lines **light rays**. Only the light rays needed to outline the shadow are drawn. Notice that the direction of each ray is shown.

To obtain light rays and beams in activities, a device called a **ray box** is used. One type of ray box is shown in Figure 22-4. One end of the box has mirrors so it acts as three light sources. The other end acts as a single source of light rays. The use of a ray box is suggested for the activity that follows.

Activity 22A The Formation of Shadows

PROBLEM ■ What causes the various parts of shadows?

APPARATUS ■ ray box; power supply; small object (such as a rubber stopper)

 CAUTION Whenever you use a ray box, take care not to drop it; injuries can be caused by the broken glass.

PROCEDURE ■

1. Place the ray box and object on a piece of paper. Aim a light beam from one source toward the object. Draw and label the shadow formed *behind* the object.
2. Aim light beams from two directions toward the object. (Use either the mirrored end of the ray box or two ray boxes.) Draw a diagram of the shadow behind the object. Shade the different parts of the shadow, and label them.
3. Repeat #2 with light coming from three directions. In this case you should have an umbra, two dark penumbras, and three light penumbras.

ANALYSIS ■

1. Which statement best explains why shadows are formed?
   (a) Light bends easily around corners.
   (b) Light is a form of energy.
   (c) Light travels in straight lines.
   (d) Light may come from many types of sources.
2. When two sources are used, how many sources must be blocked by the object to produce:
   (a) the umbra?
   (b) the penumbra?
3. When three sources are used, how many sources must be blocked to produce:
   (a) the umbra?
   (b) the dark penumbra?
   (c) the light penumbra?
4. Summarize what causes the various parts of shadows.

APPLICATIONS ■

1. On a sunny day, how could you use the length of your shadow to tell when "high noon" is?
2. Why might it be important to understand the formation of shadows if you were employed as:
   (a) a lighting expert at a live theatre
   (b) a portrait photographer

22.3 The Transmission of Light

As light travels from one place to another it displays several properties or characteristics. Three of those properties are discussed in this section.

The fact that **light travels in straight lines** was shown in the shadow activity. It can also be observed in the beam of light of a movie projector or a laser.

DID YOU KNOW?

*T*he "deadly" rays from laser guns used in science fiction movies are visible only if the laser light reflects off numerous particles, such as particles of mist or smoke. The same principle is used in laser shows and concerts.

Another illustration of light travelling in straight lines is the formation of **eclipses**. Eclipses of the sun or moon occur when light from the sun is blocked by the moon or the earth. Figure 22-5 shows how an eclipse of the moon occurs. This is called a **lunar eclipse**. An eclipse of the sun, a **solar eclipse**, can only occur when the moon is between the earth and the sun.

Figure 22-5 A lunar eclipse: Notice that four light rays are needed to outline the shadow of the eclipse. Two rays are drawn from the top of the sun, and two from the bottom. (Sizes and distances in this diagram are not to scale.)

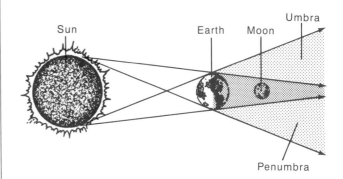

Another property of light energy is that **it does not need a material in which to travel**. This is different from sound energy, which must travel through particles of air or other material. In fact, light travels fastest when there are no particles at all, in other words, in a vacuum. That is why light from the sun and stars can reach us through the vacuum of outer space. (If light could not travel in a vacuum, imagine what would happen to the bell-in-a-vacuum demonstration in Figure 15-1, Section 15.2. The bell would disappear!)

One other property of light is its very fast speed. All radiant energy, including light, travels at a **speed of 3.0×10^8 m/s** in a vacuum. That speed is only slightly less in air, so we use the same value for calculations. At a speed of 3.0×10^8 m/s, light could travel all the way across Canada in about $\frac{1}{50}$ of a second!

PRACTICE

5. What property of light corresponds to the fact that we can't see around corners?
6. The diagram illustrates how a solar eclipse occurs. Redraw the diagram exactly in your notebook. Complete the diagram to show the formation of shadows. Label the place on the earth where the observers would see a total eclipse of the sun.

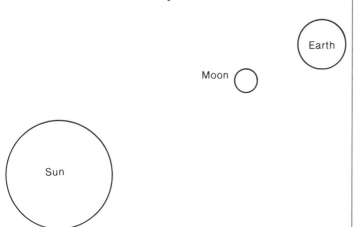

7. Assume light takes 500 s to reach the earth from the sun. How far is the earth from the sun? ($d = vt$)
8. The distance light travels in one year is called a *light year*. Calculate that distance, assuming there are 3.2×10^7 s in a year.
9. The average distance from the earth to the moon is 4.0×10^8 m. How long does it take light to travel from the earth to the moon? $\left(t = \dfrac{d}{v} \right)$

22.4 How Light Behaves When it Strikes Objects

First we defined light. Then we studied sources of light and how light is transmitted. Now we will study what happens when light strikes various objects or materials.

Figure 22-6 shows a photograph of materials that treat light in three different ways.

The glass and the water are **transparent**. They allow light to pass through easily.

The ice is **translucent**. It allows some light to pass through, but it does not allow a clear image to be seen through it.

The spoon is **opaque**. No light passes through it. All the light is either absorbed or reflected.

Light energy is easily absorbed by dark, dull surfaces. It is easily reflected by shiny, smooth surfaces. An apparatus that demonstrates this is the Crookes' radiometer, shown in Figure 22-7.

When bright light is aimed toward the radiometer, the vanes spin rapidly. The shiny surfaces reflect light. The dark surfaces absorb light energy, which changes to thermal energy. This energy in turn warms nearby air particles. The particles jump off the dark surfaces, forcing the vanes to spin in one direction.

Finally, the way light reflects off a shiny surface depends on how smooth the surface is. Two possible situations of reflection are shown in Figure 22-8.

Figure 22-6 Transparent, translucent, and opaque objects

Figure 22-7 The radiometer

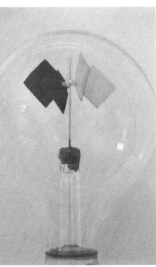

Figure 22-8 Reflection of light off shiny surfaces

(a) Smooth surface

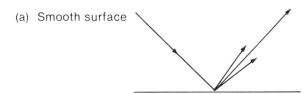

(b) Rough surface

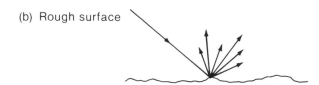

PRACTICE

10. Name two other objects that are:
    (a) transparent
    (b) translucent
    (c) opaque

11. Why is it better to wear white clothing than black clothing on a hot, sunny day?
12. Which of Newton's laws of motion (Chapter 6) is demonstrated when the air particles jump off the black surface of a radiometer? Explain your answer.

22.5 Reflection of Light in a Plane Mirror

Several new terms must be introduced before you begin experimenting with mirrors. The following definitions are illustrated in Figure 22-9.

(1) An **incident ray** is a ray of light travelling from the source to some object, such as a mirror.
(2) A **reflected ray** is a ray of light that bounces off an object.
(3) A **normal** (N) is a line at an angle of 90° to the surface where the incident ray strikes. (A normal is not a light ray.)
(4) The **angle of incidence** ($\angle i$) is the angle between the incident ray and the normal.
(5) The **angle of reflection** ($\angle r$) is the angle between the reflected ray and the normal.

Figure 22-9 Plane-mirror definitions

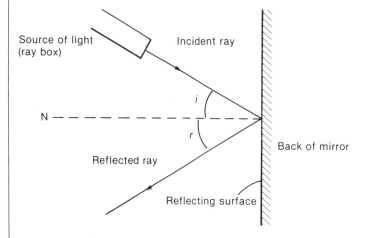

Activity 22B Plane-Mirror Reflection

PROBLEM ■

(a) What is the law of reflection for a plane mirror?

(b) How can rays be used to locate an image in a plane mirror?

(c) What are the characteristics of an image in a plane mirror?

Figure 22-10 For Activity 22B: Only the incident rays are shown. You must find the reflected rays.

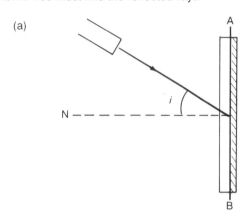

(a)

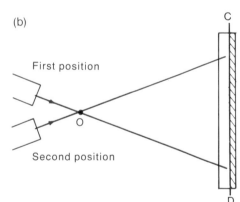

(b)

APPARATUS ■ ray box with a single-slit window; plane mirror; protractor

PROCEDURE ■

1. Look at the mirror to see how it is made. The reflecting surface is probably at the back of the glass.

 CAUTION Before handling mirrors or glass, check that there are no chips or sharp edges which might cut your hands.

2. Draw a line AB on a piece of paper. Stand the mirror vertically so its reflecting surface is along AB, as shown in Figure 22-10(a).

3. Aim an incident ray from the ray box to the mirror. Use small dots to mark the incident and reflected rays. Remove the ray box and mirror and use a straight edge to draw the rays.

4. Draw a normal from the point where the rays meet at the mirror. Label and measure the angles of incidence and reflection.

5. Repeat #2 to #4 using two new diagrams and distinctly different angles.

6. Draw a line CD and a point O on a piece of paper as shown in Figure 22-10(b). Locate the image (I) of the object (O) in the mirror in the following way:

   (a) Find a set of incident and reflected rays with the ray box in the first position. Move the ray box to the second position, and find another set of rays. (The incident rays must go through O.)

   (b) Remove the mirror and extend the reflected rays straight back behind the mirror, because that is where they *appear* to come from.

   (c) Find the point where the extended lines meet. This is the image (I).

7. Use the following technique to determine how accurate the image location found in #6 is. Stand a pencil vertically at the object location. Stand a second pencil behind the mirror at the image location. Look into the mirror from various directions to see how closely the image of the first pencil lines up with the pencil behind the mirror. (If the image and the second pencil line up exactly, the image location is good.)

8. Look into a plane mirror. Is the image upright or inverted? Is the image smaller than the object, larger, or the same size?

ANALYSIS ■

1. For each diagram in Procedure #4 and #5, how does the angle of incidence compare to the angle of reflection? If your diagrams and results are accurate, you will be able to write the law of reflection.

2. In the diagram for Procedure #6, how does the distance between the image and the mirror compare to the distance between the object and the mirror?

3. Describe how light rays can be used to locate an image in a plane mirror.

4. What are the characteristics of an image in a plane mirror?

22.6 Ray Diagrams for Plane Mirrors

A ray diagram can be used to locate the image of an object seen in a mirror. The rays are drawn so that the law of reflection ($\angle i = \angle r$) is obeyed.

Consider object OB in Figure 22-11(a). From point O two incident rays are drawn. The normals and reflected rays are then drawn. To find the image (I), the reflected rays must meet, so they are extended behind the mirror. Then all the rays from point O reflect off the mirror and appear to come from point I.

The same procedure is used to find the image of B. That image is labelled M. Then the total image, IM, can be drawn.

In Figure 22-11(a), the distance from the object to the mirror equals the distance from the image to the mirror. This provides a short cut for finding an image in a plane mirror. An example of this short cut is shown in Figure 22-11(b).

Figure 22-11 Locating an image in a plane mirror

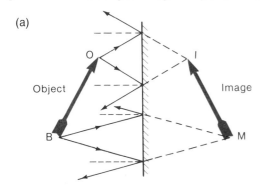

(a)

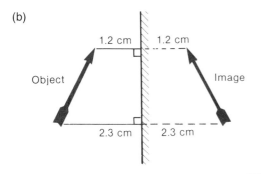

(b)

After an image has been located in a ray diagram, we can describe the image. Four characteristics are generally needed to describe each image.

(1) **Attitude:** Is the image upright or inverted?
(2) **Size:** Is the image larger than the object, smaller, or the same size?
(3) **Type:** Is the image real or imaginary? A **real image** can be placed onto a screen, as you will observe later in the chapter. The light rays that create the real image actually meet each other. An **imaginary image** cannot be placed on a screen. The light rays that create such an image only appear to meet each other. To see an imaginary image in a mirror, you have to look into the mirror. In a single mirror an imaginary image is upright. (An imaginary image is also called a *virtual* image.)
(4) **Location:** Is the image in front of the mirror, or behind it?

PRACTICE

13. State the angle of reflection if the angle of incidence is:
    (a) 22°   (b) 75°   (c) 0°
14. Describe the image in a plane mirror by stating its:
    (a) attitude   (b) size   (c) type   (d) location
15. Copy each diagram into your notebook. Locate the image of the object.

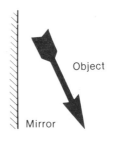

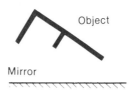

22.7 Applications of Plane Mirrors

Plane mirrors are commonly used as looking glasses. But they also have other interesting applications.

For example, in an arcade shooting gallery a plane mirror is used in some machines. Figure 22-12 shows the type of machine in which a rifle shoots light that bounces off a mirror to a target below. A direct hit is recorded if the light strikes a sensitive part of the target. The image of the target appears straight ahead and at the distance illustrated in the diagram.

Figure 22-12   Changing the direction of light in a shooting gallery

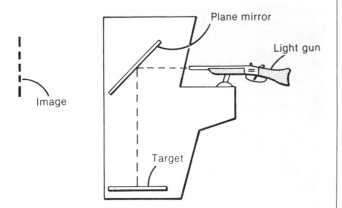

Another application of plane mirrors comes from the fact that when two mirrors are placed at an angle to each other, multiple images are seen. The smaller the angle, the greater the number of images. At 90° between the mirrors, three images are formed, and at 60°, five images are formed. (Refer to Appendix F.) A kaleidoscope, shown in Figure 22-13, has two plane mirrors at an angle of 60° to each other. Coloured glass or plastic crystals are placed between the mirrors. Thus, five identical images of the crystal pattern can be seen at any one time. As the kaleidoscope is turned, new patterns are formed.

Figure 22-13   The kaleidoscope

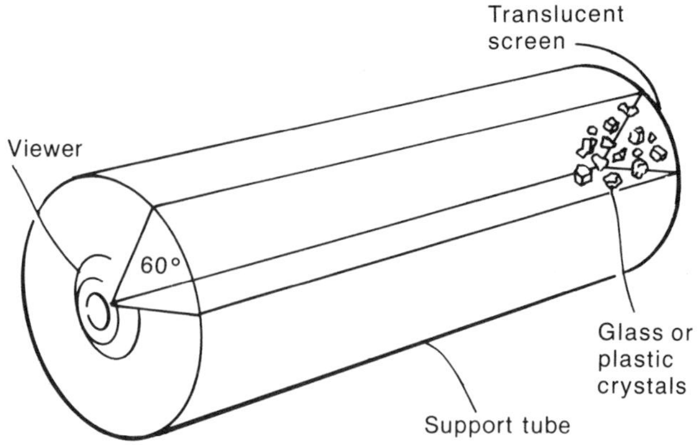

PRACTICE

16. Try this. Obtain two plane mirrors. Hold them at angles to each other of 90° and less. Observe how multiple images can be obtained.
17. Find out how a plane mirror is used in the devices listed below. Describe your findings.
    (a) a single-lens reflex camera
    (b) a one-way mirror
    (c) an ophthalmoscope

22.8   Curved Mirrors

Although plane mirrors are very common, they are not the only type of mirror used. Curved mirrors, both concave and convex, also have many applications.

A **concave mirror** has a reflecting surface that curves inwards. A **convex mirror** has a reflecting surface that bulges outwards. Refer to Figure 22-14.

In Figure 22-14 there are two symbols, C and r, that should be defined. The point C is the **centre of curvature** of the circle from which the mirror is made. The distance r is the **radius of curvature** of a curved mirror. It is the distance from the centre of curvature to the reflecting surface.

Figure 22-14 Curved mirrors

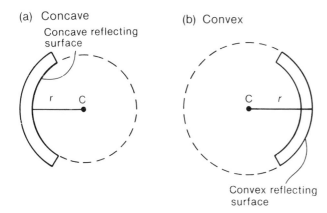

(a) Concave

Concave reflecting surface

(b) Convex

Convex reflecting surface

Other definitions for curved mirrors are illustrated in Figure 22-15. The **principal axis** (P.A.) of a curved mirror is the line drawn through C that strikes the **vertex** (V), which is the middle of the mirror. The **focal point** (F) is the position where parallel incident rays meet when they reflect. The **focal length** (f) is the distance from F to the reflecting surface.

Figure 22-15 Curved-mirror definitions

(a) Concave

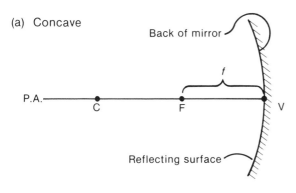

Back of mirror

P.A.

C   F   V

Reflecting surface

(b) Convex

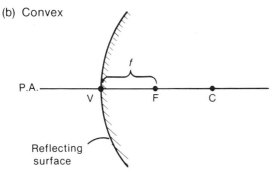

P.A.

V   F   C

Reflecting surface

PRACTICE

18. The diagrams represent curved mirrors. For each mirror:
    (a) state whether it is concave or convex
    (b) measure its radius of curvature

(i)

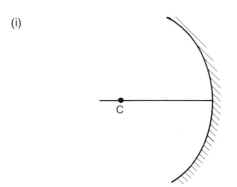

C

(ii)

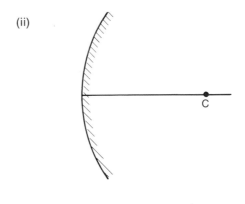

C

(iii)

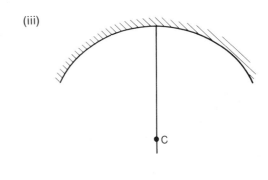

C

Activity 22C Reflection in a Circular Concave Mirror

PROBLEM ■ For a circular concave mirror:

(a) what is the ratio of the radius of curvature to the focal length?

(b) what are the rules for light rays that strike the mirror?

APPARATUS ■ ray box with single-slit and triple-slit windows; circular concave mirror

PROCEDURE ■

1. Set the mirror flat on a piece of paper and draw its shape. Aim a single light ray toward V so it reflects onto itself. Draw that ray. Now move the ray box around and find a second ray that reflects onto itself, and draw it. Repeat this for a third ray, as shown in Figure 22-16(a). The point where the rays meet is C. Measure the radius of curvature, r. Label both C and r in your diagram.

Figure 22-16

(a)

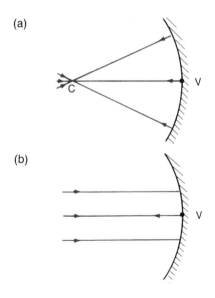

(b)

2. Set the triple-slit window into the ray box, and check to be sure the emerging rays are parallel. Draw the shape of the mirror on a new diagram. Aim three *parallel* rays of light toward the mirror so that the middle ray strikes V and reflects onto itself. See Figure 22-16(b). Draw all incident and reflected rays. The point where the reflected rays meet is F. Label it and measure the focal length, f.

3. Starting a new diagram, aim a single ray, P.A., toward the middle of the mirror so it strikes V and reflects onto itself. See Figure 22-17. Use the measurements found in #1 and #2 to label points C and F. Use a single ray to determine each of three important *rules* for concave-mirror reflection. Draw all the rays on your diagram. The rays used to determine these rules are:

(a) an incident ray parallel to the principal axis (and close to it)

(b) an incident ray through F (at a small angle to the principal axis)

(c) an incident ray through C (but not along the principal axis)

Figure 22-17

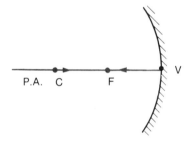

ANALYSIS ■

1. Describe what method can be used to locate C for a circular concave mirror.

2. Describe how to locate F for a circular concave mirror.

3. Use the measurements in Procedure #1 and #2 to calculate the ratio of $\frac{r}{f}$. How close is this ratio to $\frac{2}{1}$?

4. (a) Through what point does an incident ray parallel to the principal axis reflect?

   (b) Where does the incident ray through F reflect?

   (c) Where does the incident ray through C reflect?

5. Summarize the rules for light rays that strike a circular concave mirror.

1. What is the focal length of a concave mirror whose radius of curvature is:
   (a) 12 cm?   (b) 60 mm?   (c) 4.6 cm?
2. What is the radius of curvature of a concave mirror whose focal length is:
   (a) 2.1 cm?   (b) 24 mm?   (c) 5.8 cm?
3. The word converge means to come together. Explain why a concave mirror may be called a converging mirror.
4. List some uses of concave mirrors.

Figure 22-18   Images in concave mirrors

(a) Object close to mirror

22.9   Images in Concave Mirrors

An image can be described as having four main characteristics: attitude, size, type, and location. These were defined in Section 22.6. The characteristics of the image in a concave mirror depend on where the object is located.

Figure 22-18(a) shows an image in a concave mirror when the object is close to the mirror. The image is upright, larger than the object, and imaginary. Its location is behind the mirror, which will be proved using diagrams in Section 22.10.

Diagram (b) shows an image when the object is just beyond the focal point. In this case, the image is inverted, larger than the object, real, and located in front of the mirror. It is real because it can be placed onto a screen. You can look at the screen to see the image; you do not have to look at the mirror. When a single mirror is used, a real image is inverted.

PRACTICE

19. Try these.
    (a) Hold a glass concave mirror at arm's length and view an object far away in the room. Describe the image by stating its attitude, size, and type.
    (b) Hold a concave mirror at arm's length and look at your image in the mirror. Slowly move the mirror toward you until it just touches the tip of your nose. Describe what happens to the size of your image as the mirror approaches.

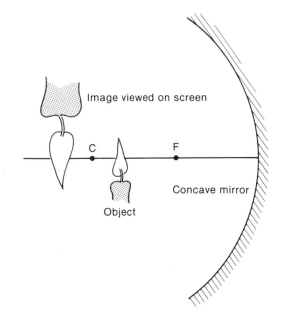

(b) Object just beyond the focal point

Activity 22D Reflection in a Circular Convex Mirror

PROBLEM ■ For a circular convex mirror:
(a) what is the ratio of the radius of curvature to the focal length?
(b) what are the rules for light rays that strike the mirror?
(c) what are the characteristics of the image?

APPARATUS ■ ray box with single-slit and triple-slit windows; convex mirror (circular); convex mirror (glass)

PROCEDURE ■
1. Design a procedure to determine the centre of curvature, C, and the radius of curvature, *r*, of the circular convex mirror. Use Procedure #1 in the previous activity and Figure 22-19(a) as references. Notice that the rays reflecting from a convex mirror spread apart, so they do not meet. To make the rays meet, you must extend them straight back (using broken lines) behind the mirror.
2. Design a procedure to determine the focal point, F, and focal length, *f*, of the convex mirror. Use as references Procedure #2 in the previous activity and Figure 22-19(b).

Figure 22-19

(a)   (b)

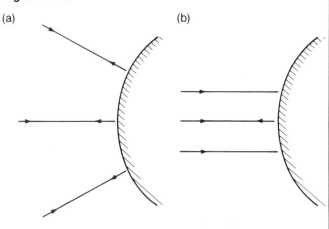

3. Design a procedure to determine three important rules for convex-mirror reflection. Use Figure 22-20 and Procedure #3 in Activity 22C as references. To determine the rules use:
(a) an incident ray that is parallel to the principal axis
(b) an incident ray that is aimed toward F
(c) an incident ray that is aimed toward C

Figure 22-20

(a)

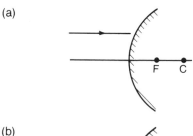

(b)

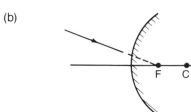

(c)

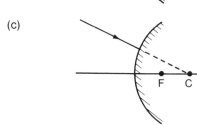

4. View the image of an object seen in a convex mirror made of glass. Describe the image by stating its attitude, size, and type.

ANALYSIS ■
1. What extra step must be taken to locate C and F in a convex mirror compared to a concave mirror?
2. (a) Calculate the ratio of $\frac{r}{f}$ for the convex mirror.

   (b) How does this ratio compare to the ratio of $\frac{r}{f}$ for the concave mirror?
3. (a) For an incident ray parallel to the principal axis, what point does the incident ray line up with?
   (b) Where does an incident ray toward F reflect?
   (c) Where does an incident ray toward C reflect?
4. What are the rules for light rays that strike a circular convex mirror?

APPLICATIONS ■
1. The word diverge means to spread apart. Explain why a convex mirror may be called a diverging mirror.
2. List some uses of convex mirrors.

22.10 Ray Diagrams for Curved Mirrors

A ray diagram can be used to locate the image of an object in a curved mirror. The method we will use here involves the rules for curved-mirror reflection that you learned in the previous two activities. (Those rules are actually based on the fact that $\angle i = \angle r$ for all mirrors, although we did not prove it in the activities.)

In the sample problems that follow notice that the reflected rays must meet in order to locate an image. In the first case the reflected rays actually meet in front of the mirror. Thus, the image is real. In the second case the reflected rays do not meet unless they are extended behind the mirror. Thus, the image is imaginary.

Sample Problem 1

Use a ray diagram to find the image of a 2.0 cm high object located 10 cm from a concave mirror that has a focal length of 2.5 cm. State the attitude, size, type, and location of the image.

Solution If $f = 2.5$ cm, then $r = 5.0$ cm. Draw a concave mirror with $r = 5.0$ cm. Label C and

F. Draw the object sitting on the principal axis. (This saves a lot of time.) Use three incident rays and reflected rays, according to the rules, to locate the image.

The image is inverted, smaller than the object, real, and in front of the mirror.

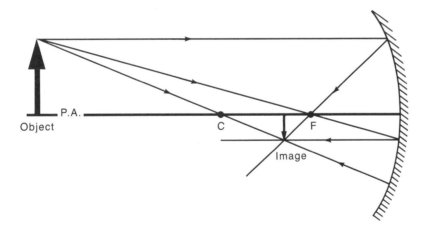

Sample Problem 2

Repeat sample problem 1 using a convex mirror and an object distance of 6 cm and a focal length of 3.0 cm.

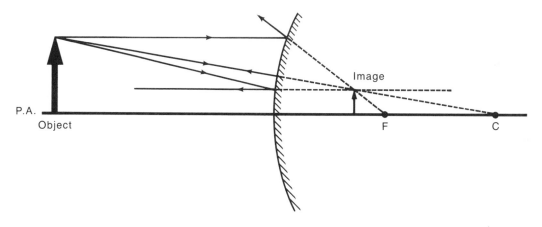

Solution   The image is upright, smaller than the object, imaginary, and behind the mirror.

PRACTICE

20. Draw a fully labelled ray diagram to locate the image of the object for each situation described in the chart below. In each diagram use two rules, and draw the object 1.5 cm high. For each image, state its attitude, size, type, and location.

Type of mirror	Focal length (cm)	Distance of object to mirror (cm)
(a) Concave	3.0	12.0
(b) Concave	4.0	8.0
(c) Concave	4.0	6.0
(d) Concave	4.0	4.0
(e) Concave	4.0	2.0
(f) Convex	3.0	10.0
(g) Convex	3.0	3.0

21. Based on your diagrams in #20, answer these questions.
    (a) What is the only type of mirror that can produce a real image?
    (b) What type of image is produced when an object is located closer than the focal point of a concave mirror?
    (c) Where must an object in front of a concave mirror be located to produce no image?
    (d) What type of image does a convex mirror always produce?

22.11 Applications of Curved Mirrors

Concave mirrors

Figure 22-21 shows four uses of concave mirrors.

A car headlight, in diagram (a), has the source of light near the focal point of the mirror. Light reflects off the mirror to form a directed beam.

Concave mirrors are used to concentrate sunlight. A solar cooker, illustrated in diagram (b), has the cooking pot located at the focal point of the mirror. Diagram (c) shows a large solar collector used for scientific research. It is located in the Pyrenees Mountains in Southern France.

Diagram (d) illustrates how a concave mirror is used in a reflecting telescope. Huge telescopes (up to 6 m in diameter) collect much light, so astronomers can view distant stars which are not visible through small telescopes.

Figure 22-21   Applications of concave mirrors

(a) Headlight of a car

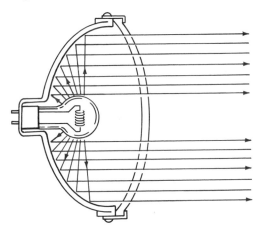

(b) Solar cooker

(c) Solar reflector

(d) Reflecting telescope

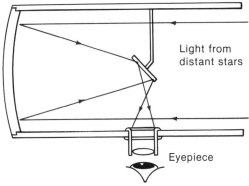

Concave mirror

Light from distant stars

Eyepiece

Convex mirrors

Images in convex mirrors are always upright and smaller than the object. Therefore convex mirrors allow the viewer to see over a wide angle. Such mirrors are used in stores to discourage shoplifting. They are also used as rear-view mirrors on trucks, buses, and motorcycles. (See Figure 22-22.) When using a convex mirror, a driver must be careful because a vehicle is much closer than it appears in the mirror.

Figure 22-22   A convex mirror gives a wide-angle view.

Words to Know

light	normal
luminous	angle of incidence
incandescent	angle of reflection
fluorescent	real image
phosphorescent	imaginary image
chemiluminescent	concave mirror
umbra	convex mirror
penumbra	principal axis
transparent	radius of curvature
translucent	focal length
opaque	

Chapter Objectives

Having completed this chapter, you should now be able to:

1. Describe the importance of light energy.
2. Give a basic definition of light.
3. List sources of light energy.
4. Name the parts of a shadow.
5. Draw diagrams of solar and lunar eclipses.
6. List characteristics of light as it is transmitted from one place to another.
7. Define and give examples of objects that are transparent, translucent, and opaque.
8. Explain the difference between absorbing, reflecting, and transmitting light energy.
9. State the law of reflection for mirrors.
10. In a diagram locate the image of an object in a plane mirror.
11. State the meaning of the following terms for curved mirrors: concave, convex, centre of curvature, radius of curvature, principal axis, vertex, focal point, and focal length.
12. Know and apply the ratio $\frac{r}{f}$ for curved mirrors.
13. State three rules used to draw ray diagrams for curved mirrors.
14. For each image in a mirror, state its attitude, size, type, and location.
15. Draw a ray diagram to find the image of an object located at various distances from a curved mirror.
16. State applications of all types of mirrors.

Chapter Review

1. What is light? (22.1))
2. (a) What is an incandescent object?
   (b) State four examples of incandescent objects. (22.1)
3. What property of light is illustrated by the formation of shadows? (22.2, 22.3)
4. Name the type of eclipse in which the sun's light is blocked off by the moon. (22.3)
5. Describe evidence that light travels in a straight line. (22.3)
6. How fast does light travel in a vacuum? (22.3)
7. The nearest star to our sun is about 4 light years away. Use your answer to Practice #8 to find the distance to the nearest star. (22.3)
8. As the space probe Voyager sped past the distant planet Neptune, it sent photographs back to the earth using signals that travelled at the speed of light. If the signals travelled 4.5 billion kilometres (or 4.5×10^{12} m), how long did they take to reach the earth? (22.3)
9. From each pair of materials listed, choose the material that absorbs light more easily. (22.4)
   (a) a black surface; a white surface
   (b) a transparent material; an opaque material
   (c) a smooth surface; a rough surface
   (d) a dull surface; a shiny surface
10. State the law of reflection for mirrors. (Act. 22B, 22.6)
11. Describe the differences between a real image and an imaginary image. (22.6)
12. If you stand 60 cm in front of a plane mirror, how far are you from your image in the mirror? (22.6)
13. Each diagram shows an object in front of a plane mirror. Draw the diagrams in your notebook and locate the images. (22.6)

14. For circular curved mirrors, state the ratio of:
    (a) $\frac{r}{f}$ (b) $\frac{f}{r}$ (Act. 22C, Act. 22D, 22.10)
15. A candle flame, 2.0 cm high, is used as an object to demonstrate images in curved mirrors. For each situation described below, draw a ray diagram to locate the image, and state the four characteristics of the image. (22.10)
    (a) The flame is 5.5 cm from a concave mirror with a 7.0 cm radius of curvature.
    (b) The flame is 2.0 cm from the mirror in (a).
    (c) The flame is 6.0 cm from a convex mirror with a 5.0 cm radius of curvature.
16. Assume you have a shiny tablespoon. How would you hold the spoon to obtain an image of yourself that is:
    (a) small and imaginary?
    (b) small and real?
    (c) large and imaginary? (22.8 to 22.10)
17. The diagram shows one way of heating water using solar energy.

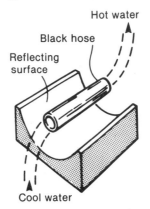

Hot water

Black hose

Reflecting surface

Cool water

(a) Describe at least two ways in which this is an application of topics in this chapter.
(b) How would you determine where to position the black hose for the best heating effects?

(a)

(b)

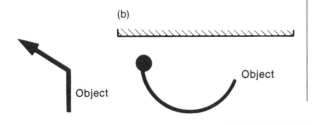

Object

Object

CHAPTER 23

Refraction and Lenses

Main Ideas

- Light can bend as it travels from one material into another.
- When light strikes the inside surface of a transparent material at certain angles, it can become trapped inside the material.
- Light reflecting inside a material has several applications, including the use of binoculars and fibre optics.
- A lens uses the bending of light to produce an image.
- The image produced by a lens depends on the type of lens and the distance between the object and the lens.
- A ray diagram can be used to locate the image in a lens.

When light enters a transparent material, it can bend, and in some cases it can reflect inside the material. This is what causes diamonds to sparkle. The bending of light allows the use of lenses, and it is applied in glass fibres to transmit telephone messages. Many of the applications of the principles examined in this chapter can be found in Chapter 24.

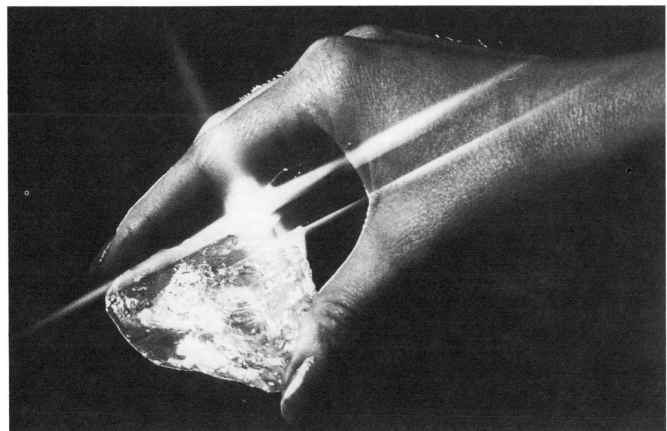

23.1   Refraction of Light

Have you ever noticed that the sun appears to change colour as it is setting? Or, looking down, have you ever noticed the distortion as you walk in clear, waist-deep water? Such effects occur because of the bending of light.

In the previous chapter you learned that light travels in straight lines. That is true as long as the light is travelling in one uniform material. However, when light travels from one material into another, it can bend. This bending is called **refraction**.

Figure 23-1(a) shows a beam of light travelling from air into a block of glass. The light refracts upon entering the glass. (Some of the light also reflects off the side of the block.) The reason the light refracts is that its speed changes. Light travels more slowly in the glass than in the air. This results in a change in direction. Another example of how a change in speed causes a change in direction is illustrated in Figure 23-1(b). The wheels of a car change direction when they travel from pavement to sand, as shown in the diagram.

Refraction can be observed in various circumstances. For example, if a ruler is placed into a beaker of water, the ruler appears to be bent, as shown in Figure 23-2. This is caused by the refraction of light as it leaves the water.

Figure 23-1   Refraction

(a) Refraction of light

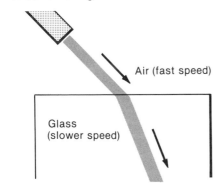

Air (fast speed)

Glass
(slower speed)

(b) Refraction of a set
of wheels

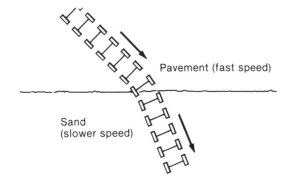

Pavement (fast speed)

Sand
(slower speed)

Figure 23-2   Observing the effect of refraction

Certain symbols are used to label diagrams of refraction of light. Figure 23-3 shows a typical refraction diagram with several of these symbols. The normals are drawn at 90° to the surfaces where the rays enter and leave the prism. The angles of incidence ($\sphericalangle i$), refraction ($\sphericalangle R$), and emergence ($\sphericalangle e$) are measured between the normal and the ray. You will use these symbols in Activity 23A.

Figure 23-3   Symbols used in refraction diagrams

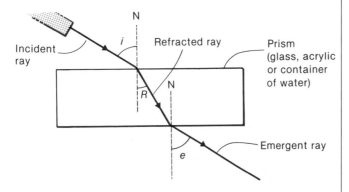

PRACTICE

1. Try this. Obtain a coin, a small opaque dish, a small beaker, and some water. Place the coin in the dish, and position your eyes so you just miss seeing the coin, as illustrated in Figure 23-4(a). Slowly add water to the dish without moving the coin. Describe what you observe. Explain the effect, using as reference Figure 23-4(b).

Figure 23-4   For Practice #1

(a) Before adding water

(b) After adding water

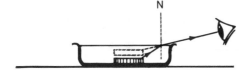

Activity 23A   Refraction in a Rectangular Prism

PROBLEM ■
(a) What happens to a ray of light as it travels from air into another material, then back into air?
(b) What are the laws of refraction?

APPARATUS ■   ray box with single-slit window; rectangular solid block (made of glass or acrylic); rectangular plastic box to hold water; protractor

 CAUTION   Inspect all glass or acrylic objects for chips or sharp edges which may cut your hands.

Figure 23-5

(a)

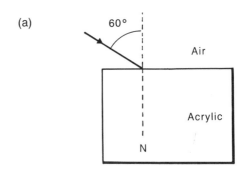

(b)

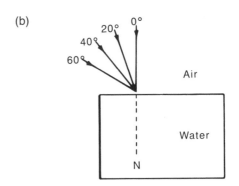

PROCEDURE ■
1. Place the solid block on a page and draw its outline. Use a broken line to draw a normal, as shown in Figure 23-5(a). Draw an incident ray so that ∡ i = 60°. Repeat this procedure using three more diagrams and angles of 40°, 20°, and 0° from the normal.
2. Aim a single ray along the incident ray in the first diagram. Draw the ray that emerges on the opposite side of the block. Remove the block and draw the entire path of the light. Label and measure the angles of refraction (∡ R) and emergence (∡ e).
3. Repeat #2, using the other angles of incidence.
4. Repeat #1 to #3, using water in a plastic container. You can draw all the rays on one diagram if you place them near one corner, as shown in Figure 23-5(b).
5. Tabulate the measurements in a chart similar to the one below.

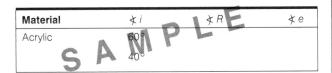

Material	∡ i	∡ R	∡ e
Acrylic	60°		
	40°		

ANALYSIS ■
1. (a) When light travels at an angle from a material of low density (such as air) to one of higher density (such as water), does it bend away from or toward the normal?
   (b) When light travels at an angle from a material of high density to one of lower density, does it bend away from or toward the normal?
2. When light travels from air into another material, at what angle of incidence is there no refraction?

3. For each ray observed, how does the angle of incidence in air compare to the angle of emergence in air?
4. How does refraction in water compare to refraction in glass or acrylic?
5. In which substance, water or the solid block, do you think light travels faster? What evidence do you have for your answer?
6. Describe what happens to a ray of light as it travels from air into a more dense material, then back into air.
7. State two laws of refraction. (These are based on your answers to Analysis #1.)

APPLICATION ■ Two swimmers, G and B, stand at the edge of a clear lake. B bets he can stand on the rock he sees and the water will be at his waist. G bets he is wrong because she thinks the rock is too far below the surface.
(a) According to the diagram, who is right?
(b) Why was the other swimmer wrong? (A ray diagram will help you explain your answer.)

23.2 Total Internal Reflection

It is possible for light in a transparent material to reflect inside the material. This can occur only when the material is surrounded by less dense, transparent material. The effect can be explained by considering refraction.

You have learned that when light travels from a material of high density (such as acrylic) into one of lower density (such as air), it refracts away from the normal. This means that the angle of emergence in air is greater than the angle in the acrylic. This is shown in diagram (a) of Figure 23-6.

In diagram (b) the angle in the acrylic has increased, and the angle of emergence is almost 90°. When this happens, the white light actually starts splitting up into rainbow colours. Also, some light is internally reflected; in other words, some light reflects off the inside surface of the acrylic.

When the light just disappears along the surface of the plastic, as in diagram (c), the angle in the acrylic is called the **critical angle**, $\angle c$. For any angle in the acrylic greater than the critical angle, **total internal reflection** occurs. This is shown in diagram (d). Total internal reflection can occur in any transparent material surrounded by less dense material. Figure 23-6(e) shows laser light internally reflecting in water.

Figure 23-6 Explaining total internal reflection

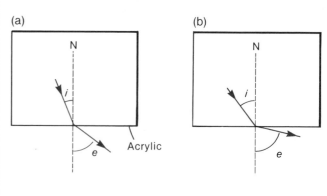

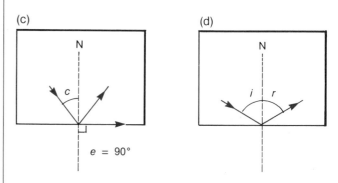

(e) Total internal reflection of laser light in water

Activity 23B Internal Reflection

PROBLEM ■

(a) What is the critical angle of acrylic (or other materials) surrounded by air?

(b) What is an application of total internal reflection?

APPARATUS ■ ray box with single-slit and double-slit windows; semicircular acrylic block; 2 triangular acrylic prisms (45°, 90°, 45°)

Figure 23-7

(a)

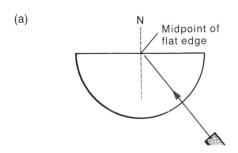

Midpoint of flat edge

N

(b)

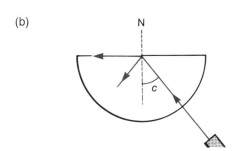

N

c

(c)

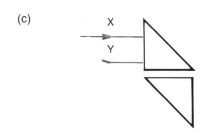

X

Y

PROCEDURE ■

1. Place the semicircular block on your page and draw its outline. Aim a single ray from the curved side directly toward the *middle* of the flat edge as shown in Figure 23-7(a). Complete the diagram.

2. Slowly move the ray box around until you can see the rainbow colours near the flat edge. Be sure the ray continues to strike the midpoint of the flat edge. Move the box slightly farther until the light in the air disappears. See Figure 23-7(b). Mark the rays. Remove the block, draw the normal, and measure the critical angle, ⊀ c, for acrylic. Have the teacher check your value.

3. Start a new diagram with the same block. Aim a single ray from the curved side so that the angle inside the acrylic is greater than ⊀ c. Complete the diagram of total internal reflection. Label and measure the angles of incidence and reflection.

4. A periscope is an interesting application of total internal reflection. To see how light travels in a periscope, set up the triangular prisms as shown in Figure 23-7(c). Aim two rays, X and Y, as shown, and draw the paths followed by those rays.

ANALYSIS ■

1. Describe how you could judge when the critical angle occurred.

2. What is the critical angle of acrylic surrounded by air?

3. Does the law of reflection for mirrors ($⊀ i = ⊀ r$) apply for total internal reflection?

4. What is an application of total internal reflection?

5. In your diagram of the periscope, are the final rays upright or inverted when compared to the incident rays? How do you know?

APPLICATION ■ The critical angle of ordinary glass is 42°. Which of the following angles of light rays in glass would result in total internal reflection?
(a) 35°   (b) 50°   (c) 43°   (d) 3°

23.3 Applications of Total Internal Reflection

Figure 23-8 Applications of total internal reflection

(a) The periscope

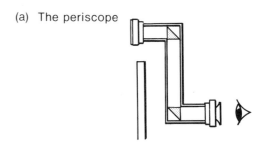

Plane mirrors reflect light just like prisms that allow total internal reflection. However, plane mirrors have disadvantages. They tarnish easily so they do not last as long as prisms. Also, they absorb more light than prisms. Thus, internal reflection in prisms is used where reflection in mirrors might not be good enough.

The principle of the periscope was described in the previous activity. A more detailed diagram of a periscope is shown in Figure 23-8(a).

Bicycle reflectors also use total internal reflection. Light from a car behind the bicycle strikes the reflector and bounces back toward the car. This is illustrated in Figure 23-8(b).

Prisms that provide total internal reflection are used in binoculars, shown in Figure 23-8(c). Without prisms, the binoculars would have to be made longer to give the same enlargement of images.

An important application of internal reflection occurs in fibre optics. This is the study of how light acts in thin solid strands of glass called fibres. Once light enters a fibre it continues to travel inside the fibre. If the fibre is curved, the light strikes the inside of the fibre and internally reflects. In the field of medicine, glass fibres are used to view internal parts of the body for diagnostic purposes, or during microsurgery. In the field of communications, glass fibres are replacing metal conductors used to transmit telephone and television signals as well as computerized data [Figure 23-8(d)]. In this use of fibres, laser light carries the information. (Section 25.7 describes this application further.)

(b) A bicycle reflector

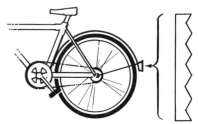

(c) The prism binocular   Other half (not shown)

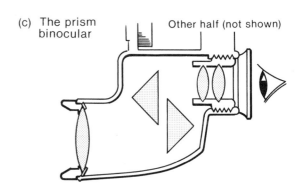

(d) Fibre optics

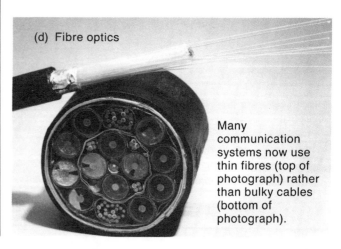

Many communication systems now use thin fibres (top of photograph) rather than bulky cables (bottom of photograph).

DID YOU KNOW?

On a hot day in the summer you may notice what looks like a pool of water lying ahead of you on a paved highway. This optical illusion is called a mirage. It occurs because of the refraction of light and some internal reflection in the layers of air above the pavement.

PRACTICE

2. Each diagram shows a light ray going from one material into another. In each case decide whether or not total internal reflection could occur in the first material.

(a)

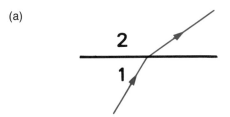

(b)

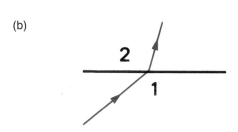

(c)

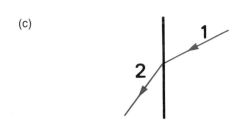

23.4 Lenses

Anyone who has used a magnifying glass to light a campfire has made use of refraction of light in a lens. Anyone who wears contact lenses or ordinary eye glasses is taking advantage of the refraction of light in lenses.

A lens is a transparent device with at least one curved edge. Whether the edge is flat or curved, the laws of refraction are obeyed. One example of how light refracts in a lens is shown in Figure 23-9.

Figure 23-9 An example of refraction of light in a lens

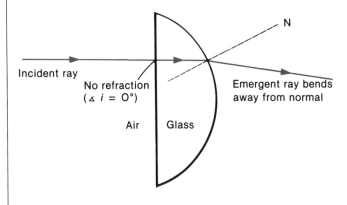

Lenses may be either convex or concave. A convex lens is thicker in the middle than at the outside edge. A concave lens is thicker at the outside edge than in the middle. Refer to Figure 23-10.

Figure 23-10 The design of lenses

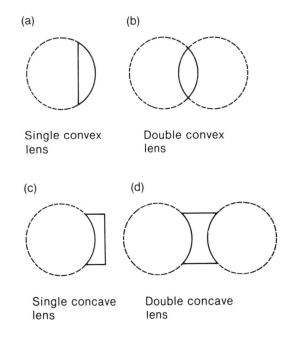

A lens has a principal axis (P.A.) just as a curved mirror does. However, a lens has two focal points and no centre of curvature. For a convex lens the **primary focal point** (P.F.) is located on the side of the lens oppo- site the source of light. The **secondary focal point** (S.F.) is located on the same side as the source. See Figure 23-11. The focal length (f) is measured to the middle of the lens, as indicated.

Figure 23-11 A double convex lens

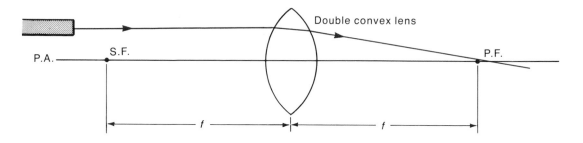

PRACTICE

3. Determine the approximate direction of the light ray as it emerges from the lens shown. (Hint: Draw a normal from the curved edge and apply the laws of refraction.)

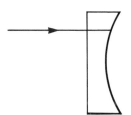

Activity 23C Convex Lenses

PROBLEM ■
1. How can the focal length of a convex lens be found?
2. What are the rules for light rays that strike a convex lens?
3. What are the characteristics of the image in a convex lens?

APPARATUS ■ ray box with single-slit and triple-slit win- dows; 2 double convex lenses (one acrylic and one glass)

PROCEDURE ■

1. Place the acrylic lens at the middle of the page and draw its outline and principal axis. Aim three parallel rays toward the lens so that the centre ray falls along the principal axis. The point where the emergent rays meet is the primary focal point (P.F.). Label it and measure the focal length (f).
2. Remove the lens and draw in the secondary focal point (S.F.) a distance f from the lens on the opposite side of the primary focal point.
3. Using your diagram and Figure 23-12 as references, perform the procedure needed to complete these rules for drawing ray diagrams for convex lenses:
   (a) An incident ray parallel to the principal axis . . .
   (b) An incident ray through the secondary focal point
   . . .
   (c) An incident ray through the middle of the lens at a small angle to the principal axis . . .

Figure 23-12 Rules for a convex lens

(a)
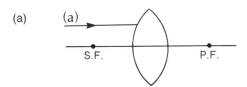

(b)
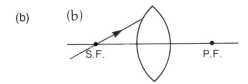

(c)
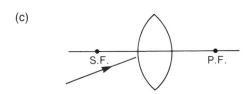

4. Hold the glass convex lens at arm's length and view objects around you. Describe the image (attitude, size, and type) when the object viewed is:
   (a) close to the lens
   (b) far from the lens

ANALYSIS ■

1. How can the focal length of a convex lens be found?
2. What are the rules for light rays that strike a convex lens?
3. List the characteristics of the image in a convex lens.

APPLICATIONS ■

1. When a convex lens is used as an ordinary magnifying glass, is the image real or imaginary?
2. Is a convex lens a converging or diverging lens? Explain your answer.
3. List devices that use at least one convex lens.

23.5 Concave Lenses

Figure 23-13 shows that for a concave lens the primary focal point is on the same side of the lens as the source of light. Compare this situation to that for a convex lens in Figure 23-11.

The light rays that are parallel to the principal axis determine where the primary focal point is. In Figure 23-13 notice that the primary focal point is found by extending the emergent ray back to the principal axis.

As with convex lenses, the focal length (f) is measured to the middle of the lens.

Figure 23-13 A double concave lens

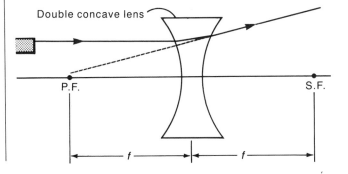

Activity 23D Double Concave Lenses

PROBLEM ■
1. How can the focal length of a concave lens be found?
2. What are the rules for light rays that strike a concave lens?
3. What are the characteristics of the image in a concave lens?

APPARATUS ■ ray box with single-slit and triple-slit windows; 2 double concave lenses (one acrylic and one glass)

PROCEDURE ■
1. Set the acrylic lens in the middle of the page and draw its outline and principal axis. Aim three parallel rays toward the lens so that the middle ray falls along the principal axis. Draw all the rays. Remove the lens and extend the emergent rays straight back until they meet. The point where they meet is the primary focal point (P.F.). Label it and measure the focal length (f).
2. Draw in the S.F. a distance f from the lens on the side of the lens opposite the P.F.
3. Using your diagram and Figure 23-14 as references, perform the procedure needed to complete these rules for drawing ray diagrams for concave lenses:
   (a) An incident ray parallel to the principal axis . . .
   (b) An incident ray toward the secondary focal point . . .
   (Hint: Remove the lens and aim an incident ray toward the S.F. Then replace the lens.)
   (c) An incident ray through the middle of the lens at a small angle to the principal axis . . .
4. Use the glass concave lens to view objects around you. Describe the images by stating their attitude, size, and type.

Figure 23-14 Rules for a concave lens

(a)

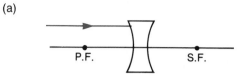

(b)

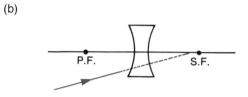

(c)

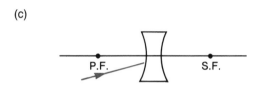

ANALYSIS ■
1. How can the focal length of a concave lens be found?
2. What are the rules for light rays that strike a concave lens?
3. List the characteristics of the image in a concave lens.

APPLICATIONS ■
1. Can an image in a concave lens be placed onto a screen? Why or why not?
2. Is a concave lens a converging or diverging lens? Explain your answer.
3. List devices that use a concave lens.

23.6 Ray Diagrams for Lenses

A ray diagram can be used to locate the image of an object situated near a lens. Ray diagrams for lenses resemble those for mirrors. Any two of the three rules learned in the activities may be used to locate an image. After the image is located, its attitude, size, type, and location can be stated.

Light that passes through a lens can refract twice, first when entering the lens and again when leaving. This double refraction is not easy to draw, so a short cut can be used. A straight line is drawn to represent the lens, so the light ray in the diagram refracts only once. The type of lens is indicated in the centre of the diagram.

Sample Problem 1

The focal length of a double convex lens is 2.5 cm. A 1.5 cm high object is located 8.0 cm from the lens. Use a ray diagram to locate the image of the object. Describe the image.

Solution Draw the diagram according to the instructions. Place the object on the principal axis. Use two or three rules to find where the refracted rays meet.

The image is inverted, smaller than the object, real, and located on the side of the lens opposite the object.

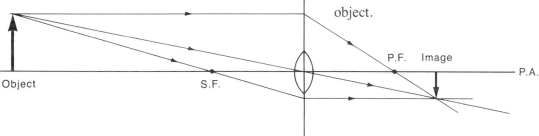

Sample Problem 2

Repeat sample problem 1, using a double concave lens.

Solution The refracted rays must be extended back to where they meet, which is on the side of the lens where the object is located.

The image is upright, smaller than the object, imaginary, and located on the same side of the lens as the object.

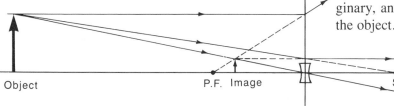

Several optical instruments, including the camera and the eye, use lenses. These applications are discussed in the next chapter.

PRACTICE

4. Draw a fully labelled ray diagram to locate the image of a 1.5 cm high object located as described in the table. In each diagram use two rules. For each image, state its attitude, size, type, and location.

Type of lens	Focal length (cm)	Distance of object to lens (cm)
(a) Convex	3.0	6.0
(b) Convex	3.0	4.5
(c) Convex	4.0	4.0
(d) Convex	4.0	2.0
(e) Concave	4.0	4.0

5. Based on your diagrams in #4, answer these questions.
   (a) What is the only type of lens that can produce a real image?
   (b) What type of image is produced when an object is located closer than the secondary focal point of a convex lens?
   (c) Where must an object in front of a convex lens be located to produce no image?
   (d) What type of image does a concave lens always produce?

Words to Know

refraction
laws of refraction
critical angle
total internal reflection
lens
convex lens

concave lens
principal axis
primary focal point
secondary focal point
focal length

Chapter Objectives

Having completed this chapter, you should now be able to:
1. Define refraction and explain why it occurs.
2. State the laws of refraction.
3. Measure the angles of incidence, refraction, and emergence in a diagram of refraction of light through a prism.
4. Describe the conditions needed for total internal reflection.
5. Define critical angle and be able to find it experimentally.
6. Explain applications of total internal reflection.
7. Draw the shapes of convex and concave lenses.
8. State what is meant by primary focal point and secondary focal point for lenses.
9. State three rules for drawing ray diagrams for both convex and concave lenses.
10. State the attitude, size, type, and location of the image seen in a lens.
11. Draw a ray diagram to find the image of an object located at various distances from a lens.

Chapter Review

1. When light travels from air into water at an angle, why does it refract? (23.1)
2. In which material, A or B, is light travelling more slowly? Explain your answer. (23.1)

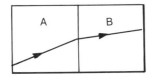

3. State the laws of refraction. (Act. 23A)
4. Draw a diagram of a 3.0 cm × 5.0 cm glass prism that has a ray of light striking the long edge such that ∡ i = 50°, ∡ R = 30°, and ∡ e = 50°. (23.1, Act. 23A)
5. The angle of incidence of a ray into a rectangular prism is 0°. What is the size of the angle of:
   (a) refraction?   (b) emergence? (Act. 23A)
6. What is meant by the term critical angle? (23.2)
7. State two conditions necessary for total internal reflection. (23.2)
8. A right-angled periscope can be used to see around corners. Assume you are given one triangular prism and two cardboard tubes. Draw a diagram of how you would arrange those pieces to make such a periscope. (23.2, Act. 23B)
9. The diagram represents a block of diamond. If the critical angle in diamond is only 24°, which of the light rays shown will reflect internally? (23.2, Act. 23B)

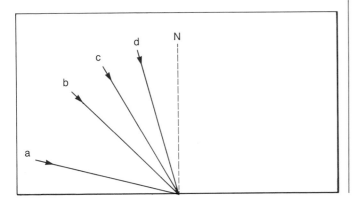

10. A double convex lens can be used to start a fire in bright sunlight. Draw a diagram of a lens (f = 5.0 cm) to explain why the lens can start a fire. (Hint: Light rays from a distant source are considered to be parallel to each other.) (23.4, Act. 23C)
11. Draw a fully labelled ray diagram to locate the image of the object for each situation described below. In each diagram use two rules. For each image that results, state its attitude, size, type, and location. (23.4 to 23.6)
    (a) A detective is inspecting part of a broken toothpick with a magnifying glass (convex lens) of focal length 6.5 cm. The piece of toothpick is 1.5 cm long and is held 3.0 cm from the middle of the magnifying glass.
    (b) A demonstration of a real image is set up using a candle flame (2.0 cm high) as the object. The flame is located 8.0 cm from the appropriate type of lens of focal length 5.5 cm. (In this diagram, show where the screen should be placed to view the real image.)
    (c) A 3.0 cm high object is located 9.0 cm from a concave lens of focal length 4.0 cm.
12. Which type of lens, concave or convex, produces images similar to the images in a convex mirror? Explain.
13. Find a reference book (or other resource) that describes fibre optics. Answer at least one of the following questions.
    (a) How is the science of fibre optics applied in medicine?
    (b) How is the science of fibre optics applied in industry?
    (c) How are fibre optics used in communication systems?
    (d) What careers rely on fibre optics?

CHAPTER **24**

Optical Instruments

A device such as a microscope can help the human eye examine enlarged images. In the field of medicine a microscope is an important device used to study cells or examine body parts closely. The microscope is just one example of an optical instrument. In this chapter you will learn how lenses in a microscope produce an enlarged image, and you will study several other optical instruments.

Main Ideas

- An optical instrument is any device that helps us see.
- A pinhole camera can be used to study how film cameras operate.
- The human eye is a sensitive and important optical instrument.
- Various optical instruments use combinations of lenses to produce an image.

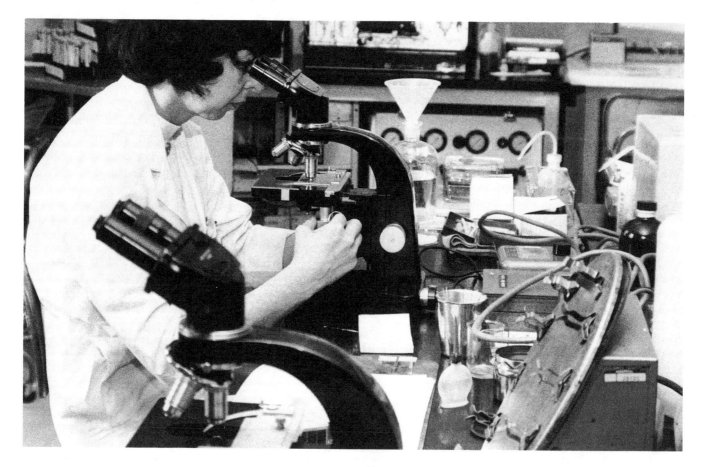

24.1 The Importance of Optical Instruments

Optical instruments are devices that help us see. The most important optical instrument is the eye. Of course, if we did not have eyes, the topic of light would have little meaning.

Optical instruments have the following important functions:

(1) **They record images:** The eye records images temporarily. A camera records images permanently.
(2) **They improve weak vision:** Eyeglasses and contact lenses help people with weak vision to see normally.
(3) **They create large images:** A microscope can make an image look hundreds of times larger than the original object. A projector places a large image onto a screen from a small photograph.
(4) **They help to view distant objects:** Binoculars and telescopes make faraway objects, such as the moon, appear much clearer than the ordinary eye can.

The activities and ideas in this chapter will give you a basic understanding of a few optical instruments. Each instrument you will study is an application of knowledge gained from the previous two chapters on the reflection and refraction of light.

PRACTICE

1. Which of the two types of image does a projector project onto a screen? (If you cannot recall the difference between a real image and an imaginary image, check back to Section 22.6.)

Activity 24A   The Pinhole Camera

PROBLEM ■   What are the characteristics of the image produced by a pinhole camera?

APPARATUS ■   pinhole camera (Figure 24-1); piece of opaque paper or aluminum foil; light source (either a small electric lightbulb or a candle); pin; glass convex lens with a focal length greater than the length of the camera

 CAUTION   If you use a candle as a light source, be sure the pinhole remains at least 20 cm away from the flame. Have another student help you here. In case of an emergency, have a fire extinguisher and a fire blanket nearby. Also, candle wax can burn your skin. Let the candle cool off before you touch it.

Figure 24-1   A simple pinhole camera

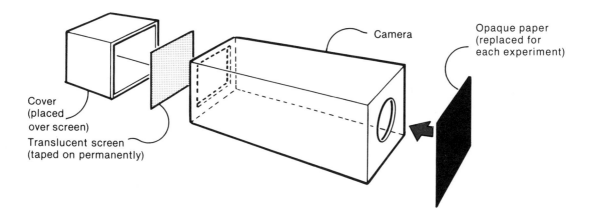

PROCEDURE ■

1. Tape the opaque paper or aluminum foil over the end opening of the camera and poke a pinhole in the middle of it. With the room lights out, aim the pinhole toward the light source, from a distance of about 30 cm. Describe the image seen on the translucent screen by stating its attitude, size, and type.
2. Determine what happens to the image on the screen when the camera is moved closer to and farther from the light source.
3. Add a second pinhole about 5 mm above the first. View the light source and describe the images.
4. Add several more pinholes in the shape of a large ''R'' and describe the effect. (A diagram of the image would help your description.)
5. Stand about one metre from the light source and hold the lens between the camera and the light source. Adjust the position of the lens until you obtain a single bright image of the light source on the screen. Describe what occurs.
6. Remove the opaque paper or aluminum foil and try to produce a clear image of the room or a scene outside using the lens in front of the camera. (In this case the room lights may have to be on.)

ANALYSIS ■

1. When an image is formed in a pinhole camera, what property of light is illustrated? Explain your answer.
2. Draw a ray diagram to show each of the following.
   (a) A flame is located close to a pinhole camera with a single pinhole. See Figure 24-2.

Figure 24-2

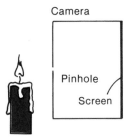

Camera

Pinhole

Screen

   (b) A flame is located far from the camera in (a).
   (c) A flame is located far from a pinhole camera with two pinholes.
3. In Procedure #6 you obtained an image similar to one that you found in Practice #4, Section 23.6. Which diagram in #4 relates to Procedure #6?

4. What are the attitude and type of image produced by a pinhole camera?
5. What happens to the size of the image in a pinhole camera as the distance to the object viewed increases?
6. What type of lens can be used to concentrate the light of several pinhole images into one bright image?

APPLICATION ■ What type of lens should be used in a real camera to produce a real image?

24.2   Modern Cameras

A camera is an optical device that can make a permanent record of a scene. The image is recorded on a film that is sensitive to light.

A pinhole camera can be used to take a picture. However, the pinhole does not let in much light, so a long time is needed to expose the film. To overcome this problem, a convex lens is used.

In the mid-1800s cameras used a lens and a single photographic plate. In 1889 roll films were invented, so cameras became more practical. It was not until 1935 that an efficient way of taking colour photographs was invented.

The modern camera box contains the following main parts:

(1) A **convex lens** gathers light and focusses it onto a film.
(2) A **shutter** controls the amount of light striking the film when the picture is taken. The shutter's speed and size of opening can be adjusted.
(3) A **film** records the image and is later developed to give a permanent picture.
(4) A **viewfinder** allows the photographer to see what he or she is photographing.

Figure 24-3 shows two common types of 35 mm cameras. They are called 35 mm cameras because 35 mm of film is exposed each time a picture is taken.

In both cameras shown in Figure 24-3, the image on the film is inverted. The photographer, however, wants to see an upright image in the viewfinder, so this is done in one of two ways. In a simple camera a small

Figure 24-3 35 mm cameras

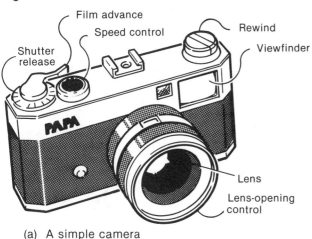

(a) A simple camera

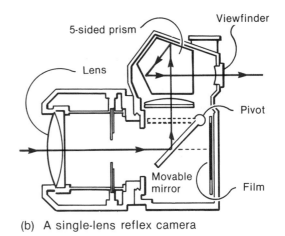

(b) A single-lens reflex camera

separate viewfinder is used. In a single-lens reflex camera a plane mirror and a five-sided prism causing total internal reflection are used. The plane mirror flips up for an instant when the picture is taken.

PRACTICE

2. State the attitude and type of image that occurs on the film of a modern camera.
3. List careers that apply the use of cameras or the principles of photography.

24.3 The Human Eye

The human eye is a fascinating optical instrument. Although the details of how we see are complex, we can compare the seeing process to a colour television system.

Figure 24-4(a) shows the basic set-up of a television system. Diagram (b) illustrates how a similar system allows us to see.

Figure 24-4 Systems that create images

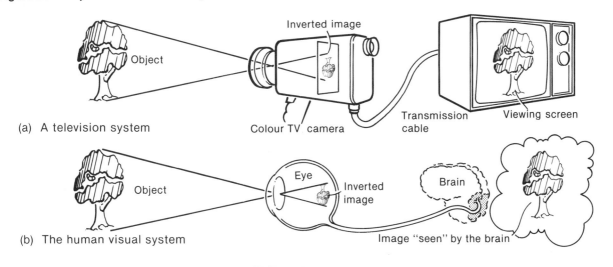

(a) A television system

(b) The human visual system

The human eye, with an average diameter ranging from 20 mm to 25 mm, has many features to help us see. Figure 24-5 shows the basic structure of the eye.

Light rays that enter the eye are focussed by both the cornea and the lens. The cornea is a fixed transparent layer at the front of the eye. Light refracts a large amount as it passes through the cornea. Then the light refracts slightly as it passes through the convex lens. The image is focussed on the back of the eye, just as the image in a camera is focussed on the film.

The lens is somewhat flexible so that its shape can be controlled by muscles. When you look at faraway objects, the lens has a normal shape, and the muscles are relaxed. When you look at a close object, the muscles force the lens to become thicker so the image remains in focus. That is why eyestrain results if you look at nearby objects too long.

The **pupil** of the eye is the "window" through which light enters the lens. It appears black because most of the light that enters a human eye is absorbed inside. The pupil is surrounded by the iris, the coloured portion of the eye. The iris controls the size of the pupil. In bright light the pupil becomes small, and in dark light the pupil becomes large to let in more light. You have likely experienced walking into a dark room or theatre. You are unable to see until your pupils have become larger. One way to overcome this problem is to cover one eye for a while before you enter the theatre.

Two important liquids, the **aqueous humour** and **vitreous humour** help the eyeball maintain its shape. The aqueous humour has the added function of supplying cells to repair damage to the cornea or lens.

Figure 24-5 The structure of the right eye as viewed from above

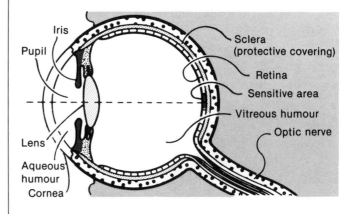

At the rear of the eye is the light-sensitive **retina**. It consists of numerous blood vessels, nerves, and two types of receptors. There are an estimated 120 million **rods** in each eye that are sensitive to black and white. There are also more than 6 million **cones** that are sensitive to colours. (Colour vision is discussed in the next chapter.)

When you look straight at an object, the clearest part of the image is located in the region marked "sensitive area" in Figure 24-5. The image is inverted and real. The information received by the rods and cones is sent through the **optic nerve** to the brain. Then the brain interprets what you see.

At the point where the retinal nerves join the optic nerve, a **blind spot** occurs. The blind spot is noticed only when one eye is closed. Figure 24-6 illustrates how you can find your own blind spot.

Figure 24-6 Determining your blind spot

1

Hold the book at arm's length. Cover your left eye and stare at the number 1 with your right eye. Move the book toward you until the 2 disappears. This

2

shows the location of your blind spot. If you move the book closer to or farther from you, the 2 will reappear.

PRACTICE

4. Name the part of the eye that performs each function listed below:
   (a) controls the amount of light entering the pupil
   (b) keeps the shape of the inside of the eye
   (c) causes most of the refraction of light entering the eye
   (d) reacts to black and white light
   (e) carries signals from the eye to the brain
   (f) allows the focussing of nearby and faraway objects

24.4 Vision Defects and Their Corrections

Normal, healthy eyes allow the formation of a clear image on the retina of the eye. A person with normal eyes is said to have 6/6 vision. This means that the eye sees clearly at a distance of 6.0 m. Someone with 6/12 vision must be 6.0 m from an object in order to see it as clearly as someone with normal eyes at a distance of 12.0 m.

> **DID YOU KNOW?**
>
> **S**ince 6 m is approximately equal to 20 feet in the Imperial system, the expression 20/20 vision corresponds to the metric 6/6 vision, both of which indicate normal vision.

If the image in the eye comes to a focus in front of the retina, the defect is called **near-sightedness**. Objects far away appear out of focus or blurry. A concave lens corrects this fault, as shown in Figure 24-7.

Far-sightedness is caused when the image comes to an imaginary focus behind the retina. Objects close to the eye are blurred. This defect can be corrected using a convex lens, as illustrated in Figure 24-8.

Figure 24-7 Near-sightedness

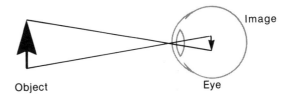

(a) The image comes to a focus in front of the retina

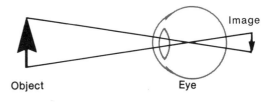

(b) A concave lens corrects the defect

Figure 24-8 Far-sightedness

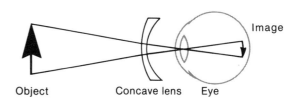

(a) The image comes to a focus behind the retina

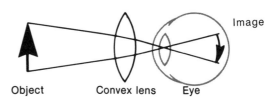

(b) A convex lens corrects the fault

Another defect, called **astigmatism**, results when the cornea has an uneven surface. Equal-sized lines in different directions appear to have different thicknesses. Figure 24-9 gives a simple test for astigmatism. The defect can be corrected using a lens that is shaped like a cylinder. In some cases it can also be corrected by wearing contact lenses. A layer of water between the contact lens and the cornea helps correct the astigmatism.

Figure 24-9   A test for astigmatism

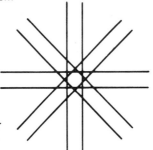

Hold the book at arm's length. View the diagram with one eye at a time. If all the lines appear equally bright, you do not have astigmatism.

Colour blindness is a defect in which certain shades of colour are not clear. Some cones in the retina do not respond to the light energy received. About 8% of all males and 0.5% of all females have some form of colour blindness.

The eye is a sensitive optical instrument. It can suffer defects other than the common ones described here. To take proper care of our eyes we should wear eye protection during sports and work activities and refrain from getting excess ultraviolet radiation. Furthermore, we should protect our eyes from strain by reading only in appropriate lighting conditions and not staring too long at close objects, such as computer screens.

PRACTICE

5. Which eye has better vision, one with 6/8 vision or one with 6/16 vision? Explain.
6. State the type of lens that can be used to correct for:
   (a) near-sightedness   (c) astigmatism
   (b) far-sightedness
7. Name careers that apply an understanding of the human eye.

24.5   Using More than One Lens in an Optical Instrument

Optical instruments have four general functions as described in Section 24.1. We have discussed how they record images and improve weak vision. In the last parts of this chapter we will discuss how they create large images and help us view distant objects.

A convex lens can be used as a magnifying glass. The image may appear two or three times larger than the object. But this is not sufficient if tiny objects, such as skin cells, are to be viewed. To obtain larger images, two or more lenses can be combined to make an instrument called a **microscope**.

Similarly, one lens by itself does not help the normal eye to view distant objects. Two or more lenses must be used together to enlarge the image of faraway objects such as stars and the moon. One optical instrument that makes distant objects appear larger and closer is called a **telescope**. (A telescope which uses lenses is called a **refracting telescope**. A reflecting telescope, which uses a concave mirror, was described in Section 22.11.)

To make a basic microscope or telescope, two convex lenses can be used. The lens that is closest to the object is called the **objective** lens. The lens that the eye looks into is called the **eyepiece**.

To see how an image is created in a two-lens instrument, refer to the three ray diagrams in Figure 24-10.

Diagram (a) shows an object located beyond the focal point of the objective lens. A real image is formed. The real image then becomes the "object" for the eyepiece in diagram (b). This object is located between the eyepiece and the secondary focal point of the eyepiece. The usual rules for drawing ray diagrams are used, even though the object is below the principal axis.

Diagrams (a) and (b) are combined to obtain (c). The result is a complete ray diagram of a two-lens instrument. Notice that the final image is larger than the original object.

Many microscopes and refracting telescopes have three or more lenses. Extra lenses are added to get an even larger image, or to create an upright image.

Figure 24-10   A two-lens optical instrument

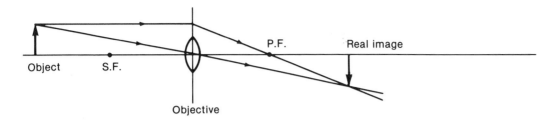

(a) The objective lens creates a real image

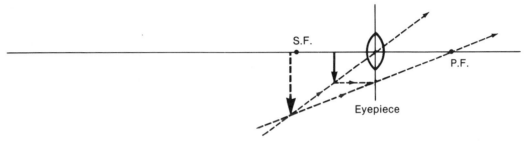

(b) The eyepiece creates an enlarged image
of the first real image

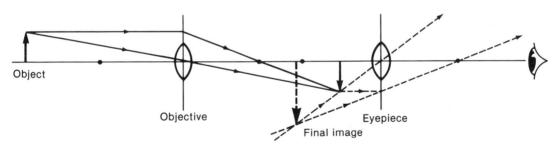

(c) Diagrams (a) and (b) are combined

PRACTICE

8. In Figure 24-10(c), state the attitude, size, and type
of the final image compared to the original object.

Activity 24B   The Microscope and Refracting Telescope

PROBLEM ■ What are the similarities and differences between a microscope and a refracting telescope?

APPARATUS ■ several glass convex lenses (with focal lengths ranging from 5 cm to 20 cm); optical bench apparatus

PROCEDURE A: THE MICROSCOPE ■

1. Obtain two lenses and determine their focal lengths. One way to find the focal length is shown in Figure 24-11.
2. Place the lenses in the holders on the optical bench so they are separated by the sum of their focal lengths. (See Figure 24-12.) Place the screen holder almost twice the focal length of the objective away from the objective. Insert a piece of paper with small printing into the screen holder.
3. Look through the eyepiece and move the lenses and your eye back and forth until you find the clearest and largest image. The image should be inverted and larger than the object if the system is acting like a microscope.
4. Repeat #1 to #3 using various combinations of lenses; for example, objective f = 5.0 cm and eyepiece f = 5.0 cm; objective f = 5.0 cm and eyepiece f = 10 cm. Try to discover which combination gives the largest and clearest image.

Figure 24-11   Finding the focal length of a convex lens

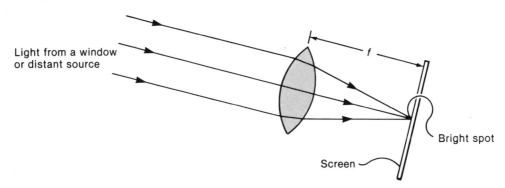

Figure 24-12   An optical bench set up

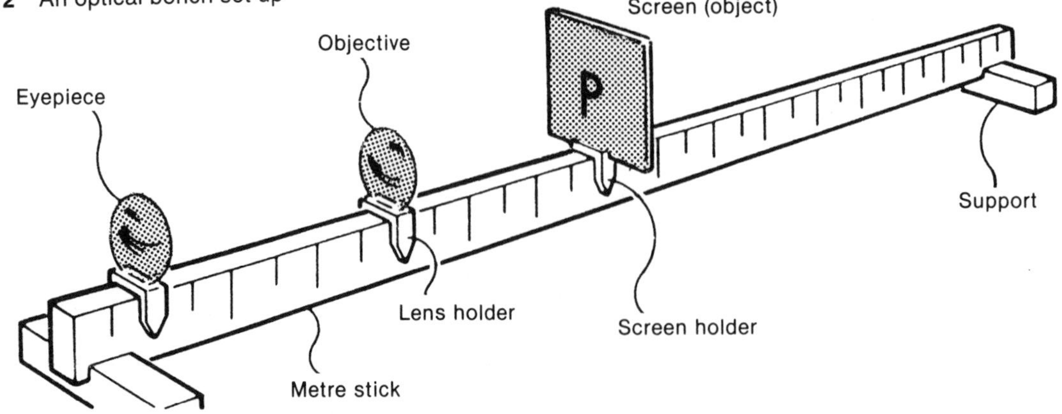

PROCEDURE B: THE REFRACTING TELESCOPE ■

1. Obtain two lenses and determine their focal lengths.
2. Place the eyepiece at one end of the optical bench. Place the objective a distance equal to the sum of the focal lengths away from the eyepiece. (The screen holder is not needed for the telescope.)
3. Look through the eyepiece at a distant object. Move the lenses and your eye until you obtain the clearest and largest image of the object. Describe that image.
4. Try various combinations of lenses to discover which combination will give the largest image of the same object. Describe your observations.

ANALYSIS ■ What are the similarities and differences between a microscope and a refracting telescope?

APPLICATION ■ List careers that involve the use of microscopes or telescopes. Find out the type of training needed to engage in one of these careers.

Words to Know

shutter	near-sightedness
viewfinder	far-sightedness
pupil	astigmatism
retina	colour blindness
rods	microscope
cones	refracting telescope
blind spot	

Chapter Objectives

Having completed this chapter, you should now be able to:

1. Describe ways in which optical instruments help us see.
2. Draw a ray diagram to locate the image in a pinhole camera and describe that image.
3. Compare a lens camera with a pinhole camera.
4. Describe the functions of the main parts of a camera.
5. State the names and functions of the main parts of the human eye.
6. Describe defects of the human eye and corrections for those defects.
7. Draw a diagram to show how the final enlarged image is created in a two-lens optical instrument.
8. Make a basic refracting telescope and microscope, given two lenses.

Chapter Review

1. Name two optical instruments that are used to:
   (a) record images
   (b) improve weak vision
   (c) create large images
   (d) help view distant objects   (24.1)
2. What happens to the size of the image in a pinhole camera when the object is moved farther from the camera?   (Act. 24A)
3. In what ways does a lens camera differ from a pinhole camera?   (Act. 24A, 24.2)
4. State the type of image (real or imaginary) in each of the following:
   (a) pinhole camera
   (b) lens camera
   (c) television camera
   (d) human eye   (Act. 24A, 24.2, 24.3)

5. State the main function of these parts of the human eye:
   (a) cornea
   (b) lens
   (c) iris
   (d) retina   (24.3)

6. Set up an experiment to determine the angle from your line of vision ($\sphericalangle\, a$ in the diagram) at which your blind spot occurs.

   Compare your value with that of other students. (24.3)

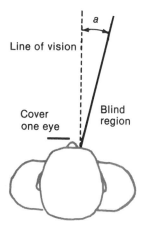

7. (a) What is near-sightedness and how can it be corrected?
   (b) What is far-sightedness and how can it be corrected?   (24.4)

8. Draw a ray diagram to locate the final image in a two-lens instrument using the diagram below as a guide. Label your diagram.   (24.5)

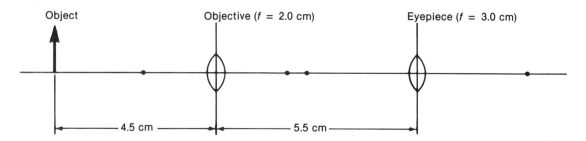

9. Describe how a microscope and refracting telescope are:
   (a) similar   (b) different   (24.5, Act. 24B)

CHAPTER 25

Colour and Lasers

In this chapter you will study the properties of light that cause different colours, as well as applications of colour. You will also learn about lasers and how they are used to make holograms.

One thing that humans have in common with bees, apes, and goldfish is that they are able to see colours. Most animals are not so lucky. Their eyes are sensitive to black and white only. Their world would seem very dull to us.

It would be hard to imagine a world without colour. Most of us take for granted the beauty of sunsets, flower blossoms, rainbows, and colourful underwater life. We have also become used to seeing spectacular laser shows, like the one shown in the photograph.

Scientists admit they do not fully understand how we see colours. They do, however, agree on the important fact that colours could not exist without light.

Main Ideas

- More than one method can be used to split light up into its spectral colours.
- Light colours can be added together to produce other colours.
- The colour an object appears depends on the light it is viewed in as well as on the light colours it absorbs.
- Applications of colour include the rainbow, colour vision, and colour television.
- The light visible to the human eye is only a small portion of the electromagnetic spectrum.
- The laser is a special type of light with countless uses, including holography.

25.1   The Visible Spectrum

For thousands of years stories were told and poems written about rainbows. But the reason why rainbows formed was not fully understood. Then, in 1666, Sir Isaac Newton made a famous discovery that was later used to explain rainbows. Newton allowed a narrow beam of sunlight to pass through a solid glass prism, and observed that the white light split up into many colours (Figure 25-1). This band of colours visible to the human eye is called the **visible spectrum**. A rainbow is an example of the visible spectrum.

Figure 25-1   Newton's discovery showed that white light is made of many different colours.

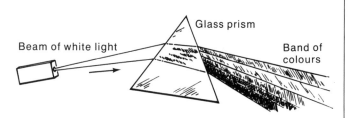

Beam of white light

Glass prism

Band of colours

The process of splitting white light into its spectral colours using a prism is called **dispersion**. When light travels from air into another material, such as glass, it refracts because its speed decreases. The amount the speed decreases depends on the colour of the light. The colour that slows down the most refracts the most. You will discover which colour slows down the most in the next activity.

Another way to split white light into the spectrum is to pass the light through a *diffraction grating*. Recall from Chapter 12 that **diffraction** is the bending of a wave at it passes through an opening. A diffraction grating has thousands of parallel lines or openings. When white light passes through these lines it bends, and the light waves undergo interference. The waves with the shortest wavelengths bend the least. In Activity 25A you will discover which colour has the shortest wavelength, and you will compare the spectrum produced by a grating with the spectrum produced by a prism.

Activity 25A   Observing the Visible Spectrum

PROBLEM ■   How does a spectrum produced by a prism compare to a spectrum produced by a grating?

APPARATUS ■   ray box with a single-slit window; equilateral triangular prism (acrylic or glass); incandescent light bulb with straight filament; diffraction grating

PROCEDURE ■

1. Place the prism on white paper and aim a beam of light toward it, as shown in Figure 25-1. Adjust the position of the light beam to obtain the best spectrum.

2. Draw a diagram showing how the white light is dispersed. Label the positions of the six main colours (red, orange, yellow, green, blue, and violet).

3. View the incandescent light bulb through a diffraction grating. Hold the grating so the colours are parallel to the filament in the bulb (Figure 25-2). Describe what you observe, and draw a diagram showing the spectrum.

Figure 25-2   Viewing white light through a grating

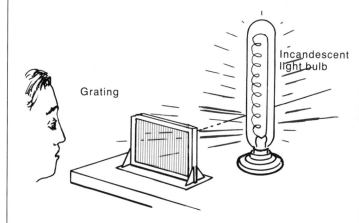

Grating

Incandescent light bulb

1. (a) Which colour bends the most when dispersion occurs in a triangular prism?
   (b) Which colour slows down the most as white light travels from air into a prism? (Refer to Section 25.1.)

2. (a) In the diffraction grating pattern, which colour spread out the least from the source?
   (b) Which colour has the shortest wavelength? (Refer to Section 25.1.)

3. In one case, red bends the most, and in the other it bends the least. Which is which?

4. How does a spectrum produced by a prism compare to a spectrum produced by a grating?

APPLICATIONS ■

1. A spectroscope is a device used to observe the spectrum produced by various light sources. Which do you think would be a more convenient spectroscope, one with a prism, or one with a grating? Why?

2. Sunlight consists of more radiant energies than our eyes can see. It also has invisible radiations beyond the visible spectrum. Two such radiations are called **infrared** and **ultraviolet**. Include these invisible radiations where you think they belong in your first diagram of the spectrum.

25.2 Additive Colour Mixing

If white light can be split up into many colours, can those colours be recombined to produce white light? Sir Isaac Newton performed experiments to answer this question. He discovered that the colours of the spectrum can be recombined to produce white (or nearly white) light. See Figure 25-3.

Figure 25-3 The colours of the spectrum can be added together to produce white light.

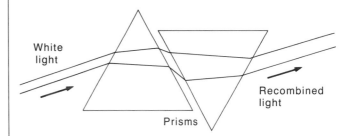

Are all the colours of the spectrum needed to produce white light? You will explore this question in the next activity, in which you will add light colours. The process of adding light to light is called **additive colour mixing**. Three definitions are important when learning what colours result when light colours are mixed.

(1) The **primary light colours** are the three light colours that, when added together, produce white light.

(2) The **secondary light colours** are the colours produced when pairs of primary light colours are mixed.

(3) **Complementary light colours** are any two colours that, when added together, produce white light.

Activity 25B   Mixing Light Colours

PROBLEM ■

(a) Which colours are the primary light colours and which are the secondary light colours?

(b) What are the complementary light colours of red, blue, and green?

Note: Two colours should be defined for this activity. *Cyan* (pronounced si'an) is a greenish-blue colour. *Magenta* (with a soft "g") is a pinkish-purple colour.

When observing colours in this activity you may notice that what should be white appears to be yellowish. This occurs because better results can only be obtained with high-quality equipment not always available to schools.

APPARATUS ■   ray box with 2 mirrors at one end (or 3 ray boxes); set of 6 plastic or glass filters (red, green, blue, yellow, cyan, and magenta); white screen

PROCEDURE ■

1. Place a green filter and a red filter in the ray box as shown in Figure 25-4(a). Adjust the mirror so that the two colours of light overlap on a nearby white screen. Record the colour observed.

2. Repeat #1 for the following colour combinations:
   (a) green and blue   (d) blue and yellow
   (b) blue and red   (e) red and cyan
   (c) red, green, and blue (f) green and magenta

ANALYSIS ■

1. Draw a colour chart like the one shown in Figure 25-4(b). Use the first letter of each colour (R, G, B, Y, C, M, and W) to complete it. The W means white. Have your teacher check the chart.

2. Which colours are the primary light colours and which are the secondary light colours? (See Section 25.2.)

3. What are the complementary light colours of red, blue, and green? (See Section 25.2.)

APPLICATION ■   The lighting crew in a live theatre uses lights with red, green, and blue filters. Assume a director wants a white object to appear yellow. What filters should the lighting crew use?

Figure 25-4   For Activity 25B

(a) Adding red light and green light

(b) Colour chart

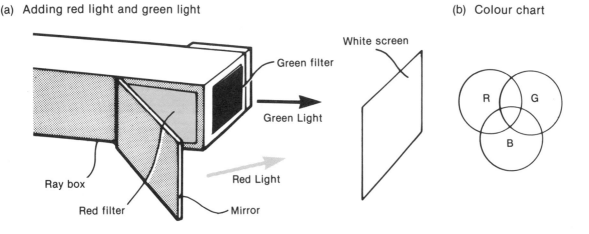

25.3 The Subtraction of Light Colours

The addition of light colours, as you discovered in Activity 25B, results from the interaction of light with light. The subtraction of light colours, however, results from the interaction of light with matter. When light strikes matter, some or all of it is absorbed, or subtracted, by the matter. Any light not absorbed is reflected from the matter or transmitted through it. For example, when white light strikes a red rose, red is reflected and the other colours are absorbed.

To predict what colours are absorbed by an object of a specific colour, you can use the colour chart from Activity 25B. The following results tend to be observed for objects that absorb light:

(1) An object of a primary light colour absorbs the other primary light colours. (For example, a blue filter absorbs red and green light, and transmits blue.)

(2) An object of a secondary light colour absorbs its complementary colour. (For example, a yellow filter absorbs blue, but transmits red and green. It also transmits yellow, which is made up of red and green.)

To relate these observations to the next activity, refer to Figure 25-5. It illustrates how to predict the colour transmitted through a filter when light reflects from an opaque object. The prediction does not always come true because the colours of opaque objects and filters are not pure.

Figure 25-5 Predicting the colour transmitted through a filter

(a) A yellow object viewed through a green filter appears green.

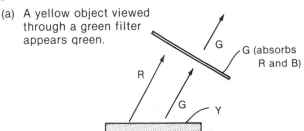

G (absorbs R and B)

(b) A yellow object viewed through a blue filter appears black.

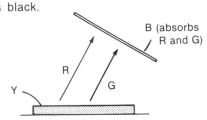

B (absorbs R and G)

Activity 25C Subtracting Light Colours

PROBLEM ■ What colours are absorbed by colour filters that are the primary and secondary light colours?

APPARATUS ■ set of colour filters (or coloured lights); set of coloured opaque objects (Both sets should have these colours: red, green, blue, yellow, cyan, and magenta.)

PROCEDURE ■

1. In your notebook set up a chart like the one shown.
2. View a red object through each of the colour filters, one at a time. Record the colours seen, in your chart. It is a good idea to record both the colour observed and the colour that should occur according to the theory in Section 25.3.

		Colour of opaque object in white light					
		Red	Green	Blue	Yellow	Cyan	Magenta
Colour of filter or light	Red						
	Green						
	Blue						
	Yellow						
	Cyan						
	Magenta						
		Colour seen by observer					

3. Repeat #2 for an object that is green, then one that is blue, and so on. Complete your chart.

ANALYSIS ■

1. State the primary light colours reflected by an opaque object that is:
   (a) red
   (b) yellow
   (c) cyan
2. Explain why a red object viewed in green light or through a green filter should appear black.
3. Explain why a magenta object viewed in red light or through a red filter should appear red.
4. What colours are absorbed by colour filters that are the primary light colours?
5. What colours are absorbed by colour filters that are the secondary light colours?

25.4 Subtractive Colour Mixing

You have likely had the experience of mixing two paints or colour pigments together to get a third colour. For example, if you mix yellow and cyan pigments, you get green pigment. The process of mixing colour pigments together to obtain new colours is called **subtractive colour mixing**.

To understand why colours are subtracted when pigments are mixed together, we will summarize what was observed in the previous activity. This summary is based on what should occur in an ideal situation.

Filters and opaque objects are similar in that they absorb (subtract) certain colours. Figures 25-6 and 25-7 show what happens to the primary light colours that strike filters and opaque objects. Study these diagrams carefully to see how they are similar.

Figure 25-6 White light striking filters

(a) Clear filter

(b) Red filter

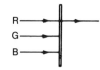

(c) Green filter

(d) Blue filter

(e) Yellow filter

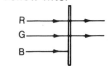

(f) Cyan filter

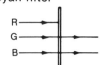

(g) Magenta filter

(h) Black filter

Figure 25-7 White light striking opaque objects

(a) White object

(b) Red object

(c) Green object

(d) Blue object

(e) Yellow object

(f) Cyan object

(g) Magenta object

(h) Black object

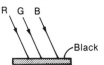

Colour pigments absorb light energies just as filters and opaque objects do. Colour pigments, however, can be mixed together to absorb more light energies. Figure 25-8 gives two examples of mixing colour pigments. Again, study the diagrams carefully.

Figure 25-8 Mixing colour pigments (in white light)

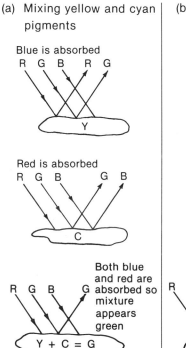

(a) Mixing yellow and cyan pigments

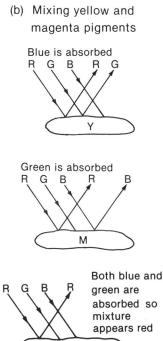

(b) Mixing yellow and magenta pigments

Three colour pigments can be mixed to obtain black pigment. Those three pigments — yellow, cyan, and magenta — are called the **primary pigment colours**. When any two primary pigments are mixed, a **secondary pigment colour** results. The secondary pigment colours are red, green, and blue.

Try not to confuse light colours with pigment colours. The primary light colours (R, G, and B) are the secondary pigment colours. The secondary light colours (Y, C, and M) are the primary pigment colours.

Sample Problem 1

What colour is transmitted when cyan light (B, G) strikes a filter that is:
(a) blue?   (b) red?   (c) yellow?

Solution
(a) blue (A blue filter transmits blue and absorbs green. Cyan is made up of blue and green.)
(b) no colour, or black (A red filter absorbs both green and blue.)
(c) green (A yellow filter absorbs blue.)

Sample Problem 2

What colours are reflected when magenta light strikes a yellow object?

Solution Magenta light is made up of red and blue. A yellow object absorbs blue, so only red can reflect. The object appears red.

PRACTICE

1. State the colour(s) transmitted in each case:
   (a) white light (R, G, B) strikes a red filter
   (b) white light (R, G, B) strikes a cyan filter
   (c) red light strikes a green filter
   (d) yellow light (R, G) strikes a red filter
2. State the colour(s) reflected off each opaque object:
   (a) white light (R, G, B) strikes a magenta object
   (b) blue light strikes a green object
   (c) blue light strikes a magenta object
   (d) cyan light strikes a yellow object
3. What colour results when the following pigments are mixed?
   (a) Y + M   (c) C + M
   (b) Y + C   (d) Y + C + M

25.5 Applications of Colour

The rainbow

To see a rainbow, the observer must be in a position between the raindrops and the sun, as shown in Figure 25-9(a). The sun's rays travel to the water droplets where some of them internally reflect and travel to the observer.

Figure 25-9(b) shows a beam of light that enters a single droplet of water. The light undergoes dispersion; in other words, it refracts and splits into its spectral colours. The various colours reflect off the inside surface of the droplet (total internal reflection). When the light leaves the droplet, it remains split into the same colours seen in the dispersion activity.

In diagram (b) violet light is entering the observer's eye. The observer would have to look slightly higher in the sky to see red light from other droplets. The resulting arrangement of colours is illustrated in diagram (c).

Figure 25-9 How a rainbow is produced

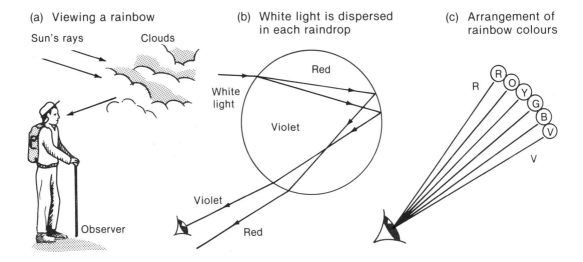

(a) Viewing a rainbow

Sun's rays   Clouds

Observer

(b) White light is dispersed
    in each raindrop

Red

White
light

Violet

Violet

Red

(c) Arrangement of
    rainbow colours

R

R
O
Y
G
B
V

V

Colour television

If you look at a colour television screen closely, you will notice thousands of tiny dots or bars.

 CAUTION *If you try this, do not stare at the screen for more than a minute. Harmful radiation may be emitted when the television is turned on.*

The dots or bars on the screen are arranged in groups of three. You can likely guess the colours of the dots. They are the primary light colours, red, green, and blue.

Three electron guns, one for each colour of dot, are located at the back of the television. At selected instants they send electrons toward the dots on the screen. Each time a dot is struck by electrons it gives off light energy. To produce blue light, only blue ones are struck. To produce yellow light, both green and red dots are struck. Black results when none are struck. In fact, a great number of colours can be created by properly aiming the electrons at the coloured dots. Refer to Figure 25-10.

Figure 25-10 Basic operation of a colour television

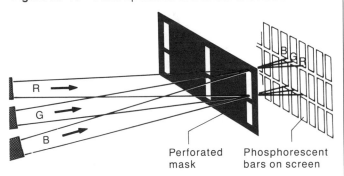

Perforated mask   Phosphorescent bars on screen

Colour vision

The human eye is well adapted to see colours of light. The retina at the back of the eye has both rods and cones. (This was discussed in Section 24.3.) The rods react to black and white when light strikes them. The cones, which are important for this discussion, react to colours.

One theory of colour vision is that there are three types of cones. Each type of cone reacts to one primary light colour (red, green, or blue). The cones can react in various combinations to give all the shades of colour we see. For instance, if the cones sensitive to green and blue are stimulated equally, we see cyan.

An interesting way to demonstrate the theory of three types of cones is to stare at a coloured object until your eyes become tired or fatigued. To observe this "retinal fatigue", place a small, bright red object on a white background. Stare at the centre of the object for about 40 s. Then stare intently at one spot on a piece of white paper. Try to explain what you observe.

When you stare at a red object, the red cones in your retina become fatigued. Then when you stare at a white surface, which reflects red, green, and blue light, only your green and blue cones react. Thus, you see the colour cyan.

Colour vision is very complex. Scientists are researching to try to prove (or disprove) the theory of three types of cones.

PRACTICE

4. Would you look to the east or west in order to try to see a rainbow a few hours before sunset? Explain your answer.
5. Which cones in the human eye must be activated in order to see the colour magenta?
6. If you stare at a bright yellow circle and then stare at a white piece of paper, you see a blue circle. Explain why this happens.
7. In a colour television, which dots must be struck by electrons in order to create:
   (a) cyan?
   (b) white?
   (c) black?

25.6 Light Theory and the Electromagnetic Spectrum

Light is a form of energy. In some ways it acts the way particles act. In other ways it acts more like waves. Scientists have a special name for a package of energy that acts like a particle and a wave: they call it a **photon**.

In the study of waves (Chapter 14) you learned that waves have a wavelength and a frequency. Light waves or photons also have wavelengths and frequencies. Each colour in the visible spectrum has a different wavelength and frequency, as shown in Figure 25-11. Notice that as the frequency increases, the energy also increases. Notice also that as the frequency increases the wavelength decreases. This can be verified by considering the universal wave equation, $v = f\lambda$, in which v is the speed of light, 3.0×10^8 m/s.

Photons are created by the changing motion of charged particles. (This was discussed in Section 21.7.) Both electric and magnetic forces are involved in changing the motion of these particles. Thus, the resulting photons are called **electromagnetic waves**.

Visible light is only a small portion of the entire set of electromagnetic waves. The entire set, called the **electromagnetic spectrum**, is illustrated in Figure 25-12. Once again notice that the high-frequency waves have high energies. Also notice that infrared light has lower frequencies than visible light. (''Infra'' means below.) Ultraviolet light has higher frequencies than visible light. (''Ultra'' means above.)

PRACTICE

8. Direct sunlight contains large amounts of ultraviolet light, which can cause sunburn. Why is ultraviolet light more likely to cause sunburn than visible light? (Hint: Compare the energies of the photons.)

Figure 25-11 The visible spectrum

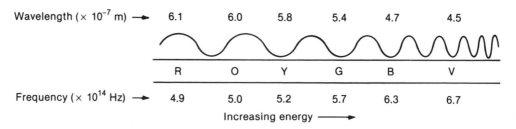

Figure 25-12 The electromagnetic spectrum

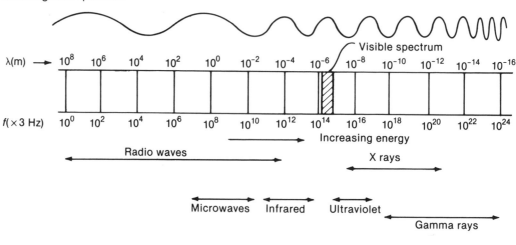

25.7 The Laser: An Application of Light

The laser provides an appropriate conclusion to the topic of light. We will look at why laser light is unique, and at some of the countless uses of lasers.

Properties of laser light

A laser is a source of light energy that is different from other sources. Most light sources, such as incandescent lamps, give off many wavelengths of light, as illustrated in Figure 25-13(a). A laser, however, usually gives off light of only one wavelength at a time. That is why laser light has a pure colour. Not only are the waves the same wavelength, but they are also in step with each other, as shown in Figure 25-13(b).

Figure 25-13 Comparing white light with laser light

(a) White light from an incandescent source consists of waves of many wavelengths.

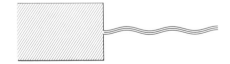

(b) Light from a laser consists of waves which are in step and have a single wavelength.

Lasers can be controlled to emit either continuous beams or pulses that are as short as a billionth of a second. Also, they can be made to emit either visible or invisible wavelengths of light. In any case, the waves spread out very little as they travel.

How a laser operates

Since the invention of the laser in 1960, many types of lasers have been developed. Some common lasers use a gas, such as carbon dioxide, or a mixture of helium and neon gas. Some use liquids, while many use solids. They all operate on the principle that energy from some source is given to particles in the laser. When these particles lose their extra energy, they emit it in the form of laser light.

One example of this process is found in the helium-neon gas laser. (This is the type of continuous-beam laser found in many schools.) The mixture of gases consists of about 85% neon and 15% helium. This mixture is placed in a tube that has a small concave mirror at each end. The tube is connected to high-voltage terminals. When a high electric potential difference (voltage) is applied to the tube, the helium atoms gain energy. These atoms collide with the neon atoms, giving their extra energy to them. The excited neon atoms in turn give off their extra energy in the form of light waves. Many of these waves reflect back and forth between the mirrors, causing other excited neon atoms to emit light of the same wavelength. This process builds up quickly, and soon the light starts coming out of the mirror at one end of the laser. This mirror reflects about 95% of the light that strikes it, and transmits the rest. The process is shown in Figure 25-14.

Figure 25-14 Basic operation of a helium-neon gas laser

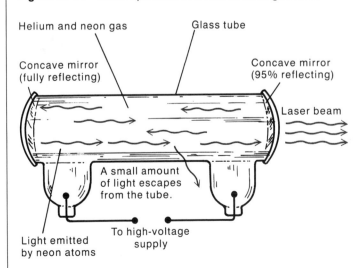

Uses of lasers

Numerous uses have been found for the unique properties of laser light. Laser light in the form of a continuous visible beam provides accurate alignment during the construction of skyscrapers, tunnels, roads, and bridges. Laser beams are used to survey land and sea coasts that are difficult to approach. Laser beams are also combined with lenses, prisms, and mirrors to entertain people at concerts and laser shows. One example was shown in the photograph at the beginning of the chapter.

In industry, lasers are used to cut metals and other materials quickly and accurately. Lasers can be used to drill fine holes and weld joints. These processes are computer-controlled. See Figure 25-15.

Figure 25-15 This photograph shows holes drilled by a laser in a hair.

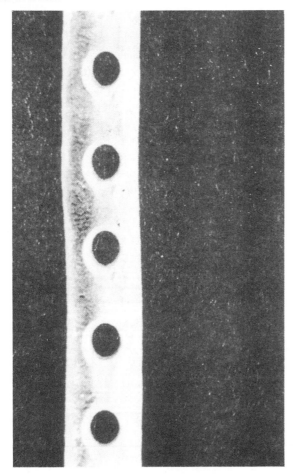

In the field of communication, lasers are having a great impact. Many offices and communication systems are linked with fine glass fibres through which laser light travels, carrying information with it. (Fibre optics was discussed in Section 23.3.) Audio and visual signals and data base information are coded into a tiny solid-state laser, no larger than a single grain of salt. The coded information travels along the laser beam in the fibres, then is detected by another tiny laser. This laser decodes the information. Eventually all our communication will be done in this way.

Lasers are used in the field of medicine. A laser can cut like an ultra-fine knife while healing the wound as it cuts. Or it can vaporize a blood clot, which consists of hardened red blood cells. Some cancer diagnosis and treatments are carried out effectively with lasers.

Likely you have experienced the clear, pure sound produced by a compact disc system. Concentrated laser light reflects off the disc as the disc spins rapidly in the player. Information is encoded on the disc in numerous pits and is detected in the reflected laser light. Laser light does not damage the disc, so the disc should last far longer than records or magnetic tapes. See Figure 25-16.

Information about numerous other applications of the laser can readily be found. One more application, holography, is presented in the next section.

PRACTICE

9. List differences between ordinary white light and laser light.
10. Describe how you would use two laser beams to be sure that the height of bottles passing by on a conveyor belt is always the same.
11. Research and report on modern uses of the laser.
12. List careers that involve laser usage.

Figure 25-16 The basic arrangement of a laser system in a compact disc player

(a) Information is coded onto the disc in the form of tiny pits arranged in circles.

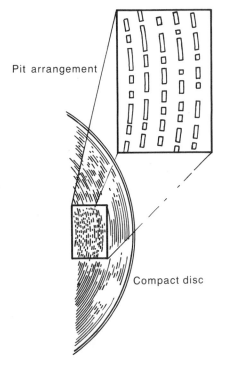

Pit arrangement

Compact disc

(b) As the disc spins around, a laser beam reflects off the raised parts, but *not* off the pits. The on-off signals are received by a photodiode that changes the signals into electric signals to produce sound.

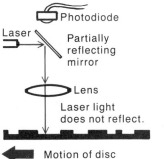

Photodiode

Laser

Partially reflecting mirror

Lens

Laser light does not reflect.

Motion of disc

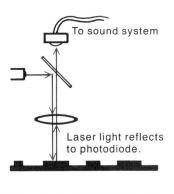

To sound system

Laser light reflects to photodiode.

25.8 Holography

Holography is the process of encoding information on a surface using the interference of light waves. The surface on which the information is encoded and stored is called a **hologram**. The word hologram stems from the Greek *holos*, which means whole, and *gramma*, which means something recorded. A hologram may be compared to a picture, which is the end result of the process of photography. However, a picture is a flat, two-dimensional representation, whereas a hologram appears to have depth, or three dimensions; in other words, it is "whole".

When you first look at a hologram, it may appear to be an untidy, boring pattern of lines. If so, you are seeing an interference pattern of light waves stored in the hologram. Interference is a property of all waves. In Unit 6, you observed the interference of sound waves, as well as waves on ropes, coiled springs, and water. Light waves also can interfere. In fact, the diffraction grating (used in part of Activity 25A) produced a type of interference pattern. Figure 25-17 shows two types of interference patterns. One is a regular pattern, the other irregular. Such patterns can be produced only when the wavelengths of light remain constant. That is why lasers are needed to produce holograms.

Almost all of the holograms produced take advantage of the fact that a lot of information can be stored in a very small space. Some uses of such holograms are:

- to act as lenses and mirrors
- to split light beams into two or more beams, sometimes up to millions of tiny beams
- to add light beams together
- to help scan the Universal Product Code in stores (Figure 25-18)
- to make optical computing systems that perform operations millions of times faster than electronic computer systems
- to make "heads-up displays" in aircraft and other vehicles

Figure 25-17 Examples of interference patterns

(a) This pattern is produced when two sources of waves interfere in two dimensions.

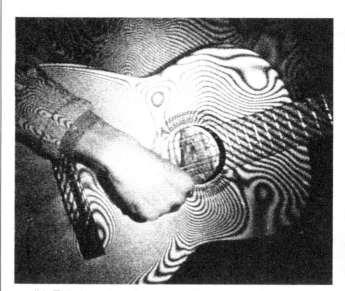

(b) This is an interference pattern on a hologram.

Figure 25-18 An example of the Universal Product Code

Let us look at this last example in greater detail. A pilot looking straight ahead can see a detailed image of the control panel with all the information seemingly suspended in the air. This prevents the need to look at the control panel. Not only does this save time in case of an emergency, but it means the pilot can keep his or her eyes focussed at infinity. In the future, heads-up displays may become common in automobiles.

Only about 5% of all holograms are the artistic three-dimensional images on a two-dimensional surface. These viewing holograms are the ones seen on some magazine covers and in some specialty stores. Looking at such a hologram is like looking through a window. If you move your head up and down or from side to side, you get different views. If part of the hologram is covered over, you can look "through" it at a different location and still see the whole scene.

To make a viewing hologram, two sets of light beams must reach the holographic plate. (This plate or film has an emulsion sensitive to light, so it is just like a photographic plate.) One way to accomplish this is shown in Figure 25-19. A single laser beam is split into two, a **reference beam** and a **subject beam**. The reference beam goes directly to the holographic plate or film. The subject beam reflects off the subject, then arrives at the holographic plate. The waves of the subject beam interfere with the waves of the reference beam according to the shape of the subject. The wavelengths are so tiny (about 100 times smaller than the thickness of a hair) that even breathing as the exposure is made can spoil the interference pattern.

After the holographic plate is exposed to the laser light, it is developed just like a regular photograph. The resulting hologram contains a permanent interference

Figure 25-19 One way of making a hologram

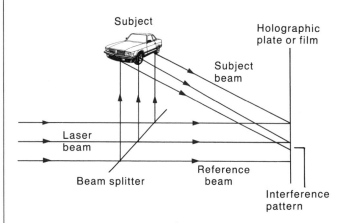

pattern that can be viewed in laser light or white light, depending on the type of hologram.

There are many other ways of making viewing holograms. (One of these is suggested in the next activity.) Ways have been found of encoding motion into a hologram. However the problems of producing three-dimensional movies using holography have not been solved at this time.

PRACTICE

13. Research and report on modern developments in laser holography.

Activity 25D Making a Hologram

PROBLEM ■ What are the properties of a student-made reflection hologram?

APPARATUS ■ helium-neon laser (with a power in the range of about 1 mW); concave lens; large paper clamp; subject to be holographed (A bright object, such as a quarter or a shiny toy, is recommended.); holographic plate sealed until needed; photographic safety light (green is preferred); photographic developing trays, chemicals, and tongs; water supply

Note: Holographic film can be used in place of a holographic plate. However, the film must be held firmly between two glass plates to prevent motion during exposure.

CAUTION
Do not let laser light enter your eyes directly. This can cause permanent damage.
Follow the safety instructions provided with the photographic developing chemicals.

PROCEDURE PART A: GETTING READY ■
1. Seal the room so no light can enter through the windows or doors.
2. Mix the developing chemicals according to the manufacturer's instructions. You will require a developer, a stop bath, a fixer, and running water for rinsing.
3. Set up the apparatus (without the holographic plate) as illustrated in Figure 25-20 (overleaf). Line up the laser light with the lens so the subject is fully illuminated. Notice that when the holographic plate is later installed just ahead of the subject, the reference beam is the one directly from the laser, and the subject beam is the one that reflects off the subject back to the plate.
4. Discuss the exposure time needed for your situation. For example, only 1 s may be needed for a 5 mW laser, whereas about 3 s may be needed for a 1 mW laser. Also, read the instructions in Part B before the room lights are put out.

Figure 25-20   Set-up for making a reflection hologram

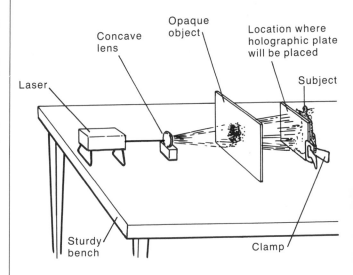

PROCEDURE PART B: PRODUCING THE HOLOGRAM ■
1. Place an opaque object between the lens and the subject. This is the shutter in the holographic system. Turn on the safety light and turn off the room lights. Obtain a holographic plate from its sealed container and place it so its emulsion side (the rougher side) touches the subject. Be sure the subject and holographic plate are as stable as possible. Reseal the container with the unused holographic plates.
2. Get everybody and everything to be perfectly still while you open the shutter (by removing the opaque object) for a very brief time.
3. Follow the steps for developing the plate. The developing stage is important. Make sure the hologram does not become over-developed.

ANALYSIS ■
1. After the developing and rinsing are completed, turn on the room lights and view the hologram by reflected light from an incandescent bulb or the sun. Compare your hologram with those made by other students.
2. Describe what changes you would make to try to obtain a better hologram next time.

APPLICATION ■   How would you alter the procedure to try to obtain a double image in one hologram?

Words to Know

visible spectrum
dispersion
diffraction
diffraction grating
additive colour mixing
primary light colours
secondary light colours
complementary light
   colours

subtractive colour mixing
primary pigment colours
secondary pigment colours
photon
electromagnetic waves
electromagnetic spectrum
laser
holography
hologram

Chapter Objectives

Having completed this chapter, you should now be able to:

1. Explain why dispersion of white light occurs in a triangular prism.
2. Compare the spectrum produced by diffraction with the spectrum produced by dispersion.
3. List the colours of the visible spectrum.
4. Define primary and secondary light colours.
5. Predict the colour of light that results from mixing two or three primary light colours.
6. Distinguish between additive colour mixing and subtractive colour mixing.
7. Predict the colour of an opaque object seen through a coloured filter.
8. Define primary and secondary pigment colours.
9. Predict the colour of a pigment made of a mixture of two or three primary pigments.
10. Explain how a rainbow is formed.
11. Compare colour vision with colour television.
12. Explain what is meant by the visible spectrum and the electromagnetic spectrum.
13. Describe briefly the operation and some uses of a laser.
14. Define holography and explain the basic steps in making a simple hologram.

Chapter Review

1. What is the dispersion of white light? (25.1)
2. Explain why blue light refracts more than yellow light when the two colours enter a prism from the same direction. (25.1)
3. What is observed when white light is viewed through a diffraction grating? (25.1, Act. 25A)
4. List in order the colours of the visible spectrum. (25.1, Act. 25A, 25.6)
5. What light colour results when the following light beams are added together?
   (a) red and green   (c) magenta and green
   (b) blue and yellow   (Act. 25B)
6. Bright white fabrics gradually become yellowish. The whiteness can be restored by using a bleach that adds a certain colour to the yellowed fabrics.
   (a) What primary light colours are reflected by yellow?
   (b) What other primary light colour should be added to create white?
   (c) Why do bleaches have "bluing agents"? (25.2 to 25.4)
7. Why does a red rose appear red in white light? (25.3, 25.4)
8. Why does a red rose appear black in blue light? (25.3, 25.4)
9. If black objects absorb all light energies, how can we see them? (25.3, 25.4)
10. Fluorescent lighting in stores has a lot of blue light and very little red. Is this an advantage or disadvantage when customers are choosing an appropriate shade of red lipstick? (25.4)
11. A man who is designing his own restaurant wants it to have a colourful interior. He decides to use blue lighting in a room having no other source of light.
    (a) State what colour a customer would see when looking at:
      (i) a red rose
      (ii) white plates
      (iii) green lettuce
      (iv) a rare steak (reddish centre)
      (v) yellow beans
    (b) What would you suggest that the man should do to improve the situation? (25.4)
12. What two paints can be mixed together to obtain a paint that is:
    (a) red?   (b) green?   (c) black? (25.4)
13. How do the colours of the rainbow compare to the colours produced when white light passes through a triangular prism?
14. When seen from the ground, a rainbow has the shape of an arc. What do you think its shape would be when viewed from an airplane high above the raindrops?
15. Describe the similarities between colour vision and colour television. (25.5)
16. Try this. Set up a pendulum about 1 m in length. Stand about 5 m or more from the pendulum.
    (a) Hold a red filter over your left eye. Keeping *both* eyes open, watch the pendulum as it swings perpendicular to your line of sight. Describe the motion observed.
    (b) Repeat (a) with the filter over your right eye.
    (c) Repeat the experiment using filters of different colours.
17. Describe the ways in which visible light differs from the rest of the electromagnetic spectrum. (25.6)
18. A certain laser produces electromagnetic waves having a wavelength of 2.0×10^{-10} m. Are the waves visible? (25.6, 25.7)
19. List three properties of laser light. (25.7)
20. Where does a helium-neon laser obtain energy to produce light? (25.7)
21. A double balloon consists of a small green balloon inside a clear, colourless balloon. Both are fully blown up. A visible laser beam is aimed toward the set, and the green balloon bursts inside the other one.
    (a) What are two possible colours of the laser beam? Explain your answer.
    (b) Why does the outer balloon not break?
22. Describe how a viewing hologram is made.

23. The polarization of light provides evidence that light travels by means of transverse waves.

    (a) Obtain two polaroid filters and discover what you can as light passes through both of them.

    (b) Discover what you can by viewing the glare off a horizontal surface through a single polaroid filter.

    (c) Place a plastic ruler or protractor between two polaroid plates. Rotate one of the plates slowly, and describe what you discover.

    (d) Research and report on the uses of polarized light.

Atomic Physics

How big is an atom? It is little wonder that many people have difficulty visualizing the size and appearance of an atom. No one has ever seen an atom. Its appearance can only be deduced from indirect evidence gained by analysing the effects of high-energy particles and rays such as X rays. The nuclei of atoms contain vast amounts of energy. Nuclear energy can be very beneficial if it can be controlled. Unfortunately, in nuclear reactions there are still many risks involved, such as possible exposure to radioactive emissions. This unit is about atomic physics and includes information about atoms, radioactivity, and nuclear reactions.

Information gained in this unit will be useful to you if you plan a career in nursing, dental technology, medical technology, pharmacy, or radiopharmacy. Knowledge of atomic physics is also essential in diagnostic radiology, radiation therapy, X-ray technology, occupational health and safety technology, and forensic science.

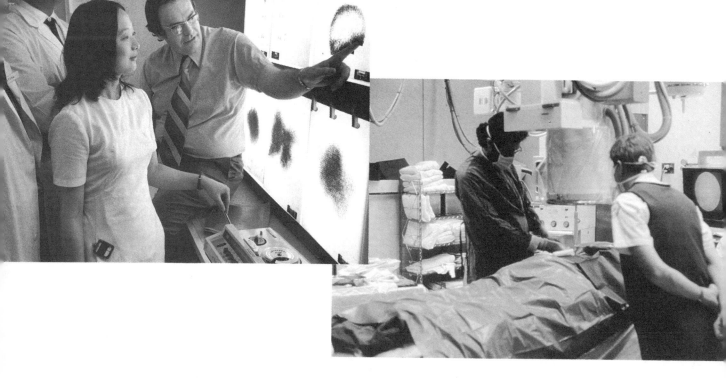

- Diagnostic radiologists and radiation therapy technicians help in discovering and treating many illnesses. Rapid expansion in this field of therapy is providing a wide area for employment.

- The Canadian Forces seek young men and women familiar with atomic physics for a wide variety of careers. One of the Canadian Forces' strengths as a potential employer is its custom of paying members while they further their studies in a specific field.

Knowing the information in this unit will be especially useful if you plan a career in any of the areas already mentioned, as well as nuclear power generation, and the field of nuclear waste transportation. Much practical information about training for, and working in, any of the careers mentioned can be obtained from talking to someone already in that field, and from your local community college, university, guidance office, or counselling centre.

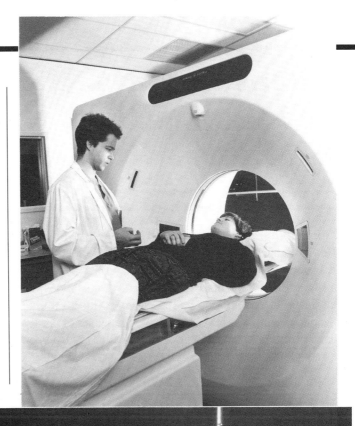

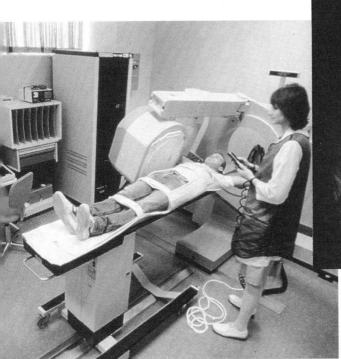

CHAPTER 26

Atoms, X Rays, and Radioactivity

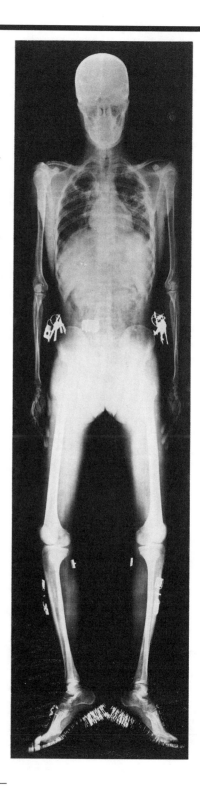

This photograph, made with X rays approximately 100 years ago, shows a fully clothed man. Evidently the X rays could pass through his clothes and skin, but not through his bones, his keys, the nails in his shoes, or the metal clasps holding up his garters. Since the time the photograph was taken, many practical uses of X rays have been found. The dangers of X rays have also been discovered.

Part of this chapter is devoted to the discovery, uses, and dangers of X rays. The majority of the chapter deals with natural radioactivity. It, too, has both uses and dangers. The study of X rays and radioactivity will help in your understanding of the structure of atoms.

Main Ideas

- The discovery of X rays and radioactivity has added to the understanding of what matter is made of.
- X rays can be both useful and harmful.
- Radioactivity occurs naturally; it is happening around us at all times.
- Various ways can be used to detect radioactive emissions.
- Radioactive substances have an average half-life that can be found experimentally.
- Radioactive substances can be both hazardous and useful.

26.1 From Classical to Modern Physics

Toward the end of the 1800s, scientists were confident they knew most of nature's secrets about matter and energy. They believed that matter was made up of tiny atoms, which could not be divided into smaller parts. They thought they understood motion, forces, and such energies as thermal energy and light. The physics up to that time is called **classical physics**.

Then in 1895 an important discovery broke the spell of confidence. That year marked the beginning of what we call **modern physics**. Listed below are some of the important events of modern physics.

- 1895—discovery of X rays
- 1896—discovery of radioactivity
- 1905—special theory of relativity
- 1911—discovery of the nucleus
- 1919—observation of the first nuclear reaction
- 1920—naming of the proton
- 1932—discovery of the neutron
- 1939—discovery of nuclear fission
- 1942—first sustained reaction in a nuclear reactor
- 1948—invention of the transistor
- 1960—invention of the laser

Today's physicists know there are many tiny particles besides protons, neutrons, and electrons. They no longer are confident they know everything. On the contrary, they admit there is much to learn. They continually search for new particles and ideas.

PRACTICE

1. Review the following in class:
   (a) the structure of an atom (Section 17.3)
   (b) the parts of the electromagnetic spectrum that have high-energy waves (Section 25.6)

26.2 The Discovery and Use of X Rays

In 1895 a German physicist named Wilhelm Roentgen (1845-1923) was experimenting in his darkened laboratory. He had a glass tube with invisible particles travelling in it and black paper surrounding it. On a table near the tube were some crystals that he was not even paying attention to. Suddenly he noticed that the crystals were glowing in the dark. He decided to search for the cause of the glow.

After experimenting, Roentgen discovered that the particles travelling in the glass tube struck the end of the tube, giving up much energy. That energy was given off in the form of invisible rays that could travel through black paper as well as cause certain crystals to glow. The rays he had accidentally discovered had no name. He decided to call them **X rays**.

> ### DID YOU KNOW?
>
> The glass tube being used by Roentgen when he discovered X rays is called a cathode-ray tube. The particles (or "cathode rays") travelling in the tube are now known to be high-speed electrons. Modern television tubes, with their electron guns, are based on cathode-ray tubes.

After more experimenting, Roentgen found that the X rays from his tube could pass through flesh and reveal bone structure on a film. He made the photograph shown in the chapter introduction.

Later it was learned that X rays travel in straight lines at the speed of light. They belong to the high-energy end of the electromagnetic spectrum. (That spectrum, discussed in Section 25.6, contains radio waves, microwaves, infrared light, visible light, ultraviolet light, and gamma rays.)

X rays are very useful for medical purposes. They are used to take X-ray photographs of teeth, bones, and internal organs. Figure 26-1 shows a typical X-ray photograph. X rays can also be used to treat some types of cancers. They are aimed toward the cancerous cells in an attempt to kill them without destroying the surrounding healthy tissue.

X-ray cameras are used to check the contents of baggage at airports. The rays can pass through leather, plastic, and cloth, but they are absorbed by metal objects such as guns and knives.

Figure 26-1 This X-ray photograph shows a distinct fracture of a child's leg. The ring shape near the top is a metal splint used to support the leg.

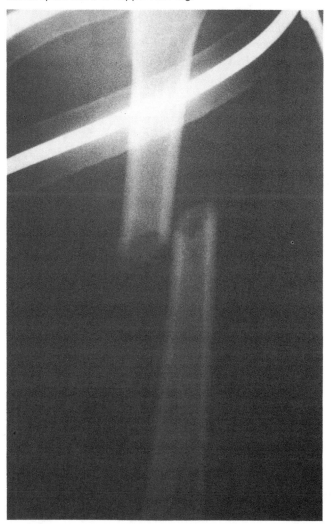

In industry, X rays are used to control the thickness of machined parts, and to detect flaws inside metal. X rays can also be used to etch microcircuits onto computer chips. These chips are smaller than chips etched with ultraviolet light because X rays have very short wavelengths.

X rays are not always useful. In fact, they can be very harmful, especially when too many of them strike certain cells in the body. X-ray photographs of your teeth or body should be taken only when necessary. If possible, a lead shield, which absorbs X rays, should be used to protect areas where unwanted rays may do damage. Pregnant women should be particularly aware that X rays can cause permanent damage to an unborn child.

PRACTICE

2. (a) What do X rays have in common with other waves in the e.m. (electromagnetic) spectrum?
   (b) In what ways are X rays different from other waves in the e.m. spectrum?
3. (a) List substances that are transparent to X rays.
   (b) List substances that are opaque to X rays.
4. When a person needs several X-ray photographs of his or her teeth, a lead shield is placed around the neck just under the chin. Why is this wise?
5. Research and report on the use of X rays in industry, scientific research, or medicine.

26.3 The Discovery of Radioactivity

Just a few months after Wilhelm Roentgen discovered X rays, a French scientist named Henri Becquerel made another accidental discovery. Becquerel, who lived from 1852 to 1908, was experimenting with minerals that he thought might give off X rays when struck by sunlight. To test his hypothesis, he intended to use photographic film which, he knew, was sensitive to X rays.

One cloudy day in 1896 he stored some uranium samples on an unexposed, covered film in a drawer. Four days later, just for interest, he developed the film, expecting to see nothing. To his amazement, the film had been exposed. Some invisible energy had passed through the opaque cover of the film and had exposed it. Becquerel had discovered **radioactivity**, which is the emission of particles and/or energy from the nucleus of an atom.

Becquerel's experiment can be repeated in the laboratory. If a radioactive substance is placed on an unexposed film for three or four days, it will cause the film to be exposed. An example of this is shown in Figure 26-2.

Figure 26-2 The photograph shows the faint outline of a radioactive watch, which was built in the 1950s. The watch was left on an unexposed film for three days before the film was developed.

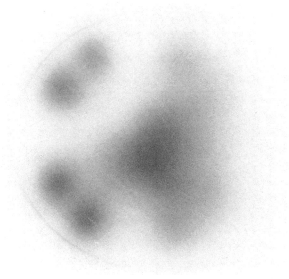

Soon after Becquerel's discovery, Marie Curie (1867-1934) and her husband Pierre (1859-1906) began to analyse the chemical that was the source of radioactive emissions. They discovered other elements that were highly radioactive. See Figure 26-3.

Many more experiments were performed to find out more about radiation. We now know that when a radioactive substance gives out emissions, it turns into a different substance. We also know that there are three types of emissions given off by radioactive substances:

(1) **Alpha** (α) **particles** have a positive charge and are fairly slow moving.
(2) **Beta** (β) **particles** have a negative charge, are much lighter than alpha particles, and are fast moving.
(3) **Gamma** (γ) **rays** are high-energy radiations, not particles; thus, they have no mass. They belong to the electromagnetic spectrum.

Methods of detecting and using radioactive emissions will be discussed later in the chapter. As you study radioactivity, remember that these emissions come from the nucleus of an atom.

Figure 26-3 Marie and Pierre Curie

PRACTICE

6. Which waves have higher energies, X rays or γ rays? (Hint: Refer to Figure 25-12 in Section 25.6.)

Activity 26A Indirect Evidence of Radioactivity

PROBLEM ■ What are the properties of the tracks left by emissions from a radioactive source in a cloud chamber?

APPARATUS ■ cloud chamber; dry ice; alcohol; radioactive source(s); piece of cloth; masking tape

Figure 26-4 Design of a simple cloud chamber

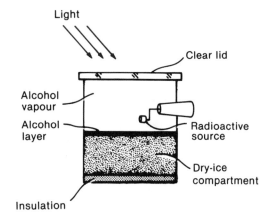

Light
Clear lid
Alcohol vapour
Alcohol layer
Radioactive source
Dry-ice compartment
Insulation

CAUTION
Use gloves or tongs to handle dry ice. It can "burn" the skin.
Use tongs or washable gloves to handle a radioactive source, and wash your hands after handling it. Never aim the source toward a person, and do not allow it to come in contact with your mouth.

PROCEDURE ■

1. Place the dry ice in the lower compartment of the cloud chamber, as illustrated in Figure 26-4. Add a layer of alcohol to the chamber and check to be sure that the chamber is level. Place the lid on the chamber.
2. Record the name of the radioactive source and the type(s) of particles it emits. Put it in the appropriate position. Allow the vapour to settle for three or four minutes.
3. Observe and describe the tracks. Draw diagrams of the shapes and sizes of the tracks. (If very few tracks are seen, try rubbing the lid of the container with a cloth.)
4. If a different type of source is available, use it to repeat #1, #2, and #3.
5. Remove the radioactive source. Cover the hole where it was positioned with masking tape. Wait for a few minutes, and then determine if there are any tracks visible in the vapour.

ANALYSIS ■

1. Did the tracks from a single source have different shapes and lengths? Explain your answer.
2. If more than one source was used, compare the tracks from the various sources.
3. In Procedure #5 you may have noticed tracks caused by "background radiation". Speculate on what this expression means.
4. List the properties of tracks left by emissions from a radioactive source in a cloud chamber.

APPLICATION ■ Compare the tracks in the cloud chamber with the vapour trails left by high-flying aircraft.

Activity 26B   Measuring Radioactivity

PROBLEM ■
(a) How can the emissions from various radioactive sources be measured?
(b) What happens to the number of emissions detected as the distance from the radioactive source increases?

APPARATUS ■   Geiger tube; electronic scaler; source of beta particles (e.g., strontium 90); holder for the source; various other sources (e.g., a smoke detector with a radioactive source, an old watch with a radioactive dial, etc.); tongs and washable gloves; graph paper

 CAUTION   Only the teacher should handle the strontium source. See also the caution notes in Activity 26A.

PROCEDURE ■
1. Connect the Geiger tube to the electronic scaler, and learn how to adjust and read the scale on the scaler. (For example, does the scaler indicate the average counts per second, the average counts per minute, the total count per minute, etc.?) Set the scaler counter to zero.
2. Observe the radiation detected from a variety of sources and from various directions from those sources.
3. Record the background radiation (the surrounding natural radiation) for 1.0 min. Repeat this measurement five times to obtain an average value. Record the value.

4. Have your teacher place the beta source in a holder 10 cm (or other appropriate distance) from the Geiger tube. Find the average count for 1.0 min, and subtract the background radiation. Record this detected radiation.
5. Repeat #4 at distances of 20 cm, 30 cm, 40 cm, and 50 cm. Record the data in a table.

ANALYSIS ■
1. How can the emissions from radioactive sources be measured?
2. Does a radioactive source emit radiations in only one direction? Explain your answer.
3. Make a general comparison of the sources used in this activity.
4. Plot a graph of the radioactive count detected (vertical axis) against the distance from the beta source (horizontal axis). What happens to the number of emissions detected as the distance from the radioactive source increases?

APPLICATION ■
What safety precaution(s) should be considered when finding a location for a smoke-detector containing a radioactive source?

26.4 Detecting Radioactive Emissions

Radioactive emissions (α, β, and γ emissions) cannot be detected by any of our senses, including our sight. Thus, evidence that they exist must come from some other means. One method of detecting radioactive emissions is through the use of photographic film. This is how Henri Becquerel discovered radioactivity. You have observed two other methods in Activities 26A and 26B, namely by using a cloud chamber and a Geiger counter system. Let us look in more detail at these two methods of detecting radioactivity.

A cloud chamber is a container that has a layer of alcohol resting on a cold surface, as was shown in Figure 26-4. The cold temperature, provided by solid carbon dioxide (dry ice), is needed so that the alcohol does not evaporate too quickly. As the alcohol evaporates, alcohol vapour (a "cloud") forms in the chamber. A radioactive source provided with the chamber is placed in the vapour.

Although you cannot see the radioactive emissions in a cloud chamber, you can see where they have travelled. The action is like the vapour trail of a jet aircraft high in a clear sky. You may not be able to see the jet, but you can see the trail it leaves behind.

Figure 26-5   Tracks seen in the chamber

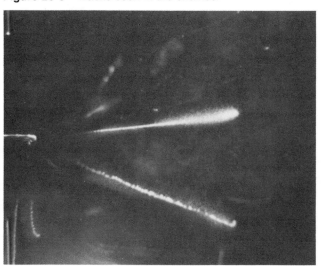

In a cloud chamber the radioactive emissions cause the alcohol vapour to become charged electrically. These charged particles attract other vapour particles, and soon they condense and form tracks of visible droplets. That allows you to see where the emissions have travelled. Figure 26-5 shows a photograph of some tracks in a cloud chamber.

The vapour tracks have three different shapes, depending on what caused them:

(1) α particles are heavy, so their tracks are short, fat, and straight.
(2) β particles are light and fast moving, so their tracks are longer, thinner, and often curved.
(3) γ rays are high-energy waves that do not by themselves create tracks. However, they can cause electrons in the atoms of the vapour to escape. These electrons can in turn leave tracks similar to tracks left by β particles.

To obtain quantitative (numerical) measurements of radioactive emissions, a Geiger counter can be used. As you observed in Activity 26B, this counter consists of a Geiger tube (named after its inventor) connected to an electronic scaler or counter. Often this device is also attached to a loudspeaker that can create clicking sounds. (Don't confuse a Geiger counter with a metal detector which also emits clicking sounds.) Other types of detectors besides the Geiger counter are also used.

The quantity of emissions from a radioactive source is called the **activity**. The accepted unit of activity is the becquerel (Bq), named after Henri Becquerel.

1 Bq = 1 emission/s

Thus, an activity of 2.0 Bq is the same as 2.0 emissions per second or 120 emissions per minute.

One becquerel is a very low rate of activity. Thus, the kilobecquerel (kBq) or the megabecquerel (MBq) are often used, where 1 kBq = 10^3 Bq and 1 MBq = 10^6 Bq. For example, a person undergoing tests for a kidney problem may have radioactive iodine with an activity of 7 MBq injected into his or her bloodstream.

PRACTICE

7. Why are the tracks left by alpha and beta particles in a cloud chamber different?

8. A certain source has an activity of 5 Bq. How many emissions come from the source in one minute?

9. Calculate the activity (in Bq) of a source that:
   (a) has 500 emissions in 10 s
   (b) has 2500 emissions in 20 s
   (c) has 4200 emissions in 1.0 min

10. To prepare for a thyroid scan, a patient swallows a solution of radioactive iodine that has an activity of 4.0 MBq. Determine the number of emissions that come from the source in:
    (a) 1 min
    (b) 1 h

Activity 26C Absorbing Radioactive Emissions

PROBLEM ■
(a) What materials are effective in absorbing each of the three types of radioactive emissions?
(b) How does the thickness of a material affect its ability to absorb radioactive emissions?

APPARATUS ■ sources of α, β, and γ emissions; Geiger counter system; samples of absorbing materials; tongs; washable gloves

CAUTION Your teacher will let you know if you can handle the radioactive sources available and will advise you of safety precautions.

PROCEDURE ■
1. Write out a list of procedure steps you would follow to solve the problems given. Include safety precautions. Graphing data may help you analyse the second problem.
2. Carry out and report on your activity. At the end of the report try to add applications. (For example, how would you suggest storing the radioactive sources used here, in a safe way?)

26.5 Developing a Model of the Atom

After the discovery of X rays and radioactivity, scientists searched for the answer to the question, "What is an atom made of?"

In 1897 an Englishman, Sir Joseph J. Thomson (1856-1940), discovered that atoms contain electrons with negative charges. Then he reasoned that because the atoms were neutral, they must also contain some positively charged material to neutralize the negative electrons. He developed a model or description of an atom as shown in Figure 26-6.

Then in 1911 in England, Ernest Rutherford (1871-1937) performed an important experiment to check

Figure 26-6 J. J. Thomson's model of the atom

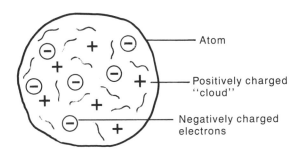

Thomson's model of the atom. Rutherford aimed α particles at a thin sheet of gold foil. All around the foil was a screen that could detect the positively charged α particles. See Figure 26-7(a) (overleaf).

Figure 26-7 Rutherford's gold-foil experiment

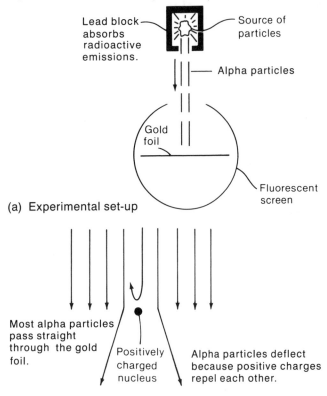

(a) Experimental set-up

Lead block absorbs radioactive emissions.
Source of particles
Alpha particles
Gold foil
Fluorescent screen

Most alpha particles pass straight through the gold foil.

Positively charged nucleus

Alpha particles deflect because positive charges repel each other.

(b) Observations

Rutherford discovered that almost all the α particles went straight through the gold foil. A few particles were deflected or reflected, as illustrated in Figure 26-7(b). He concluded that the positively charged part of each atom must be concentrated in a small nucleus of the atom. His model of the atom is shown in Figure 26-8.

By 1920 scientists knew that the atom contained electrons travelling around a nucleus. The nucleus contained positively charged **protons** as well as some other particles. Those particles were finally discovered in 1932 by James Chadwick (1891-1974), an English physicist. The particles had a neutral charge and were named **neutrons**. Now the model of the atom was more complete. Figure 26-9 shows a 1932 model of an oxygen atom.

Today's scientists believe that electrons travel in regions, not in set orbits as shown in Figure 26-9(a). Thus, they use a simplified model of the atom, as shown in diagram (b).

Figure 26-8 Rutherford's model of the atom

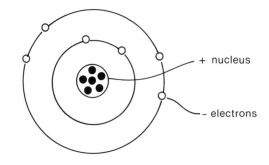

+ nucleus

– electrons

Figure 26-9 Models of the oxygen atom

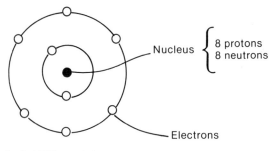

Nucleus { 8 protons / 8 neutrons

Electrons

(a) A 1932 model

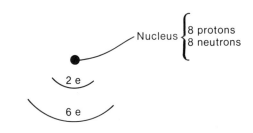

Nucleus { 8 protons / 8 neutrons

2 e

6 e

(b) A present-day model

PRACTICE

11. Name the type of charge on:
    (a) an electron   (c) a neutron
    (b) a proton   (d) a nucleus
12. What reasoning led J. J. Thomson to think that an atom must contain a positive charge?
13. Explain why beta particles or gamma rays could not have worked in place of alpha particles in Rutherford's gold-foil experiment.

26.6 Atoms, Elements, and Isotopes

You probably know that water is made up of hydrogen and oxygen (H_2O). Hydrogen and oxygen are examples of elements. An **element** is a substance that cannot ordinarily be divided into other substances.

All atoms of one element have the same number of protons. For example, every hydrogen atom has one proton and every oxygen atom has eight protons. The number of protons in each atom is called the element's **atomic number**.

Protons and neutrons have nearly equal masses. An element's **atomic mass number** is the sum of the number of the protons and neutrons in each atom. For instance, an atom of oxygen has 8 protons and 8 neutrons, so its atomic mass number is 16.

Electrons, which have hardly any mass, travel in regions around the nucleus. Each region can hold a certain maximum number of electrons. For example, the region closest to the nucleus can hold up to two electrons and the next region up to eight. In a neutral atom the total number of electrons is the same as the total number of protons.

There are more than 100 known elements. The first 18 elements are listed in Table 26-1 in the order of their atomic numbers. Each box in Table 26-1 contains the element's symbol, atomic number, electron arrangement for a neutral atom, and atomic mass. (The atomic mass will be explained shortly. It is not the same as the atomic mass number.)

Table 26-1 The First Eighteen Elements

H — Hydrogen	B — Boron	F — Fluorine	Al — Aluminum	Cl — Chlorine
He — Helium	C — Carbon	Ne — Neon	Si — Silicon	Ar — Argon
Li — Lithium	N — Nitrogen	Na — Sodium	P — Phosphorus	
Be — Beryllium	O — Oxygen	Mg — Magnesium	S — Sulphur	

Sample Problem 1

For an atom of the element sodium (Na) having a mass number of 23, state the:
(a) number of protons in the nucleus
(b) number of neutrons in the nucleus
(c) number of electrons in the third region

Solution
(a) 11
(b) 23 − 11 = 12
(c) 1

Table 26-2 Some Common Isotopes

Element	Name	Symbol	Comment
Hydrogen	Hydrogen	^1_1H	Most abundant form of H
	Deuterium	^2_1H	
	Tritium	^3_1H	Radioactive
Carbon	Carbon-12	$^{12}_6C$	Most abundant form of C
	Carbon-13	$^{13}_6C$	
	Carbon-14	$^{14}_6C$	Radioactive
Uranium	Uranium-232	$^{232}_{92}U$	Radioactive
	Uranium-235	$^{235}_{92}U$	Radioactive
	Uranium-238	$^{238}_{92}U$	Radioactive; most abundant form of U

The **atomic mass** is the average mass of the atoms of an element. When measured in kilograms, this mass is extremely small (in the order of 10^{-28} kg). A more convenient way to express atomic mass is in terms of a carbon atom of atomic mass number 12. One twelfth of the mass of this atom is called one **atomic mass unit**, symbol u. You should be able to see from Table 26-1 that the atomic mass of helium would be 4 u.

Notice in Table 26-1 that some of the atomic masses are not whole numbers. Sulphur, for instance, has an atomic mass of 32.1 u. This results from the fact that many elements have isotopes. An **isotope** is a substance whose atoms have the same number of protons but a different number of neutrons than other atoms of the same element. Most sulphur atoms have 16 protons and 16 neutrons (atomic mass number of 32). A few sulphur atoms have 16 protons and 19 neutrons (atomic mass number of 35). The average atomic mass works out to 32.1 u.

Refer to Table 26-2 for a list of some of the isotopes of three elements. Again, the number on the lower left-hand side indicates the atomic number. However, the number on the upper left-hand side represents the atomic mass number of the isotope.

PRACTICE

14. For an atom of the element fluorine (F), state the:
    (a) atomic number
    (b) number of neutrons in the nucleus, assuming the atomic mass number is 19
15. Find the number of neutrons in an atom of:
    (a) nitrogen (atomic mass number 14)
    (b) hydrogen (atomic mass number 1)
    (c) tritium (atomic mass number 3)
16. Draw a model similar to that shown in Figure 26-9(b) of an atom of:
    (a) beryllium
    (b) helium
    (c) phosphorus
17. Calculate the number of neutrons in each isotope of uranium listed in Table 26-2.

26.7 Half-Life

As the nuclei (plural of nucleus) of a sample of a radioactive isotope emit particles, they become nuclei of a different element. The average length of time for half the original nuclei to become other nuclei is called the **half-life** of the radioactive isotope. After one half-life has elapsed, the rate of emissions is half of the original rate.

As an example, consider an isotope that has an average half-life of eight days. Assume you have a sample that emits at a rate of 1000 Bq. Eight days later the activity will be half the original, or 500 Bq. After another eight days, the activity will be 250 Bq, and so on. When plotted on a graph, this half-life example yields a smooth curve, as shown in Figure 26-10.

Half-lives of radioactive substances range from a small fraction of a second to billions of years.

Figure 26-10 Graphing a half-life curve: half-life $= 8$ d

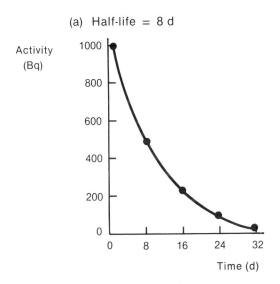

(a) Half-life $= 8$ d

PRACTICE

18. A certain sample of radioactive substance has an activity of 100 Bq at time 0.0 h. The half-life of the substance is 2.0 h. Calculate the activity when the time is:
    (a) 2.0 h (b) 4.0 h (c) 6.0 h

Activity 26D Measuring Half-Life

PROBLEM ■ How can graphing be used to determine the half-life of a radioactive isotope?

APPARATUS ■ radioisotope mini-generator; Geiger counter system; 10 mL glass beaker; stopwatch; graph paper

Note: The "mini-generator" is a commercially available kit that uses a radioactive isotope of long half-life to produce a different isotope with a short half-life. Some examples of half-lives are 2.6 min, 100 min, and 64 h. Your teacher will mix the chemicals in the mini-generator and provide you with an isotope at the appropriate moment.

 CAUTION Use tongs or washable gloves, and wear goggles to handle a liquid radioactive source. Never aim the source toward a person, and do not allow it to come in contact with your mouth.

PROCEDURE ■
1. Set up a table of data based on the one shown in Table 26-3.

Table 26-3 Observations and Calculations for Activity 26D

Time period (min)	1st	3rd	5th	7th	9th	11th	13th
Background activity							
Recorded activity							
Actual activity							

SAMPLE

2. Set up the Geiger counter system to determine the average background radiation. (This procedure was done in Activity 26B, but should be repeated here.) Be sure any radioactive sources are far away. Record the average value all across the second row of your table.
3. Arrange the apparatus so you will be able to take activity readings soon after the isotope is available. Obtain the liquid isotope in the beaker from your teacher. Place the beaker close to the Geiger tube, and do not move it for the remainder of the activity.
4. Determine the activity for the first full minute, do not take any reading for the next full minute, then find the activity for the third full minute, etc. Continue until the activity is only about 10% of the highest activity. Enter your observations in the data table.

ANALYSIS ■

1. Use subtraction to complete the final row of the data table.
2. Plot a graph of the actual activity (vertical axis) against the time period. Join the points on the graph with a smooth curve.
3. How does the shape of the curve on the graph compare to the curve on the graph in Figure 26-10?
4. Use the graph to determine the approximate half-life of the radioactive isotope used. (To do this, find the time for the actual activity to drop to half of a specific value. This calculation can be done more than once and an average can be taken.)
5. Indium-113m has a half-life of 100 min; barium-137m has a half-life of 2.6 min; and oxygen-15 has a half-life of 2.0 min. Was the isotope you used in this activity one of these? How can you tell?

APPLICATION ■ How do you think radioactive isotopes in hospitals are provided?

26.8   Uses of Radioactivity

Radioactive dating

The process of using the half-life of a radioactive substance to find the age of some object is called **radioactive dating**. It is a valuable aid to archaeologists, geologists, and historians.

Consider, as an example, the problem of determining the age of a wooden bowl found at some ancient burial site. During its lifetime, the tree from which the bowl was made absorbed both carbon-12 ($^{12}_{6}C$) and radioactive carbon-14 ($^{14}_{6}C$). After the tree died its carbon-12 content remained the same because it was no longer taking in carbon dioxide. However, its carbon-14 content gradually decreased due to radioactive emissions. After about 5730 years, the carbon-14 emissions would be reduced to half. (The half-life of carbon-14 is 5730 years.) Thus, scientists can determine the age by measuring the ratio of carbon-14 to carbon-12 in a sample of the tree.

Carbon-14 dating can be used on any object that was alive at some time. However, the process is inaccurate for ages greater than about 30 000 years.

Radioactive dating can also be used to determine the age of rocks and mineral deposits. Uranium-238 ($^{238}_{92}U$), with a half-life of 4.5×10^9 years, has been used to determine that some rocks on earth are about 4×10^9 years old!

Radioactive tracers

Very small amounts of a radioactive substance can be injected into the liquid of a system. As the isotope travels in the liquid through the system, it continually gives off emissions. These emissions help a detector trace the path of the isotope and thus analyse the system. In most cases, the emissions are gamma rays.

Sodium-24 ($^{24}_{11}Na$), with a half-life of 15 h, is often used in biological systems, such as the human body or plants, to trace the flow of blood, food, or water. Iron-59 ($^{59}_{26}Fe$) can be used as a tracer in mechanical systems, such as an engine, to trace the flow of lubricating oil.

DID YOU KNOW?

Some tracers used in humans must be swallowed or inhaled. For example, radioactive iodine-131 used to test the thyroid can be swallowed in a liquid or capsule, and zenon-133 gas used to test lungs can be inhaled.

Radiation therapy

Cobalt-60 ($^{60}_{27}Co$), a radioactive source of γ rays, is used in radiation therapy or treatment. Gamma rays, like X rays, travel through some cells but are absorbed by others. In radiation therapy, γ rays are aimed from several directions at a cancerous growth. If the radiation is successful, the cancer cells absorb the γ rays and are then destroyed by them. Figure 26-11 shows just one of the many types of devices used in hospitals for radiation therapy.

Figure 26-11 The cobalt-60 source in this machine emits gamma rays that kill cancerous cells.

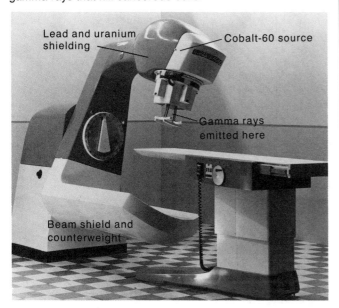

Lead and uranium shielding

Cobalt-60 source

Gamma rays emitted here

Beam shield and counterweight

Industrial applications

Radioactive sources can be used to control the thickness of manufactured products such as paper, steel, and aluminum foil. If the product becomes too thick, it absorbs more radiation and adjustments can then be made.

Sources of γ rays can be used to detect flaws inside metal parts. Gamma rays can penetrate where visible light and even X rays cannot.

Food preservation

A variety of foods — including some spices, grains, fruits, vegetables, meat, and fish — can be preserved effectively using γ rays. These rays cause chemical reactions to occur within the food. The new chemicals react with proteins and other substances in mould, bacteria, and insect larvae. This process reduces the growth of the harmful organism, or may kill it completely. See Figure 26-12.

Figure 26-12 The potato with the sprouts was not exposed to radiation. The other potato was exposed to γ rays. Both potatoes were harvested 8.5 months before this photograph was taken.

Food preservation using γ rays has advantages. Energy is saved because the treated food needs less refrigeration. Fewer chemical preservatives, some of which may be harmful to humans, are required. World food shortages may be lessened. And exotic foods from other parts of the world can be made available to North Americans.

The disadvantages of using γ rays to preserve food are not certain. Scientists are researching to determine if any chemical changes produced by the rays may be harmful to humans. Furthermore, consumers are not aware that food preserved with γ rays is not radioactive.

PRACTICE

19. Assume that a 2000 Bq source of sodium-24 (half-life of 15 h) is injected into a body. How long will it take the activity to decrease to 250 Bq?

20. Research and report on modern developments in the use of radioactivity.

21. Discuss careers that apply a knowledge of radioactivity.

26.9 Hazards of Radiation

The scientists who discovered radioactivity about 100 years ago did not at first realize the dangers of high-energy emissions (α, β, and γ). Today, much more is known about the health hazards of radioactive emissions, and everyone should be aware of them.

When a radioactive emission strikes a living cell, it can cause molecules within the cell to become charged electrically. The charged molecules may prevent the cell from functioning properly or growing. The charged molecules may also prevent reproduction of the cell. When this occurs in the body, the functions of the body can deteriorate. In other cases, the charged molecules may cause the cells to multiply more rapidly than normal. This is one way that cancer can begin.

Charged molecules in cells can also cause long-term effects. If the cells are located in the reproductive organs, the damage can be passed on to the offspring. The effects on future generations are not known.

It is obvious that exposure to radiation should be avoided if possible. People who work with or near radioactive sources should take care not to receive radiation doses that exceed the recommended dose. Patients who require radiation should also be aware of the hazards involved.

Words to Know

classical physics	becquerel
modern physics	element
X rays	atomic number
radioactivity	atomic mass
alpha particles	atomic mass number
beta particles	isotope
gamma rays	half-life
activity (radiation)	radioactive dating

Chapter Objectives

Having completed this chapter, you should now be able to:

1. Compare the time periods called classical physics and modern physics.
2. State the uses and dangers of X rays.
3. Define radioactivity and state the three types of emissions from a radioactive substance.
4. Describe the shapes of tracks in a cloud chamber left by radioactive emissions.
5. Define background radiation.
6. Define and use the unit of radiation activity.
7. Name materials that absorb radioactive emissions.
8. Name and compare the three main types of particles that make up an atom.
9. Define element and write the symbols of common elements.
10. Draw a model of an atom, given its mass number and atomic number. (This is required only for the first 18 elements.)
11. Define isotope.
12. Define the half-life of a radioactive substance and plot a half-life curve on a graph.
13. Given the activity of a radioactive sample, find the activity after one, two, or three half-lives.
14. Describe uses and hazards of radioactivity.

Chapter Review

1. What discovery marked the end of classical physics and the beginning of modern physics?   (26.1)

2. The X rays used to view luggage at airports can damage high-speed film. What type of material may be used to protect a film from exposure?   (26.2)

3. In past centuries one of the substances in artists' paints was lead. Today, little or no lead is used in such paints. How could X rays be used to distinguish a genuine old masterpiece from a modern fake of that masterpiece? (26.2)

4. From what part of the atom does radioactivity originate? (26.3)

5. Name the three types of emissions from radioactive sources and the kind of charge on each emission. (26.3)

6. (a) In what ways are X rays and γ rays similar?
   (b) In what ways are they different? (26.2, 26.3)

7. List three methods of detecting radioactivity. (26.3, 26.4)

8. What is meant by the term background radiation? (Act. 26A, 26.4)

9. Assume you are asked to make a container to store a β source. What materials and design would you use? (Act. 26C)

10. At an activity of 10 Bq, calculate how many emissions a source would send out in:
    (a) 1.0 min   (b) 3.0 min   (26.4)

11. Sketch the shape of a graph that illustrates the relationship between the *activity* detected (vertical axis) and
    (a) the *distance* from the radioactive source (Act. 26B)
    (b) the *thickness* of a barrier between the source and the detector (Act. 26C)

12. (a) What do all atoms of the same element have in common?
    (b) What name is given to atoms with the same number of protons but different numbers of neutrons? (26.6)

13. Which of the following substances are elements? H, H_2O, He, Na, NaCl, H_2SO_4, Al   (26.6)

14. Draw a model of an atom of:
    (a) fluorine-19
    (b) carbon-12
    (c) carbon-14   (26.5, 26.6)

15. An experiment was performed to measure the half-life of iodine-131 ($^{131}_{53}I$). The following activities were recorded at noon on each observation day.

Observation day	0	4	8	12	16
Activity (Bq)	10 000	7100	5000	3500	2500

(a) Plot a graph of the activity.
(b) According to the graph, what is the half-life of iodine-131?
(c) What would be the activity on day 24? (26.7 and Act. 26D)

16. An important property of radioactive emissions not considered in this chapter is how they act in a magnetic field. If all three emissions (α, β, and γ) pass near a magnet, as illustrated in Figure 26-13, one of them changes direction a lot, one changes direction only slightly, and one continues in a straight line.

(a) Predict which type of emission acts which way. Give reasons for your prediction by considering the properties of the emissions.
(b) Discuss your predictions in class. (This discussion may be enhanced by a demonstration of a cathode-ray tube influenced by a magnetic field.)
(c) Research this topic in a reference book and report on your findings.

Figure 26-13 Radioactive emissions in a magnetic field

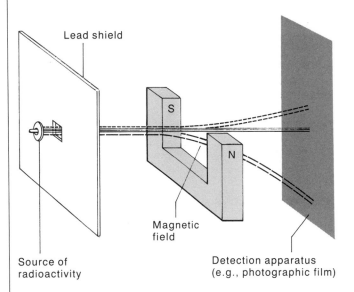

Lead shield

S

N

Magnetic field

Source of radioactivity

Detection apparatus (e.g., photographic film)

CHAPTER 27

Using Nuclear Energy

The photograph shows part of a nuclear generating station in the final stages of construction. Much knowledge of physics and technological skill are required to design and build such a structure. Nuclear generating stations are a benefit because they provide a continuous supply of large amounts of electrical energy. But the risks of using nuclear energy are so great that many people doubt that the benefits are worth the risks.

In this chapter you will learn about two types of nuclear reactions, fission and fusion. You will see that they have both benefits and risks. One of the serious risks is possible exposure to radioactive emissions, the main topic of the previous chapter.

Main Ideas

- Vast amounts of energy are stored in the nuclei of atoms.
- Energy released from atomic nuclei can be of benefit if it is controlled.
- Nuclear generating stations provide a peaceful use of controlled nuclear energy.
- Many risks are involved in using nuclear energy.
- Nuclear fusion has the potential to be a large source of energy in the future.
- Physics is an ever-growing, ever-changing field of study.

27.1 The Force that Binds the Nucleus

In Chapter 26 you learned that the nucleus of an atom contains neutrons and protons. Neutrons have a neutral electric charge and protons have a positive electric charge.

Since protons are positively charged, they repel each other (like charges repel). This repelling must be overcome by some powerful force in order to hold the protons in the nucleus.

The force that binds the particles of the nucleus together is called the **strong nuclear force**. This force acts between all protons and neutrons. It results only when the particles are extremely close together.

Although scientists do not fully understand the strong nuclear force, they do know that it is sometimes not strong enough to hold the nucleus together. That is when the nucleus splits up into smaller parts, giving off radioactivity, as discussed in Chapter 26.

Whenever the strong nuclear force is weakened, and the nucleus splits, energy is released. It is the creation and use of this energy that you will study in this chapter.

PRACTICE

1. When a nucleus is held together, which force is stronger, the repelling electric force or the attracting nuclear force? How can you tell?

27.2 Nuclear Fission

In the type of nuclear activity (called "radioactivity") discussed in Chapter 26, the nucleus of an atom emitted alpha or beta particles, as well as energy. Such activity can occur for both light and heavy elements. However, another type of activity, called nuclear fission, occurs only for heavy elements.

Nuclear fission, discovered in 1939, is the splitting up of a large nucleus into smaller nuclei that are nearly equal in size. Fission is accompanied by the release of neutrons and a large amount of energy.

In a fission reaction the mass of the original nucleus is greater than the sum of the masses of the resulting nuclei. In other words, some mass disappears. That lost mass changes into energy.

Figure 27-1 Albert Einstein (1879-1955)

It was Albert Einstein (1879-1955, Figure 27-1), the famous German scientist, who first predicted that matter and energy could interchange in a nuclear reaction. His well-known equation states that the amount of energy created when some mass disappears equals the product of the mass and the square of the speed of light.

$$E = mc^2 \text{ where } c = 3.0 \times 10^8 \text{ m/s}$$

Sample Problem 1

If 1.0 kg of a substance changes entirely into energy, how much energy is created?

Solution
$$\begin{aligned} E &= mc^2 \\ &= 1.0 \text{ kg} \times (3.0 \times 10^8 \text{ m/s})^2 \\ &= 9.0 \times 10^{16} \text{ J} \end{aligned}$$

Until 1905 scientists believed that matter could not be created or destroyed (law of conservation of mass) and energy could not be created or destroyed (law of conservation of energy). Then Einstein proposed the relation $E = mc^2$, and the conservation laws had to be joined into one law. Now, the law of conservation of mass-energy states that:

For an enclosed system, the total amount of mass-energy remains constant.

An element commonly used for nuclear fission is uranium. Most uranium nuclei do not undergo fission easily. However, one isotope, uranium-235, can be made to split by bombarding it with a neutron. (An alpha particle is not used because it would be repelled by the nucleus.) The extra neutron is absorbed by the uranium-235, creating an unstable isotope, which almost immediately splits into two smaller nuclei, releasing neutrons and energy.

A typical uranium fission reaction is:

uranium-235 + neutron → uranium-236
→ strontium-90
+ xenon-143
+ 3 neutrons
+ energy

Using symbols, the equation for this reaction is:

$$^{235}_{92}\text{U} + ^{1}_{0}\text{n} \rightarrow ^{236}_{92}\text{U}$$
$$\rightarrow ^{90}_{38}\text{Sr}$$
$$+ ^{143}_{54}\text{Xe}$$
$$+ 3^{1}_{0}\text{n}$$
$$+ \text{energy}$$

In the fission reaction above, the three neutrons are capable of joining with other uranium-235 nuclei. Every time such a nucleus absorbs one neutron, it splits up and emits three more neutrons. Soon thousands and then millions of nuclei will be splitting up. This process is called a **chain reaction**. It is illustrated in Figure 27-2. A tremendous amount of energy is released in a chain reaction.

Figure 27-2 The beginning of a chain reaction

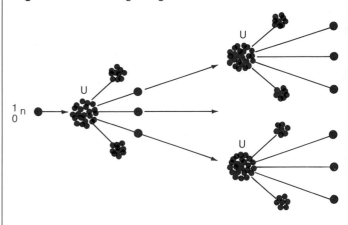

A fission bomb is designed on the principle of chain reactions. The bomb is made up of two separate masses of a material that can undergo fission. The masses are too small to start a chain reaction until they are joined together. When the barrier separating the masses is broken by a chemical explosion, a chain reaction begins, and the bomb explodes. This is illustrated for a uranium fission bomb in Figure 27-3. (A more important and peaceful use of the energy released in chain reactions is the topic of the next section.)

Figure 27-3 The structure of a uranium fission bomb

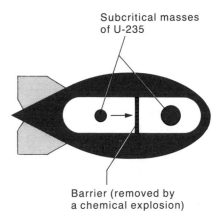

Subcritical masses of U-235

Barrier (removed by a chemical explosion)

PRACTICE

2. When a nucleus undergoes fission, what products result?

3. Calculate the amount of energy released if the following amounts of matter change entirely into energy:
   (a) 500 g (0.5 kg)
   (b) 2.0 kg
   (c) 10 kg

27.3 Using Nuclear Fission to Generate Electricity

One of the most important uses of nuclear fission is in nuclear reactors. In such devices a controlled fission process causes a substance such as uranium to split into new substances with the release of much energy.

There are at least eight different designs for nuclear reactors. We will study the details of the reactor designed in Canada. Then we will look briefly at reactor designs used in the United States and Europe.

The nuclear reactor designed and built in Canada is called the **CANDU** reactor. This name indicates that the reactor is **CAN**adian in design, uses **D**euterium (^2_1H) as its moderator, and uses **U**ranium as its fuel.

Fuel for the CANDU reactor

Uranium dioxide is the fuel used in a CANDU reactor. Most of its uranium atoms are $^{238}_{92}U$, but a small number (0.7%) are the fissionable $^{235}_{92}U$.

The fuel is pressed into pellets and placed in long metal tubes, called pressure tubes, each tube having a mass of about 300 kg (Figure 27-4). Hundreds of these tubes are placed horizontally into an assembly called a **calandria**. The horizontal arrangement has the advantage that the tubes can be replaced one at a time without shutting down the entire reactor. See Figure 27-5 and the photograph at the beginning of the chapter.

Figure 27-4 Fuel for a CANDU reactor

 Pellet

(a) Uranium dioxide powder is pressed into a pellet.

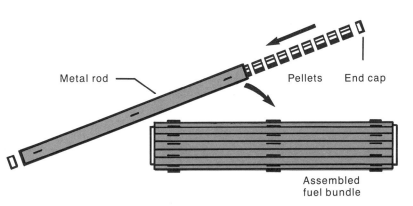

Metal rod — Pellets   End cap

Assembled fuel bundle

(b) The pellets are inserted into metal rods, which are then bundled.

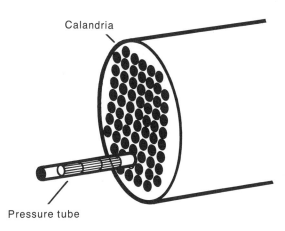

Calandria

Pressure tube

(c) The bundles are inserted into pressure tubes, which are placed into the calandria.

Figure 27-5 In the calandria of a CANDU reactor the fuel rods are horizontal. This allows the rods to be replaced by using the mechanical device shown in the photograph. The calandria shown is located at the Pickering Generating Station, Pickering, Ontario.

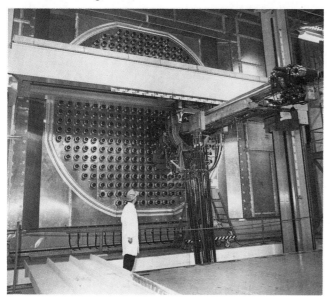

In order for the neutrons to react with the uranium-235 nuclei, they must travel slowly enough to be absorbed. Therefore, they must be slowed down to increase the chances of reaction. A substance that causes neutrons to slow down is called a **moderator**.

The moderator used in a CANDU reactor is heavy water. Its chemical name is deuterium oxide (D_2O) because it contains deuterium and oxygen. Deuterium (D or ^2_1H) is an isotope of hydrogen that was mentioned in Section 26.6. Each deuterium atom has one proton and one neutron. It is the extra neutron that helps prevent heavy water from absorbing neutrons from the fission reaction. That is why heavy water is an excellent moderator.

> **DID YOU KNOW?**
>
> The neutrons released during a fission reaction travel at speeds of up to 42 000 km/s. The moderator slows them down to about 3 km/s.

Controlling the fission reaction

When uranium-235 is bombarded with neutrons, it splits up. This creates new substances as well as high-speed neutrons and energy. The neutrons are needed to continue the chain reaction, but they must be controlled so that the desired number are absorbed by the uranium nuclei.

The number of neutrons is regulated by using **control rods** that absorb neutrons. These rods, often made of cadmium, can be moved into or out of the calandria to adjust the number of neutrons striking the uranium-235.

Producing steam in the reactor

The energy released from the fission reaction heats a substance called a **coolant**. The coolant, again heavy water, delivers its thermal energy to ordinary water, which in turn changes to steam. Then the steam is directed through huge turbines to make them spin. Refer to Figures 27-6 to 27-8.

Creating electricity

The ultimate purpose of a nuclear generating station is to produce electricity. The spinning turbines are connected to alternating current (AC) generators. The generators create electrical energy, which is delivered to consumers.

Figure 27-6 The basic operation of a nuclear generating station

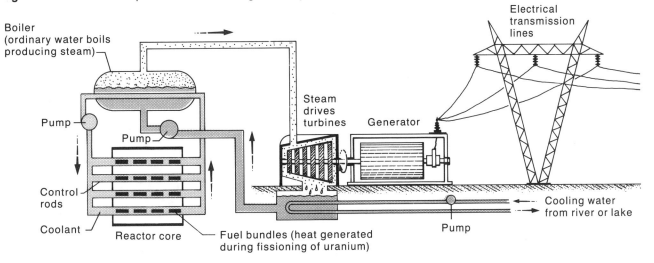

Boiler
(ordinary water boils
producing steam)

Pump

Pump

Control
rods

Coolant

Reactor core

Fuel bundles (heat generated
during fissioning of uranium)

Steam
drives
turbines

Generator

Electrical
transmission
lines

Cooling water
from river or lake

Pump

Figure 27-7 Installing parts of a turbine

Figure 27-8 This is the Pickering nuclear generating station located on Lake Ontario. It has eight reactor buildings.

Other types of reactors

One type of reactor used widely in the United States and Europe is called the **pressurized water reactor**, or **PWR**. It was developed from a system used to operate nuclear-powered submarines. Ordinary water (H_2O) is used as both the moderator and the coolant. Ordinary water absorbs neutrons more easily than heavy water. This creates the need to enrich the uranium fuel so it is between 2% and 4% of the fissionable U-235. To achieve a high temperature without boiling, the coolant is under high pressure. This explains the name of the reactor. Just as in the CANDU reactor, the coolant delivers energy to a water-and-steam circulation system. The steam drives turbines, and so on. A disadvantage of this type of reactor is that it must be shut down for refuelling every 12 to 18 months. See Figure 27-9.

Other types of reactors include the boiling water reactor, the high-temperature gas-cooled reactor, and the fast breeder reactor. You might be able to guess some of the properties of these reactors just by their names. Much literature is available describing the benefits and risks of these types of reactors.

PRACTICE

4. Describe the main differences between a nuclear generating station and a hydro generating station (Section 21.3).
5. Describe the advantage of placing the pressure tubes horizontally in a CANDU reactor.
6. In a CANDU reactor, name the mechanism or substance that:
   (a) controls the *number* of neutrons striking the atoms of fuel
   (b) controls the *speed* of the neutrons
7. Why is heavy water a good moderator?
8. Compare the CANDU and PWR systems using these headings:
   (a) meaning of name
   (b) fuel used
   (c) coolant used
   (d) moderator used
   (e) distinguishing features

Figure 27-9   The basic design of a PWR

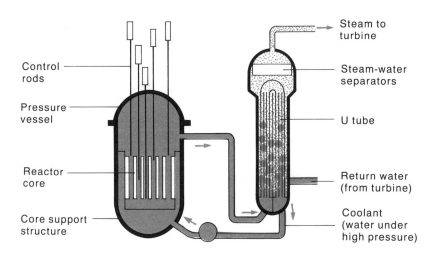

27.4 Risks of Using Nuclear Reactors

We have seen some of the benefits of using nuclear energy to generate electricity. Large amounts of energy can be produced using fuels that do not occupy much space. Furthermore, the world's supply of uranium, the main fuel used in reactors, will be ample for hundreds of years. But there are many risks involved in using nuclear energy. We will consider the major ones here.

Career risks

People whose jobs involve working close to uranium and other radioactive substances are subject to hazards. For example, workers in uranium mines are exposed to radiation. This radiation can lead to cancerous growths, particularly in the lungs. Efforts have been made to reduce these risks.

Workers at other stages of the nuclear industry are also exposed to hazards. These stages include milling the uranium, refining the fuel, operating the reactor, and handling nuclear wastes. Precautions are taken to keep the risks to a minimum. Refer to Figure 27-10.

Accidental risks

In April of 1986, a major disaster occurred at the Chernobyl nuclear reactor in the U.S.S.R. The reactor, which used graphite as its moderator, overheated and burned, a condition called *meltdown*. Deadly radiation was sent into the atmosphere, and spread across thousands of square kilometres. It will take many years to recover from this disaster.

The Chernobyl incident is not the only serious one. Another incident occurred at the Three Mile Island reactor in Pennsylvania, U.S.A. in 1979. (See Practice #12.) Although nuclear reactors have features intended to prevent such incidents, it is obvious that disasters can and do occur. They may be caused by equipment failure, an earthquake or other natural event, or human failure (which evidently was the cause of the Chernobyl incident).

Figure 27-10 Safety considerations for nuclear-industry workers

(a) This international symbol is used to warn people of dangerous radiation.

(b) As workers leave a high-risk area at a nuclear plant, this device checks the amount of radiation they received, and cleans their shoes.

The CANDU reactor has features to prevent meltdown and radioactive emissions. (The amount of uranium in each reactor is too small to cause a nuclear explosion, so the major concern is meltdown.) If a loss of coolant occurs, the *emergency core cooling system* begins to act. Then, if further precautions are needed, the *containment system* starts to operate. In case of a very serious emergency, the reactor is shut down completely, using any of two or three independent systems. These systems, which are illustrated in Figure 27-11, are:

- dumping the moderator into a safety tank below the calandria
- dropping shutoff rods into the calandria
- pumping ''liquid poison'' into the moderator to dilute it

Thermal effects

All fossil fuel and nuclear generating stations produce thermal energy that is either recycled or discarded as waste heat. Some of the discarded heat goes into the atmosphere near the station, but most of it is carried by water into a nearby lake, river, or ocean. This hot water may alter the ecosystem and cause problems for underwater life.

Figure 27-11   Shutdown systems in a CANDU reactor

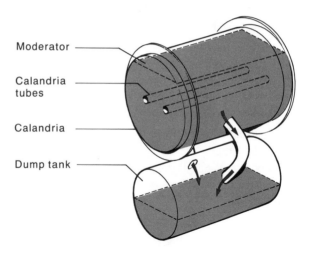

(a) Draining of the moderator

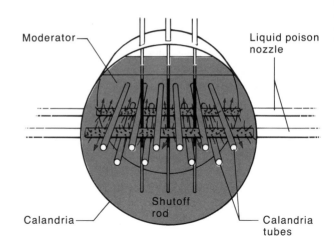

(b) Using shutoff control rods and liquid poison

Radioactive wastes

Radioactive wastes are a major problem facing the nuclear industry and our society. *Reactor wastes*, also called *low-level wastes*, are associated with materials used in maintenance operation at the nuclear reactor. These wastes are generally buried at disposal sites. They comprise only about 1% of the wastes at a nuclear reactor.

Spent-fuel wastes, also called *high-level wastes*, result from the nuclear reactions. About 99% of all nuclear wastes are found in the spent (used) fuel. The spent fuel generates a large amount of heat and emits much radiation. Furthermore, the fuel has a long half-life. Thus, it poses a large problem.

Currently, spent fuel is stored underwater in pools at reactor sites. As the piles of nuclear waste become larger, research is continuing to find a permanent solution to the problems involved in the storage and transportation of nuclear wastes. (See Figure 27-12.)

Figure 27-12 Researching the safe transport of nuclear wastes: A truck carrying a newly designed container has just crashed into a concrete barrier. Even though the crash occurred at a speed of 130 km/h, the container remained undamaged.

What choices do we have?

We have observed that there are both benefits and risks to generating electricity using nuclear reactors. People who oppose reactors have succeeded in forcing the number of proposed reactors to be reduced. In some regions, laws have been passed preventing the construction of new reactors until the problem of safe permanent storage of wastes has been solved.

People who promote nuclear reactors point to the relatively good safety record of the CANDU reactor. They also remind us that the use of fossil fuels to generate electricity has problems and serious risks. These include a limited supply of such fuels, costly transportation (especially for coal), the creation of environmental pollution, and possible hazardous working conditions, as proven by disasters in coal mines and offshore oil rigs.

Scientists, politicians, and citizens must together accept the responsibility of choosing wisely between the benefits and the risks. Everyone must also learn to conserve energy and promote the use of renewable sources of energy, such as solar energy. These steps will help ensure that future generations are not left with problems that may be impossible to solve.

PRACTICE

9. Three common ways of generating electricity in North America are with fossil fuels (especially coal, oil, and natural gas), with water at dams, and at nuclear reactors. For each of these methods, make lists of benefits and risks. In comparing these lists, what conclusion do you come to?

10. Why is spent fuel a major problem in the nuclear industry?

11. Choose one type of reactor, for example the CANDU reactor. Research and report on the safety features of that reactor.

12. Research and report on the incidents that occurred at Three Mile Island (March, 1979) and/or Chernobyl (April, 1986). Discuss the causes, short-term effects, and long-term effects of the incidents.

27.5 Nuclear Fusion

Nuclear fusion is the joining together of two small nuclei to make a larger nucleus. The mass of the final nucleus is less than the sum of the masses of the original nuclei. In other words, some mass disappears. As in nuclear fission, the lost mass changes into energy ($E = mc^2$). The energy from a fusion reaction is even greater per gram of reactants than the energy from a fission reaction.

One example of a fusion reaction is the collision of two fast-moving deuterium nuclei creating a helium nucleus, a neutron, and energy (Figure 27-13). The equation for this reaction is:

$$\text{{}^2_1H} + \text{{}^2_1H} \rightarrow \text{{}^3_2He} + \text{{}^1_0n} + \textbf{energy}$$

Nuclear fusion is the basic source of energy in our universe. It goes on continually in the sun and stars where hydrogen and other light elements fuse into heavier elements. In fact, it is believed that nuclear fusion is the process by which all elements have formed from atoms of hydrogen.

Figure 27-13   The fusion of two deuterium nuclei

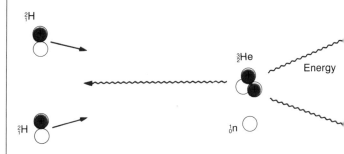

Scientists have been able to create fusion reactions on earth. A hydrogen bomb is an example of a use of fusion that is neither peaceful nor controlled. However, scientists are searching for ways of controlling fusion reactions. They are attempting to use large magnetic fields or lasers to obtain the high temperatures needed for fusion. If they are successful, we may have an answer to our energy-supply problems. An almost endless number of hydrogen nuclei obtained from ocean water may be available for energy through fusion. Furthermore, fusion does not create as many radioactive by-products as does fission. Figure 27-14 shows one possible design of a nuclear fusion reactor.

Figure 27-14   The basic design of a laser fusion reactor

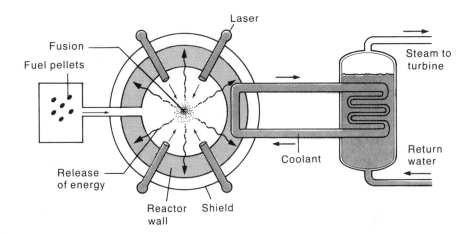

PRACTICE

13. Nuclear fusion on the sun changes an estimated 4×10^9 kg of mass into energy each second.
    (a) Calculate the amount of energy emitted by the sun each second.
    (b) What is the power rating of the sun?
    $$\left(P = \frac{E}{t}\right)$$

14. What features are common to the fusion reactor (Figure 27-14) and the fission reactors (Figure 27-6 and Figure 27-9)?

15. One type of reactor that uses magnetic fields to produce nuclear fusion is called the *tokamak*. Research and report on this type of reactor.

D I D   Y O U   K N O W ?

The sun's mass is so huge (about 2×10^{30} kg) that we need not worry about the "death" of the sun for billions of years.

27.6   Physics — Past, Present, and Future

Throughout this textbook you have seen glimpses of how science and physics developed in the past. The philosophers in ancient Greece laid the foundations of scientific thought. Famous scientists such as Galileo Galilei and Isaac Newton greatly advanced the study of physics. With them came developments in experimentation, measurement, and careful observation.

You have explored specific details of several areas of physics. Some of those details include the study of mechanical forces and energy, power, thermal energy, sound energy, electrical energy, electric and magnetic forces, light energy, and nuclear energy. A model of the structure of matter was developed, and you have learned how matter and energy interact.

You have also learned that physics is linked with technology and society. As the principles of physics were developed, they often were applied in technology.

As technology developed, new discoveries were made possible in physics. And science and technology have made available a wide variety of careers. In many cases our society has benefitted from both the scientific and technological developments. But in some ways the developments have had serious negative effects on our society. Hearing about these effects may help you appreciate the need for energy conservation and care of the environment.

But this study has not given a complete view of physics. No one textbook could do that. In fact, the more we learn about the subject of physics, the more there is to learn.

Thus, the process called the scientific method continues. We hypothesize, we experiment, we analyse, we predict the results of a new situation, and we start all over again. The researchers of "particle physics" tell us there may be hundreds of subatomic particles that have no explanation. They believe that every particle has an antiparticle. When a particle collides with its antiparticle, the two destroy each other, producing energy.

Astronomers make us feel very small by telling us how many billions of stars there are. They believe that the chances are high that somewhere else life exists in advanced forms. Much remains to be learned from the study of the universe.

Physicists are trying to solve two basic questions about nature:

• Is there a fundamental particle that makes up all other particles?

• Is there a unified theory that can explain all of nature's forces?

Where will all this knowledge and these questions lead us in the future? The development of computers will give us more leisure time. We may be able to watch three-dimensional television using laser technology. Communication systems will make our planet seem very small. Perhaps we will learn more about how humans think so we can make wise decisions about our future.

This brings us to the end of this study, but it represents the beginning of a huge frontier of knowledge in the subject of physics and its relationship to our society.

PRACTICE

16. The *quark* is a particle that may be a fundamental particle of nature. Evidence shows, for example, that a proton is made of three quarks. Research the properties of quarks, and write a report on your findings.

Words to Know

strong nuclear force	calandria
nuclear fission	control rods
law of conservation of	moderator
mass-energy	coolant
chain reaction	pressurized water reactor
CANDU reactor	nuclear fusion

Chapter Objectives

Having completed this chapter, you should now be able to:

1. Name and describe the force that binds the particles of the nucleus together.
2. Define nuclear fission.
3. Calculate the amount of energy produced when a given amount of mass changes into energy ($E = mc^2$).
4. Describe how a chain reaction is set up.
5. Explain the basic operation of a nuclear generating station.
6. State benefits and risks of using nuclear energy to generate electricity.
7. Name sources of electrical energy other than nuclear energy.
8. Define nuclear fusion.
9. State the contributions of physics to our society in the past, present, and future.

Chapter Review

1. Name and describe the force that binds the particles of the nucleus together. (27.1)
2. Compare nuclear fission and nuclear fusion. (27.2, 27.5)
3. Calculate the amount of energy released when the following quantities of matter change entirely into energy:
   (a) 3.0 kg
   (b) 400 g
   (c) 600 kg (27.2)
4. Describe how a chain reaction begins. (27.2)
5. State the function of each of the following components of a CANDU nuclear reactor:
   (a) uranium
   (b) control rods
   (c) moderator
   (d) coolant
   (e) steam
   (f) generator (27.3)

6. (a) What is another name for deuterium oxide?
   (b) What are the uses of this chemical in a CANDU reactor? (27.3)
7. Do you think the benefits exceed the risks in using nuclear fission reactors to produce electricity? Explain your answer.
8. The fast breeder reactor is a controversial reactor. It has some of the greatest advantages of all fission reactors, but also some of the greatest risks. Use reference books to discover why.
9. What is the main source of energy in the sun? (27.5)
10. List three ways that you think you could use to help conserve energy in the future.

The Metric System

Metric prefixes

Prefix	Symbol	Factor by which the standard unit is multiplied		
exa	E	10^{18}	=	1 000 000 000 000 000 000
peta	P	10^{15}	=	1 000 000 000 000 000
tera	T	10^{12}	=	1 000 000 000 000
giga	G	10^{9}	=	1 000 000 000
mega	M	10^{6}	=	1 000 000
kilo	k	10^{3}	=	1 000
hecto	h	10^{2}	=	100
deca	da	10^{1}	=	10
standard unit		10^{0}	=	1
deci	d	10^{-1}	=	0.1
centi	c	10^{-2}	=	0.01
milli	m	10^{-3}	=	0.001
micro	μ	10^{-6}	=	0.000 001
nano	n	10^{-9}	=	0.000 000 001
pico	p	10^{-12}	=	0.000 000 000 001
femto	f	10^{-15}	=	0.000 000 000 000 001
atto	a	10^{-18}	=	0.000 000 000 000 000 001

Système International (SI) fundamental quantities and their base units

Fundamental quantity	Base unit	Symbol
Length or distance	metre	m
Mass	kilogram*	kg
Time	second	s
Electric current	ampere	A
Temperature	kelvin	K
Amount of substance	mole	mol
Luminous intensity	candela	cd

*The kilogram is the only base unit having a prefix. The gram proved to be too small for practical purposes.

Derived quantities often used in physics, and their units

Dervied quantity	Unit	Symbol
Force	newton	N
Pressure	pascal	Pa
Energy	joule	J
Power	watt	W
Frequency	hertz	Hz
Electric resistance	ohm	Ω
Electric potential difference	volt	V
Radiation activity	becquerel	Bq

APPENDIX B

Scientific Notation

Extremely large and small numbers are awkward to write in long form. To avoid the problem, measurements are often recorded in **scientific notation**, also called "standard form." In this notation, one non-zero digit is placed before the decimal point and the other digits after it. The best way to see the usefulness of scientific notation is to study examples of large and small numbers.

Calculations involving very large and small numbers are also much easier when scientific notation is used. For example, the product of

$$150\ 000\ 000\ 000 \times 4\ 200\ 000\ 000$$

is more easily written as

$$1.5 \times 10^{11} \times 4.2 \times 10^{9} = 6.3 \times 10^{20}.$$

When multiplying or dividing using scientific notation, it is best to multiply or divide the non-exponents, then multiply or divide the powers of 10 by adding or subtracting the exponents. In general,

$$10^{a} \times 10^{b} = 10^{a+b}, \text{ and } 10^{a} \div 10^{b} = 10^{a-b}.$$

Examples of scientific notation

Quantity measured	Approximate measurement	Scientific notation
Mass of the earth	6 000 000 000 000 000 000 000 000 kg	6×10^{24} kg
Distance to the Andromeda galaxy	19 000 000 000 000 000 000 000 m	1.9×10^{22} m
Distance from the earth to the moon	380 000 000 m	3.8×10^{8} m
Thickness of a spider web strand	0.000 005 m	5×10^{-6} m
Mass of a proton	0.000 000 000 000 000 000 000 001 7 g	1.7×10^{-24} g

Measurement Errors and Significant Digits

The number of students in a classroom is an exact number. However, the length of the classroom is a measurement that is not an exact number. Measurements can never be exact. They always have some form of error.

There are two main types of error. A **random error** is simply a haphazard error; sometimes the measurement is higher than the true value, and sometimes it is lower. For example, if you are measuring the time for 10 vibrations of a pendulum, you may start the stopwatch a little soon, or a little late. This type of error can be reduced by taking the average of several readings.

A **systematic error** is an error caused by a problem with the measuring device or the person using it. Some examples are a metre stick with worn ends, a stopwatch that always runs slow, and a dial instrument that is not properly zeroed. One way to reduce this type of error is to add or subtract the known error.

A common source of error in reading scales is **parallax**. This is the apparent shift in an object's position when the observer changes position. (Parallax error can be either random or systematic.) To observe an example of parallax, cover your left eye and hold the index finger of your outstretched right arm so it appears to cover a distant object. Then switch eyes, and observe how the distant object appears to change position. To prevent parallax, always view a dial or scale directly, not from an angle.

Each recorded measurement should consist of digits known for certain, and one estimated digit. These digits are called **significant digits**. Consider, for example, the measurement of the length of a notebook page. You might find that its length lies somewhere between 27.3 and 27.5 cm, so you would record its length as 27.4 cm. The first two digits are known for certain, and the last one is estimated. Thus, the measurement has 3 significant digits.

When zeros are included in a measurement, the following rules apply:

- Zeros placed before other digits are not significant: 0.0054 m has 2 significant digits.
- Zeros placed between other digits are always significant: 6003 g has 4 significant digits.
- Zeros placed after other digits behind a decimal are significant: 4.30 kg has 3 significant digits.
- To judge whether zeros at the end of a number are significant, scientific notation must be used. For example, 6200 km has an unknown number of significant digits. However,

6.2×10^3 km has 2 significant digits.

6.20×10^3 km has 3 significant digits.

6.200×10^3 km has 4 significant digits.

High-precision instruments (see Chapter 2) provide measurements with more significant digits than other instruments. If errors are reduced to a minimum, the measurement is accurate, in other words it is close to the true value. The difference between *precision* and *accuracy* can be illustrated with a micrometer calliper that is not properly zeroed. The reading may be *precise*, perhaps to three significant digits, but it is not *accurate* unless the systematic error is reduced.

Calculating and Rounding Answers

Measurements are often used to perform calculations. For example, the surface area of a page can be calculated by multiplying the length by the width. When such calculations are made, the final answer should be written with a logical number of significant digits.

When adding or substracting measured quantities, the final answer should have no more than one estimated digit. For example, let us add
84.3 cm + 62.4 cm + 31.82 cm.

84.3 cm	The "3" is estimated.
62.4 cm	The "4" is estimated.
31.82 cm	The "2" is estimated.
178.52 cm	Both the "5" and the "2" are estimated.

Thus, the answer should be rounded to one estimated digit; the answer is 178.5 cm.

When multiplying or dividing measured quantities, the final answer should have as many significant digits as the original measurement with the *least* number of significant digits. For example,
10.4 mm × 108.6 mm = 1129.44 mm^2
should be rounded to 3 significant digits. Thus, the answer is 1130 mm^2, or more exactly, 1.13×10^3 mm^2.

When calculated answers must be rounded to the correct number of significant digits, the following rules should apply. Each example given is rounded to 2 significant digits.

- If the first digit to be dropped is 4 or less, the preceding digit is not changed.
  e.g., 8.74 becomes 8.7
- If the first digit to be dropped is 6 or more, the preceding digit is raised by 1.
  e.g., 6.36 becomes 6.4
- If the digits to be dropped are a 5 followed by digits other than zeros, the preceding digit is raised by 1.
  e.g., 3.45123 becomes 3.5
- If the digit to be dropped is a 5 (or a 5 followed by zeros), the preceding digit is not changed if it is even, but it is raised by 1 if it is odd.
  e.g., 2.65 becomes 2.6
  2.75 becomes 2.8

Graphing

In graphing experimental results, the **independent variable**, the one controlled by the experimenter, is placed along the horizontal axis. The **dependent variable**, which depends on the independent one, is placed along the vertical axis. (In simple terms, the dependent variable is the quantity you are trying to find.) The graph should be given a title. Scales should be chosen to occupy as large a portion of the graph paper as possible. The axes should be labelled with the names of the quantities being plotted and their units.

Points on a graph are obtained by plotting ordered pairs obtained from the experiment. If the points plotted appear to line up fairly closely, a single straight line of best fit should be drawn. Once a straight line is obtained on a graph, the slope of the line can be calculated using either of these equations:

$$\text{slope} = \frac{\text{rise}}{\text{run}} \quad \text{or} \quad \text{slope} = \frac{\Delta y}{\Delta x}$$

where Δy is the change in the value plotted on the vertical axis and Δx is the corresponding change in the value on the horizontal axis.

When calculating the slope of a line on a graph, always include units, because they indicate the meaning of the slope.

Sample Problem

An experiment is performed to determine the mass of various volumes of a certain liquid. The data obtained are placed in a table, as shown.

Volume (L)	0	0.5	1.0	1.5	2.0	2.5	3.0
Mass (g)	0	395	780	1180	1590	1980	2360

(a) Plot a graph of the data and draw the line of best fit.

(b) Calculate the slope of the line, and state what it represents.

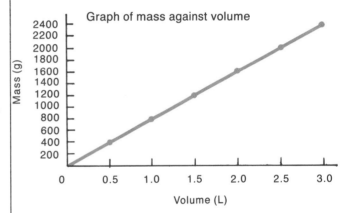

Solution

(a) Refer to the graph shown.

(b) slope $= \dfrac{\Delta y}{\Delta x}$

$\quad = \dfrac{2370\,\text{g} - 0.0\,\text{g}}{3.0\,\text{L} - 0.0\,\text{L}}$

$\quad = 790\,\text{g/L}$

Thus, the slope of the line is 790 g/L, which represents the density of the liquid.

Derivations of Equations

In the text certain equations are used without a complete explanation regarding their origin. The derivations of those equations are beyond the goals of the text but are included here for reference.

Section 7.4 $E_K = \dfrac{mv^2}{2}$

Assume that an object, starting from rest, has an amount of work, E, done on it. By the law of conservation of energy, that work is transformed into kinetic energy possessed by the object. Thus,

$$E_K = E$$
$$= Fd$$

where F is the unbalanced force ($F = ma$) that causes the object to accelerate for a distance d given by the relation $d = v_{ave}t$. (v_{ave} is the average or half-time speed.)

Therefore, $E_K = (ma)(v_{ave}t)$

Now, $a = \dfrac{\Delta v}{t}$

$\quad\quad = \dfrac{v_f}{t}$ (The object started from rest and reached a final speed of v_f.)

Thus, $E_K = \dfrac{m(v_f)(v_{ave}t)}{t}$

$\quad\quad = mv_f v_{ave}$

Since $v_{ave} = \dfrac{1}{2}v_f$, we conclude that $E_K = \dfrac{mv_f^2}{2}$

or $E_K = \dfrac{mv^2}{2}$

Section 10.4 ''For every centimetre difference between the water levels there is a pressure difference of 100 Pa or 0.1 kPa.''

The force of gravity pulling down on a 1.0 kg mass is about 10 N. A force scale can be used to show this fact.

The density of water is 1000 g/L, which is the same as 1.0 g/mL or 1.0 g/cm³. This means that the force of gravity pulling down on 1.0 cm³ of water is 10 N ÷ 1000 or 0.01 N.

Now imagine a cube of water 1.0 cm on each side. The bottom of the cube has a surface area of 1.0 cm². If the cube is resting on a surface, it exerts a pressure of:

$$p = \dfrac{F}{A}$$
$$= \dfrac{0.01\ \text{N}}{0.0001\ \text{m}^2} \quad\quad (1.0\ \text{cm}^2 = 0.0001\ \text{m}^2)$$
$$= 100\ \text{N/m}^2, \text{which is } 100\ \text{Pa or } 0.1\ \text{kPa}$$

This proves the original statement.

Activity 10B ''The force on 1.0 mL of water is 0.01 N.'' This fact is explained above.

Section 18.9 ''For a series circuit, $R_T = R_1 + R_2$.''
Experimentally, it was found that for a series circuit having resistors R_1 and R_2, the current (I) remains constant in the circuit and the total potential rise (V_T) equals the sum of the individual potential drops ($V_1 + V_2$).

Using Ohm's law, $R_T = \dfrac{V_T}{I}$

$$R_T = \dfrac{V_1 + V_2}{I}$$
$$R_T = \dfrac{V_1}{I} + \dfrac{V_2}{I}$$
$$\therefore R_T = R_1 + R_2$$

Section 18.9 "For a parallel circuit, $\frac{1}{R_T} = \frac{1}{R_1} + \frac{1}{R_2}$."

Experimentally it was found that for a parallel circuit having resistors R_1 and R_2, the potential difference (V) remains constant and the total current (I_T) equals the sum of the individual currents ($I_1 + I_2$).

Using Ohm's law, $R_T = \dfrac{V}{I_T}$ or $\dfrac{1}{R_T} = \dfrac{I_T}{V}$

$$\frac{1}{R_T} = \frac{I_1 + I_2}{V}$$

$$\frac{1}{R_T} = \frac{I_1}{V} + \frac{I_2}{V}$$

$$\frac{1}{R_T} = \frac{1}{R_1} + \frac{1}{R_2}$$

Section 19.4 $P = VI$

For this derivation we will introduce a new symbol, Q, representing charge.

Current (I) is defined as the amount of charge (Q) that passes through a circuit each second (t) (Section 18.3). Thus,

$$I = \frac{Q}{t} \quad \text{or} \quad Q = It.$$

Potential difference or voltage (V) is defined as the amount of energy (E) given to a certain amount of charge (Q) (Section 18.4). Thus,

$$V = \frac{E}{Q} \quad \text{or} \quad E = VQ.$$

Now power is $P = \dfrac{E}{t}$ (where $E = VQ$)

$$P = \frac{VQ}{t} \quad \text{(where } Q = It\text{)}$$

$$P = \frac{V(It)}{t} \quad \text{(divide the } t\text{)}$$

$$\therefore P = VI$$

Section 22.7 "At 90° between the mirrors, three images are formed."

The number of images (n) formed by two mirrors at various angles to each other is given by the equation

$$n = \frac{360°}{a} - 1$$

where a is the angle between the mirrors.

SELECTED ANSWERS

Chapter 1

PRACTICE
4. (a) 0.017 s
   (b) 60 Hz
5. (a) 0.25 s
   (b) 50 s
   (c) 7.7 s
6. (a) 0.20 Hz
   (b) 40 Hz
   (c) 0.59 Hz

REVIEW
3. (a) 7.5 s
   (b) 0.13 Hz
4. 0.11 s
5. 91 Hz
9. (a) 0.60 s
   (b) 0.10 s

Chapter 2

REVIEW
1. (a) 7.5 cm
   (b) 240 m
2. (a) about 160 paces
   (b) about 130 m
3. 11.7 m (or about 12 m)
4. 1.4×10^9 km
5. (a) 42 cm; 0.42 m
   (b) 0.338 m; 338 mm
   (c) 400 000 m
   (d) 19 m; 1900 cm
   (e) 0.15 km
7. 12.22 m; 12.2 m; 12 m
8. 8.57 cm

Chapter 3

PRACTICE
1. (a) 6.84 m^2 (or 6.8 m^2)
   (b) 864 mm^2 (or $8.6 \times 10^2 \text{ mm}^2$)
   (c) $10\ 000 \text{ m}^2$ (or $1.0 \times 10^4 \text{ m}^2$)

2. (a) $60\ 000 \text{ m}^2$
   (b) 6 ha
3. (a) 61 cm^2
   (b) $7.1 \times 10^2 \text{ m}^2$
   (c) $7.5 \times 10^2 \text{ mm}^2$
4. (a) 3.0 m^2
   (b) $36.00
5. (a) $1.1 \times 10^2 \text{ m}^2$
   (b) 11 bundles
8. (a) 2700 kg/m^2
9. (a) 1400 g/L
   (b) 1400 kg/m^3
10. $16\ 000 \text{ kg/m}^3$
11. (a) $m = DV$
    (b) $V = \dfrac{m}{D}$
12. (a) 840 kg
    (b) 5.5 L

REVIEW
2. (a) $90\ 000 \text{ m}^2$
   (b) 9 ha
   (c) $18\ 000
3. 2.5 cm^2
4. (a) 1000 kg/m^3
5. (a) 0.50 m by 0.20 m by 0.15 m
   (b) 0.015 m^3
   (c) 8500 kg/m^3
6. (a) 120 cm^3
   (b) 5.5 g/cm^3
7. $1.3 \times 10^3 \text{ g/L}$
8. 36 kg
9. $1.1 \times 10^3 \text{ m}^3$

Chapter 4

PRACTICE
2. (a) 2.0 m/s
   (b) 50 m/s
   (c) 62 m/s
3. 333 m/s
4. 30 cm/s
5. (a) $d = vt$
   (b) $t = \dfrac{d}{v}$

446

6. (a) 174 m (or 1.7×10^2 m)
   (b) 16 s
7. 1440 m (or 1.4×10^3 m)
8. 11 400 km (or 1.1×10^4 km)
9. 25 h
11. B, C
14. (a) 4.0 cm/s
    (b) 8.0 m/s
    (c) 0.5 m/s

REVIEW
3. 12.5 m/s
4. 3.0×10^8 m/s
5. 4032 m, or 4.0 km
6. 112 s
7. (a) 0.2 s
9. (a) 16 cm/s
   (b) 8.0 cm/s
   (c) 4.0 cm/s
   (d) 2.0 cm/s
10. B, C

Chapter 5

PRACTICE
1. (a), (d), (e)
2. (a), (d)
3. (a) 12 (m/s)/s
   (b) 17 (m/s)/s
   (c) −5.0 (m/s)/s
4. 13 (m/s)/s
5. 4 (km/h)/s
6. −0.1 (m/s)/s
7. (a) $\Delta v = a \Delta t$

   (b) $\Delta t = \dfrac{\Delta v}{a}$
8. (a) 63 m/s
   (b) 20 s
9. 300 s (or 5 min)
10. A collision will occur because it
    would take 22.5 s to stop.
11. 20 m/s
12. A
13. (a) 5.0 (m/s)/s
    (b) 12.5 (m/s)/s
    (c) 500 (m/s)/s

14. The final accelerations are:
    (i) 4 (m/s)/s
    (ii) 10 (m/s)/s
    (iii) 200 (m/s)/s
15. (a) 9.8 m/s
    (b) 19.6 m/s
    (c) 29.4 m/s

REVIEW
3. (a) 20 (m/s)/s
   (b) 37 (m/s)/s
5. 0.2 (m/s)/s
6. −20 (km/h)/s
7. 40 m/s
8. 3.5 s
10. (a) 2.5 (m/s)/s
    (b) 5.0 (m/s)/s
11. (d) 8 (m/s)/s
12. 160 (cm/s)/s
14. 34.3 (m/s)/s
16. (a) no
    (b) yes

Chapter 6

PRACTICE
2. (a) 2 N
   (b) 4 N
   (c) 10 N
9. (a) 0.25 (m/s)/s
   (b) 2.5 (m/s)/s
   (c) 80 (m/s)/s
10. (a) 25 000 N (or 2.5×10^4 N)
    (b) 125 N
    (c) 1.6×10^5 N

11. $m = \dfrac{F}{a}$
12. 1.6 kg
13. (a) 2940 N
14. (a) 147 N
    (b) 147 N
16. (a) 89 N
    (b) 258 N
25. (a) 0.06
    (b) 0.3
26. $f = \mu N$
27. 110 N

REVIEW

6. 2.0 (m/s)/s
7. 300 N
8. 3.0 kg
9. 588 N
18. (a) 147 N
    (b) 0.34
    (c) wood
19. 60 N
20. 0.34

Chapter 7

PRACTICE

2. 125 J
3. zero
4. (a) 0.98 N
   (b) 1.96 J
6. (b) 80 000 J (or 8.0×10^4 J)
8. (a) $F = \dfrac{E}{d}$

   (b) $d = \dfrac{E}{F}$
9. (a) 20 N
   (b) 0.5 m
10. (a) 0.0 J
    (b) 2.94 J
11. 68 600 J (or 6.9×10^4 J)
12. (a) $m = \dfrac{E_P}{gh}$

    (b) $h = \dfrac{E_P}{mg}$
13. (a) 0.5 kg
    (b) 1.5 m
14. (a) 200 J
    (b) 400 000 J (or 4.0×10^5 J)
    (c) 120 J
15. (a) $m = \dfrac{2E_K}{v^2}$

    (b) $v = \sqrt{\dfrac{2E_K}{m}}$
16. (a) 4.0 kg
    (b) 5.0 m/s
17. (a) 50 J
20. 5.0 W

21. 2.5 W
22. 40 W
23. (a) $E = Pt$

    (b) $t = \dfrac{E}{P}$
24. (a) 7200 J
    (b) 50 s

REVIEW

2. 29 400 J (or 2.9×10^4 J)
3. 120 N
4. 3000 m, or 3.0 km
5. 1.4×10^3 J
6. 1.0 kg
7. 5.0 m
8. (a) 4.0 J
   (b) 16 J
   (c) 36 J
9. 2.0 kg
10. 3.0 m/s
12. 60 W
13. (a) 2.35×10^5 J
    (b) 2.35×10^6 J
    (c) 163 W
14. 3.6×10^5 J
15. 500 000 s, or about 139 h

Chapter 8

PRACTICE

2. (a) 150 N·m
   (b) 250 N·m
3. zero
4. (a) $d = \dfrac{T}{F}$

   (b) $F = \dfrac{T}{d}$
5. 0.22 m
6. 150 N
7. (a) 2nd class
   (b) 3rd class
   (c) 3rd class
   (d) 1st class
8. (a) 110 N·m
   (b) 810 N·m
9. (a) 6.8 N·m
   (b) 78 N·m

11. (a) 90 N
    (b) 200 N
    (c) 400 N

12. (a) $d_E = \dfrac{F_L d_L}{F_E}$

    (b) $F_L = \dfrac{F_E d_E}{d_L}$

    (c) $d_L = \dfrac{F_E d_E}{F_L}$

13. (a) 1.0 m
    (b) 300 N
    (c) 0.1 m

14. (b) 1.2 m
    (c) 1.5 m

15. 200 N

16. (a) 6.0 cm
    (b) 2.0 cm

23. (b) and (d) are stable

25. (d), (a), (b), (c)

REVIEW

1. 90°

4. 360 N·m

5. 6.0 N·m

7. no (840 N·m; 810 N·m)

8. 120 N

9. 1.5 m

10. 200 N

11. (a) 0.5 m
    (b) 120 kg

Chapter 9

PRACTICE

4. (a) 0.8 N/m
    (b) 8000 N/m
    (c) 80 N/m

5. (a) 100 N/m
    (b) 50 N/m
    (c) 25 N/m

6. (a) 0.055 m
    (b) 400 N/m

7. (a) $F = k\Delta L$

    (b) $\Delta L = \dfrac{F}{k}$

8. 500 N

9. 0.05 m, or 5 cm

REVIEW

3. (a) A
    (b) C

5. (b) 5000 N/m

6. 600 N

7. 2.5 m

8. (a) 100 N/m
    (c) 30 N
    (d) 38 N

Chapter 10

PRACTICE

4. (a) 5 Pa
    (b) 800 Pa
    (c) 20 000 Pa, or 20 kPa

5. 2 500 000 Pa, or 2500 kPa

7. (a) $F = pA$

    (b) $A = \dfrac{F}{p}$

8. (a) 0.55 N
    (b) 0.8 m²

9. 80 000 N (or 8.0×10^4 N)

10. 2.0 m²

13. 62 kPa

19. (a) 1.0 kPa
    (b) 1.8 kPa
    (c) 3.4 kPa

20. 302.8 kPa (or 303 kPa)

22. (a) 750 N
    (b) 19 200 N
    (c) 4800 N

23. 2400 N

24. 500 N

26. 620 N

REVIEW

2. 40 000 N (or 4.0×10^4 N)

3. 4000 N (or 4.0×10^3 N)

5. 240 000 N (or 2.4×10^5 N)

6. (a) 0.2 m²

10. 7.2 kPa

11. 365 kPa

12. 9 kPa to 19 kPa

15. (a) 100 kPa
    (b) 250 kPa

17. 2500 N and 35 000 N
18. 600 N
20. 0.5 N
21. (a) 4.0 N
    (b) 12 N
22. (a) 3.0 N
    (b) 3.0 N

Chapter 11

PRACTICE
1. A pear shape would provide excellent streamlining.
9. The ball will curve downward to the left.

Chapter 12

PRACTICE
23. (a) 0.048
    (b) 0.22
    (c) 5.25
24. about 5.2

REVIEW
12. about 1.6

Chapter 13

PRACTICE
1. 6000 J
2. 9600 J
3. (a) 0.5 kg
   (b) 20°C
   (c) 2000 J/(kg·°C)
4. (a) 130 J/(kg·°C)
   (b) 1.3×10^2 J/(kg·°C)
5. (a) 2.1×10^5 J
   (b) 7.5×10^4 J
   (c) 2.6×10^4 J
6. (a) 5.0×10^4 J
   (b) 9.0×10^5 J
   (c) 6.7×10^3 J
8. (a) 840 J/(kg·°C)

9. (a) 450 J/(kg·°C)
14. (a) 4.2×10^5 J/kg
    (b) 4.2×10^5 J
15. 2.1×10^6 J/kg
16. (a) 3.4×10^6 J
    (b) 1.3×10^8 J
    (c) 4.4×10^4 J
17. 1.3×10^5 J

REVIEW
4. 2.9×10^5 J
5. (a) 2.4×10^4 J
   (b) 2400 J/(kg·°C)
6. (a) 1.2×10^5 J
   (b) 4.6×10^4 J
   (c) 4.2×10^4 J
   (d) 1.8×10^4 J
7. (a) 2.0×10^4 J
8. (a) 920 J/(kg·°C)
12. (a) 3.3×10^5 J/kg
    (b) 4.0×10^4 J/kg
13. (a) 2.0×10^6 J/kg
    (b) 2.3×10^6 J/kg
14. (a) 5.0×10^5 J
    (b) 3.3×10^5 J
15. 3.3×10^6 J

Chapter 14

PRACTICE
2. (b) 8.5 cm
3. (b) 4 cm
4. 200 cm
5. 24 cm
6. $f = 0.4$ Hz, $T = 2.5$ s
7. 0.42 s
8. 25 Hz
13. (a) 30 m/s
    (b) 3 m/s
    (c) 80 m/s
14. (a) 4.0 m/s
    (b) 20 m/s
    (c) 80 m/s
15. (a) $f = \dfrac{v}{\lambda}$

    (b) $\lambda = \dfrac{v}{f}$

16. (a) 600 Hz
    (b) 0.05 m
17. (a) 100 Hz
    (b) 0.01 s
18. 6.0 cm
22. 4.0 m
23. 4.0 m

REVIEW
 2. 4 cm
 6. (a) 1.5 s
    (b) 0.60 s
    (c) 4 s
 7. (a) 20 Hz
    (b) 210 Hz
    (c) 60 Hz
 9. (a) 0.20 s
    (b) 0.002 s
10. (a) 0.1 Hz
    (b) 4.0 Hz
13. 1500 m/s
14. 800 Hz
15. 0.67 m

Chapter 15

PRACTICE
 6. (a) 333.8 m/s
    (b) 344 m/s
    (c) 330.8 m/s
10. (a) 1500 m/s
    (b) 349 m/s
12. (a) 2 Hz
    (b) 6 Hz
    (c) 5 Hz
13. 505 Hz, 519 Hz
16. 1440 m/s
17. 150 m

REVIEW
 6. 340 m/s
 7. 2070 m
 8. (a) 347 m/s
    (b) 336.8 m/s
    (c) 326 m/s
11. (a) 1500 m/s

12. 7500 m
14. (a) 5 Hz
    (b) 4 Hz
15. 3 Hz, 5 Hz, 8 Hz
21. 1400 m/s
22. 72.5 m

Chapter 16

PRACTICE
 2. (a) 400 Hz
    (b) 640 Hz
    (c) 1160 Hz
 3. (a) 100 Hz
    (b) 160 Hz
    (c) 290 Hz
 4. (a) 1200 Hz
    (b) 4000 Hz
    (c) 1024 Hz
 6. (a) 10
    (b) 100
    (c) 1000
    (d) 10 000
 7. 80 dB
11. 44 cm
12. 120 cm

REVIEW
 7. (a) 2000 Hz
    (b) 500 Hz
    (c) 4000 Hz
    (d) 250 Hz
 9. 1000 times
16. 0.54 m
17. 351 m/s

Chapter 17

PRACTICE
 4. (a) positive
    (b) neutral
    (c) negative
    (d) positive
    (e) neutral
    (f) negative

5. electrons
6. (a) negative
7. (a) rubber becomes negative, silk positive
   (b) silk becomes negative, glass positive
   (c) glass becomes positive, cotton negative
   (d) cat's fur becomes positive, amber negative
9. neutral
11. positive
12. negative

REVIEW
5. neutral
6. (a) the electron
7. (a) positive
   (b) negative
9. (a) amber becomes negative, rubber positive
   (b) wool becomes positive, rubber negative
   (c) vinyl becomes negative, silk positive
14. (a) negative
    (b) positive
    (c) positive
    (d) negative

Chapter 18

PRACTICE
7. (a) 0.6 A
   (b) 0.08 A
   (c) 4 A
8. (a) 150 mA, that is, 0.15 A
   (b) 1.5 A
   (c) 7.5 A
10. (a) 3.5 V
    (b) 10.5 V
    (c) 210 V
17. (a) 7.0 V
    (b) 9 V
    (c) 220 V
18. (a) 5 Ω
    (b) 15 Ω
    (c) 16 Ω
    (d) 25 Ω
19. (a) $V = RI$
    (b) $I = \dfrac{V}{R}$
20. 125 V

21. 0.5 A
22. (a) 7.7 Ω
    (b) 1200 Ω
    (c) 1111 Ω
23. (a) 4 Ω
    (b) 10 Ω
    (c) 10 Ω
24. (a) 2 A
    (b) 6 V
    (c) 5 Ω
    (d) 3 Ω
25. (a) 50 V
    (b) 5 A
    (c) 10 Ω

REVIEW
7. (a) 0.35 A
   (b) 0.042 A
   (c) 0.905 V
   (d) 1.05 V
14. 10 V
16. (a) 12 Ω
    (b) 20 Ω
    (c) 20 Ω
17. (a) 21 V
    (b) 0.5 A
18. 60 V
19. 15 A
21. (a) 900 Ω
    (b) 60 Ω
22. (b) 30 V
    (c) 30 V
    (d) 60 Ω
    (e) 40 Ω
23. (b) 3 V
    (c) 3 V
    (d) 1.5 A
    (e) 1.5 Ω

Chapter 19

PRACTICE
7. (a) 360 W
   (b) 264 W
   (c) 1140 W
   (d) 3.6 W

8. (a) $V = \dfrac{P}{I}$

  (b) $I = \dfrac{P}{V}$

9. 9 V
10. 10 A
11. (a) 2.7 MJ and 5.4¢
  (b) 7.2 MJ and 14.4¢
  (c) 10.8 MJ and 21.6¢
12. (a) 0.15 kW·h and 0.9¢
  (b) 3.0 kW·h and 18¢
  (c) 6.4 kW·h and 38.4¢
13. (a) 580 kW·h
  (b) $29.00

REVIEW
4. (a) 120 V
  (b) 240 V
  (c) 120 V
6. (a) 1.8 W
  (b) 4800 W
  (c) 108 W
7. (a) 12 V
  (b) 5 A
8. 0.02 A, or 20 mA
9. 12 V
10. (a) 3.6 MJ
  (b) 5.4¢
11. (a) 300 kW·h
  (b) $15.00
12. $27.60
14. (a) 1800 W
  (b) 14 400 W
  (c) 720 W

Chapter 20

PRACTICE
12. (c) outwards, away from the magnet
13. counterclockwise
14. clockwise

REVIEW
10. (a) clockwise
  (b) counterclockwise

11. (i) left end is N
  (ii) right end is N
  (iii) both ends are S
16. (a) inwards
  (b) inwards
  (c) inwards
17. clockwise
18. (b) left end is N
  (c) counterclockwise when viewed from above

Chapter 21

PRACTICE
1. The magnetic field around the conductor must be changing.
2. (a) left and right
  (b) up and down
  (c) up and down
8. (i) step-up, 1000 V
  (ii) step-up, 1500 V
  (iii) step-down, 100 V
9. (a) $N_s = N_p \cdot \dfrac{V_s}{V_p}$

  (b) $N_p = N_s \cdot \dfrac{V_p}{V_s}$

  (c) $V_p = V_s \cdot \dfrac{N_p}{N_s}$
10. (a) 240 V
  (b) 15 000 windings
  (c) 4800 windings

REVIEW
3. (a) yes
  (b) no
  (c) yes
4. (a) The current increases.
  (b) The current increases.
  (c) The current increases.
  (d) The current stops.
8. (a) The right end becomes N.
13. 30 V
14. 60 windings
15. 200 windings
16. 120 V
17. (b)

Chapter 22

PRACTICE
7. 1.5×10^{11} m
8. 9.6×10^{15} m
9. 1.3 s
12. 3rd law
13. (a) 22°
    (b) 75°
    (c) 0°
14. The image is upright, the same size as the object, imaginary, and located behind the mirror.
18.   (i) concave, 2.5 cm
     (ii) convex, 3.5 cm
    (iii) concave, 3.0 cm
19. (a) The image is inverted, smaller than the object, and real.
21. (a) concave
    (b) imaginary
    (c) at F
    (d) imaginary

REVIEW
6. 3.0×10^8 m/s
7. 3.84×10^{16} m
8. 1.5×10^4 s, or about 4.2 h
12. 120 cm
14. (a) 2/1
    (b) 1/2

Chapter 23

PRACTICE
2. (a) yes
   (b) no
   (c) yes

REVIEW
2. B
5. (a) 0°
   (b) 0°
9. a, b, and c will internally reflect

Chapter 24

PRACTICE
1. real
2. inverted and real
4. (a) iris
   (b) vitreous humour
   (c) cornea
   (d) rods
   (e) optic nerve
   (f) lens
5. 6/8
6. (a) concave lens
   (b) convex lens
   (c) cylindrical lens or hard contact lens
8. inverted, larger than the object, and imaginary

REVIEW
4. They are all real.
6. For most people the angle is between 16° and 22°.

Chapter 25

PRACTICE
1. (a) red
   (b) cyan, blue, and green
   (c) no colour (black)
   (d) red
2. (a) red + blue (magenta)
   (b) no colour (black)
   (c) blue
   (d) green
3. (a) red
   (b) green
   (c) blue
   (d) black
4. east
5. red and blue
7. (a) blue and green
   (b) red, green, and blue
   (c) none

REVIEW
5. (a) yellow
   (b) white
   (c) white

6. (a) red and green
   (b) blue
12. (a) yellow and magenta
   (b) yellow and cyan
   (c) There are three possible answers.
       One is ''cyan and red''.
18. no
21. (a) red or blue

Chapter 26

PRACTICE

6. γ rays have higher energies than X rays.
8. 300 emissions
9. (a) 50 Bq
   (b) 125 Bq
   (c) 70 Bq
10. (a) 2.4×10^8 emissions
   (b) 1.44×10^{10} emissions
11. (a) negative
   (b) positive
   (c) neutral
   (d) positive
14. (a) 9
   (b) 10
15. (a) 7
   (b) 0
   (c) 2

17. 140, 143, 146 neutrons, respectively
18. (a) 50 Bq
   (b) 25 Bq
   (c) 12.5 Bq
19. 45 h

REVIEW

10. (a) 600 emissions
   (b) 1800 emissions
13. H, He, Na, Al
15. (b) 8 days
   (c) 1250 Bq

Chapter 27

PRACTICE

3. (a) 4.5×10^{16} J
   (b) 1.8×10^{17} J
   (c) 9.0×10^{17} J
13. (a) 3.6×10^{26} J
   (b) 3.6×10^{26} W or 3.6×10^{23} kW (This is approximately a billion billion times as much power as our largest generating station puts out!)

REVIEW

3. (a) 2.7×10^{17} J
   (b) 3.6×10^{16} J
   (c) 5.4×10^{19} J

INDEX

PHOTO CREDITS

All photos not specifically credited to another source are included by courtesy of the author, Alan J. Hirsch. Many of the remaining photos in the book were obtained through the diligent and imaginative picture research of Elaine Freedman and Will Woods.

Unit One, Opening Photos
Left to right: I.S.T.C., Mustassini, Québec; I.S.T.C., Downsview, Ontario; Courtesy, Dr. Bernie Goldman; I.S.T.C., Montreal, Québec; Toronto East General Hospital.

Chapter 2
Figure 2.5, Ontario Hydro

Chapter 3
Opening Figure, Imperial Oil Limited

Unit Two, Opening Photos
Left to right: I.S.T.C., Trout River, Newfoundland; I.S.T.C., Shippegan, New Brunswick; Sharpless/Colin Fraser; I.S.T.C., Shippegan, New Brunswick; Courtesy, Birgitte Nielsen

Chapter 4
Opening Figure, General Motors Corporation

Chapter 5
Figure 5.12, NASA; 5.13, Kitchener-Waterloo Record

Chapter 6
Opening Figure, NASA; Figure 6.1, Yerkes Observatory, University of Chicago

Chapter 7
Figure 7.8, Information Canada/Miller Services

Unit Three, Opening Photos
Left to right: I.S.T.C., Rose Bay, Nova Scotia; I.S.T.C., Toronto, Ontario; Cirque du Soleil/Martha Swope; Gérard Châtaigneau

Chapter 8
Opening Figure, David Street/National Ballet

Chapter 9
Opening Figures, Stelco Canada and B.C. Tourism; Figure 9.1, Copyright Harold Edgerton (1990); Courtesy of Palm Press, Inc.; 9.31 (a), Gouvernement du Québec; 9.32, I.S.T.C., Lion's Gate Bridge, Vancouver, B.C.; 9.35 (a) Elaine Freedman; 9.35 (b) Anglican Church of Canada; 9.36 (a), J. Gertz/Alberta Research Council; 9.36 (b) L. Lorinczi/Alberta Research Council; 9.39 (b), I.S.T.C., Expo '86, Vancouver B.C.; 9.41, Stanford Downey

Unit Four, Opening Photos
Left to right: Toronto General Hospital/Pearce A-V; Toronto General Hospital; I.S.T.C., Riverview, New Brunswick; Tony Honeywood/De Havilland Canada; Tony Honeywood/De Havilland Canada

Chapter 10
Figure 10.2, Toronto Star

Chapter 11
Opening Figure, Air Canada; Figure 11.4 (c), General Motors Corporation, Warren, Michigan

Unit Five, Opening Photos
Left to right: Ontario Hydro; I.S.T.C., Richmond B.C.; Ontario Ministry of Natural Resources

Chapter 12
Opening Figure, NASA; 12.15, John Frim; 12.27 (b), Courtesy Ford Trucks

Chapter 13
Figure 13.9, Canapress/Ralph Crane

Unit Six, Opening Photos
Left to right: National Ballet/David Street; Birgitte Nielsen; IBM; I.S.T.C., Tidal Bore Park, New Brunswick

Chapter 14
Opening Figure, First Light/Stephen Homer; 14.13 (a), (b), and (c), University of Washington College of Engineering/Library Services

Chapter 15
Opening Figure, British Airways; Figure 15.7, Leo Burnett USA Advertising; 15.11, Bruel & Kjaer Canada Ltd., Bramalea, Ontario

Chapter 16
Opening Figure, Manta Sound, Toronto/Sy Potma; Figure 16.6, The Bettmann Archive, Inc.; 16.20, The National Arts Centre, Ottawa, Ont.; 16.21 (a), Bell-Northern Research Ltd., Ottawa

Unit Seven, Opening Photos
Left to right: I.S.T.C., Mississauga, Ontario; Ford of Canada News Services; Ontario Hydro; IBM Canada; I.S.T.C. Montreal, Québec

Chapter 17
Opening Figure, Pat Morrow/First Light; Figure 17.2, Fisher Scientific Collection; 17.19, The Ontario Science Centre, Toronto

Chapter 18
Figure 18.2, NASA; 18.3, Pacific Gas and Energy, San Francisco, California

Chapter 19
Opening Figure, Ontario Hydro

Chapter 20
Opening Figure, Courtesy Dofasco, Hamilton

Chapter 21
Opening Figure, Hydro Québec; Figure 21.8 (b), Ontario Hydro; 21.8 (c), Ontario Hydro; 21.10 (a), Arco Solar, Inc.

Unit Eight, Opening Photos
Left to right: Alan Hirsch; Toronto East General Hospital; Toronto General Hospital; Spar Aerospace

Chapter 22
Opening Figure, NASA; Figure 22.1, John Wiley & Sons

Chapter 23
Opening Figure, Diamond Information Center;
Figure 23.8 (d), Bell-Northern Research Ltd., Ottawa

Chapter 25
Opening Figure, L. Michael Roberts, Laserist; Figure 25.17, Lumonics

Unit Nine, Opening Photos
Left to right: Toronto East General Hospital; Ontario Hydro; Toronto East General Hospital; Robert C. Ragsdale, F.R.P.S.

Chapter 26
Opening Figure, The Deutches Museum, Munich; Figure 26.3, AIP Niels Bohr Library; 26.11, Atomic Energy of Canada; 26.12, Brookhaven National Laboratory

Chapter 27
Opening Figure, Ontario Hydro; Figure 27.1, AIP Niels Bohr Library; 27.5, Ontario Hydro; 27.7, Ontario Hydro; 27.8, Ontario Hydro; 27.10 (b), Ontario Hydro; 27.12, Ontario Hydro